MediaGuardian

Media Directory

2004

Edited by **Emily Bell** and **Chris Alden**

Researched by **Toni Hanks**
Additional Research: **Ben Siegle, Louise Richards**

The Guardian and MediaGuardian are
trademarks of the Guardian Media Group plc
and Guardian Newspapers Ltd.

Guardian Books is an imprint of
Guardian Newspapers Ltd.

A CIP record for this book is available from
the British Library

ISBN 1-84354-041-X

Distributed by Atlantic Books
An imprint of Grove Atlantic Ltd
Ormond House
26–27 Boswell Street
London WC1N 3JZ

Cover Design: Two Associates
Text Design: Bryony Newhouse

Sub-edited by Liane Katz and Martin Nicholls
Proofread by Peter Gibbs and Kathleen Gill
Indexed by Diana Le Core and Bryony Newhouse
Further research: Sheila Caffrey, Sue Jeffels,
Tom Lutz, Vinutha Mallya, James Merino,
Michelle Ross, Mo Smith, Janice Woods,
Bulent Yusuf

Data compiled on behalf of Guardian Newspapers Ltd
by Loughborough University

Data cleaned by Broadsystems Ltd

Disclaimer
*We have taken all steps possible to ensure the accuracy
of the data in this directory. If any information
is incorrect, please send an email with updated
details to* mediadirectory@guardian.co.uk

Printed by Biddles

Contents

Introduction

There is no such thing as a quiet year in media, but even by the frenetic standards of recent years we are in the middle of an extraordinary time. So it seems appropriate that we have chosen now to relaunch the Guardian Media Guide and produce a new Media Directory, expanding our coverage and combining MediaGuardian analysis with the most comprehensive media listings available in book form.

The directory gives readers a flavour of the big issues and how they affect the shape of the future media industry, but it is also above all a practical source book for media professionals and an invaluable guide to students wanting to work in the media.

The past year has proved to be a defining one for many aspects of the industry: in Britain we had a new Communications Act which lays out the biggest changes to the ownership rules for commercial television for a decade, we had the war in Iraq which saw an unprecedented level of reporting from embedded and unilateral reporters, and a worldwide audience embracing 24-hour news and the internet in astonishingly high numbers.

We saw reporting methods subjected to extreme scrutiny and the bonds of trust between media and reader, viewer and listener tested. After the war, news in the UK was dominated by the row surrounding the BBC's reporting of the affair, which in turn led first to the apparent suicide of BBC source and government scientist Dr David Kelly, and then to the Hutton inquiry. In the US, the New York Times issued an unprecedented apology after it emerged that Jayson Blair, one of its brightest young reporters, had systematically fabricated dozens of pieces. Add to this the fundamental changes being wrought in radio, television and online media by the arrival of digital technologies, and we are once again challenged in terms of how to fit it all in.

On a more personal note for the Guardian, as the Media Directory was going to press the Guardian lost Hugo Young, who died at the age of 64. Hugo Young was our foremost political commentator and the chairman of our owner, the Scott Trust. Both through his words and deeds he enforced a belief in the value of an independent media to the functioning of democracy – something as important now as it ever has been in the past.

Emily Bell

Iraq: the media war

We did not know it at the time, but the media war for Iraq began on the night of September 2, 2002. The world summit on sustainable development was drawing to a close; the first anniversary of the World Trade Centre attacks was approaching; and in the US, the pressure for war was rising. That day, in an aeroplane high above Africa, Tony Blair turned to his PR chief, Alastair Campbell, and told him: we need a dossier on Iraq.

For Mr Campbell, it was a memorable conversation – and not only because the dossier, when published, became one of the cornerstones of the case for war. He had cause to recall it almost nine months later when, after a conversation between a Today programme journalist and an MoD weapons expert, he became the centre of damaging allegations about his role at the highest level of government. It was a row that became a test of strength between Downing Street and the BBC – culminating in the death of the weapons expert and the appearance of a prime minister before a public inquiry for only the second time in history. By the time Mr Campbell tendered his resignation in August 2003 – still denying any wrongdoing – he looked a man ready to spend more time with his family.

September 2002 to February 2003: the PR offensive

At first, all went smoothly. Mr Blair, talking on home ground in Sedgefield the next day, promised an Iraq dossier within "a few weeks". The document duly appeared on September 24 – and included the sensational claim that Iraq was able to deploy weapons of mass destruction within 45 minutes. The Evening Standard splashed with four words: "45 minutes to attack".

The war dance that followed is well documented. Mr Blair helped broker a UN resolution in November, warning Iraq of "serious consequences" if it did not disarm; in December, he told troops to prepare for battle; in January, he said war could go ahead even if inspectors did not find weapons of mass destruction.

Then February, a nightmare month for the spinners: no Unmovic evidence for WMD; no UN support for a second resolution; a Labour rebellion against war; huge public protest; and perhaps most humiliatingly, a second, "dodgy" dossier based in parts on an academic thesis almost seven years old. Not only was Mr Blair failing to persuade a divided public of the case for war, but his personal popularity was plunging. Even as a US-led invasion grew ever more inevitable, it seemed, the British government was losing trust – and although the public was finally moved to support its troops, the issue was to re-emerge when WMD were not immediately found.

March and April 2003: war

When war began, some 2,000 journalists from around the world were in the Gulf to cover it – with varying degrees of accuracy. First, about 600 journalists were **embedded** with British and US troops; the biggest single exercise in the embedding of journalists to date. The system gave reporters unprecedented access to advancing positions, not to mention protection. It was successful in meeting the demands of 24-hour news –

"The fact is that war is full of violence, death and destruction"

Jihad Ballout, al-Jazeera press officer (March 2003)

many embeds were uncensored and allowed to broadcast live from the battlefield. But there was more than a suspicion of military control: columns with journalists in them, it sometimes seemed, were less liable to be involved in frontline firefights.

Journalists operating independently did not necessarily fare better. Those in Baghdad – who numbered more than 200, almost all based in the Palestine Hotel on the city's main square (later shelled by a US tank: see page 8) – were **monitored** by Iraqi authorities. Some, such as a Channel 4 News crew who found Scud missiles hidden in residential Baghdad, self-censored to avoid expulsion from Iraq.

In the TV studios and newspaper offices, editors had to steer a line between coalition **propaganda** and its sometimes wild Iraqi equivalent, typified by information minister Mohammed Saeed al-Sahaf, dubbed "comical Ali". The result was frequent confusion. Umm Qasr was reported captured at least nine times before it was, leading the BBC's deputy director of news, Mark Damazer, to say the public was "less well-informed than it should be". Reports of an uprising in Basra, transmitted worldwide, proved unsubstantiated. A "Saddam torture morgue" in fact housed Iranian victims of the Iran-Iraq war. Britain was later to criticise the US-run media centre in Qatar, which it said "did not do enough to put the events of the war in context".

In Britain, the popular press split along predictable lines – the right, led by the Sun, backing Our Boys in inimitable style; and the left, led by the Mirror, castigating Mr Blair as America's "poodle". This left the broadcast media, and to an extent the broadsheets, carrying the flag for objective reporting. Yet even at an early stage of war, the **BBC** came under attack from government. Doubtless the BBC made most effort to distinguish between fact, propaganda and conjecture in its war report-ing, yet the government seemed to want a more pro-British line from its public broadcaster: minister John Reid accused the corporation of acting like a "friend of Baghdad", to firm rebuttals from the BBC.

Of the news networks, **Sky News** was transformed from the fledgling service that had covered the first Gulf war. With an established reputa-tion for breaking stories quickly, it dominated multichannel ratings, with BBC News 24 and ITV News well behind. Yet in July 2003, correspondent James Forlong was to resign after admitting a report from submarine HMS Splendid had been faked; he reported that the submarine was "beneath the waters of the Persian gulf" and showed a cruise missile being fired, when in fact the pictures were library footage and the vessel was docked.

The **US media** were less sceptical than the British. One network, NBC, sacked a reporter for telling Iraqi journalists that the US had misjudged the determination of Iraqi forces; radio group Clear Channel even organised pro-war rallies. Fox News was infamously and unashamedly pro-war, although Britain's independent television commission – later to be subsumed into Ofcom – decided it had not broken rules on "due impartiality".

Perhaps the most moving and enduring images of war – the toppling of Saddam Hussein's statue on April 9, and the rescue of private Jessica Lynch – turned out to be stage-managed to a greater or lesser extent. No more than 100 Iraqis greeted the statue's fall, critics said, and it was dislodged with the help of US forces. This was reported at the time, but perhaps outweighed by the power of the images. The Lynch story was attacked by the BBC's Correspondent programme – which alleged that Lynch was in little danger, and being treated as well as could be expected in an Iraqi hospital – as "one of the most stunning pieces of news management ever conceived".

In the Arab world, Qatar-based **al-Jazeera** focused on the horrors of war. Mr Blair criticised the channel for broadcasting pictures of two dead British soldiers lying in a road – an image the BBC had trouble broadcasting weeks later, even after pixellating it and notifying family members. The BBC's Mark Damazer was left reflecting on the difference between its coverage and that shown globally: "We've been too static and our credibility with international audiences is on the line. BBC World is showing one thing and other channels around the world are showing something different."

May and June 2003: the Gilligan affair

With the war over, the foreign affairs select committee investigated the decision to invade – and some journalists began to focus on rumours of unease in the intelligence services before war began. On Thursday May 29, **Andrew Gilligan**, of the BBC Radio 4's flagship current affairs programme, Today, reported one, particularly damaging allegation. He quoted an unattributed "senior intelligence source" saying that the British government's September dossier on Iraq's weapons of mass destruction – and particularly the 45-minute claim – had been "made sexier" at Downing Street.

At first, the story did as such stories do – it commanded attention for a couple of days, amid denials, and began to fade – at which Gilligan stirred the nest. He repeated the allegations in the Mail on Sunday, quoting his source saying there was no evidence for the 45-minute claim. "I asked him how this transformation happened. The answer was single word. 'Campbell.' What? Campbell made it up? 'No, it was real information. But it was included against our wishes because it wasn't reliable.'"

The next day, another BBC journalist – Newsnight correspondent **Susan Watts** – reported a "senior official" claiming the intelligence services came under heavy pressure over the 45-minute claim.

On Tuesday, five days after the original Today report, the government began its counter-attack. First, Commons leader **John Reid** blamed "rogue elements" in the security services; and on Friday Tony Blair's official spokesman listed what he called a "series of inaccuracies" in Gilligan's report.

By now, the **foreign affairs committee** had taken note. First Gilligan and then Mr Campbell were questioned. On June 19 Gilligan described his source as "one of the senior officials in charge of drawing up the dossier ... a source of long standing, well known to me, closely connected with the question of Iraq's weapons of mass destruction, easily sufficiently senior to be worth reporting". On the 25th Mr Campbell hit back. "I know we are right in relation to that 45-minute point. It is completely and totally untrue. It is – I don't use this word lightly – it is actually a lie."

With that, the row had become a stand-off. The BBC stood by its story, with director of news Richard Sambrook citing an "unprecedented level of pressure" from Number 10. The government appeared to hold its fire: until July 4, when – five weeks after the row began – the MoD released a statement saying an "unnamed official" had come forward, turning a crisis about WMD into a different kind of affair altogether: a game of hunt the mole.

Andrew Gilligan:
reported damaging claims
(Reuters/Russell Boyce)

Dr David Kelly: expert on Iraqi weapons
(National Pictures)

July 2003: The death of Dr David Kelly

Details about Gilligan's source began to slip out almost as soon as the MoD's press release. On July 5, Tom Baldwin reported in the Times that Gilligan's source was a scientist working in Iraq. Next day a statement from the BBC governors, intended to defend Gilligan, reiterated that he was a "senior intelligence source". On July 8, the MoD released a statement saying an official admitted speaking to Gilligan, but that he had made no comment regard to the 45-minute claim, except to say that it was "probably for impact"; the BBC's response was that the description did not match Gilligan's source "in some important ways". Next day, as rumours began to spread, the MoD confirmed a name to journalists; and by July 10, the Times, the Guardian and the Financial Times had named the source of Gilligan's allegations as Dr David Kelly.

Enter, again, the foreign affairs committee. With the BBC still refusing to name the scientist as the source of its information, Dr Kelly appeared before MPs on July 15. There he admitted meeting both Gilligan and Watts; but said Gilligan's account of Campbell's intervention in the 45-minute claim "was not a factual record ... from the conversations I had with him, I don't know how he could have had the authority to make the statements he is making." MPs on the committee concluded that Dr Kelly was "most unlikely" to be Gilligan's source.

Still the government called on the BBC to confirm its source: "All they they have to do is say yes or no," Mr Blair told the Commons – "why don't they?" On July 17, Gilligan faced the foreign affairs committee for a second time. Even as Gilligan was being branded an "unsatisfactory witness", Dr Kelly told his wife that he was going for a walk: when he failed to return home that night, his family called the police. At 9.20am next day, a body was found in woods: on July 19, police confirmed that the body to be that of Dr David Kelly.

At an inquest, it emerged that Dr Kelly had died from an "incised wound" to the left wrist – the assumption being that the scientist had committed suicide at the pressure of the media storm surrounding him. He was buried on August 6.

August 2003: The Hutton inquiry

With Dr Kelly's family grieving, both sides moderated their tone – in the short term, at least. The government announced there would be an independent judicial inquiry, headed by Lord Hutton; the BBC confirmed that Dr Kelly was indeed the source of both its journalists' reports. But at this, others weighed in. The Mail on Sunday deputy editor, Roderick Gilchrist, said Mr Campbell was in a "disturbed psychological state" and "out of control"; while former cabinet member Peter Mandelson described Andrew Gilligan as a "loose cannon" on, of all programmes, Today. Meanwhile the press took sides: the Murdoch-owned Sun and Times, currently pro-Blair, cast the BBC as the villain of the piece; the Mail and Mirror, for very different reasons, blamed Blair.

The inquiry itself had a brief but inexact remit: to investigate the "circumstances surrounding" Dr Kelly's death. But there was no doubting its thoroughness. Reams of emails, dossiers and other documents, in all stages of drafting, began to pour in to Lord Hutton's team – and from there, when the inquiry started, into the public domain.

Neither side escaped criticism. For the BBC, **Gilligan** was first through the mill – his notes, made on a palmtop computer, took some interpreting; "with hindsight", he told the inquiry, he wished he had

Reporting the war **Alan Rusbridger**

The following is part of a speech delivered by Alan Rusbridger, editor-in-chief of the Guardian, at a Guardian/New York Magazine conference on War Reporting in New York, 23 July 2003.

In covering the Iraq war, the main issue newspaper editors agonised over is perhaps one which, in retrospect, needn't have caused so much fretting.

It's the question of where, in a war of this sort, do you want your reporters to be? How do you cover it?

The obvious answer: everywhere. But there were times when the answer was not so obvious.

Two British broadsheets pulled their correspondents out of Baghdad before the war began, citing either safety or anxieties about the usefulness or reliability of their copy. Some American news organisations did the same.

That was a fairly fundamental challenge to the common-sense assumption that most solvent media organisations would want as many viewpoints as possible.

Given the scale of embedding journalists, I suppose my gut feeling is that it seems a bit churlish to complain about getting frontline access after years of complaining that we've been kept away from the action. So I remain less worried than some about what is, after all, a new name for an old routine. You would be mad to rely on embeds for your only news about war. Of course they can only see a pinprick – though this was more of a problem for TV, which often seemed intoxicated by the incredible pictures whizzing back from the front. There are questions about tone and language. Do you dress in battle dress? Not if you can help it.

Do you use the word "we" to suggest a sense of shared endeavour? No.

At least one of The Guardian's three embeds – a photographer – swears he would never do it again. He truly felt constrained and unable to take the pictures he wanted to take. But the evidence seems to be that, faced with having to report uncomfortable things, reporters went ahead and reported them.

What about the unembedded unilateral journalists? Yes please. If we're honest, most of them were only semi-unilaterals. They might have been free to roam by day. But they needed fuel, food, water and, sometimes protection. Which came from an understanding and generally supportive US army. But there was nevertheless a great value to the Guardian in having James Meek driving up from Kuwait to Baghdad with a translator in tow – free to speak to Iraqis as he went, free to give a perspective of the country and the war other than the one seen from the turret of an Abrams tank. James gave a deeply textured account of the road to Baghdad which simply couldn't have been written by any of the embeds.

Were we right to keep reporters in Baghdad? I genuinely can't see any reason why not. Yes, they were – initially at least – working under restrictions. But none of those I've spoken to seems to think that they were unduly compromised by this. And it may or may not be significant that most of the obvious examples of misleading reporting came, not from the reporters actually inside Baghdad, but from journalists elsewhere, some of them travelling with the coalition forces.

A few examples of where the stories became confused: the non-existent tank convoy leaving Basra, the non-uprising in Basra, the non-taking of Umm Qasr. Then there was the Sky News dispatch from the submarine beneath the Persian Gulf – actually a staged piece of action filmed in dock and spliced with some library footage. In the US the spinning of the rescue of Jessica Lynch raised questions about the way the story was reported.

And so on.

This is not to make any claims for the truthfulness of the Baghdad regime. It simply points out that the journalists who were working there haven't been caught out in putting out any disinformation from their minders. They were all experienced: they used their journalistic skills. None of these glaringly wrong or manipulated stories was the result of disinformation pumped out by Baghdad.

For the Guardian, there was huge value in having Suzanne Goldenberg in Baghdad. She was there 89 days, and her reporting – before, during and after the war – was remarkable for the way it humanised the people who were, in conventional war reporting terms, supposed to be the enemy. In many past wars – right up to what the British tabloids couldn't resist calling "the Argies" and the baby-killing Iraqis of Gulf war one – reporters could be relied upon to play their part in dehumanising the enemy. And here was a woman reporter writing, day after day, sympathetic accounts of everyday people in Baghdad as they waited for war, or suffered under its assault.

Such reporting may well, in future, make it harder to get a civilian consensus for fighting wars against other civilian populations. That is something politicians and soldiers will have to factor into their thinking.

And once the bombs started falling, and the American army finally shot its way into town and the mortuaries filled to overflowing the bodies, we had a witness there – filing extraordinarily graphic and moving pieces.

In retrospect, was there any question that it was right to keep reporters in Baghdad?

I really can't see it. I've yet to hear a convincing case for saying that reporters shouldn't be on the ground to witness what was being done in our name.

been more careful about his claim that Downing Street knew the 45-minute claim to be false. Internal BBC memos showed that where Gilligan's editor at Today, Kevin Marsh, was originally happy with his journalism – "great stories, well handled and well told" – he later found it marred by "loose use of language and lack of judgment". **Watts**, meanwhile, revealed rigorous notes and tapes confirming beyond doubt that Dr Kelly had said Mr Campbell inserted the 45-minute claim; but showed concern at BBC bosses' "attempt to mould them so that they were corroborative, which I felt was misguided and false". Meanwhile, emails revealed that **BBC governors** had harboured doubts about the original report: chairman Gavyn Davies criticised the "repeatedly inappropriate tone" used by presenter John Humphrys on May 29, acknowledging also that Gilligan's Mail on Sunday article on June 1 weakened the BBC case; while governor Dame Pauline Neville-Jones thought a denial by the joint intelligence committee – which she once chaired – should have been more prominently reported. Most embarrassingly of all, it emerged that the description of Dr Kelly as a "senior intelligence source" was added at the BBC press office's behest: a case, perhaps, of the BBC doing its own sexing-up.

But if that gave ammunition to the anti-Beeb lobby, there was plenty too for the anti-Blairs. Two officials from the **defence intelligence staff**, it emerged early on, wrote letters of protest about how intelligence had been presented. Documents showed how the September dossier was **drafted and redrafted** in the weeks leading up to publication: on September 5 2002, Mr Campbell said it needed a "substantial rewrite … as per TB's discussion", with the 45-minute claim making its first appearance five days later; a third draft, circulated on the 15th, was dismissed by Jonathan Powell, Mr Blair's chief of staff, as doing "nothing to demonstrate a threat, let alone an imminent threat from Saddam". After further exchanges between Mr Campbell and the joint intelligence committee, the dossier said on the 19th that "the Iraq military *may be able* to deploy *chemical or biological* weapons within 45 minutes of an order to do so" (our italics); but by the time of publication, on the 24th, the 45-minute claim had been firmed up again. On September 19, it emerged, **Dr Kelly** suggested 12 to 14 amendments to the dossier – including one on the mention of a factory producing a poisonous gas, described in the dossier as of "particular concern". In an email to Dr Kelly, one intelligence officer described its inclusion as "another example supporting our view that you and I should have been more involved in this than the spin merchants in this administration". **Dr Brian Jones**, a retired branch head of the defence intelligence analysis staff, told the inquiry his department had been concerned about "the tendency … to, shall we say, over-egg certain assessments, particularly in relation to the production of chemical weapons".

Mr Campbell and **Mr Blair**, appearing at the inquiry, both defended themselves against the central claim. Mr Campbell said he "had no input, output, influence upon it whatever at any stage of the process"; while Mr Blair raised the stakes: "You … have this extraordinary allegation which, if it were true, would mean we had behaved in the most disgraceful way, and I would have to resign as prime minister".

A separate argument turned on what, or who, caused Dr Kelly's death. Defence secretary **Geoff Hoon**, it transpired, had overruled his most senior civil servant to insist Dr Kelly appear before the select committee; while Mr Campbell isolated Mr Hoon further, saying he thought the

Alastair Campbell: resigned in August
(The Guardian/Dan Chung)

"naming strategy" was wrong, Mr Hoon said he was unaware that Downing Street was briefing journalists with clues. **Richard Hatfield**, MoD head of personnel, said: "I find some difficulty in squaring the press's desire to know the name of Dr Kelly with the press's criticism of us for providing it to them". As for **Dr Kelly himself**, it emerged that he had felt put "through the wringer" by the MoD: he was a private man, said one psychologist, who had suffered a profound "loss of self-esteem" by being forced to face the foreign affairs committee as he did.

On August 29 2003, almost a year after the idea of an Iraq dossier was first raised, Mr Campbell announced his **resignation**. Although the departure had been expected, the timing surprised journalists who expected him to wait until Lord Hutton delivered his verdict. Some said he had got out early in case Hutton called against him; others said he had wanted to leave a year before. Next day, he was pictured at Turf Moor, home of Burnley FC, doing exactly he had promised to do: spending more time with his family.

After Campbell: an end to government by spin?

At the time of writing, Lord Hutton's take on the circumstances surrounding the death of Dr David Kelly remains unknown. What is known is that before and during war in Iraq, and with whatever degree of justification, there was a profound loss of trust in the apparatus surrounding Tony Blair. Downing Street had since 1997 been synonymous with a culture of "spin": with Britain at war, the degree and importance of that spin appeared to increase. In Iraq, many journalists had expressed concern that the US-led coalition, of which Britain was a part, had attempted to control the flow of information: truth, they feared, was being subverted to political – even moral – ends. Dr Kelly thought it, we now know; Andrew Gilligan thought it; significant elements of the intelligence and journalistic community thought it too. Mr Campbell as much as admitted that the view was spreading when he told the Hutton inquiry just how damaging Gilligan's report could be. The government had spun itself into a corner, it seemed, from which the only defence was attack.

There are lessons for journalists too. Most basic was the importance of tapes or shorthand notes; if it were not for the evidence of Susan Watts, Gilligan's story might have turned belly-up early on. Second, it is remarkable what different journalists will do with similar information: where Gilligan ran his story on the basis of a single, uncorroborated source, Watts thought Dr Kelly's comments about Mr Campbell to be a "gossipy aside". Third, there is the question of how far the media spotlight on Dr Kelly may have contributed to his death. Fourth, it is arguable that the BBC, indignant at being dubbed a "friend of Baghdad" by a Labour minister and yet the "Blair Broadcasting Corporation" by sections of the rightwing press, was desperate – perhaps too desperate – to exert its independence before its charter renewal in 2006. Governments, it seems, do not have a monopoly on spin.

With Mr Campbell gone, there are calls for a new start: a lower profile for the Downing Street press office; an end to the lobby system with its cosy, off-the-record briefings; in short, a stronger wall between propaganda and truth. We can hope. Yet as every conflict has ever shown, the greatest damage is often wreaked when two truths collide: caught in the middle of the latest struggle was Dr David Kelly.

Chris Alden

■ Safety of journalists

The Iraq war was devastating in terms of safety for journalists.
Some 16 media workers died during the war, including two – cameramen
Jose Couso and Taras Protsyuk – killed in an attack on the Palestine Hotel,
Baghdad, on 8 April. The US admitted that the hotel was shelled by one of
its tanks – although, to illustrate the difficulty of finding truth in the fog of war,
Israeli website Debka.com later alleged that the explosion was planted by Iraqi
military intelligence. In June, the family of Couso announced that it was taking
legal action against the soldiers responsible.

Perhaps the worst outcry was reserved for the killing of Reuters cameraman
Mazen Dana, who was shot dead by US troops in August while filming outside
a Baghdad prison. The chief executive of Reuters, Tom Glocer, said: "The latest
death is hard to bear. That's why I am calling upon the highest levels of the US
government for a full and comprehensive investigation into this terrible tragedy."

Two months earlier, BBC world affairs editor John Simpson had called
on the US government to investigate why more journalists were killed
by its soldiers than by any other means during the Iraq war.

Journalists killed and missing during war in Iraq

Dead

Tareq Ayyoub, Al-Jazeera cameraman
David Bloom, NBC TV correspondent
Veronica Cabrera, freelance camerawoman for Argentina's America TV
Jose Couso, Tele Cinco cameraman
Kaveh Golestan, freelance BBC cameraman
Michael Kelly, American journalist and Washington Post columnist
Christian Liebig, journalist for German Focus magazine
Terry Lloyd, ITN correspondent
Paul Moran, freelance Australian cameraman
Kamaran Abdurazaq Muhamed, BBC translator
Julio Anguita Parrado, reporter for El Mundo, Spain
Mario Podesta, freelance reporter for Argentina's America TV
Taras Protsyuk, Reuters cameraman
Gaby Rado, Channel 4 News foreign affairs correspondent

Missing

Fred Nerac, French ITN cameraman
Hussein Osman, Lebanese translator

Detained and believed to have been released

Marcin Firlej and **Jacek Kaczmarek**, Polish journalists who escaped after being captured south of Baghdad;
seven Italian journalists

The Communications Act 2003

It was a long time coming. In July 2003, after 30 months of parliamentary scrutiny, 26 standing committee sessions, 17 days of debate and more than 500 amendments, New Labour's much heralded Communications Act was passed. With it, five pillars of the regulatory landscape – the broadcasting standards commission, the independent television commission, the radio authority, the radiocommunications agency and Oftel – all disappeared, and in December 2003 transferred their powers to a single body, **Ofcom**.

The idea seems straightforward enough: Ofcom centralises media regulation, concentrating the powers of five fiefdoms into a single organisation. But the main aim, commentators were quick to see, was deregulation. The Communications Act removes key restrictions on media ownership: including, most controversially, rules preventing newspaper owners or overseas moguls – say, for example, **Rupert Murdoch** – from taking over a terrestrial British broadcaster such as Five.

But the moguls did not get it all their own way. A rearguard action fought in the Lords by Labour peer Lord Puttnam – who promised to fight "in every respect, the provision that would allow Five or any terrestrial channel to be wholly or partially owned by any large newspaper group" – led to an 11th-hour **public interest test** to be applied in the event of major media takeovers such as these. The test would assess the "share of voice" companies have across media sectors.

The duty of Ofcom, we were told in early 2003, was to "favour light-handed regulation" – but also to "intervene when necessary". There are two power structures: the main board, made up entirely of government appointees such as Ed Richards,

former media policy adviser at No 10; and a separate "content board" with broader media experience to regulate standards. From the point of view of media ownership, the legislation is indeed light-handed; powers to intervene apply mostly to content.

The light touch: media ownership

The Communications Act brings down barriers to media ownership in Britain, in particular:

- allowing overseas giants to buy British broadcasters such as ITV and Five;
- relaxing rules on cross-media ownership and cross-platform promotion, which restricted newspaper owners from buying more than 20% of a terrestrial TV station;
- abolishing radio legislation preventing companies from broadcasting to more than 15% of the total number of potential listeners, or owning more than one commercial national radio licence. New rules instead require at least two independent radio stations per area, who can each own up to 55% of the population coverage.

Last-minute amendments softened the impact of this deregulation, forcing Ofcom to:

- assess whether any takeovers are in the public interest, according to the "share of voice" companies have across media sectors;
- accord citizens rights alongside those with an economic interest in its decisions (an amendment expressly opposed by Ofcom chairman Lord Currie);
- apply a "localness" test to local radio mergers.

Peer pressure: Lord Puttnam (right) battled with culture secretary Tessa Jowell over foreign ownership of the media

The government has also agreed to underwrite Ofcom's legal fees and damages if media giants choose to appeal its decisions.

The regulation of television advertising is also relaxed: Ofcom has the power to hand over day-to-day responsibility to a self-regulatory body similar to the advertising standards authority – which currently handles non-broadcast media. The ban on political advertising on television is set to remain.

Ofcom is not designed to regulate press and internet content, but the new legislation does cover newspaper mergers and acquisitions, which may be referred to the competition commission in cases of "exceptional public interest".

A significant last-minute change to the Act, however, was a series of amendments devoted to protecting the independent television production industry; in particular a code of practice ensuring that all rights for programmes remain with the production company (not the broadcaster) unless negotiated otherwise.

In June, the government also proposed relaxing the proposed ban on ITV gaining full ownership of its news service provider, ITN, which also provides news for Channel 4 and Five.

Intervention where necessary: the content board

As a counterweight to its deregulatory stance on ownership, the Communications Act provides for tougher regulation of media content. If Five changed hands or increased its audience share, for example, Ofcom would review its public service responsibilities, and could also set quality standards for the producer of the channel's news service. But

Ofcom will be unable to enforce a channel's public service remit unless the channel's failure had been serious and "not excused by economic or market conditions".

As part of its duty to regulate the way channels stick to public service remits, meanwhile, Ofcom has indicated it will launch an investigation into the commitment to religious programming on ITV and Channel 4.

The **BBC** is broadly outside Ofcom's remit, but by no means immune: the board will have the power to fine it up to £250,000 for breaches of taste and decency. This is as nothing, however, compared to the threat hanging over the licence fee, which currently accounts for more than 75% of the BBC's income. As one of its first duties, Ofcom is expected to conduct a detailed investigation into public service broadcasting; the BBC is then subject to a wholesale review of its funding when its charter comes up for renewal in 2006. What Ofcom recommends between now and then may be crucial to the BBC's existence in its present form.

The press still self-regulates through the **press complaints commission** (PCC). At a culture select committee inquiry into privacy and media intrusion led by Labour MP Gerald Kaufman – during which the PCC came under severe pressure over its role and remit – it was suggested (notably by Independent editor Simon Kelner) that Ofcom could act as an ombudsman for the PCC; but the committee recommended an independent ombudsman instead.

For more on the PCC and regulation of the press, see page 23; for more on privacy, see page 239; for a full list of Ofcom board members and their histories, see the panel below.

Ofcom board (all are government appointees)	Content board
Chairman	**Chairman**
David Currie, (Lord Currie of Marylebone), *economist*	Richard Hooper*
Deputy chairman	**Deputy chairman**
Richard Hooper, *former chairman of the Radio Authority**	Sara Nathan*
Chief executive	**Other members**
Stephen Carter, *former managing director of NTL*	Adam Singer, *former chief executive of Telewest*
Executive members	Floella Benjamin, *independent production company owner*
Ed Richards, *Downing Street policy adviser*	*and former children's TV presenter*
Kip Meek, *founder of Spectrum Strategy consultancy*	Jonathan Edwards, *Olympic gold medallist and Songs of*
Non-executive members	*Praise presenter*
David Edmonds, *director general of Oftel*	Kath Worrall, *formerly director of broadcasting at Border*
Ian Hargreaves, *former editor of the Independent and*	Pam Giddy, *former BBC producer and director of Charter88*
the New Statesman	Kevin Carey, *vice-chairman of Royal National Institute for*
Sara Nathan, *former editor of Channel 4 News and*	*the Blind*
*non-executive member of the Radio Authority**	Matthew MacIver, *chief executive of general teaching council*
Millie Banerjee, *former director of BT and Channel 4*	*for Scotland*
	Sue Balsom, *former vice-chair of the broadcasting council*
	for Wales
	Rosemary Kelly, *former head of public affairs at the BBC in*
* *on both boards*	*Northern Ireland*

The MediaGuardian 100

The MediaGuardian 100 list is the definitive guide to the most powerful movers and shakers in one of the UK's most vibrant industries. This, the third year of its publication, has been the most controversial so far with the BBC director general, Greg Dyke, taking on the mantle of Rupert Murdoch as the UK's most powerful media executive. A panel of experienced media watchers gleaned from the worlds of politics, journalism, advertising and the internet judged entrants using three criteria: cultural influence, economic clout and political power.

The BBC, Ofcom, women and new media were the big winners – the cash-rich corporation's cultural clout across TV, radio, and online was considered stronger than ever; new regulators are on the scene; women are more prominent than before with 19 places in the top 100; and new media has shown no signs of becoming "old" with the arrival of Apple chief Steve Jobs and emergence of a new generation of mini media moguls in the form of "bloggers". Mr Murdoch, who this year realised his dream of achieving a global satellite TV network with the acquisition of DirecTV, is of course number two. But the case for the BBC's dominance will be put under the microscope in the coming year in the run-up to charter renewal in 2006. It will need to prove beyond doubt that its burgeoning interests across all media are a force for the good, not bad.

Profiles by John Plunkett

1. Greg Dyke

Job: director general, BBC *Age:* 56
Industry: broadcasting, publishing, new media
Company turnover: £3.4bn *Staff:* 24,000
Salary: £469,000. *2002 ranking:* 2

Greg Dyke's BBC is the most powerful force in British broadcasting. BBC1 is the most popular channel, BBC Radio's lead over its commercial rivals is its biggest ever, its internet empire is unprecedented in its scale and depth, and the corporation has resurrected digital terrestrial television from the ashes of ITV Digital. The commercial arm, BBC Worldwide, had revenues of over £700m and profits of around £100m – in addition to the £2.5m which the BBC receives from the licence fee. But with charter renewal in 2006, Mr Dyke's task will be to persuade the BBC's critics that it is not anti-competitive, nor is it dumbing down, and that it remains a force for the public good.

2. Rupert Murdoch

Job: chairman and chief executive, News Corporation
Age: 72 *Industry:* broadcasting, publishing, new media
Company turnover: £11.9bn *Staff:* 34,000
Salary: £5.5m *2002 ranking:* 1

Rupert Murdoch has branded "paranoid" those critics who suggest he has sewn up a deal with Tony Blair to buy Channel Five. But to paraphrase Henry Kissinger, even paranoids have monopolists. The chairman and chief executive of News Corporation is, in global terms, the most powerful man in television. When he finally took control of US satellite operator DirecTV in a £4.1bn deal in April 2003, his worldwide pay-TV empire was extended to 110 million viewers across four continents. His broadcast empire is set to expand further in the UK, with provisions in the Communications Act that allow him to purchase Five – if, that is, he can satisfy Lord Puttnam's "public interest test".

3. David Currie

Job: chairman, Ofcom *Age:* 56 *Industry:* regulation
Annual budget: £120m *Staff:* 1,000 *Salary:* £133,000
2002 ranking: new entry

As chairman of Ofcom, Lord (David) Currie is in charge
of the most powerful regulator the UK television, radio
and telecommunications industries have ever seen
– see page 9.

4. Gavyn Davies

Job: chairman, BBC *Age:* 52 *Industry:* broadcasting
Salary: £66,000 *Worth:* £135m *2002 ranking:* 11

With Gavyn Davies lies the responsibility of securing the
future of the licence fee in the run-up to the renewal of
the BBC's royal charter in 2006. It is as simple (or as
complicated) as that.

5. Sir Christopher Bland

Job: chairman, British Telecom *Age:* 65
Industry: telecommunications *Company turnover:* £24.6bn
Staff: 108,600 *Salary:* £512,000 (including benefits)
2002 ranking: 6

Sir Christopher Bland is the sort of businessman who
tackles a £29bn debt mountain for the challenge of it,
when his past achievements mean he doesn't really need
to get out of bed.

6. Rebekah Wade

Job: editor, the Sun *Age:* 35 *Industry:* publishing
Circulation: 3.52 million *2002 ranking:* 53

As the most influential newspaper editor in Britain,
Rebekah Wade is the most powerful woman in the media
– see page 20.

Rebekah Wade: most powerful editor

7. Paul Dacre

Job: editor-in-chief, Associated Newspapers *Age:* 54
Industry: publishing *Circulation:* 2.3 million (Daily Mail)
Salary: £834,000 *2002 ranking:* 7

No other editor of a national newspaper has so many
admirers or detractors as Paul Dacre.

But it is a sign of his influence that both Gordon
Brown and David Blunkett felt compelled to heap
praise on the Daily Mail editor at a dinner in his
honour in 2003.

8. Stephen Carter

Job: chief executive, Ofcom *Age:* 38
Industry: regulation *Annual budget:* £120m
Staff: 1,000 *Salary:* £350,000 *2002 ranking:* new entry

Stephen Carter pipped Patricia Hodgson to become
the first chief executive of super-regulator Ofcom –
and the man who will arguably have more influence
on the direction of TV and radio in the UK than any
previous watchdog.

9. Richard Desmond

Job: chief executive, Northern and Shell,
Express Newspapers *Age:* 50 *Industry:* publishing
Circulation: Daily Express 907,265;
Sunday Express 875,740; Daily Star 856,133;
Daily Star Sunday 485,454 *Company turnover:* £405m
Salary: £21m (including a £20.3m bonus)
2002 ranking: 27

Richard Desmond's Daily Star is the newspaper success
story of the decade.

The once ailing red-top is now the fastest growing
newspaper in the country, up nearly 10% year-on-year
to more than 850,000.

10. Mario Monti

Job: competition commissioner, European Union
Age: 60 *Industry:* all media *2002 ranking:* 23

Not for nothing is Mario Monti nicknamed
"Super Mario". The European Union's competition
commissioner is one of the most powerful men
in Europe, and has won a string of victories against
some of the world's largest media organisations.

11. Tony Ball
Job: chief executive
Company: BSkyB
Industry: broadcasting, new media
2002 ranking: 4

12. Bill Gates
Job: chairman and founder
Company: Microsoft
Industry: new media
2002 ranking: 10

13. Steve Jobs
Job: chief executive and founder
Company: Apple Computer
Industry: new media
2002 ranking: new entry

14. Charles Allen
Job: chairman
Company: Granada
Industry: broadcasting
2002 ranking: 12

15. Michael Green
Job: chairman
Company: Carlton Communications
Industry: broadcasting
2002 ranking: 13

16. Dawn Airey
Job: managing director, Sky Networks
Company: BSkyB
Industry: broadcasting
2002 ranking: 33

17. Eileen Gallagher
Job: managing director,
   Shed Productions; chair of Pact
Industry: broadcasting
2002 ranking: 93

18. Sly Bailey
Job: chief executive
Company: Trinity Mirror
Industry: publishing
2002 ranking: new entry

19. Les Hinton
Job: executive chairman
Company: News International
Industry: publishing
2002 ranking: 22

20. Richard Hooper
Job: deputy chairman, Ofcom
Industry: media regulation
2002 ranking: new entry

21. Sir Christopher Meyer
Job: chairman, press complaints
   commission
Industry: publishing
2002 ranking: new entry

22. Jana Bennett
Job: director of television
Company: BBC
Industry: broadcasting
2002 ranking: 42

23. Mark Thompson
Job: chief executive
Company: Channel 4
Industry: broadcasting
2002 ranking: 14

24. Alastair Campbell
Job: director of communications,
   10 Downing Street, until 2003
Industry: public relations
2002 ranking: 43

25. Ashley Highfield
Job: director of new media
Company: BBC
Industry: broadcasting, new media
2002 ranking: new entry

26. Arun Sarin
Job: chief executive
Company: Vodafone
Industry: telecommunications
2002 ranking: new entry

27. Dame Marjorie Scardino
Job: chief executive
Company: Pearson
Industry: publishing, new media
2002 ranking: 28

28. Conrad Black
Job: chairman
Company: Hollinger International
Industry: publishing
2002 ranking: 18

29. Piers Morgan
Job: editor, the Daily Mirror
Industry: publishing
2002 ranking: 19

30. Niall FitzGerald
Job: chairman
Company: Unilever
Industry: consumer goods
2002 ranking: 34

31. Tessa Jowell
Job: culture secretary
Industry: politics
2002 ranking: joint 39

32. Jenny Abramsky
Job: director of radio and music
Company: BBC
Industry: broadcasting
2002 ranking: 46

33. David Mansfield
Job: chief executive
Company: Capital Radio
Industry: broadcasting
2002 ranking: 37

34. Ralph Bernard
Job: executive chairman
Company: GWR
Industry: broadcasting
2002 ranking: 38

**35. Anthony McPartlin and
   Declan Donnelly**
Job: presenters; independent
   TV producers
Industry: broadcasting
2002 ranking: new entry

36. Patricia Hewitt
Job: secretary of state,
   Department of Trade & Industry
Industry: politics
2002 ranking: joint 39

Eileen Gallagher (17th):
highest climber since 2002

The Guardian/Frank Baron

37. Tom Moloney
Job: chief executive
Company: Emap
Industry: publishing, broadcasting
2002 ranking: new entry

38. Alan Rusbridger
Job: editor of the Guardian,
   executive editor of the Observer
Industry: publishing, new media
2002 ranking: 32

39. Mark Byford
Job: director, World Service and
   global news
Company: BBC
Industry: broadcasting
2002 ranking: 44

40. Chris Wright
Job: chairman
Company: Chrysalis
Industry: broadcasting, music
2002 ranking: new entry

41. Kevin Marsh
Job: editor of the Today programme,
   Radio 4
Company: BBC
Industry: broadcasting
2002 ranking: new entry

42. Roger Parry
Job: chief executive
Company: Clear Channel International
Industry: broadcasting, advertising
2002 ranking: new entry

43. David Puttnam
Job: freelance policy adviser,
   film producer
Industry: politics, broadcasting
2002 ranking: new entry

44. Nigel Pickard
Job: director of programmes
Company: ITV
Industry: broadcasting
2002 ranking: new entry

Sir Martin Sorrell (45th): furthest faller since 2002

45. Sir Martin Sorrell
Job: group chief executive
Company: WPP
Industry: advertising, marketing
2002 ranking: 5

46. Lorraine Heggessey
Job: controller, BBC1
Company: BBC
Industry: broadcasting
2002 ranking: 51

47. Kevin Lygo
Job: director of television
Company: Channel 4
Industry: broadcasting
2002 ranking: 55

48. Nicola Shindler
Job: founder and executive producer
Company: Red Productions
Industry: TV production
2002 ranking: new entry

49. Robert Thomson
Job: editor, the Times
Industry: publishing
2002 ranking: 25

50. JK Rowling
Job: author
Industry: publishing
2002 ranking: new entry

51. Jane Root
Job: controller, BBC2
Company: BBC
Industry: broadcasting
2002 ranking: 73

52. Barry Cox
Job: deputy chairman
Company: Channel 4
Industry: broadcasting
2002 ranking: 57

53. John Witherow
Job: editor, the Sunday Times
Industry: publishing
2002 ranking: 69

54. Andrew Marr
Job: political editor, BBC; presenter, Start the Week (Radio 4)
Industry: broadcasting
2002 ranking: 75

55. Crispin Davis
Job: chief executive
Company: Reed Elsevier
Industry: publishing, new media
2002 ranking: 60

56. Trevor Kavanagh
Job: political editor, the Sun
Industry: publishing
2002 ranking: 61

57. Max Clifford
Job: founder
Company: Max Clifford Associates
Industry: public relations
2002 ranking: 52

58. Jane Lighting
Job: chief executive
Company: Channel Five
Industry: broadcasting
2002 ranking: new entry

59. Sarah Hunter
Job: special adviser, Downing Street
Industry: politics
2002 ranking: new entry

60. Barclay Knapp
Job: president and chief executive officer
Company: NTL
Industry: broadcasting, new media, telecommunications
2002 ranking: 49

61. Tony O'Reilly
Job: executive chairman
Company: Independent News & Media
Industry: publishing
2002 ranking: 65

62. Chris de Lapuente
Job: vice-president and managing director
Company: Procter & Gamble UK and Ireland
Industry: consumer goods
2002 ranking: 67

63. Matthew Freud
Job: chairman
Company: Freud Communications
Industry: public relations
2002 ranking: 86

64. Jonathan Ross
Job: TV and radio presenter
Industry: broadcasting
2002 ranking: new entry

65. Ian Hislop
Job: editor, Private Eye
Industry: publishing, broadcasting
2002 ranking: 56

66. John Pluthero
Job: chief executive
Company: Energis
Industry: telecommunications, new media
2002 ranking: 71

67. Ricky Gervais
Job: actor, co-creator, co-writer and co-producer of The Office; DJ on London radio station Xfm; stand-up comic
Industry: broadcasting
2002 ranking: new entry

68. Charles Moore
Job: editor, Daily Telegraph
Industry: publishing
2002 ranking: 63

69. Terry Mansfield
Job: president and chief executive
Company: National Magazine Company
Industry: publishing
2002 ranking: 74

70. Nick Elliott
Job: controller of drama
Company: ITV
Industry: broadcasting
2002 ranking: 77

71. Andrew Gowers
Job: editor, Financial Times
Industry: publishing
2002 ranking: 68

72. Jeremy Paxman
Job: presenter, Newsnight and University Challenge on BBC2; author
Industry: broadcasting
2002 ranking: 78

73. Richard Littlejohn
Job: columnist, the Sun; presenter, Sky News
Industry: publishing
2002 ranking: 64

74. Tim Bowdler
Job: chief executive
Company: Johnston Press
Industry: publishing
2002 ranking: 79

75. Douglas McCorkindale
Job: chairman, president and chief executive
Company: Gannett
Industry: publishing
2002 ranking: new entry

76. John McVay
Job: chief executive, Pact
Industry: production
2002 ranking: new entry

77. Dominic Lawson
Job: editor, Sunday Telegraph
Industry: publishing
2002 ranking: 81

78. Alan Yentob
Job: director of drama and entertainment and children's programmes
Company: BBC
Industry: broadcasting
2002 ranking: 82

79. Nicholas Coleridge
Job: managing director
Company: Conde Nast
Industry: publishing
2002 ranking: 83

80. Roger Alton
Job: editor, Observer
Industry: publishing
2002 ranking: 84

81. Nikki Hemming
Job: chief executive
Company: Sharman Networks
(owner of Kazaa)
Industry: new media
2002 ranking: new entry

82. Martin Bashir
Job: Interviewer/presenter,
Tonight with Trevor McDonald
Industry: broadcasting
2002 ranking: new entry

83. Stef Calcraft
Job: partner
Company: Mother
Industry: advertising
2002 ranking: new entry

84. Simon Kelner
Job: editor, Independent
Industry: publishing
2002 ranking: 85

85. Trevor Beattie
Job: chairman
Company: TBWA/London
Industry: advertising
2002 ranking: new entry

86. Richard Sambrook
Job: director of BBC News
Company: BBC
Industry: broadcasting
2002 ranking: 88

87. Helen Boaden
Job: controller, Radio 4
Company: BBC
Industry: broadcasting
2002 ranking: 96

88. Mark Frith
Job: editor, Heat
Industry: publishing
2002 ranking: new entry

89. Jon Zeff
Job: head of broadcasting policy
division, Department for Culture,
Media & Sport
Industry: broadcast regulation
2002 ranking: new entry

90. Sir Trevor McDonald
Job: news anchor, ITN
Industry: broadcasting
2002 ranking: 66

91. Felix Dennis
Job: owner
Company: Dennis Publishing
Industry: publishing
2002 ranking: new entry

92. Bob Phillis
Job: chief executive
Company: Guardian Media Group
Industry: publishing, broadcasting
2002 ranking: new entry

93. Kelvin MacKenzie
Job: chairman and chief executive
Company: The Wireless Group
Industry: broadcasting
2002 ranking: 95

94. A blogger
Industry: new media
2002 ranking: new entry

95. Jane Tranter
Job: controller of drama
commissioning
Company: BBC
Industry: broadcasting
2002 ranking: new entry

96. Nicholas Hytner
Job: director, National Theatre
Industry: theatre
2002 ranking: new entry

97. Michael Jackson
Job: chairman
Company: Universal Television
Groups Worldwide
Industry: broadcasting
2002 ranking: new entry

98. Sylvia Auton
Job: chief executive
Company: IPC Media
Industry: publishing
2002 ranking: new entry

99. Michael Foster
Job: partner, Artists Rights Group;
director UMTV
Industry: broadcasting, management
2002 ranking: new entry

100. The ghost of Lord Reith
Job: first director general of the BBC
Industry: broadcasting
Age: died in 1971

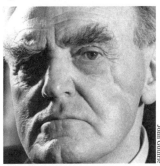

John Guthrie

**Lord Reith: in 1922, said BBC's role
was to "inform, educate and entertain"**

■ Panellists

Lord Alli
Co-founder of production company Planet 24.
Campaigner for equal rights for homosexuals
and ethnic minorities.

Mark Lawson
Journalist, broadcaster and author, perhaps
best known as presenter of Newsnight Review.
Guardian columnist since 1995.

Tess Alps
Deputy chairman of media buyer PHD. "Too much
opportunistic dross masquerading as serious analysis,
and too many current affairs shows shunted into late
night slots," she has said of today's television.

Mike Soutar
Editorial director of IPC Media, one of the most
successful magazine editors of the last 10 years.

Chris Smith
Former culture secretary; played key role in drawing
up the communications bill. Stepping down from
politics at next election to front arts management
initiative.

Emily Bell
Editor-in-chief of Guardian Unlimited. Previously
worked for the Observer as advertising correspondent,
media business editor and finally business editor.

Janine Gibson
Editor-in-chief of MediaGuardian; has previously
written for the Independent, Broadcast and Televisual.
Oversees the Guardian's G3 sections – Society,
Media, Life and Education.

Janet Goldsmith
Managing director of Universal Studios Networks UK.
Previously helped launch Meridian Broadcasting and
was managing director of SelecTV.

Press

The nationals

National newspapers are at the cultural and political heart of the UK: we buy almost 90m national papers a week, more than in any country bar Japan. Two-thirds of us say we read a national paper. But the market is crowded: there are now 10 daily papers and 11 Sundays, as listed in the table on page 23; and over the past 50 years, national dailies have lost some 2 million readers a day – even though their pagination has grown.

About half the daily papers sold in the UK are accounted for by the popular, "red-top" tabloids: the Sun, the Daily Mirror and the Daily Star. Of these, Rupert Murdoch's Sun is by far the most popular, selling 3.5m copies a day in the six months to June 2003. The mid-market tabloids – the Daily Mail and the Daily Express – account for more than a quarter of daily sales: of these, the Mail sells more than twice as many papers as its rival. Broadsheets – the Daily Telegraph, the Times, the Guardian, the Independent and the Financial Times – account for the rest of sales: the Telegraph leads the way with just under a million, although its readership is ageing and it depends significantly on discounted subscription sales.

The Sunday market is similar. Murdoch's News of the World leads the sales march, far outselling its rival, the Sunday Mirror; the Mail on Sunday outstrips the Sunday Express; but the Sunday Times leads broadsheet sales ahead of the Sunday Telegraph, the Observer and the Independent on Sunday.

Popular tabloids

The daily tabloids are traditionally distinguished by their party politics, with the **Sun** on the right wing and the **Daily Mirror** on the left. War in Iraq brought a new dimension to the rivalry. The Sun, despite its reservations about the prime minister, Tony Blair, backed the decision to go to war in Iraq, capitalising the words "Our Boys" in traditional and inimitable style; feature writer Katy Weitz resigned at what she called the paper's "gung-ho" attitude. The Daily Mirror opposed war, with editor Piers Morgan pursuing a "serious news" agenda in the face of falling circulation, often clearing the front page to promote articles by radical leftwingers such as John Pilger.

In March, Rebekah Wade, the **News of the World** editor who had pioneered the controversial "naming and shaming" of paedophiles, moved across to become the first female editor of the **Sun**. Rumours of Page 3's demise proved unfounded in the first issue, when the slot was filled by the topless model "Rebekah from Wapping". Wade's first editorial was a carefully worded piece saying the paper's patience with Tony Blair was "wearing thin", leaving open the option of an anti-Blair stance after war in Iraq.

"We should always be looking for someone to blame"

James Murray, Sunday Express news editor, in an emailed memo to staff (July 2003)

Wade's replacement at the News of the World was Andy Coulson, the journalist famous for being photographed with celebrities in the Sun's Bizarre column in the 1990s. **People** editor Neil Wallis left to become Coulson's deputy. Completing the editorial merry-go-round, **Sunday Mirror** deputy editor Mark Thomas became new editor of the People.

Morgan's Mirror bravely pursued its "serious" agenda, but its circulation continued to suffer: in March 2003, sales of the paper fell below 2m for the first time in 70 years. Analysts warned that the editor might have been given too much power by Trinity Mirror executives; but the arrival in January of Sly Bailey, formerly chief executive at magazine group IPC, suggested change. The year also saw a succession of journalists leave the newspaper's flagship celebrity column, 3am Girls. "I'm going to sort this showbusiness thing out if it kills me," Morgan told the Press Gazette at the time.

The **Daily Star** served up its usual diet of cod-celebrity news with little mention of international affairs, and watched its circulation rise. Meanwhile the **Daily Star Sunday**, launched in September 2002, hit the ground running with a circulation of more than 475,000* in the first six months of 2003. Worst affected was the People, which saw its circulation fall 15% year on year.

All circulation figures exclude bulks (see explainer, page 21)

Mid-markets

The **Daily Mail** continues to dominate the middle market. The paper – socially and politically conservative, yet read by more women than men – bared its teeth during the "Cheriegate" affair that dominated the

---

■ Wade's world

The first female editor of the Sun, Rebekah Wade, stepped into the editor's chair in January 2003 as if born to it. Within minutes, by wearing a Page 3 badge on her lapel, she dispelled any notion that she would ditch the paper's topless models; within a day, she had steered the paper's editorial line right of Tony Blair; and within a week, in a notorious "Mr Men" caricature, she had offended every Rastafarian, asylum seeker and ethnic Albanian in Britain. Not bad for a few days' work.

But for Wade, it wasn't just a few days. Since starting at the News of the World magazine as a 20-year-old feature writer in 1990, she has spent her career learning the tenets of life under Rupert Murdoch. For the "red-tops' red-top", as the hacks put it, editorship of the

Rebekah Wade: appearing before culture select committee

Sun was the fulfilment of a scarcely concealed ambition.

That ambition has made her enemies. David Yelland, editor when she was his deputy, was said in particular to distrust her. But as a pro-Blair paper under Yelland, the Sun had lost some of the tenacity and irreverence of the MacKenzie years. Wade's brief is to put it back.

So far she has campaigned to save the pound, challenged "asylum madness", and been gung-ho in support of war in Iraq. So far, so Sun. She is married to former soap star Ross Kemp, has a talent for schmoozing celebrities, but keeps a low media profile. Her easy mix of conservatism and tabloid instinct have made her a textbook example of how to get on at NewsCorp.

At times she sails too close to the masthead. At the News of the World she "named and shamed" paedophiles, only pulling the campaign after police opposition and anti-paedophile riots in Portsmouth. She has also admitted Murdoch titles paid police for information. Most recently, a News of the World investigation into a plot to kidnap Victoria Beckham – started under Wade's editorship – led to a collapsed trial and recriminations all round, although the paper escaped censure from the press complaints commission.

What of the future? After the Portsmouth riots, a question mark remains over Wade's judgment – but her talent and sense of mischief should see her through the trouble. And with New Labour under increasing pressure and a showdown looming over Europe, those qualities are precisely what a Murdoch paper needs.

■ Explainer: ABCs

• **What are ABCs?** ABCs are circulation figures published by the Audit Bureau of Circulations, an independent company that monitors and verifies sales of newspapers and magazines.

• **How often do ABCs come out?** Newspaper ABCs are published each month. Magazine ABCs are published every six months, covering January-June and July-December each year.

• **What do the ABCs include?** The ABC publishes the number of copies of a publication sold at full price and sent to subscribers, but also "bulks": copies distributed free to targeted places such as hotels and airlines. In order to prevent non-targeted dumping of issues merely to bump up circulation, the ABC has completed a review of how it collates and records these bulk sales. *In future,* the number of bulks that can be declared must be reported by target audience (ie airline passengers, train passengers, hotel customers etc). The price paid for each discounted copy must also be declared within price bands relative to the cover price. Emap and National Magazines both had to reissue lower circulation figures for January to June 2002 after listing too many free giveaways as paid-for bulks. The embarrassing errors affected 23 magazines in total.

• **What is the press doing about it?** Many publishers – including Emap and many regional newspapers – have now stopped giving away free or discounted copies, leading to lower circulation but greater transparency in the figures. Many nationals are also reducing the number of bulks and discounted copies they distribute.

media in December 2002, in which the prime minister's wife, Cherie Blair, admitted contacting the solicitor of Peter Foster, a convicted Australian fraudster who was facing deportation, for advice on buying some flats in Bristol. After initial scepticism, the paper later backed her husband over war in Iraq; then in June 2003 conducted its own poll calling for a referendum on the new European constitution. The newspaper's editor, Paul Dacre, earned £830,000 in 2002, it was announced, making him Britain's best paid national newspaper editor. But the intense 14-hour days perhaps took their toll: Dacre had major heart surgery in 2003 and took two months off.

The Mail's slanging match with the **Daily Express** – its closest rival for right-of-centre readers – continued. In a rare interview, Dacre called Express owner Richard Desmond an "appalling man" who is bad for British journalism; Desmond hit back by calling Mail owner Lord Rothermere "arrogant". Plugging his possible launch of a London evening paper to rival the Evening Standard, Desmond said he wasn't going to be beaten by a man whose ancestors sympathised with Hitler; Lord Rothermere said Desmond's words were "unfounded slander". The advertising standards authority also had to be called in to police a row over a mailshot by (Daily Mail owner) Associated attacking the Express; the regulator refuted the Mail's claim that readers had permanently defected from the Express in their "thousands".

The Mail later turned its guns on the Daily Telegraph, the right-of-centre broadsheet. After the Telegraph axed its "Peterborough" diary column, the Mail appropriated the title for itself.

Cost-cutting continued at Desmond's Express. Journalists protested at a plan to move up to 100 production jobs to the paper's offices near Preston. Desmond also confirmed he had considered producing sections of its magazine supplements in India – but said the idea had been dismissed.

At the **Sunday Express**, meanwhile, journalists received an email in July 2003 from news editor Jim Murray ordering a change in editorial style. As well as aiming for "six sex stories a week", the memo said, the paper needed to "be on the side of the middle classes ... We should always be looking for someone to blame!"

Broadsheets

The right-of-centre **Daily Telegraph** still sold the most of the daily broadsheets – but its headline circulation figure dipped below a million for the first time in almost 50 years, as it decided to cut back on bulk sales (see explainer, opposite). In February it redesigned its front page, expanded its comment section and ditched its "Peterborough" column in preference of the more metropolitan "London spy". It also tweaked the masthead. But in May there were fears of a cash crisis at the paper's owner, Hollinger, which suspended the rights of some of its shareholders to redeem their stock for cash.

It is not always easy to define the **Times**: it lies somewhere between the respectable, conservative Thunderer of old and the more downmarket paper of the price-war years. Under Robert Thomson, it has tried to concentrate on accessible presentation. One of Thomson's first changes was replacing the traditional diary with clock logo ("too mannered", said Thomson) with the Thunderer, a column designed to give journalists and others a chance to rant; but the redesign of the T2 tabloid proved unpopular. The paper scored a coup in late 2002 by serialising the diaries of Edwina Currie; and it hired Tina Brown, the former editor of Talk magazine, as a weekly US columnist. In its leader columns, it used measured tones to advocate war against Iraq. Circulation was significantly down, at below 620,000 for the six months to June 2003 (all figures exclude bulks).

The left-of-centre **Guardian** made a series of changes to the body of the paper in March 2003. It moved the weekly Editor supplement inside the broadsheet section, turning it into a daily page of comment and analysis from other publications around the world; and gave more prominence to media news, giving MediaGuardian a daily page within the business section. In its leader columns, the Guardian urged caution at every stage of war. Circulation remained stable at about 386,000 from January to June.

The Observer continued to expand, launching Observer Music Monthly to complement its monthly magazines on food and sport. Its circulation remained solid at above 430,000.

In most trouble were the **Independent** and the **Independent on Sunday**; both papers' circulation declined to below 185,000. Chief executive Ivan Fallon said he thought cost-cutting at the paper had gone far enough; but March 2003 saw boss Tony O'Reilly sell the group's profitable regional newspapers to raise cash. The papers were the most anti-war of the broadsheets: the Independent on Sunday printed posters attempting to lure readers away from the Observer.

The **Financial Times**' circulation slipped in Britain as the global economic outlook turned bleak: with profits falling to £1m in 2002 from £31m the year before, the paper launched a £3m revamp and marketing campaign in April. The idea was to widen the paper's appeal to allow the paper compete with the improved business sections of other broadsheets: "We want to re-emphasise that we are a newspaper for the business community and are the only newspaper you need to read that will give you everything you need to know," editor Andrew Gowers told the Observer. The paper also launched a Saturday magazine, and planned to launch an Asia edition in autumn 2003.

The bottom line

The advertising recession hit the newspaper industry hard in 2002: nationals lost 6.4% of their advertising revenue, which fell to under £2bn (just 13.7% of total UK spend). Advertisers pulled campaigns in early 2003 as images of the Iraqi war dominated pages. Broadsheet and mid-market newspapers at least increased their sales by about 130,000 in the first few days of war, but circulation departments warned that the rise would not be sustained.

Faced with rising distribution costs and uncertain advertising revenue, newspapers agreed to cooperate to increase their share of advertising: the Newspaper Marketing Agency, chaired by Maureen Duffy, was formed to market papers to the public. But as the Sun and the Daily Mirror continued their spat, and the Daily Mail picked fights with both the Daily Telegraph and the Daily Express, not all analysts held out hope for the move. "It's akin to chairing the Israeli-Arab peace talks," Ellis Watson, former marketing director of the Sun, told MediaGuardian.co.uk at the time. With their eyes firmly on the bottom line, almost all newspapers claimed to have abandoned the "price wars" once and for all. The Mirror put its price up to 32p throughout the country, and the Sun signalled that it would also return to full cover price.

National Sunday circulations

	Editor	Jan–Jun 03	Jan–Jun 02	% change
Tabloids				
News of the World	Andy Coulson	3,875,857	3,953,525	−1.96
Mail on Sunday	Peter Wright	2,278,959	2,289,835	−0.47
Sunday Mirror	Tina Weaver	1,643,936	1,758,140	−6.49
People	Mark Thomas	1,120,222	1,318,034	−15.01
Sunday Express	Martin Townsend	881,556	831,223	6.05
Daily Star Sunday	Hugh Whittow	472,228	–	–
Broadsheets				
Sunday Times	John Witherow	1,639,130	1,393,694	−1.76
Sunday Telegraph	Dominic Lawson	710,581	726,950	−2.25
Observer	Roger Alton	430,546	427,701	0.66
Independent on Sunday	Tristan Davies	182,646	191,106	−4.43

all figures exclude bulks

National daily circulations

	Editor	Jan–Jun 03	Jan–Jun 02	% change
Tabloids				
Sun	Rebekah Wade	3,525,993	3,441,396	2.46
Daily Mail	Paul Dacre	2,350,541	2,353,287	−0.12
Daily Mirror	Piers Morgan	1,989, 174	2,109,630	−5.71
Daily Express	Chris Williams	902,325	878,911	2.66
Daily Star	Peter Hill	851,781	758,836	12.25
Broadsheets				
Daily Telegraph	Martin Newland*	911,584	954,067	−4.45
Times	Robert Thomson	616,308	662,597	−6.98
Financial Times	Andrew Gowers	434,907	458,149	−5.07
Guardian	Alan Rusbridger	386,585	386,468	0.03
Independent	Simon Kelner	184,016	191,360	−3.84

Source: ABC, www.abc.org.uk   * replaced Charles Moore in September 2003

The Guardian, the Independent, the Telegraph and the Times all raised their cover prices by 5p in September and October 2002. Charles Moore, the Telegraph's editor, insisted his paper was still too cheap: "The Telegraph costs 55p for something like a novel and is 100 times more interesting," he said. The Observer also went up 10p to £1.30, and the Sunday Times was up 20p to £1.40.

Privacy and regulation

There was a gladiatorial scrap in 2003 over the future of the press complaints commission (PCC), the self-regulatory body for newspapers and magazines. The arena was the culture select committee inquiry into privacy and media intrusion, headed by Labour MP Gerald Kaufman.

Appearing before the committee, editors divided along tabloid-broadsheet lines. Independent editor Simon Kelner told the committee there were "real problems" with the PCC, and called for an ombudsman to act as a court of appeal; Guardian editor Alan Rusbridger said a "further step" beyond the PCC might enable people to appeal without recourse to law.

THAT NATURE CORRESPONDENT'S SNOOPING ROUND AGAIN, CALL THE PCC.

Tabloid editors and PCC executives were subjected to more of a grilling. Sun editor Rebekah Wade admitted payments had been made to police – prompting MP Chris Bryant to ask Les Hinton, News International chairman and PCC code committee chairman, if it was "time for you to clean up your act". The same MP asked PCC director Guy Black why People editor Neil Wallis was sitting on the commission when he had two adjudications against him: "You might as well have Neil Hamilton and Jonathan Aitken sitting on the committee for parliamentary standards."

Piers Morgan was typically bullish, characterising his appearance before the committee as a "ritual bollocking". Paul Dacre, editor of the Daily Mail, joined other editors in dismissing the idea of an ombudsman, calling it "repugnant". He later told Press Gazette that Kelner had betrayed the industry: "He sits on the moral high ground on his tiny, diminishing, heavily subsidised circulation and sits in judgment on the industry. His comments were yet again based on a total misconception of how the PCC works."

Perhaps predictably, the inquiry's final report in June 2003 was an assault on the excesses of tabloid journalism. Running to 60 pages, it recommended a privacy law – rejected by the culture secretary, Tessa Jowell, the same afternoon – and proposed to fine editors for breaching the PCC code.

The committee was critical of the running of the PCC, saying it should be more proactive and proceed immediately to adjudication if the complainant wants it to do so. It called for a ban on payments to police for information; increased lay membership; the independent ombudsman to hear appeals; adjudications to be more prominently published; and for editors of persistently offending newspapers to stand down from the commission: a policy of "three strikes and you're out".

Sir Christopher Meyer, incoming chairman of the PCC, kept a low profile over the issue after the report's publication – despite having put forward an eight-point reform plan that fell some way short of the committee's report. Indeed, it was broadsheet editors who had their own reasons to be angry in July, when the Guardian was found in breach of the PCC code by paying prisoner John Williams for his column, "A Life Inside". Editors of all five national dailies wrote to the PCC to protest at its interpretation of the code.

▶▶ NATIONAL NEWSPAPER CONTACTS, page 36

"Yes, Anthea, I feel guilty about what we have done to you"
Piers Morgan (April 2003)

PCC adjudications, January to July 2003

- **January 2003:** The PCC partially upholds a complaint by Bernie Ecclestone and his wife and daughter about an article in the Mail on Sunday, saying "intimate details" of Ms Ecclestone's relationship with her boyfriend John Keterman – "including an account of its sexual aspect" – were in breach of the code.

- **February 2003:** The People is found to have breached the code by publishing pictures of actress Julie Goodyear sitting in her back garden, taken using long-lens photography.

- **May 2003:** The Independent is cleared of anti-Semitism over a cartoon depicting the Israeli prime minister, Ariel Sharon, eating a baby as tanks and helicopters attack a town, in allusion to the Goya painting "Saturn devouring one of his own children". Solicitors for Mr Sharon argue that the cartoon alluded to the "blood libel" that Jews preyed on Christian children; but the PCC accepts the cartoonist's position that he had intended to satirise an Israeli attack on Gaza City as a form of "macabre electioneering".

- **July 2003:** The Sun is found guilty of "one of the most serious forms of physical intrusion into privacy" by publishing transcripts of taped telephone calls involving Peter Foster – the convicted conman at the centre of the "Cheriegate" affair – and his mother.

- **July 2003:** The Guardian learns that the PCC is to exonerate the News of the World for paying £10,000 to convicted criminal Florim Gashi, the witness at the centre of the collapsed "Posh kidnap" trial. The adjudication is delayed, however, following an unprecedented intervention from the attorney general.

- **July 2003:** The PCC finds the Guardian to be in breach of its code by paying prisoner John Williams £720 for an article, ruling that sections describing encounters with Jeffrey Archer are not in the public interest. Editors of all five national daily broadsheets write to the PCC in protest.

"I'm more inclined to shoot from the hip than not"

Sir Christopher Meyer, incoming chairman of the Press Complaints Commission (April 2003)

National newspaper ownership			
Group name	**Market share Jan–Jun 03**	**Titles**	**Executive control**
News International	35.2%	Sun Times Sunday Times News of the World	Rupert Murdoch
Daily Mail and General Trust	19.0%	Daily Mail Mail on Sunday	Lord Rothermere
Trinity Mirror	17.1%	Daily Mirror Sunday Mirror People	Victor Blank
Northern and Shell	13.8%	Daily Express Daily Star Sunday Express Daily Star Sunday	Richard Desmond
Hollinger International	7.2%	Daily Telegraph Sunday Telegraph	Conrad Black
Guardian Media Group	3.2%	Guardian Observer	Scott Trust
Pearson	3.0%	Financial Times	Pearson board
Independent Newspapers	1.5%	Independent Independent on Sunday	Tony O'Reilly

Market share based on national daily and Sunday ABCs, January to June 2003

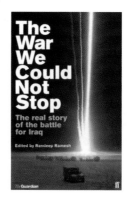

The regionals

Key contact

Newspaper Society
Bloomsbury House
74–77 Great Russell St
London WC1B 3DA
020 7636 7014
ns@newspapersoc.org.uk
www.newspapersoc.org.uk

Mergers and acquisitions

- **October 2002:** Scottish Radio Holdings buys four small Scottish titles – including the Wee County News – from the UK's fourth-biggest newspaper publisher, Johnston Press. Estimated circulation: 34,000.

- **December 2002:** Newsquest (Gannett) buys the Glasgow Herald, Glasgow Evening Times and Sunday Herald from the Scottish Media Group for a reported £216m. Estimated circulation: 251,000.

- **March 2003:** Newsquest in action again, buying Independent News and Media's regional newspapers in London. The deal was referred to the competition commission in May, but if approved it would see 45 papers – including the Hackney Gazette, the Kentish Times Series and the Barking & Dagenham Post – change hands for £60m. Estimated circulation: 600,000.

Consolidation, consolidation, consolidation: that is the reality for Britain's regional press. With Newsquest's purchase of Independent News & Media's 45 London newspapers in March 2003, more than 75% of regional newspaper circulation was controlled by just four owners. In the six months to June 2003, the same four – Trinity Mirror, Newsquest (owned by US behemoth Gannett), the Daily Mail & General Trust and Johnston Press – sold or distributed more than 50m of the 69m papers circulated each week, and owned 799 of the 1,300 titles.

Fewer than 100 regional titles were dailies; but together, dailies commanded more than half of the circulation (36.7m copies a week). By contrast there were 23 Sunday papers, circulating 2.3m copies; 535 weekly paids, selling almost 6.5m; and 643 weekly frees, distributing almost 24.7m copies.

The Newspaper Society, which lobbies for the publishers of regional and local newspapers, is passionate about the strength of the industry. Some 84% of UK adults read a regional newspaper, it boasts, compared with 68% who read a national newspaper; since 1999, regional press coverage (readership) has grown by 1.9%, while national press coverage has fallen by 4.7%. Regional press has a high "solus readership": 40% of those who read a regional paper do not read a national daily. The industry employs about 34,000 people, nearly a quarter of whom are editorial staff.

But for the past two years, regional circulation has been on the slide; about 3m fewer papers are now sold or distributed than in the six months to December 2000. This can partly be explained by the decision by many papers to stop giving away copies for free or at discounted prices; the idea being to increase the percentage of actively purchased and full rate sales (see explainer on ABCs, page 21). It is also slightly offset by the good performance of weekly papers (so often seen as the poor relations to the dailies); weeklies increased their circulation for the fourth successive year to December 2002, and the Kent Messenger, the top-selling paid weekly, sold more than 60,000 copies a week in 2002–03.

The biggest-selling regional daily was once again the Daily Record in Scotland; but it lost almost 10% of its circulation in the year to June 2003, selling 514,000 copies, after being hit by the price war between the Sun and the Scottish Daily Mirror. It hit further trouble in February 2003, when it faced a boycott by fans of Glasgow Celtic FC over its coverage over a fracas in Newcastle between a photographer and several Celtic players. Editor Peter Cox eventually left in May, after claiming to have secured an exclusive interview with Prince William which then fell through. Cox was replaced by Bruce Waddell.

The biggest selling Sunday title was the Daily Record's stablemate, the Sunday Mail.

London's Evening Standard was again the biggest selling regional evening title. New editor Veronica Wadley initially presided over a fall in circulation, dipping below 400,000 in December 2002 amid accusations of making the paper too similar to the Daily Mail; but in January 2003 sales bounced back over 424,000 in the run-up to the introduction of the congestion charge in London. The Standard's sister titles, Metro, performed well in seven cities throughout the UK; but the group faced a possible challenge to its supremacy, as Richard Desmond revealed plans to launch a free evening paper in London (see box).

Advertising expenditure on regional newspapers rose by 1.3% to £2.9bn in 2002 – over 20% of total UK ad spend. In particular, Johnston Press, the fourth largest regional media company, reported strong advertising growth in the second half of 2002.

▶▶ REGIONAL NEWSPAPER CONTACTS, page 37

"Richard Desmond is an appalling man. He is bad for British journalism. He is bad for public life and he is bad for civilised standards"

Daily Mail editor Paul Dacre on Richard Desmond (September 2002)

"I don't want to sound like Jesus, but this is what I was born to do. They are everything I hate and I am everything they hate"

Richard Desmond on the Daily Mail (April 2003)

■ Can Desmond take on the Standard and win?

Richard Desmond: taking on London?

Richard Desmond's Express Newspapers ruffled feathers at the Evening Standard in 2003, revealing plans to launch an evening free paper to compete against it in London under editor Nick Ferrari. Desmond released mock-ups of his freesheet, which he said would have an initial print run of 500,000 and be called the Evening Mail or the London Evening Mail. But Associated, owners of both the Standard and the Daily Mail, went to court in June and effectively gained control of the "Mail" trademark in London for themselves.

Some commentators suspected that Desmond's move might be a bluff, designed only to put the wind up Associated. If the launch does go ahead, the freesheet – probably titled PM – would be run as a tight ship with a large amount of news agency copy, the formula used so successfully by Associated's free urban morning titles, Metro.

Express Newspapers would also have a tough battle against the Standard's stranglehold on distribution outlets in London: the Standard has agreements in place with station owners London Underground and Railtrack, plus its own vendors on the streets outside. Desmond is hoping to break this stranglehold by taking the case to the office of fair trading.

In the regions

- Harry Blackwood, the Hartlepool Mail editor who became embroiled in a political row after a man in a monkey costume beat Labour's candidate in the Hartlepool mayoral election, was sacked in March after three-and-a-half years in the job. Blackwood had accused local MP Peter Mandelson of attempting to get him sacked, but the former Northern Ireland minister denied the claim. Mail owners Johnston Press gave no reason for the dismissal, but denied that political pressure could have any bearing on editorial policy.

- Former Matlock Mercury editor Don Hale, who won an OBE after successfully campaigning against Stephen Downing's conviction for the murder of Wendy Sewell in 1973, defended his work after Derbyshire police said Mr Downing remained the "only suspect" for the killing. Ms Sewell's widower suggested in February that Hale had distorted evidence, but Hale said: "I know my submissions were fair."

- Sir Ray Tindle, owner of more than 120 local newspapers, ordered his editors to block the publication of letters or articles opposing war in Iraq. "I do this, not just as a proprietor to the newspapers, but as someone who served as a British soldier from 1944 to 1947 in the Far East," said Sir Ray.

Top 10 publishers, July 2003

	Papers	Weekly circ	% share
Trinity Mirror	234	15,833,079	23.1
Newsquest	212	10,594,420	15.4
Northcliffe Newspapers Group *	105	9,011,708	13.1
Johnston Press	241	8,373,902	12.2
Associated Newspapers*	7	6,485,985	9.5
Guardian Media Group	44	2,609,191	3.8
Archant	62	2,445,852	3.6
Midland News Association	19	2,149,244	3.1
Independent News & Media**	27	1,503,255	2.2
DC Thomson	3	1,218,051	1.8
Top 10	**954**	**60,224,687**	**87.8**
All publishers	**1,286**	**68,621,913**	**100**

* owned by Daily Mail and General Trust
** selling regional newspapers to Newsquest
Source: Newspaper Society

Top 10 frees Jan-June 2003

	Distribution
Metro London	426,552
Manchester Metro News	300,101
Nottingham & Long Eaton Topper	212,113
The Glaswegian (19 May–29 June)	161,889
Southampton Advertiser	153,250
Nottingham Recorder	152,989
Herald & Post, Edinburgh (5 May–29 June)	147,926
Wirral Globe	134,756
Bexley Dartford & Gravesend News Shopper	131,825
Kingston Guardian	128,895

Source: Newspaper Society

Top 20 paid regionals Jan–June 2003

	Circulation	Year-on-year %	Frequency	Editor
Sunday Mail, Scotland*	621,721	−7.2	Sunday	Allan Rennie
Sunday Post, Dundee	547,256	−5.8	Sunday	David Pollington
Daily Record, Scotland*	514,000	−9.4	morning	Bruce Waddell
Evening Standard, London*	418,891	0.5	evening	Veronica Wadley
Express & Star, West Midlands	169,527	−3.1	evening	Adrian Faber
Manchester Evening News	158,143	−2.6	evening	Paul Horrocks
Liverpool Echo (Mon–Fri)	142,837	−2.9	evening	Mark Dickinson
Birmingham Evening Mail	113,973	−6.4	evening	Roger Borrell
Belfast Telegraph	108,615	–	evening	Edmund Curran
Leicester Mercury	99,258	−3.5	evening	Nick Carter
Newcastle Evening Chronicle (Mon–Fri)	96,831	−2.7	evening	Paul Robertson
Evening Times, Glasgow (Mon–Fri)	95,761	−3.0	evening	Charles McGhee
Sunday Life, Belfast	92,843	−3.4	Sunday	Martin Lindsay
Press & Journal, Aberdeen	92,406	–	morning	Derek Tucker
Sunday Sun, Newcastle	88,583	−4.6	Sunday	Peter Montellier
Sunday Mercury, Birmingham	87,997	−6.5	Sunday	David Brookes
Shropshire Star	86,196	−2.4	evening	Sarah Jane Smith
Herald, Glasgow	85,932	−6.0	morning	Mark Douglas-Home
Dundee Courier & Advertiser	85,234	−2.9	morning	Bill Hutcheon
Yorkshire Evening Post, Leeds (Mon–Fri)	85,064	−6.2	evening	Neil Hodgkinson

Source: Newspaper Society

Keeping it local **Charlie Burgess**

The regional press has always been regarded as the poor relation in the printed media business in Britain when compared to the huge circulations of the daily tabloids and the glossiness of the, er, glossy magazines. But this position belies the economic might of the regionals and their ability to speak to their local communities.

The money side is impressive. Ad spending in the regional press last year amounted to nearly £2.9bn, representing 21% of total ad spend in the UK and second only to TV. And while the spend in national papers dropped by 14.5% in the years 2000–02, the regionals were up by 3.9%. Total spend in the regional press is nearly six times the total spend on radio, and more than the combined total for direct mail, poster, radio, internet and cinema. The regional press is the only above-the-line media to have increased ad spend every year for the last decade.

Circulations, while none spectacularly huge in themselves, add up in total to 68 million a week. The basic trends are that metropolitan evenings are faring badly, but weeklies are doing well – 54% of them increased their circulation in the six months from January to June this year, compared to the same period a year ago.

So it seems people want the very local news that weeklies provide by the bucketload – and that advertisers recognise this.

So where is the downside? First, there is the state of the big metropolitan evenings – and mornings – who suffer because they are in competition with the nationals and other news outlets.

Second, journalists in the provincial press lag way behind their national cousins. The obvious reason for this is that regional groups pay the local market rate, and most groups operate near monopolies in their areas. This is also why print journalists in the US are comparatively badly paid.

Third, there is the perceived threat that a plurality of voices is being snuffed out by the increasing dominance of a few huge owners. The top four companies – Trinity Mirror, Newsquest (part of US company Gannett), Northcliffe (owned by Associated) and Johnston Press – account for almost 64 per cent of the total circulation. One by one the locally owned groups are selling out. The corporate owners, however, counter this by saying they allow their papers to be locally managed and that they benefit from sharing back office costs and big investment in state-of the-art regional printing centres.

And it's true. Even the local Women's Institute flower arrangements look a lot better in colour. And keeping it local seems to be the way to stay ahead. Finding a way to reprint the local telephone directory on a weekly basis seems to do the trick.

Charlie Burgess is media editor of the Guardian and non-executive director of CN Group, a local media company based in Cumbria

Magazines

Launches and folds

Launches

- July 2003: Trash, bi-monthly from Condé Nast and Ministry of Sound
- July 2003: Jaunt, shopping and travel glossy from Sibella Publishing
- March 2003: Word, glossy monthly on music, books and entertainment, from Development Hell
- March 2003: New!, Richard Desmond's latest celebrity offering
- February/March 2003: Sunday Times Travel magazine, glossy contract title published by River Publishing every two months
- October 2002: Closer, celebrity weekly from Emap Elan
- Winter 2002: ThreeSixty, upmarket travel and lifestyle quarterly

Folds:

- July 2003: Muzik. Latest victim of dance music magazine fallout
- December 2002: Ministry, casualty of the dance magazine collapse
- September 2002: Menswear (Emap Communications), merges with Drapers Record
- August 2002: PC Magazine (VNU). Title folds with 100,000 readers, but magazine maintains internet presence

By comparison with the rest of the media, magazines are in fair health. There are over 8,000 separate periodical titles carrying advertising in the UK, as listed by British Rate and Data (Brad), of which about two-thirds are business titles and one-third consumer. Total magazine circulation was almost 79m copies in 2002, up more than 3% on the year before.

Consumer magazines performed best: circulation rose 3.2% year-on-year in the six months to June 2003, and ad spend rose to £785m over 2002 – recovering all the ground lost in the difficult first six months of the year. Most publishers promised new launches: IPC, the country's biggest consumer publisher, pledged £2m for a "launch factory" headed by Mike Soutar at King's Reach Tower, and Emap also said it was in "launch mode".

TV magazines continued to top the newsstand ABCs, but a new generation of celebrity titles took all the plaudits. Hello! and OK! made headlines as they went to court over Catherine Zeta-Jones' wedding (see Law, page 242) – but both lost ground to Emap's Heat and the new market leader, IPC's Now. OK! owner Richard Desmond responded by launching New!, a magazine bearing some similarities to Now in look and feel, and sold more than 300,000 copies.

In the women's glossy market, Glamour consolidated its position ahead of long-time market leader Cosmopolitan. But although Cosmo's shopping-and-orgasms formula seemed dated in the UK, it continued to work worldwide: 2003 saw the magazine launch its 50th international edition.

The lads' mags began to find their level after the boom-and-bust of the late 1990s. FHM put on 3.4% in January to June 2003, but remained some way off its 1999 peak of over 700,000. But in July former Loaded editor James Brown sold his company IFG, publisher of Jack magazine, to Felix Dennis for £5.1m.

Sylvia Auton became the new chief executive of IPC in March, replacing Sly Bailey, who had joined Trinity Mirror. Emap rejoined the FTSE-100 in September 2002, and posted better than expected profits in 2003.

Both National Magazines and Emap had to restate their circulation figures for a total of 23 magazines for January to June 2002, after free bulks had been included in the headline figure (see explainer on ABCs). Worst affected was clubbers' magazine Mixmag, which revealed a 26.2% drop to 74,070, compared with a 0.1% decline reported in August; the magazine posted another sharp fall in January 2003, as readers appeared to desert the dance sector.

Business press and trades

Perhaps two-thirds of magazines in the country are business titles: Brad lists more than 5,300 business magazines and newspapers which accept advertising, but some estimates say there are as many as 10,000 if every journal and newsletter is taken into account. More than 175,000 people are said to be employed in the industry.

But it has been a difficult period for the sector. The business press thrives on offering advertisers access to a clearly defined market, and so depends on them for more than three-quarters of its revenue – but its share of total spend in the UK fell by 9.4% in 2002, to £1.1bn (less than 8% of total). Reed Business Information was one publisher forced to trim its cost base at the start of 2003, axing five senior posts in a major restructuring.

In June 2003 Jean Morgan, reporter on journalists' trade paper Press Gazette, retired after 19 years in the job. Editors and senior hacks queued up to offer plaudits. According to the Sun's editor, Rebekah Wade: "In this industry no one is irreplaceable but, in Jean, I think we have found the exception."

Customer magazines

Customer magazines – publications produced on contract for companies, and often distributed free of charge for marketing purposes – are a fast-growing industry. The sector was worth £313m in 2002, up 7.6% on the previous year, and 18% on 2000; while 11 out of the top 20 consumer titles in July to December 2002 were customer magazines. As in other areas of the media industry, the sector is consolidating, as independent contract publishers are bought by larger media services groups and by mainstream publishers.

▶▶ MAGAZINE CONTACTS, page 63

Further reading

■ Press

MediaGuardian
media.guardian.co.uk/presspublishing
Press Gazette: weekly trade magazine
www.pressgazette.co.uk

■ Books

The Shipping News E ANNIE PROULX, FOURTH ESTATE (1993)
The tale of Quoyle, who finds his peace via car wrecks on the front page
Scoop EVELYN WAUGH, PENGUIN MODERN CLASSICS
Classic Fleet Street satire
More Corrections and Clarifications IAN MAYES, GUARDIAN (2002)
Latest collection of corrections that have appeared in the Guardian, plus columns by readers editor Ian Mayes
Stick It Up Your Punter, The Uncut Story of the Sun Newspaper
PETER CHIPPINDALE AND CHRIS HORRIE, POCKET BOOKS (1999)
The Elements of Journalism: What the people should know and what the public should expect BILL KOVACH AND TOM ROSENTIEL,
GUARDIAN BOOKS, £7.99 Sets out the fundamental questions that all journalists – whether writing for a local newspaper or the internet, or broadcasting on radio and television – face as they compile their stories.

■ Web only

World News: newspaper search engine
www.worldnews.com
DotJournalism
www.journalism.co.uk
Poynter Online
www.poynter.org

■ Other resources

Audit Bureau of Circulations
www.abc.org.uk
Newspaper Society
www.newspapersoc.org.uk
Periodical Publishers Association
www.ppa.org.uk
Association of Publishing Agencies
www.apa.co.uk

The magazine market **Ciar Byrne**

To most people, magazines mean newsagents' racks stuffed with glossy titles on everything from teenage fashion to trout fishing, but these consumer magazines are just one element in the publishing pantheon.

Britain's £7bn magazine industry can be divided into three main sectors: titles aimed at the ordinary reader, B2B magazines for business professionals and customer magazines produced on behalf of clients.

There were 8,338 magazines listed with Brad (British Rate and Data) in 2002/2003 (down slightly from 8,460 in 2001–2002). 5,208 of these were consumer magazines and 3,130 business titles.

Advertisers spent more than £2bn on magazines during 2001, making them the largest advertising medium after television and regional newspapers.

Consumer magazines have done well in attracting advertising at a time when many media sectors have seen a slump – their share of the advertising market increased by over 11% between 2000 and 2002.

However, business titles have not fared quite so well, their share of the market having fallen slightly with the decline in recruitment advertising.

Readers spend £605m a year more on consumer magazines today than they did 10 years ago – more than 80% of the population and 84% of women read consumer titles.

The consumer magazine market is dominated by a handful of big publishers – including Emap, the National Magazine Company, Condé Nast and IPC – each of which controls a wide portfolio of titles.

IPC, the biggest magazine publisher in the UK, was taken over by the world's largest media conglomerate, AOL Time Warner, for £1.15bn in 2001.

Celebrity magazines are more popular than ever. According to official figures released in February 2003, the circulation of the four main existing titles – OK!, Hello!, Heat and Now – soared between 2002 and 2003.

OK!, which is owned by Express Newspapers boss Richard Desmond, recorded the highest circulation in the celebrity sector. However, thousands of these were bulk giveaways, whereas IPC's Now was the best seller at newsagents' counters.

Not to be put off, Mr Desmond launched another cut-price celebrity magazine, New!, in February 2003. The success of irreverent gossip weekly Heat also grew, with circulation increasing by more than 50% in the year to February 2003.

Heat publisher Emap aimed to build on its successful format by bringing out Closer, a new celebrity title aimed at an older female reader, in September 2002.

Women's magazines strutted their stuff in a market as competitive as ever. Handbag-sized glossy Glamour finally broke through the 500,000 circulation barrier to become the best-selling women's magazine thanks to its A5 format and cheaper price.

Glamour and Heat shared the prize for best consumer title of the year at the 2003 Periodical Publishers' Association (PPA) awards.

French publisher Hachette strengthened its UK arm by buying Emap out of a joint venture to publish fashion magazine Elle and "middle youth" women's title Red, and by purchasing teen magazine publisher Attic Futura for £40m in August 2002.

Former Loaded editor James Brown was forced to sell I Feel Good, the independent publishing company he founded to publish magazines such as the recently launched A5-sized men's title Jack, to Felix Dennis Publishing for £5.1m in May 2003.

In the B2B sector, 94% of business professionals read one or more publications regularly, while 70% see them as essential reading.

Customer magazines have also enjoyed a tremendous boom in recent years – the sector is now worth £366m and turnover has risen by 127% since 1995. A quick glance at the top 10 highest-circulation magazines in February 2003 shows that the first six are all customer titles, published on behalf of Sky, the AA, Orange, Boots, Safeway and Asda.

The PPA is the trade association for the UK magazine industry, representing 80% of the magazine market by turnover, comprising around 400 companies and 2,300 consumer, business and professional magazines.

Ciar Byrne is press and publishing correspondent for MediaGuardian.co.uk

Top 50 consumer magazines

	Magazine	actively purchased (%)	Jan–Jun 2003	Jan–Jun 2002	year-on-year (%)
1	Sky Customer Magazine	0	6,124,572	5,347,370	14.5
2	AA Magazine	0	4,679,950	5,040,942	−7.2
3	O Magazine	0	2,500,025	2,497,833	0.1
4	Asda Magazine	0	2,012,733	1,519,740	32.4
5	Boots Health & Beauty	0	1,870,390	2,190,897	−14.6
6	**What's on TV**	100	**1,689,621**	**1,666,475**	**1.4**
7	Safeway Magazine	0	1,505,064	1,757,190	−14.3
8	O Magazine – Pay Monthly	0	1,500,052	1,499,088	0.1
9	The Somerfield Magazine	0	1,345,789	1,362,143	−1.2
10	**Saga Magazine**	44	**1,239,221**	**1,191,120**	**4.0**
11	**Take a Break**	100	**1,225,116**	**1,207,384**	**1.5**
12	**Radio Times**	98	**1,161,019**	**1,155,064**	**0.5**
13	O Magazine – Pay As You Go	0	999,973	998,745	0.1
14	**TV Choice**	100	**967,807**	**861,810**	**12.3**
15	**BBC Pre-School Magazines**	100	**954,463**	**1,087,249**	**−12.2**
16	**Reader's Digest**	97	**860,562**	**948,865**	**−9.3**
17	**FHM**	100	**600,568**	**580,738**	**3.4**
18	**That's Life**	100	**592,036**	**590,162**	**0.3**
19	**Now**	100	**590,544**	**570,279**	**3.6**
20	Club News	0	582,346	–	–
21	**Glamour**	100	**576,832**	**520,193**	**10.9**
22	**Chat**	100	**575,585**	**515,000**	**11.8**
23	**Time – Europe**	83	**575,163**	**600,090**	**−4.2**
24	**Woman**	100	**571,482**	**631,451**	**−9.5**
25	**Heat**	100	**565,484**	**478,924**	**18.1**
26	**TV Times**	97	**529,632**	**570,809**	**−7.2**
27	Homebase Ideas	0	497,090	–	–
28	**OK! Magazine**	86	**489,882**	**575,307**	**−14.8**
29	**Woman's Own**	100	**484,705**	**518,861**	**−6.6**
30	VM The Vauxhall Magazine	0	478,018	400,100	19.5
31	Ikea Room	2	474,270	359,524	31.9
32	**Woman's Weekly**	100	**465,500**	**498,268**	**−6.6**
33	**Cosmopolitan**	100	**462,157**	**470,180**	**−1.7**
34	**The Economist**	81	**457,722**	**449,852**	**1.7**
35	Scamp's Diary	0	450,173	497,660	−9.5
36	Auto Exchange Group	0	441,790	473,471	−6.7
37	**Best**	100	**414,739**	**424,569**	**−2.3**
38	Emma's Diary Pregnancy Guide	0	405,735	406,050	−0.1
39	**Good Housekeeping**	100	**400,253**	**386,080**	**3.7**
40	**Bella**	100	**398,009**	**444,622**	**−10.5**
41	**TV Quick**	100	**394,251**	**440,080**	**−10.4**
42	**Yours**	100	**386,591**	**368,006**	**5.1**
43	**Marie Claire**	95	**376,476**	**393,748**	**−4.4**
44	**People's Friend**	100	**375,443**	**398,035**	**−5.7**
45	**Auto Trader***	100	**365,549**	**366,726**	**−0.3**
46	**BBC Gardeners' World**	99	**360,236**	**350,064**	**2.9**
47	Unlimited	0	349,500	–	–
48	**Hello**	99	**347,461**	**517,883**	**−32.9**
49	Renault Magazine	0	342,086	350,594	−2.4
50	**New!**	93	**339,035**	–	–

Source: ABC.
Newsstand titles in bold.
* Guardian Media Group

Top 10s: Women's v men's magazines

		Jan–Jun 2003	Year-on-year (%)
Women's weeklies			
1	Take a Break	1,225,116	1.5
2	That's Life	592,036	0.3
3	Now	590,544	3.6
4	Chat	575,585	11.8
5	Woman	571,482	−9.5
6	Heat	565,484	18.1
7	OK!	489,882	−14.8
8	Woman's Own	484,705	−6.6
9	Woman's Weekly	465,500	−6.6
10	Best	414,739	−2.3
	Total	**5,560,749**	**−0.4***
Women's lifestyle			
1	Glamour	576,832	10.9
2	Cosmopolitan	462,157	−1.7
3	Good Housekeeping	400,253	3.7
4	Yours	386,591	5.1
5	Marie Claire	376,476	−4.4
6	Company	330,617	5.9
7	Prima	330,045	−4.4
8	Woman & Home	283,025	7.6
9	New Woman	275,648	−9.1
10	Vogue	202,259	1.6
	Total	**3,623,903**	**+1.8***
Men's lifestyle			
1	FHM	600,568	3.4
2	Loaded	261,937	−15.2
3	Maxim	251,117	−7
4	Men's Health	218,756	1
5	GQ	120,741	3.7
6	Wallpaper	110,920	−15.4
7	Front	110,323	−21.5
8	Bizarre	101,209	4.3
9	Esquire	69,193	23.2
10	Stuff	61,977	9.6
	Total	**1,906,741**	**−3.4***

Source: ABC

* Year-on-year change refers to listed 10 titles only (not previous year's top 10)

Press Contacts

National daily newspapers

Daily Express
Express Newspapers
Ludgate House, 245 Blackfriars Rd
London SE1 9UX
020 7928 8000
news.desk@express.co.uk
www.express.co.uk

Daily Mail
Associated Newspapers
Northcliffe House, 2 Derry St
Kensington, London W8 5TT
020 7938 6000
news@dailymail.co.uk
www.dailymail.co.uk

Daily Mirror
Trinity Mirror, 1 Canada Square
Canary Wharf London E14 5AP
020 7293 3000
mirrornews@mgn.co.uk
new@mirror.co.uk
www.mirror.co.uk

Daily Sport
Sport Newspapers
19 Great Ancoats St
Manchester M60 4BT
0161 236 4466
nick.appleyard@
    sportnewspapers.co.uk
www.dailysport.net

Daily Star
Express Newspapers
Ludgate House, 245 Blackfriars Rd
London SE1 9UX
020 7928 8000
dailystarnewsdesk@dailystar.co.uk
www.dailystar.co.uk

Daily Telegraph
Telegraph Group, 1 Canada Square
Canary Wharf, London E14 5DT
020 7538 5000
dtnews@telegraph.co.uk
corporate.affairs@telegraph.co.uk
www.telegraph.co.uk

Financial Times
The Financial Times Group
1 Southwark Bridge
London SE1 9HL
020 7873 3000
news.desk@ft.com
joanna.manning-cooper@ft.com
www.ft.com

The Guardian
Guardian Media Group
119 Farringdon Rd
London EC1R 3ER
020 7278 2332
home@guardian.co.uk
press@guardian.co.uk
www.guardian.co.uk

The Independent
Independent News and Media (UK)
Independent House, 191 Marsh Wall
London E14 9RS
020 7005 2000
newseditor@independent.co.uk
m.ellison@independent.co.uk
www.independent.co.uk

The Sun
News Group Newspapers
1 Virginia St, London E98 1NW
020 7782 4000
news@the-sun.co.uk
lournacarmichael@the-sun.co.uk
www.the-sun.co.uk

The Times
Times Newspapers
1 Pennington St, London E98 1TT
020 7782 5000
home.news@thetimes.co.uk
www.thetimes.co.uk

National Sunday newspapers

The Business
Sunday Business Publishing,
PA News Centre
292 Vauxhall Bridge Rd
London SW1V 1SS
020 7961 0000
jdeacon@thebusiness.press.net
www.thebusinessonline.com
Also published on Monday

Daily Star Sunday
Express Newspapers
Ludgate House, 245 Blackfriars Rd
London SE1 9UX
020 7928 8000
sundaystar@dailystar.co.uk
www.megastar.co.uk

The Independent on Sunday
Independent News and Media (UK)
Independent House, 191 Marsh Wall
London E14 9RS
020 7005 2000
newseditor@independent.co.uk
www.independent.co.uk

The Mail on Sunday
Associated Newspapers
Northcliffe House, 2 Derry St
Kensington, London W8 5TT
020 7938 6000
news@mailonsunday.co.uk

News of the World
News Group Newspapers
1 Virginia St, London E98 1NW
020 7782 4000
newsdesk@news-of-the-world.co.uk
hayley.barlow@notw.co.uk
www.thenewsoftheworld.co.uk

The Observer
Guardian Media Group
119 Farringdon Rd
London EC1R 3ER
020 7278 2332
home@guardian.co.uk
www.observer.co.uk

The People
MGN, 1 Canada Square
Canary Wharf, London E14 5AP
020 7293 3000
peoplenews@mgn.co.uk
www.people.co.uk

The Sunday Express
Express Newspapers
Ludgate House, 245 Blackfriars Rd
London SE1 9UX
020 7928 8000
james.murray@express.co.uk
www.express.co.uk

Sunday Mirror
MGN, 1 Canada Square
Canary Wharf, London E14 5AP
020 7293 3000
news@sundaymirror.co.uk
www.sundaymirror.co.uk

Sunday Sport
Sport Newspapers
19 Great Ancoats St
Manchester M60 4BT
0161 236 4466
nick.appleyard@
    sportnewspapers.co.uk
www.sundaysport.com

The Sunday Telegraph
Telegraph Group, 1 Canada Square
Canary Wharf, London E14 5DT
020 7538 5000
stnews@telegraph.co.uk
dtnews@telegraph.co.uk
www.telegraph.co.uk

The Sunday Times
Times Newspapers, 1 Pennington St
London E98 1TT
020 7782 5000
news@Sunday-times.co.uk
lucy.dupuis@sunday-times.co.uk
www.sunday-times.co.uk

Regional press publishers

Archant

Head office
Prospect House, Rouen Rd
Norwich NR1 1RE
01603 628311
epd@archant.co.uk
www.archant.co.uk

Archant Anglia
01603 740222
www.archant.co.uk/content
/Businesses/regional/anglia.asp

Archant Central Scotland
0141 427 7878
www.archant.co.uk/content
/Businesses/regional/central
_scotland.asp

Archant Devon
01392 888444
www.archant.co.uk/content
/Businesses/regional/devon.asp

Archant East London & Essex
01708 771500
www.archant.co.uk/content
/Businesses/regional/East
_London.asp

Archant Hertfordshire
01727 866166
www.archant.co.uk/content
/Businesses/regional
/hertfordshire.asp

Archant North East Scotland
01779 472017
www.archant.co.uk/content
/Businesses/regional/ne
_scotland.asp

Archant North London
020 7433 0000
www.archant.co.uk/content
/Businesses/regional/norfolk.asp

Archant Somerset
01934 422622
www.archant.co.uk/content
/Businesses/regional/North_
London.asp

Archant Suffolk
01473 230023
www.archant.co.uk/content
/Businesses/regional
/somerset.asp

Daily Mail & General Trust

www.dmgt.co.uk

Associated Newspapers
Northcliffe House, 2 Derry St
London W8 5TT
020 7938 6000
www.associatednewspapers.co.uk

Northcliffe Newspapers Group
31–32 John St, London WC1N 2QB
020 7400 1100
www.thisisnorthcliffe.co.uk

Guardian Media Group

164 Deansgate
Manchester M3 3RN
0161 832 7200
www.gmgplc.co.uk

Independent News and Media

www.independentnewsmedia.com

Head office
2023 Bianconi Avenue
Citywest Business Campus
Naas Rd, Dublin 24, Ireland
00 353 1 466 3200

Johnston Press

www.jptalk.co.uk

Head office
53 Manor Place
Edinburgh EH3 7EG
0131 225 3361

Anglia Newspapers
01284 768911

East Lancashire Newspapers
01282 426161

East Midlands Newspapers
01733 555111

Lancashire Evening Post
01772 254841

Portsmouth Publishing and Printing
023 9266 4488

Sheffield Newspapers
0114 276 7676

South Yorkshire Newspapers
01302 819111

Yorkshire Post Newspapers
0113 243 2701

Yorkshire Weekly Newspapers
01924 375111

Newsquest Media

www.newsquest.co.uk

Head office
Newspaper House
34/44 London Rd
Morden, Surrey SM4 5BX
020 8640 8989

Herald and Times
0141 302 7000

Newsquest (Bradford)
01274 729511

Newsquest (Cheshire/Merseyside)
01925 434000

Newsquest Essex
01268 522792

Newsquest (Hereford)
01432 274413

Newsquest (Kendal)
01539 720555

Newsquest (Lancashire)
01772 824631

Newsquest (London)
020 8646 6336

Newsquest (Midlands South)
01562 633333

Newsquest (North East)
01325 381313

**Newsquest (North London, Herts
and Bucks)**
020 8359 5830

Newsquest (Oxfordshire)
01865 425262

Newsquest (Southern)
023 8042 4777

Newsquest (Southwest)
01256 461131

Newsquest (Sussex)
01273 544544

Newsquest (Wales & Western)
01633 810000

Newsquest (Wiltshire)
01793 528144

Newsquest (York)
01904 653051

Trinity Mirror

www.trinitymirror.com

Trinity Mirror
4th Floor, Rear Wing,
191–197 North Circular Rd
Dublin 7
00 353 1 8688600

UK Regional Head Office
Chronicle House, Commonhall Street
Chester CH1 2AA
01244 340151

Birmingham Post & Mail
0121 236 3366

Century Newspapers
028 9068 0000

Chester Chronicle
01244 340151

Coventry Newspapers
024 7663 3633

Derry Journal
028 7127 2200

Gazette Media
01642 245401

Liverpool Daily Post & Echo
0151 227 2000

Midland Weekly Media
0121 234 5073

Newcastle Chronicle & Journal
0191 2327500

Scottish and Universal
01698 283200

Trinity Mirror Southern
0118 950 3030

Western Mail & Echo
029 2058 3583

Avon

see **Somerset & Avon**

Bedfordshire

Bedford Times & Citizen
01234 405060
www.bedfordtoday.co.uk
Weekly (Thu)
Bedfordshire Journal
0116 233 3635
Weekly (Tue)
Bedfordshire on Sunday
01234 304403
www.seriousaboutnews.co.uk
Sunday
Biggleswade Chronicle
01767 222333
www.biggleswadetoday.co.uk
Weekly (Fri)
Dunstable Gazette
01582 700600
www.lutontoday.co.uk
Weekly (Tue)
Leighton Buzzard Observer
01525 858400
www.miltonkeynestoday.co.uk
Weekly (Tue)
Leighton Buzzard On Sunday
01908 809000
Sunday
Leighton Linslade Citizen
01525 858400
www.miltonkeynestoday.co.uk
Weekly free (Thu)
Luton Dunstable Herald & Post
01582 700600
www.lutontoday.co.uk
Weekly (Thu)
Luton News
01582 700600
Weekly (Tue)
Luton/Dunstable on Sunday
01582 700800
www.seriousaboutnews.co.uk
Sunday

Berkshire

Advertiser (Newbury)
01635 524111
www.newburynews.co.uk
Weekly (Tue)
Berkshire News
01895 255508
Weekly free (Wed)
Bracknell & Ascot Times
www.getbracknell.co.uk
Bracknell & Wokingham Standard
0118 918 3000
Weekly (Thu)
Maidenhead Advertiser
01628 680680
www.maidenhead-advertiser.co.uk
Weekly (Fri)
Newbury & Thatcham Chronicle
01635 32771
www.icberkshire.co.uk
Weekly (Thu)

Newbury Weekly News
01635 524111
www.newburynews.co.uk
Weekly (Thu)
Property Chronicle, Reading
0118 950 3030
www.icberkshire.co.uk
Weekly (Thu)
Reading & Thames Valley Guardian
01926 883688
Weekly (Fri)
Reading Central
0118 918 3000
www.readingcentral.co.uk
Weekly (Thu)
Reading Evening Post
0118 918 3000
www.getreading.co.uk
Daily
Slough & Langley Express
01753 825111
www.icberkshire.co.uk
Weekly (Thu)
Slough Observer
01753 523355
www.thisisslough.com
Weekly (Wed)
Thames Valley Weekly
01235 553444
www.courier-newspapers-
oxford.co.uk/tvw.htm
Weekly (Fri)
Thatcham News
01635 524111
www.newburynews.co.uk
Weekly (Thu)
Weekend Express
01753 825111
www.icberkshire.co.uk
Weekly (Fri)
Windsor, Ascot & Eton Express
01753 825111
www.icberkshire.co.uk
Weekly (Thu)
Windsor, Ascot & Maidenhead Observer
01753 523355
www.thisiswindsor.com
Weekly (Fri)
Wokingham Times
0118 918 3000
www.getwokingham.co.uk
Weekly (Wed)

Buckinghamshire

Buckinghamshire Advertiser
01494 792626
www.buckinghamtoday.co.uk
Weekly (Thu)
Buckinghamshire Echo
0116 222 3366
Weekly (Tue)
Bucks Advertiser
01296 318300
www.aylesburytoday.co.uk
Weekly (Fri)
Bucks Examiner
01494 792626
Weekly (Thu)

Bucks Free Press
01494 755000
www.bucksfreepress.co.uk
Weekly (Fri)
Bucks Herald
01296 318300
www.bucksherald.co.uk
Weekly (Wed)
Hillingdon Times
01494 755000
www.hillingdontimes.co.uk
Weekly (Thu)
Milton Keynes Citizen
01908 651200
www.miltonkeynes.co.uk
Weekly free (Thu)
Milton Keynes Journal
0116 233 3635
Weekly (Tue)
MK News
01908 809000
www.seriousaboutnews.co.uk
Weekly (Wed)
South Bucks Star
01494 755000
www.hillingdontimes.co.uk
Weekly (Thu)
Sunday Citizen
01908 371133
Weekly free (sun)

Cambridgeshire

Cambridge Evening News
01223 434434
www.cambridge-news.co.uk
Daily
Cambridge Crier
01223 434434
Weekly (Thu)
Cambridge Weekly News
01223 434434
www.cambridge-news.co.uk
Weekly (Wed)
Chatteris Times
01354 652621
www.cambs-times.co.uk
Weekly (Thu)
Ely Standard
01354 652621
www.ely-standard.co.uk
Weekly (Thu)
Ely Weekly News
01353 667415
www.cambridge-news.co.uk
Weekly (Wed)
Fenland Citizen
01945 586100
Weekly (Wed)
Huntingdon Town Crier
01480 402100
Weekly (Thu)
Huntingdon Weekly News
01480 467670
www.cambridge-news.co.uk
Weekly (Wed)
Hunts Post
01354 652621
www.huntspost.co.uk
Weekly (Wed)

Peterborough Citizen
01733 555111
www.peterboroughnow.co.uk
Weekly (Wed)
Peterborough Evening Telegraph
01733 555111
www.peterboroughnow.co.uk
Daily
Peterborough Herald & Post
01733 318600
www.peterborough.net
/heraldandpost
Weekly (Thu)
Ramsey Post
01354 652621
Weekly (Thu)
Soham Standard
01354 652621
www.ely-standard.co.uk
Weekly (Thu)
St Neots Town Crier
01480 402100
Weekly (Thu)
St Neots Weekly News
01480 467670
www.cambridge-news.co.uk
Weekly (Wed)
Whittlesey Times
01354 652621
www.cambs-times.co.uk
Weekly (Thu)
Wisbech Standard
01354 652621
www.wisbech-standard.co.uk
Weekly (Thu)

Cheshire

Advertiser (South Cheshire, Congleton, Sandbach, Alsager)
01788 602525
Weekly free (Thu)
Buy Sell
01270 250970
Weekly (Thu)
Chester & District Standard
01244 304500
Weekly (Thu)
Chester Chronicle
01244 340151
www.cheshirenews.co.uk
Weekly (Fri)
The Chronicle – Sandbach Edition
01959 564766
www.thisischeshire.co.uk
Weekly (Thu)
Community News
01781 602525
Weekly
Congleton Chronicle
01260 273737
www.beartown.co.uk
Weekly (Fri)
Congleton Guardian
01260 280686
www.thisischeshire.co.uk
Weekly (Fri)
Crewe & Nantwich Guardian
01925 434000
www.thisischeshire.co.uk
Weekly (Thu)

Crewe Chronicle
01270 256631
www.cheshirenews.co.uk
Weekly (Wed)
Ellesmere Port Pioneer
0151 355 5181
www.cheshirenews.co.uk
Weekly (Wed)
Ellesmere Port Standard
01244 304500
www.ellesmereportstandard.co.uk
Weekly (Thu)
Guardian Midweek
01925 434000
www.thisischeshire.co.uk
Weekly free (Tues)
Knutsford Express
0161 480 4491
www.manchesteronline.co.uk/news
papers/knutsford.html
Weekly (Thu)
Knutsford Guardian
01925 434000
www.thisischeshire.co.uk
Weekly (Wed)
Macclesfield Express
0161 480 4491
www.macclesfield-express.co.uk
Weekly (Wed)
Macclesfield Times & Poynton Times
0161 480 4491
www.manchesteronline.co.uk
/newspapers/macctimes.html
Weekly (Thu)
Mid & South Cheshire Guardian
01925 434000
www.thisischeshire.co.uk
Weekly (Wed)
Newton & Golborne Guardian
01925 434000
www.thisischeshire.co.uk
Weekly (Wed)
Northwich Guardian
01925 434000
www.thisischeshire.co.uk
Weekly (Wed)
Runcorn & Widnes Weekly News
0151 4245921
http://icccheshireonline.icnetwork
.co.uk/chroniclenewspapers
/weeklynews/
Weekly (Thu)
Runcorn and Widnes Herald & Post
0151 4245921
Weekly (Fri)
South Cheshire Mail
01270 256631
www.cheshirenews.co.uk
Weekly (Wed)
Warrington Guardian
01925 434000
www.thisischeshire.co.uk
Weekly (Thu)
Warrington Mercury
01925 434000
www.thisischeshire.co.uk
Weekly free (Fri)
Wilmslow Citizen
0161 491 5700
Fortnightly (Thu)

Wilmslow Express
0161 480 4491
www.thewilmslowexpress.co.uk
Weekly (Wed)
Winsford & Middlewich Guardian
01925 434000
www.thisischeshire.co.uk
Weekly (Wed)

Cleveland

Darlington, South Durham and North Yorkshire Herald & Post
01325 262000
www.icteesside.co.uk
Weekly (Fri)
Evening Gazette
01642 245401
www.icteesside.co.uk
Daily
Hartlepool Mail
01429 274441
www.hartlepoolmail.co.uk
Daily
Hartlepool Star
01429 274441
Weekly free (Thu)
Peterlee Star
01429 274441
Weekly free (Thu)
Stockton & Billingham Herald & Post
01642 245401
www.icteesside.co.uk
Weekly (Wed)
Teesside Focus
01332 365811
Weekly free (Mon)
Teesside Herald & Post
01642 245401
www.icteesside.co.uk
Weekly (Wed)
East Cleveland Advertiser
01325 381313
www.theclarion.co.uk
Weekly free (Fri)

Cornwall

Bude & Stratton Post
01566 772424
Weekly (Thu)
Camborne and Redruth Packet
01326 213333
www.thisisthewestcountry.co.uk
Weekly free (Wed)
Camelford & Delabole Post
01566 772424
Weekly (Thu)
Camelford, Delabole, Boscastle & Tintagel Journal Gazette
01566 772424
Weekly (Fri)
Cornish & Devon Post
01566 772424
Weekly (Thu)
Cornish Guardian
01208 78133
www.cornishguardian.co.uk
Weekly (Thu)

The Cornishman
01736 362247
www.thisiscornwall.co.uk
Weekly (Thu)
Cornish Times
01579 342174
www.liskeard-today.co.uk
Weekly (Fri)
Falmouth Packet
01326 213333
www.thisisthewestcountry.co.uk
Weekly (Thu)
Hayle Times
01736 795813
Weekly (Fri)
Helston Gazette
01326 213333
www.thisisthewestcountry.co.uk
Weekly free (Wed)
Helston Packet
01326 213333
www.thisisthewestcountry.co.uk
Weekly (Thu)
**Launceston, Holsworthy,
Bude & Stratton Journal Gazette**
01566 772424
Weekly (Fri)
Mid Cornwall Advertiser
01726 66755
www.midcornwall-today.co.uk
Monthly (middle of month)
North Cornwall Advertiser
01208 815096
www.northcornwall-today.co.uk
Monthly (first week)
Penwith Pirate
01326 213333
www.thisisthewestcountry.co.uk
Weekly free (Wed)
St Ives Times & Echo
01736 795813
Weekly (Fri)
Sunday Independent (Cornwall)
01752 206600
www.thisisthewestcountry.co.uk
Sunday
The West Briton
01872 271451
www.thisiscornwall.co.uk
Weekly (Thu)

Cumbria

Barrow Advertiser
01229 821835
www.cumbria-online.co.uk
Weekly free (Thu)
Carlisle East Cumbrian Gazette
01228 612600
www.cumbria-online.co.uk
Weekly (Thu)
Carlisle News & Star
01228 612600
www.news-and-star.co.uk
Daily (Mon–Thu)
**Cumberland and Westmorland
Herald**
01768 862313
www.cwherald.com
Weekly (Sat)

Cumberland News
01228 612600
www.cumberland-news.co.uk
Weekly (Fri)
Keswick Reminder
01768 772140
www.keswickreminder.co.uk
Weekly (Fri)
Lakeland Echo
01524 833111
www.lakelandtoday.co.uk
Weekly (Fri)
Northwest Evening Mail
01229 821835
www.nwemail.co.uk
Daily
South Lakes Citizen
01539 720555
www.thisisthelakedistrict.co.uk
Weekly free (Wed)
West Cumberland Times and Star
01900 607600
www.times-and-star.co.uk
Weekly (Fri)
Westmorland Gazette
01539 720555
www.thisisthelakedistrict.co.uk
Weekly (Fri)
Westmorland Messenger
01539 720555
www.thisisthelakedistrict.co.uk
Weekly (Wed)
Whitehaven News
01946 595100
www.whitehaven-news.co.uk
Weekly (Thu)
**Whitehaven/Workington West
Cumbrian Gazette**
01228 612600
www.cumbria-online.co.uk
Weekly (Thu)

Derbyshire

Derby Evening Telegraph
Northcliffe House, Meadow Rd
Derby, Derbyshire DE1 2DW
01332 291111
www.thisisderbyshire.co.uk
Daily
Ashbourne News Telegraph
01283 512345
www.ashbournenewstelegraph.co.uk
Weekly (Wed)
Belper Express
01332 291111
Weekly free (Tue)
Bolsover & District Advertiser
01246 202291
Fortnightly free (Wed)
Buxton Advertiser
01298 22118
www.buxtonadvertiser.co.uk
Weekly (Wed)
Buxton Times
01298 22118
Weekly free (Fri)
Chesterfield Advertiser
01246 504500
Weekly free (Fri)
Chesterfield Express
01246 504500
Weekly free (Wed)

Derby Express
01332 291111
Weekly free (Tue s)
Derby Trader
01332 253999
Weekly (Thu)
Derbyshire Times
01246 504500
www.derbyshiretimes.co.uk
Weekly (Thu)
Dronfield Advertiser
01246 202291
Weekly free (Wed)
Eckington Leader
01246 434343
Weekly (Fri)
Glossop Chronicle
0161 304 7691
Weekly (Thu)
High Peak Courier
01298 22118
Weekly free (Fri)
Ilkeston & Ripley Trader
01332 253999
Weekly (Fri)
Ilkeston Advertiser
0115 944 4411
www.ilkestonadvertiser.co.uk
Weekly (Thu)
Ilkeston Express
01332 291111
Weekly free (Tue s)
Ilkeston Shopper
0115 944 4411
Weekly free (Tue s)
Matlock Mercury
01629 582432
www.matlockmercury.co.uk
Weekly (Fri)
Peak Advertiser
01629 812159
Fortnightly free (Thu)
Peak Times
01629 582432
Weekly free (Fri)
Stratford & Banbury Why
01527 588000
Weekly free (Fri)

Devon

Brixham News
01803 862585
Weekly (Thu)
Dawlish Post
01626 355566
www.dawlish-today.co.uk
Weekly (Fri)
Evening Herald
01752 765500
www.thisisplymouth.co.uk
Daily
Exmouth Herald
01392 888444
www.archantdevon.co.uk
    /exmouthherald.asp
Weekly free (Fri)
Express and Echo
01392 442211
www.thisisexeter.co.uk
Daily

Herald Express
01803 676000
www.thisissouthdevon.co.uk
Daily
Holsworthy Post
01566 778220
Weekly (Fri)
Honiton Advertiser
01297 33034
www.honiton-today.co.uk
Weekly (Wed)
Ivybridge, South Brent and South Hams Gazette
01548 853101
www.ivybridge-today.co.uk
Weekly ((Fri)
Journal (Exmouth)
01392 888444
www.archantdevon.co.uk/journal.asp
Weekly (Thu)
Kingsbridge, Salcombe & South Hams Gazette
01548 853101
Weekly ((Fri)
Leader (Exeter)
01392 442211
Weekly (Wed)
Mid-Devon Advertiser
01626 355566
Weekly (Fri)
Mid-Devon Star
01823 365151
www.thisisthewestcountry.co.uk
Weekly (Fri)
Midweek Herald
01392 888444
www.archantdevon.co.uk
/midweekHERALD.asp
Weekly (Wed)
North Devon Gazette & Advertiser
01392 888444
www.northdevongazette.co.uk
Weekly (Wed)
North Devon Journal
01271 343064
www.thisisnorthdevon.co.uk
Weekly (Thu)
Okehampton Times
01822 613666
www.okehampton-today.co.uk
Weekly (Thu)
Ottery Advertiser
01297 33034
Weekly (Wed)
Plymouth Extra
01752 765500
Weekly free (Thu)
Plympton Plymstock & Ivybridge News
01548 853101
Weekly ((Fri)
Princetown Times
01822 613666
Weekly (Thu)
Sidmouth Herald
01392 888444
www.archantdevon.co.uk
/sidmouthHERALD.asp
Weekly (Fri)
South Devon & Plymouth Times
01803 862585
Weekly (Thu)

South Hams Gazette & Dartmouth Chronicle
01548 853101
www.dartmouth-today.co.uk
Weekly ((Fri)
Sunday Independent (Devon)
01752 206600
www.thisisthewestcountry.co.uk
Sunday
Tavistock Times Gazette
01822 613666
www.tavistock-today.co.uk
Weekly (Thu)
Teignmouth Post & Gazette
01626 355566
Weekly (Fri)
Torbay Weekender
01803 676000
Weekly (Thu)
Totnes News
01548 853101
Weekly ((Fri)
Totnes Times Gazette
01803 862585
Weekly (Thu)
Western Morning News
01752 765500
www.thisisplymouth.co.uk
Daily

Dorset

Bournemouth Advertiser
01202 554601
Weekly free (Thu)
Bridport News
01305 830930
www.thisisdorset.net/dorset
/bridportandlyme
Weekly (Fri)
Christchurch Advertiser
01425 476986
Weekly free (Thu)
Daily Echo
01202 554601
www.thisisdorset.net
Daily
Dorchester Advertiser
01305 830930
www.thisisdorset.net
Weekly (Thu)
Harborough Mail
01858 462626
www.harboroughmail.co.uk
Weekly (Thu)
Poole Advertiser
01202 675413
Weekly free (Thu)
Post Advertiser
01297 561205
Monthly free (Mon)
Swanage and Wareham Advertiser
01929 427428
www.thisisdorset.net
Weekly free (Thu)
Weymouth & Portland Advertiser
01305 830930
www.thisisdorset.net
Weekly (Thu)

Durham

Northern Echo (Darlington)
Newsquest (North East), Priestgate
Darlington, County Durham DL1 1NF
01325 381313
www.thisisthenortheast.co.uk
Daily
Chester-le-Street Advertiser
01325 381313
www.thisisthenortheast.co.uk
Weekly free (Thu)
Consett & Stanley Advertiser
01325 381313
www.thisisthenortheast.co.uk
Weekly free (Thu)
Darlington & Stockton Times
01325 381313
www.thisisthenortheast.co.uk
Weekly (Fri)
Darlington Herald & Post
01642 245401
Weekly (Fri)
Darlington, Aycliffe & Sedgefield Advertiser
01325 381313
www.thisisthenortheast.co.uk
Weekly free (Wed)
Durham Advertiser
01325 381313
www.thisisthenortheast.co.uk
Weekly free (Thu)
Peterlee Star
0191 501 7208
Weekly free (Thu)
South Durham Herald & Post
01642 245401
Weekly (Fri)
Wear Valley Advertiser
01325 427428
www.thisisthenortheast.co.uk
Weekly free (Wed)

East Sussex

The Argus
01273 544544
www.thisisbrightonandhove.co.uk
Daily
Bexhill News
01424 854242
Weekly free (Wed)
Bexhill-On-Sea Observer
01424 854242
www.bexhilltoday.co.uk
Weekly (Fri)
Brighton & Hove Leader
01273 544544
www.thisisbrightonandhove.co.uk
Weekly (Fri)
Eastbourne & District Advertiser
01323 722091
www.eastbournetoday.co.uk
Weekly free (Thu)
Eastbourne Gazette
01323 722091
www.eastbournetoday.co.uk
Weekly (Wed)
Eastbourne Herald
01323 722091
www.eastbournetoday.co.uk
Weekly (Fri)

Hastings & St Leonards News
01424 854242
Weekly free (Wed)
Hastings and St Leonards Observer
01424 854242
www.hastingstoday.co.uk
Weekly (Fri)
Hastings News
01424 854242
Weekly (Fri)
Horley Life
01273 544544
Weekly (Thu)
Rye Observer
01424 854242
www.ryeandbattletoday.co.uk
Weekly (Fri)
South Coast Leader
01273 544544
www.thisisbrightonandhove.co.uk
Weekly (Fri)
Sussex Express
01273 480601
www.sussexexpress.co.uk
Weekly (Fri)

Essex

Barking & Dagenham Post
020 8491 2000
Weekly (Thu)
Barking & Dagenham Recorder
020 8478 4444
www.recorderonline.co.uk
Weekly (Thu)
Basildon Yellow Advertiser
01268 503400
www.trinitymirrorsouthern.co.uk
Weekly (Thu)
Billericay & Wickford Gazette
01277 219222
www.thisisessex.co.uk
Weekly (Wed)
Brentwood Gazette
01277 219222
www.thisisessex.co.uk
Weekly (Wed)
Brentwood Yellow Advertiser
01268 503400
www.trinitymirrorsouthern.co.uk
Weekly free (Fri)
Brentwood, Billericay & Havering Recorder
020 8478 4444
Weekly (Fri)
Castle Point Yellow Advertiser
01268 503400
www.trinitymirrorsouthern.co.uk
Weekly free (Thu)
Chelmsford Yellow Advertiser
01268 503400
www.trinitymirrorsouthern.co.uk
Weekly free (Thu)
Clacton Gazette
01255 221221
www.thisisessex.co.uk
Weekly
Dunmow Broadcast and Recorder
01371 874537
www.dunmow-broadcast.co.uk
Weekly free

Epping & Waltham Yellow Advertiser
01268 503400
www.trinitymirrorsouthern.co.uk
Weekly free (Fri)
Essex Chronicle
01245 600700
www.thisisessex.co.uk
Weekly (Wed/Thu)
Essex Courier
01277 634635 x233
www.essexcourier.co.uk
Essex Enquirer
01277 627400
Weekly (Thu)
Essex County Standard
01206 506000
www.nqe.info
Weekly
Evening Echo
01268 522792
www.thisisessex.co.uk
Harlow Star
01279 866366
www.herts-essex-news.co.uk
Weekly (Thu)
Harold Gazette
01277 219222
www.thisisessex.co.uk
Weekly (Wed)
Harold Recorder
020 8478 4444
www.recorderonline.co.uk
Weekly (Fri)
Island Times
01702 477666
Monthly (Tue)
Leigh Times
01702 477666
Fortnightly (Tue)
Ongar and North Weald Gazette
01277 219222
www.thisisessex.co.uk
Weekly (Wed)
Rayleigh Times
01702 477666
Monthly (Tue)
Romford & Havering Post (Romford, Hornchurch & Districts)
020 8491 2000
Weekly free (Wed)
Romford Recorder
01708 771500
www.recorderonline.co.uk
Weekly (Fri)
Saffron Walden Observer
01279 866366
Weekly (Thu)
Saffron Walden Weekly News
01799 528033
Weekly (Wed)
Southend Times
01702 477666
Weekly (Tue)
Southend Yellow Advertiser
01268 503400
www.trinitymirrorsouthern.co.uk
Weekly free (Thu)
Thurrock Recorder
020 8478 4444
www.recorderonline.co.uk
Weekly (Fri)

Thurrock Yellow Advertiser
01268 503400
www.trinitymirrorsouthern.co.uk
Weekly free (Thu)
Thurrock, Lakeside & Grays Post
020 8491 2000
Weekly (Thu)
Walden Local
01799 516161
Weekly (Wed)

Gloucestershire

Cheltenham/Tewkesbury News
01242 271900
Weekly free (Thu)
Cotswold Journal
01432 274413
www.thisistewkesbury.com
/the_cotswolds
Weekly (Thu)
Forest of Dean and Wye Valley Review
01594 841113
www.forest-and-wye-today.co.uk
Weekly free (Wed)
The Forester
01594 820600
www.thisisgloucestershire.co.uk
Weekly (Thu)
Gloucester Citizen
01452 424442
www.thisisgloucestershire.co.uk
Daily
Gloucester News
01452 424442
Weekly free (Thu)
Gloucestershire Echo
01242 271900
www.thisisgloucestershire.co.uk
Daily
Gloucestershire Gazette
01453 544000
www.thisisgloucestershire.co.uk
Weekly (Fri)
Jobs Today – Cheltenham and Gloucester
01453 544000
included in all publications
Stroud News & Journal
01453 762142
www.thisisstroud.com
Weekly (Wed)
Wilts & Gloucestershire Standard
01285 642642
www.thisiscirencester.com
Weekly (Thu)

Hampshire

The News (Portsmouth)
Portsmouth Publishing & Printing
The News Centre, Military Rd
Hilsea, Portsmouth
Hampshire PO2 9SX
023 9266 4488
www.thenews.co.uk
Daily

Southern Daily Echo
Newsquest (Southern)
Newspaper House, Test Lane
Redbridge, Southampton SO16 9JX
023 8042 4777
www.dailyecho.co.uk
Daily

Aldershot Courier
01252 339760
Weekly free (Wed)

Aldershot Mail
01252 339760
www.surreyad.co.uk/Mediapack
website/aldmailframeright.htm
Weekly (Tue)

Aldershot News
01252 339760
www.aldershot.co.uk
Weekly (Fri)

Alresford Advertiser
01252 716444
Weekly free (Fri)

Alton Gazette
01420 84446
Weekly (Wed)

Alton Times & Mail
01252 716444
Weekly free (Tue)

Andover Advertiser
01264 323456
www.andoveradvertiser.co.uk
Weekly (Fri)

Basingstoke Gazette
01256 461131
www.thisishampshire.net
/hampshire/basingstoke
Weekly (Fri)

Basingstoke Observer
01256 694120
www.basingstoke.co.uk
Weekly (Thu)

Bordon Post
01730 264811
Weekly (Wed)

Bordon Times & Mail
01252 716444
Weekly free (Tue)

Eastleigh News Extra
01962 841772
www.thisishampshire.net
Weekly free (Thu)

Fareham & Gosport Journal
023 9266 4488
Weekly free (Thu)

Fareham & Gosport News
023 9266 4488
Daily

Gazette Extra
01256 461131
Weekly (Wed)

Hamble Valley Journal
023 9266 4488
Weekly free (Thu)

Hampshire Chronicle
01962 841772
www.thisishampshire.net
/hampshire/winchester
Weekly (Fri)

Hampshire & Surrey Guardian
024 7655 1796
Daily

Hants & Dorset Avon Advertiser
01722 426500
Weekly (Wed)

Hants and Surrey Post Dispatch
01420 88949
Fortnightly free (Mon)

Hart Courier
01252 339760
www.surreyad.co.uk
Weekly (Fri)

Havant & Waterlooville Journal
023 9266 4488
Weekly free (Thu)

Havant & Waterlooville News
023 9266 4488
Daily

Hayling Directory
023 9263 7870
Yearly free

Hayling Islander
023 9263 7870
www.haylingtoday.co.uk
Monthly free

Holiday Islander
023 9263 7870
Yearly free

Isle of Wight County Press
01983 521333
www.iwcp.co.uk
Weekly (Fri)

Liphook Times & Mail
01252 716444
Weekly free (Tue s)

Lymington Times
01425 613384
Weekly (Fri)

Meon Valley News
023 9226 8626
Monthly (Mon)

Mid Hampshire Observer
01962 859559
www.hantsmedia.co.uk
Weekly (Wed)

Monday Gazette
01256 461131
www.thisishampshire.net
Weekly (Mon)

New Forest Post
01590 613888
www.thisishampshire.net/
Weekly (Thu)

New Milton Advertiser
01425 613384
Weekly (Fri)

Petersfield Mail
01252 716444
Weekly free (Tue)

Petersfield Post
01730 264811
www.petersfield.co.uk
Weekly (Wed)

Portsmouth & Southsea Journal
023 9266 4488
Weekly free (Thu)

Romsey Advertiser
023 8042 4777
www.thisishampshire.net
/hampshire/romsey
Weekly (Fri)

Salisbury Journal
01722 426500
www.thisissalisbury.co.uk
Weekly (Thu)

Southampton Advertiser
023 8042 4777
Weekly (Thu)

Surrey & Hampshire Guardian
024 7663 0550
Weekly free (Thu)

Winchester News Extra
01962 841772
www.thisishampshire.net
Weekly free (Thu)

Winchester Shopper
023 8042 4777
Sunday

Hereford & Worcester

Express and Star (Kidderminster)
01384 355355
www.expressandstar.com
Daily

Alcester Chronicle
01527 453500
www.thisisworcestershire.co.uk
Weekly (Wed)

Bromsgrove Advertiser
01527 879211
www.thisisworcestershire.co.uk
Weekly (Wed)

Bromsgrove Messenger
01527 879211
www.thisisworcestershire.co.uk
Weekly (Wed)

Bromsgrove Standard & Droitwich Standard
01527 574111
www.bromsgrovestandard.co.uk
Weekly free (Fri)

Droitwich Advertiser
01527 879211
www.thisisdroitwichspa.co.uk
Weekly (Wed)

Evesham Journal
01432 274413
www.thisisworcestershire.co.uk
/worcestershire/evesham
Weekly (Thu)

Hereford Admag
01432 376120
Weekly (Wed)

Hereford Journal
01432 355353
www.herefordjournal.co.uk
Weekly free (Wed)

Kidderminster Chronicle
01562 829500
Weekly (Wed)

Kidderminster Shuttle
01562 633333
www.thisisworcestershire.co.uk
/worcestershire/kidderminster
Weekly (Wed)

Kidderminster Times
01562 633333
www.thisisworcestershire.co.uk
/worcestershire/kidderminster
Weekly (Thu)

Leominster Journal
01432 355353
www.shropshirestar.co.uk
Weekly free (Wed)

Redditch Advertiser
01527 453500
www.thisisworcestershire.co.uk
/worcestershire/redditch
Weekly (Wed)
Redditch Standard & Alcester Standard
01527 588688
www.redditchstandard.co.uk
Weekly free (Fri)
Ross Gazette
01989 562007
www.ross-today.co.uk
Weekly (Thu)
Ross-on-Wye Journal
01432 355353
www.shropshirestar.co.uk
Weekly free (Wed)
Stourport News
01299 822901
Weekly free (Thu)
Why Evesham
01527 588000
Weekly free (Fri)
Why Redditch & District
01527 588000
Weekly free (Fri)
Why Worcester, Malvern & Kidderminster
01527 588000
Weekly free (Fri)
Worcester Standard
01905 726200
www.worcesterstandard.co.uk
Weekly free (Fri)

Hertfordshire

Barnet & Potters Bar Times
020 8359 5830
www.barnettimes.co.uk
Weekly (Thu)
Borehamwood & Elstree Times
020 8359 5830
www.borehamwoodtimes.co.uk
Weekly (Fri)
Edgware & Mill Hill Times
020 8359 5830
www.edgwaretimes.co.uk
Weekly (Thu)
Harpenden Voice
01582 700800
Fortnightly (Fri)
Hemel Hempstead Gazette
01442 898408
www.hemelonline.co.uk
Weekly (Wed)
Hemel Hempstead Herald Express
01442 898408
Weekly (Thu)
Hendon & Finchley Times
020 8359 5830
www.hendontimes.co.uk
Weekly (Thu)
Hertfordshire Mercury
01992 526625
www.herts-essex-news.co.uk
Weekly (Fri)
Hertfordshire News
01926 431601
Weekly (Mon)

Hertfordshire on Sunday
01582 700800
Sunday
Hertfordshire Star
01992 526625
www.herts-essex-news.co.uk
Weekly (Wed)
Herts & Essex Observer
01279 866366
www.herts-essex-news.co.uk
Weekly (Thu)
Herts Advertiser
01727 866166
www.hertsad.co.uk
Weekly (Thu)
Hitchin Comet
01462 422280
www.thecomet.net
Weekly (Thu)
Lea Valley Star
01992 526625
Weekly (Wed)
Letchworth & Baldock Comet
01462 422280
www.thecomet.net
Weekly (Thu)
Royston Weekly News
01763 244502
www.cambridge-news.co.uk
Weekly (Wed)
St Albans & Harpenden Review
01727 834411
www.stalbansobserver.co.uk
Weekly free (Wed)
St Albans Observer
01727 834411
www.stalbansobserver.co.uk
Weekly (Thu)
Star Classified (Bishops Stortford)
01279 866366
Weekly (Thu)
Stevenage Comet
01462 422280
www.thecomet.net
Weekly (Thu)
Stevenage Herald
01462 422280
www.thecomet.net
Weekly free (Wed)
Watford Free Observer
01923 216216
www.watfordobserver.co.uk
Weekly (Thu)
Watford Review
01727 834411
www.stalbansobserver.co.uk
Weekly free (Wed)
Watford Times
01788 540295
Weekly free (Fri)
Welwyn & Hatfield Review
01727 834411
www.stalbansobserver.co.uk
Weekly (Thu)
Welwyn & Hatfield Times
01727 866166
www.whtimes.co.uk
Weekly (Wed)

Isle of Man

Isle of Man Courier
01624 695695
www.iomonline.co.im
Weekly (Thu
Isle of Man Examiner
01624 695695
www.iomonline.co.im
Weekly (Tue)
The Manx Independent
01624 695695
www.iomonline.co.im
Weekly (Fri)

Kent

Adscene
01227 767321
Weekly (Thu)
Bexley Express
020 8269 7000
Weekly free (Wed)
Bexley Mercury
020 8769 4444
www.icsouthlondon.co.uk
Weekly free
Bexleyheath & Welling Times
020 8269 7000
Weekly (Wed)
Biggin Hill News
01959 564766
www.biggin-hill-today.co.uk
Weekly (Thu)
Bromley News
01959 564766
www.bromley-today.co.uk
Weekly (Thu)
Chislehurst Times
020 8269 7000
Weekly (Thu)
Dartford Express
020 8269 7000
Weekly free (Wed)
Dartford Messenger
01474 333381
www.kent-online.co.uk
Weekly
Dartford Times
020 8269 7000
Weekly (Thu)
Dover Express
01227 767321
www.dover-web.co.uk
Weekly
Downs Mail
01622 630330
www.downsmail.co.uk
Monthly (variable)
East Kent Gazette & Sheppey Gazette
01227 767321
Weekly
East Kent Mercury
01304 365526
Weekly free
Edenbridge Chronicle
01959 564766
Weekly (Thu)
Edenbridge County Border News
01959 564766
www.edenbridge-today.co.uk
Weekly (Thu)

Faversham News
01227 475901
www.faversham.org/GENERAL
/favnews.htm
Weekly

Faversham Times
01227 767321
www.faversham.org/GENERAL
/favtimes.htm
Weekly

Folkestone Herald
01227 767321
Weekly

Gravesend Express
020 8269 7000
Weekly free (Wed)

Gravesend Messenger
01474 333381
www.kent-online.co.uk
Weekly

Gravesend Reporter
020 8269 7000
Weekly (Thu)

Herne Bay Gazette
01227 475901
Weekly

Hythe Herald
01227 767321
Weekly

Isle of Thanet Gazette
01227 767321
Weekly

Kent & East Sussex Courier
01892 681000
www.thisiskentandeastsussex.co.uk
Weekly (Fri)

Kent Messenger
01622 695666
www.kent-online.co.uk
Weekly

Kent on Sunday
01227 732223
www.kentonsunday.co.uk
Sunday

Kentish Express
01233 623232
Weekly

Kentish Gazette
01227 768181
Weekly

Maidstone News
01622 690339
Weekly (Wed)

Maidstone Adscene
01622 690339
Weekly free (Thu)

Medway Messenger (Rochester, Chatham, Maidstone, Gravesend)
01634 830600
www.kent-online.co.uk
Weekly

Medway News
01227 767321
Weekly

Medway Standard
01227 767321
Weekly

News Shopper Guide
020 8646 6336
Weekly (Thu)

Orpington & Petts Wood Times
020 8269 7000
Weekly (Thu)

Romney Marsh Herald
01227 767321
Weekly

Sevenoaks Chronicle
01732 228000
www.thisiskentandeastsussex.co.uk
Weekly (Thu)

Sheerness Times Guardian
01795 580300
Weekly

Sheppey Gazette
01227 767321
Weekly

Sidcup & Blackfen Times
020 8269 7000
Weekly (Wed)

Swanley Messenger
01474 333381
www.kent-online.co.uk
Weekly

Swanley Times
020 8269 7000
Weekly (Thu)

Thanet Times
01227 767321
Weekly

Wealden Advertiser
01580 753322
www.wealdenad.co.uk
Weekly free (Fri)

Westerham County Border News
01959 564766
www.westerham-today.co.uk
Weekly (Thu)

Whitstable Gazette
01227 768181
Weekly

Lancashire

Accrington Observer
01254 871444
www.accringtonobserver.co.uk
Weekly (Fri)

Asian News
01706 354321
www.theasiannews.co.uk
Monthly (4th Fri)

Barnoldswick & Earby Times
01282 426161
www.eastlancashireonline.co.uk
Weekly (Fri)

Bentham Guardian
01524 325325
Weekly (Fri)

Blackburn Citizen
01254 54321
www.thisislancashire.co.uk
/lancashire/blackburn
Weekly (Thu)

Blackpool & Fylde Citizen
01772 824631
www.thisislancashire.co.uk
/lancashire/blackpool
Weekly (Thu)

Blackpool Gazette & Herald
01253 400888
www.blackpoolonline.co.uk
Daily

Blackpool Reporter
01253 400800
Daily

Burnley Citizen
01254 54321
www.thisislancashire.co.uk
/lancashire/burnley
Weekly (Thu)

Burnley Express
01282 426161
www.burnleytoday.co.uk
Weekly (Tue & Fri)

Carnforth Guardian
01524 325325
Weekly (Fri)

Chorley Citizen
01257 269313
www.thisislancashire.co.uk
/lancashire/chorley
Weekly (Wed)

Chorley Guardian
01257 264911
www.chorleytoday.co.uk
Weekly (Wed)

Clitheroe Advertiser & Times
01200 422323
www.eastlancashireonline.co.uk
Weekly (Thu)

Colne Times
01282 612561
www.eastlancashireonline.co.uk
Weekly (Fri)

Fleetwood Weekly News and Chronicle
01253 772950
Weekly (Wed)

Garstang Courier
01995 602494
Weekly (Fri)

Garstang Guardian
01524 325325
www.prestontoday.net/
Weekly (Fri)

Lancashire Evening Post
01942 228000
www.lep.co.uk
Daily

Lancashire Evening Telegraph
01254 298220
www.thisislancashire.co.uk
Daily

Lancaster & Morecambe Citizen
01524 382121
www.thisislancashire.co.uk
Weekly (Thu)

Lancaster Guardian
01524 325325
www.lancastertoday.co.uk
Weekly (Fri)

Leyland Guardian
01257 264911
www.leylandtoday.co.uk
Weekly (Wed)

Longridge News
01772 783265
Weekly (Thu)

Lytham St Annes & Fylde Express
01253 724236
Weekly (Thu)

Morecambe Guardian
01524 325325
Weekly (Fri)

Morecambe Visitor
01524 325325
www.morecambetoday.co.uk
Weekly (Wed)

Nelson Leader
01282 612561
www.burnleytoday.co.uk
Weekly (Fri)
Ormskirk Champion
01704 392392
Weekly (Wed)
Pendle View
01282 612561
Weekly free (Fri)
Preston & Leyland Reporter
01942 228000
Weekly free (Thu)
Preston and Leyland Citizen
01772 824631
Weekly (Thu)
Rossendale Free Press
01706 213311
www.therossendalefreepress.co.uk
Weekly (Thu)
**Thornton, Cleveleys & Poulton
Citizen**
01772 824631
Weekly (Thu)

Leicestershire

Leicester Mercury
St George St, Leicester LE1 9FQ
0116 251 2512
www.leicestermercury.co.uk
Daily
Ashby & Coalville Mail
0116 251 2512
Weekly (Tue)
Ashby Times
01530 813101
Weekly (Fri)
Birstall Post
0116 267 4213
www.birstallpost.co.uk
Monthly free (1st of Month)
Coalville Times
01530 813101
Weekly (Fri)
Hinckley Herald & Journal
01455 891981
Weekly (Wed)
Hinckley Times
01455 891981
www.hinckley-times.co.uk
Weekly Thu)
Leader (NW Leics & S Derbys)
01530 813101
Weekly free (Wed)
Leicester Mail
0116 251 2512
www.thisisleicestershire.co.uk
Weekly free (Tue)
Leicestershire Times Today
0115 982 7828
Weekly (Fri)
Loughborough Mail
0116 251 2512
Weekly (Tue)
Lutterworth Mail
01858 462626
www.harboroughtoday.co.uk
Weekly (Thu)
Market Harborough Herald & Post
01604 614600
Weekly (Fri)

Melton Citizen
01664 410041
Weekly free (Tue)
Melton Times
01664 410041
www.meltontoday.co.uk/
Weekly (Thu)
Mountsorrel Post
0116 267 4213
4pa
Oadby & Wigston Mail
0116 251 2512
Weekly (Tue)
Rothley Post
0117 267 4213
6pa
Rutland Times
01572 757722
www.rutlandtimes.co.uk
Weekly (Thu)
Swadlincote Times
01530 813101
Weekly (Fri)

Lincolnshire

Grimsby Evening Telegraph
01472 360360
www.thisisgrimsby.co.uk
Daily
Alford Standard
01754 897120
Weekly (Wed)
Axholme Herald
01427 874417
Weekly (Fri)
Boston Focus
01205 354547
www.bostonuk.com/focus
Monthly free
Boston Standard
01205 311433
www.bostontoday.co.uk
Weekly (Wed)
Boston Target
01522 820000
Weekly (Wed)
Epworth Bells & Crowle Advertiser
01302 819111
Weekly free (Thu)
Gainsborough Standard
01302 819111
Weekly (Thu)
Gainsborough Target
01427 810148
Weekly (Fri)
Goole Courier
01405 720888
www.gooletoday.co.uk/
Weekly (Thu)
Goole Howden Thorne Courier
01302 819111
www.johnstonpress.co.uk
/yorkshire.asp
Weekly free (Thu)
Goole Times/Selby Post
01405 720110
www.selbypost.co.uk
Weekly (Thu)
Grimsby Target
01472 360360
Weekly free (Wed)

Holderness Gazette
01964 612777
holderness-online.com/
Weekly (Thu)
Horncastle News
01507 353200
www.horncastletoday.co.uk
Weekly (Wed)
Hornsea Gazette
01964 612777
Weekly (Thu)
Lincoln Target
01522 820000
Weekly (Wed)
Lincolnshire Echo
01522 820000
www.thisislincolnshire.co.uk
Daily
Lincolnshire Free Press
01775 725021
www.spaldingtoday.co.uk
Weekly (Tue)
The Local
01572 757722
Weekly (Fri)
Louth, Alford & Mablethorpe Leader
01507 353200
www.louthtoday.co.uk
Weekly (Wed)
Market Rasen Mail
01507 353200
www.marketrasentoday.co.uk
Weekly (Wed)
**Rutland & Stamford Mercury &
Citizen**
01780 762255
www.stamfordmercury.co.uk
Weekly (Fri)
SE Lincolnshire Target Series
01205 315000
Weekly (Wed)
Scunthorpe Evening Telegraph
01724 273273
www.thisisscunthorpe.co.uk
Daily
Scunthorpe Target
01724 273273
Weekly (Thu)
Skegness Standard
01507 353200
www.skegnesstoday.co.uk
Weekly (Wed)
Skegness Target
01205 315000
Weekly (Wed)
Sleaford Standard
01529 413646
Weekly (Wed)
Sleaford Target
01522 820000
Weekly (Wed)
Spalding Guardian
01775 725021
www.spaldingtoday.co.uk
Weekly (Thu)
Spalding Herald
01775 713723
Monthly free (1st of the month)
Spalding Post
01733 318600
Weekly (Thu)
Spilsby Standard
01754 897120
Weekly (Wed)

Spilsby Target
01205 315000
Weekly (Wed)

Stamford Citizen
01780 762255
Weekly free (Tue)

Stamford Herald & Post
01733 318600
Weekly (Thu)

London

Evening Standard
Associated Newspapers
Northcliffe House, 2 Derry St
Kensington, London W8 5TT
020 7938 6000
news@standard.co.uk
www.thisislondon.co.uk
Daily

Metro London
020 7651 5200
www.metro.co.uk
Daily

Barnes, Mortlake & Sheen Times
020 8940 6030
www.richmondandtwickenham
times.co.uk
Weekly (Fri)

Barnet Press
020 8367 2345
Weekly (Thu)

Brent & Wembley Leader
020 8427 4404
www.trinitymirrorsouthern.co.uk
Weekly free (Fri)

Brentford, Chiswick & Isleworth Times
020 8940 6030
www.richmondandtwickenham
times.co.uk
Weekly (Fri)

Bromley & Beckenham Times
020 8269 7000
Weekly (Thu)

Bromley Express
020 8269 7000
Weekly free (Wed)

Bromley News Shopper
020 8646 6336
www.newsshopper.co.uk
Weekly (Thu)

Camden Chronicle
020 8340 6868
Weekly (Thu)

Camden New Journal
020 7419 9000
www.camdennewjournal.co.uk
Weekly (Thu)

Camden Times
020 8962 6800
Weekly (Wed)

City of London & Dockland Times
020 7247 2524
Fortnightly (Mon)

Clerkenwell & Islington News
020 7778 0042
Weekly (Thu)

Croydon Advertiser
020 8763 6666
www.iccroydon.co.uk
Weekly (Fri)

Croydon Borough Post
020 8763 4433
Weekly (Wed)

Docklands & City Recorder
020 8472 1421
Weekly (Wed)

Docklands News
020 7473 2488/3990
www.docklandsnews.com
Monthly (last Fri)

Ealing & Acton Gazette
020 8579 3131
Weekly (Fri)

Ealing & Uxbridge Times
01494 755000
www.hillingdontimes.co.uk
Weekly free (Thu)

Ealing Informer
020 8579 3131
Weekly (Wed)

Ealing Leader
020 8579 3131
Weekly (Fri)

Ealing Times
01494 755000
www.ealingtimes.co.uk
Weekly (Wed)

East End Life
020 7364 3059
Weekly free (sun)

East London Advertiser
020 7790 8822
Weekly (Thu)

East London Enquirer
01277 627400
Weekly (Thu)

Eltham and Greenwich Times
020 8269 7000
Weekly (Wed)

Enfield Advertiser
020 8367 2345
Weekly (Wed)

Enfield Gazette
020 8367 2345
Weekly (Thu)

Enfield Independent
020 8359 5959
www.enfieldindependent.co.uk
Weekly (Wed)

Erith & Crayford Times
020 8269 7000
Weekly (Wed)

Greater London Advertiser
024 7625 1627
Weekly (Wed)

Greater London Review
01895 252423
Weekly free (Fri)

Hackney Gazette
020 7790 8822
Weekly (Thu)

Hammersmith and Fulham Chronicles
020 8943 5171
Weekly (Thu)

Hammersmith Times
020 8962 6800
Weekly (Wed)

Hampstead and Highgate Express
020 7433 0000
www.hamhigh.co.uk
Weekly (Fri)

Haringey Advertiser
020 8367 2345
Weekly (Wed)

Haringey Independent
020 8359 5959
www.haringeyindependent.co.uk
Weekly (Fri)

Harrow & Sudbury Chronicle
020 8962 6800
Weekly (Wed)

Harrow Leader
020 8427 4404
www.trinitymirrorsouthern.co.uk
Weekly free (Fri)

Harrow Observer
020 8427 4404
Weekly (Thu)

Harrow Times
01923 216216
www.harrowtimes.co.uk
Weekly (Thu)

Havering Herald
01708 771500
Weekly (Wed)

Havering Yellow Advertiser
01268 503400
Weekly free (Thu)

Hayes and Harlington Gazette
020 8770 7171
Weekly (Wed)

Heathrow Villager
020 7515 3710
Weekly (Sat)

Hendon Times
www.hendontimes.co.uk

Highbury & Islington Express
020 7433 0000
www.islingtonexpress.co.uk
Weekly (Fri)

Hounslow & Chiswick Informer
020 8572 1816
Weekly (Fri)

Hounslow Chronicle
020 8572 1816
Weekly free (Thu)

Hounslow Chronicles
020 8943 5171
Weekly (Thu)

Hounslow Guardian
020 8940 6030
www.hounslowguardian.co.uk
Weekly (Thu)

Hounslow Informer
020 8943 5171
Weekly free (Fri)

Hounslow, Feltham & Hanworth Times
020 8940 6030
Weekly (Fri)

Ilford & Redbridge Post
020 8491 2000
Weekly free (Wed)

Ilford Recorder
020 8478 4444
www.recorderonline.co.uk
Weekly (Thu)

Islington Gazette
020 8340 6868
Weekly (Wed)

Kensington & Chelsea News
020 8577 4348
Weekly (Fri)

Kensington Times
020 8962 6800
Weekly (Wed)

Kilburn Times
020 8962 6800
Weekly (Wed)

Kingston & Surbiton Times
020 8940 6030
Weekly (Fri)

Kingston Informer
020 8943 5171
www.trinitymirrorsouthern.co.uk
Weekly (Thu)

Lewisham News Shopper
020 8646 6336
www.newsshopper.co.uk
Weekly (Thu)

Lewisham and Greenwich Mercury
020 8769 4444
www.icsouthlondon.co.uk
Weekly free

Mayfair Times
020 7839 2455
Monthly free 1st Mon

Mitcham, Morden & Wimbledon Post
020 8769 4444
www.icsouthlondon.co.uk
Weekly free (Fri)

Newham Recorder
020 8472 1421
www.recorderonline.co.uk
Weekly (Thu)

Paddington Times
020 8962 6800
Weekly (Wed)

Richmond & Twickenham Times
020 8940 6030
www.richmondandtwickenhamtimes
.co.uk
Weekly (Fri)

Richmond Borough Guardian
020 8940 6030
www.kingstonguardian.co.uk
Weekly (Thu)

Ruislip & Northwood Informer
01895 451000
Weekly free (Fri)

South London Press
020 8769 4444
www.icsouthlondon.co.uk
Weekly (Tue , Fri)

Southall Gazette
020 8579 3131
Weekly (Fri)

The Star
01494 755000
Weekly free (Thu)

Stratford & Newham Express
020 7790 8822
Weekly (Wed)

Streatham Guardian
020 8646 6336
www.streathamguardian.co.uk
Weekly (Thu)

Teddington & Hampton Times
020 8940 6030
Weekly (Fri)

Tottenham & Wood Green Journal
020 8340 6868
Weekly (Thu)

Uxbridge & Hillingdon Leader
01895 451000
Weekly free (Thu)

Uxbridge & W Drayton Gazette
01895 451000
Weekly (Tue)

Uxbridge Informer
01895 451000
Weekly (Wed)

Uxbridge Leader
01895 451000
Weekly free (Wed)

Wandsworth Guardian
020 8646 6336
www.wandsworthguardian.co.uk
Weekly (Thu)

Wembley & Kingsbury Chronicle
020 8962 6800
Weekly (Wed)

West End Extra
020 7419 9000
Weekly (Fri)

Westender
020 7607 6060
Monthly free (last week in month)

Westminster Independent
020 8961 3345
www.londonlocals.co.uk
Weekly (Fri)

Westminster Times
020 8962 6800
Weekly (Wed)

The Wharf
020 7510 6306
www.icthewharf.co.uk
Weekly free

Willesden & Brent Chronicle
020 8962 6800
Weekly (Wed)

Manchester

Manchester Evening News
164 Deansgate
Manchester M3 3RN
0161 832 7200
www.manchesteronline.co.uk
Daily

The Advertiser (Prestwich, Whitefield & Radcliffe)
01706 354321
www.manchesteronline.co.uk
/newspapers/prestwich.html
Weekly (Fri)

Area News Today
0161 272 7711
Fortnightly (Fri)

Bolton Evening News
01204 522345
www.thisisbolton.co.uk
Daily

Bolton Journal
01204 522345
www.thisisbolton.co.uk
Weekly (Thu)

Bury Journal
0161 764 9421
www.thisisbury.co.uk
Weekly (Wed)

Bury Times
0161 764 9421
www.thisisbury.co.uk
Weekly (Tue, Fri)

Chronicle Weekend (Oldham)
0161 633 2121
www.oldham-chronicle.co.uk
Daily

Heywood Advertiser
01706 360626
www.heywoodadvertiser.co.uk
Weekly (Wed)

Leigh Journal
01942 672241
www.thisislancashire.co.uk
Weekly (Thu)

Leigh Reporter
01942 603334
www.leightoday.co.uk
Weekly free (Thu)

Metro North West
0161 832 7200
www.metronorthwest.co.uk
Weekly (Fri)

Middleton & North Manchester Guardian
0161 643 3615
www.middletonguardian.co.uk
Weekly (Thu)

Oldham Evening Chronicle
0161 633 2121
www.oldham-chronicle.co.uk
Daily

Prestwich & Whitefield Guide
0161 764 9421
www.thisisbury.co.uk
Weekly (Fri)

Radcliffe Times
0161 764 9421
www.thisisbury.co.uk
Weekly (Thu)

Rochdale Express
01706 354321
www.manchesteronline.co.uk/news
papers/rochdaleexpress.html
Weekly free (Fri)

Rochdale Observer
01706 354321
www.rochdaleobserver.co.uk
2Weekly (Wed/Sat)

Sale & Altrincham Messenger
0161 908 3360
www.thisistrafford.co.uk/trafford
/sale__altrincham
Weekly (Wed)

The Salford Advertiser
01706 354321
www.manchesteronline.co.uk
/newspapers/salford.html
Weekly (Fri)

South Manchester Reporter
0161 480 4491
www.southmanchesterreporter.co.uk
Weekly (Thu)

Stockport Citizen
0161 491 5700
www.thisislancashire.co.uk
Fortnightly (Thu)

Stockport Express
0161 480 4491
www.stockportexpress.co.uk
Weekly (Wed)

Stockport Times
0161 480 4491
www.manchesteronline.co.uk/news
papers/stockporttimeseast.html
Weekly (Thu)

Stretford & Urmston Messenger
0161 908 3360
www.thisistrafford.co.uk/trafford
/stretford__urmston
Weekly (Thu)
Tameside Advertiser
0161 480 4491
www.tamesideadvertiser.co.uk
Weekly (Wed)
Tameside Glossop Advertiser
0161 339 7611/8200
www.manchesteronline.co.uk
/newspapers/glossop.html
Weekly free (Thu)
Tameside Reporter
0161 304 7691
Weekly (Thu)
Wigan Evening Post
01942 228000
www.wigantoday.net
Daily
Wigan Observer
01942 228000
www.wigantoday.net
Weekly (Tue)
Wigan Reporter
01942 228000
www.wigantoday.net
Weekly (Thu)
Wythenshawe World
0161 998 4786
Fortnightly free (Fri)

Merseyside

Liverpool Post & Echo
Old Hall St, Liverpool L3 9JQ
0151 227 2000
www.icliverpool.co.uk
Formby Champion
01704 392392
www.championline.net
Weekly (Wed)
Freestyle
01704 392392
Monthly (Fri)
Kirkby Extra
0151 547 2000
Monthly (1st Wed)
Knowsley Challenge
0151 236 2426
www.knowsleychallenge.co.uk
Monthly (15th)
Maghull Champion
01704 392392
www.championline.net
Weekly (Wed)
Marketplace
0151 906 3000
Weekly (Thu)
Skelmersdale Champion
01704 392392
www.championline.net
Weekly (Wed)
Southport Champion
01704 392392
www.championline.net
Weekly (Wed)
St Helens Star
01925 434000
www.thisisst-helens.co.uk
Weekly (Thu)

St Helens, Prescot & Knowsley Reporter
01744 22285
Weekly (Wed)
Target
0151 906 3000
Fortnightly (Wed)
Wirral Globe
0151 906 3000
www.thisiswirral.co.uk
Weekly (Wed)
Wirral Target Property Newspaper
0151 906 3000
Fortnightly free (Wed)

Norfolk

Eastern Daily Press
Archant Norfolk, Prospect House
Rouen Rd, Norwich NR1 1RE
01603 628311
www.edp24.co.uk
Daily
Bury Free Press
01284 768911
www.buryfreepress.co.uk
Weekly
Dereham & Fakenham Times
01603 628311
www.edp24.co.uk
Weekly (Thu)
Diss Express
01379 642264
Weekly (Fri)
Diss Mercury
01603 628311
www.edp24.co.uk
Weekly (Fri)
Evening News
01603 628311
www.eveningnews24.co.uk
Daily
Great Yarmouth & Gorleston Advertiser
01493 601206
www.advertiser-online.co.uk
Weekly (Thu)
Great Yarmouth Mercury
01603 628311
www.edp24.co.uk
Weekly (Tue)
Lynn News
01553 761188
www.lynnnews.co.uk
Weekly (Tue , Fri)
Norfolk North Advertiser
01603 740222
www.advertiser-online.co.uk
Weekly (Fri)
North Norfolk & Broadland Town & Country News
01692 582287
Monthly (Fri nearest 1st/Month)
North Norfolk News
01603 628311
www.edp24.co.uk
Weekly (Thu)
Norwich Advertiser
01603 740222
www.advertiser-online.co.uk
Weekly (Fri)

Swaffam Mercury
01603 628311
www.edp24.co.uk
Monthly
Thetford Citizen
01284 768911
www.johnstonpress.co.uk/anglia
Weekly
Thetford, Brandon & Watton Times
01603 628311
www.edp24.co.uk
Weekly (Wed)
Wymondham & Attleborough Mercury
01603 628311
www.edp24.co.uk
Weekly (Fri)

North & East Yorkshire

Beverley Guardian
01377 241122
www.beverleytoday.co.uk
Weekly free (Fri)
Bridlington Gazette & Herald
01262 606606
www.bridlingtontoday.co.uk
Weekly free (Tue s)
Bridlington Free Press
01262 606606
www.bridlingtontoday.co.uk
Weekly (Thu)
Craven Herald & Pioneer
01274 729511
www.cravenherald.co.uk
Weekly (Wed)
Driffield Times
01377 241122
www.driffieldtoday.co.uk
Weekly (Wed)
Easingwold Advertiser & Weekly News
01347 821329
www.ghsmith.com/advertiser
Weekly (Thu)
East Riding News
01482 887700
Monthly
Evening Press
01904 653051
www.thisisyork.co.uk
Daily
Filey & Hunmanby Mercury
01723 363636
www.scarboroughtoday.co.uk
Weekly (Sat)
Harrogate Advertiser
01423 564321
www.harrogatetoday.co.uk
Weekly (Fri)
The Herald, Harrogate
01423 564321
www.harrogatetoday.co.uk
Weekly (Tue)
Hull Daily Mail
01482 327111
www.hulldailymail.co.uk
Daily
Knaresborough Post
01423 564321
www.knaresboroughtoday.co.uk
Weekly (Fri)

North Yorkshire Advertiser
01325 381313
www.thisisdarlington.co.uk/the
_north_east/advertiser/ny
Weekly free (Tue)

North Yorkshire Herald & Post
01642 245401
www.ncjmediainfo.co.uk
Weekly (Fri)

Northallerton, Thirsk & Bedale Times
01423 564321
Weekly (Fri)

Malton and Pickering Mercury
01723 363636
www.maltontoday.co.uk
Weekly (Wed)

Pateley Bridge & Nidderdale Herald
01423 564321
www.nidderdaletoday.co.uk
Weekly (Fri)

Pocklington Post
01723 363636
www.pocklingtontoday.co.uk
Weekly (Fri)

Ripon Gazette & Boroughbridge Herald
01423 564321
www.ripontoday.co.uk
Weekly (Fri)

Scarborough Evening News
01723 363636
www.scarboroughevveningnews.co.uk
Daily

Selby Chronicle
01924 375111
www.selbytoday.co.uk
Weekly free (Fri)

Selby Post
01405 720110
www.selbypost.co.uk
Weekly (Thu)

Selby Star
01904 653051
www.yorkandcountypress.co.uk
/york/ycp/star
Weekly free (Wed)

Selby Times
01924 375111
www.selbytoday.co.uk
Weekly (Thu)

Sheffield & South Yorkshire Times Today
0115 956 8858
Weekly free (Wed)

Trader
01723 352269
Weekly free (Thu)

Wetherby, Boston Spa & Tadcaster News
01423 564321
www.harrogatetoday.co.uk
Weekly (Fri)

Whitby Gazette
01947 602836
www.whitbytoday.co.uk
2Weekly (Tue , Fri)

York Advertiser
01904 653051
www.yorkandcountypress.co.uk
/york/ycp/ad
Weekly free (Sat)

York Star
01904 653051
www.yorkandcountypress.co.uk
/york/ycp/star
Weekly free (Wed)

Yorkshire Express
0115 956 8858
Weekly free (Wed)

Yorkshire Gazette & Herald
01904 653051
www.thisisryedale.co.uk
Weekly (Wed)

Northamptonshire

Brackley Post
01604 614600
Weekly (Fri)

Chronicle and Echo (Northampton)
01604 467000
www.northantsnews.com
Daily

Corby Citizen
01536 506100
Weekly (Thu)

Corby Evening Telegraph
01536 506100
www.northantsnews.com
Daily

Corby Herald & Post
01604 614600
Weekly (Thu)

Daventry Express
01327 703383
www.daventryonline.co.uk
Weekly (Fri)

Kettering Evening Telegraph
01536 506100
www.northantsnews.com
Daily

Kettering Herald & Post
01604 614600
Weekly (Thu)

Northampton Mercury
01604 467000
Weekly (Thu)

Northamptonshire Journal
0116 233 3635
Weekly (Tue)

Northants Herald & Post
01604 614600
Weekly (Thu)

Northants on Sunday
01536 506100
Sunday

Towcester Post
01604 614600
Weekly (Fri)

Wellingborough & East Northants Evening Telegraph
01536 506100
www.northantsnews.com
Daily

Wellingborough & Rushden Citizen
01536 506100
Weekly (Thu)

Wellingborough & Rushden Herald & Post
01604 614600
Weekly (Thu)

Northumberland

Berwick Advertiser
01289 306677
www.berwicktoday.co.uk
Weekly (Thu)

Hexham Courant
01434 602351
www.hexham-courant.co.uk
Weekly (Fri)

Morpeth Herald
01670 510522
www.morpethtoday.co.uk
Weekly (Thu)

Newcastle Times
01332 205900
Weekly (Thu)

News Post Leader
0191 251 8484
www.blyth-wansbecktoday.co.uk
Weekly

Northumberland Gazette
01655 602234
www.northumberlandtoday.co.uk
Weekly

Northumberland Herald and Post
0191 232 7500
Weekly (Wed)

Whitley Bay News Guardian
0191 251 8484
www.northtynesidetoday.co.uk
Weekly

Nottinghamshire

Alfreton Chad
01623 456789
www.johnstonpress.co.uk
/yorkshire.asp
Weekly (Fri)

Ashfield Chad
01623 456789
www.ashfieldtoday.co.uk
Weekly (Wed)

Dukeries Advertiser
01636 681234
Weekly (Fri)

Eastwood & Kimberley Advertiser
01773 713563
www.eastwoodadvertiser.co.uk
Weekly (Fri)

Eastwood Shopper
01773 713563
Weekly free (Wed)

Hucknall & Bulwell Dispatch
01623 456789
www.hucknalltoday.co.uk
Weekly (Fri)

Mansfield & Ashfield Recorder
01623 420000
Weekly free (Wed)

Mansfield Chad
01623 456789
www.mansfieldtoday.co.uk
Weekly (Wed)

Newark Advertiser
01636 681234
www.newarkadvertiser.co.uk
Weekly (Fri)

North Notts Journal
0115 982 7337
Weekly (Wed)

Nottingham & Trent Valley Journal
0115 982 7338
Weekly (Wed)

Nottingham and Long Eaton Topper
0115 969 6000
www.toppernewspapers.co.uk
Weekly free (Wed)

Nottingham Evening Post
0115 948 2000
www.thisisnottingham.co.uk
Daily

Nottingham Recorder
0115 948 2000
www.thisisnottingham.co.uk
Weekly free (Wed)

Observer (Mansfield & Ashfield)
01623 456789
Weekly (Thu)

Retford and Bawtry Guardian
01909 500500
www.retfordtoday.co.uk
Weekly (Thu)

Retford Trader
01909 500500
Weekly free (Thu)

Retford, Gainsborough & Worksop Times
01777 702275
Weekly (Thu)

South Notts Advertiser
01636 681234
Weekly (Fri)

Trader Pictorial
01636 681234
Weekly (Wed)

Worksop Guardian
01909 500500
www.worksoptoday.co.uk
Weekly (Fri)

Worksop Trader
01909 500500
Weekly free (Wed)

Oxfordshire

Banbury Cake
01295 256111
www.thisisoxfordshire.co.uk
/oxfordshire/ news/banbury.html
Weekly (Thu)

Banbury Citizen
01295 227777
Daily (Fri)

Banbury Guardian
01295 227777
www.banburyguardian.co.uk
Daily free

Bicester Advertiser
01865 425262
www.thisisoxfordshire.co.uk
/oxfordshire/ news/bicester.html
Weekly (Fri)

Henley Standard
01491 419444
www.henleystandard.co.uk
Weekly (Fri)

Herald Series
01865 425262
www.thisisoxfordshire.co.uk/oxford
shire/ about_us/titles/herald.html
Weekly (Thu)

Oxford Courier
01235 553444
www.courier-newspapers
-oxford.co.uk
Weekly (Thu)

Oxford Journal
01235 553444
www.courier-newspapers
-oxford.co.uk/journal.htm
Weekly (Fri)

Oxford Mail
01865 425262
www.thisisoxfordshire.co.uk
Daily

Oxford Star
01865 425262
www.thisisoxfordshire.co.uk
Weekly (Thu)

Oxford Times
01865 425262
www.thisisoxfordshire.co.uk
Weekly (Fri)

Oxfordshire Guardian
01926 431601
Weekly (Thu)

Oxfordshire Weekly
01865 425262
www.thisisoxfordshire.co.uk
Weekly (Wed)

South Oxfordshire Courier
01235 553444
www.courier-newspapers
-oxford.co.uk
Weekly (Thu)

Thame Gazette
01296 318300
www.aylesburytoday.co.uk
Weekly (Fri)

Witney & West Oxfordshire Gazette
01865 425262
www.thisisoxfordshire.co.uk/oxford
shire/news/witney.html
Weekly (Wed)

Shropshire

Shropshire Star
Shropshire Newspapers
Ketley, Telford
Shropshire TF1 5HU
01952 242424
www.shropshirestar.com
Daily

Bridgnorth Journal
01746 761411
www.bridgnorthjournal.co.uk
Weekly (Fri)

Ludlow Journal
01952 242424
www.ludlowjournal.co.uk
Weekly free (Fri)

Newport & Market Drayton Advertiser
01952 811500
www.marketdraytonadvertiser.co.uk
Weekly (Fri)

Oswestry & Border Counties Advertiser
01691 655321
www.bordercountiesadvertiser.co.uk
Weekly (Wed)

Shrewsbury Admag
01743 241414
Weekly (Thu)

Shrewsbury Chronicle
01743 248248
www.shrewsburychronicle.co.uk
Weekly (Thu)

South Shropshire Journal
01952 242424
www.southshropshirejournal.co.uk
Weekly (Fri)

Telford Journal
01952 242424
www.telfordjournal.co.uk
Weekly free (Thu)

Somerset & Avon

Bristol Evening Post
Temple Way, Bristol BS99 7HD
0117 934 3000
www.epost.co.uk
Daily

Bath Chronicle
01225 322322
www.thisisbath.co.uk
Daily

Bath Times
01225 322322
Weekly (Wed)

Bridgwater Mercury
01823 365151
www.thisisthewestcountry.co.uk
Weekly (Tue)

Bridgwater Star
01823 365151
www.thisisthewestcountry.co.uk
Weekly (Thu)

Bridgwater Times
01749 672430
Weekly (Thu)

Bristol Observer
0117 934 3000
www.thisisbristol.com
Weekly free (Thu)

Burnham & Highbridge Times
01749 672430
Weekly (Thu)

Burnham & Highbridge Weekly News
01823 365151
Weekly (Thu)

Central Somerset Gazette
01823 365151
www.thisissomerset.co.uk
Weekly (Fri)

Chard Advertiser
01935 471764
www.chard-today.co.uk
Weekly free (Fri)

Chard & Ulminster News
01823 365151
www.thisisthewestcountry.co.uk
Weekly (Wed)

Chew Valley Gazette
01275 332266
www.chewvalleygazette.co.uk
Monthly (Fri)

Clevedon Mercury
01275 335140
www.thisissomerset.co.uk
Weekly (Thu)

Crewkerne Advertiser
01935 471764
www.crewkerne-today.co.uk
Weekly free (Fri)
Frome Times
01225 704761
www.frometimes.com
Fortnightly free (Thu)
The Journal (Wells, Central Somerset, Shepton Mallet)
01749 672430
www.thisissomerset.co.uk
Weekly (Thu)
Mid Somerset Times
01749 672430
Weekly (Thu)
North Somerset Times
01934 422622
www.thewestonmercury.co.uk
Weekly (Wed)
Somerset County Gazette
01823 365151
www.thisisthewestcountry.co.uk
Weekly (Fri)
Somerset Guardian (Midsomer Norton/Radstock/Keynsham)
01225 322322
Weekly (Thu)
Somerset Standard
01225 322322
www.thisissomerset.co.uk
Weekly (Thu)
Sunday Independent (Bristol & Somerset)
01752 206600
www.thisisthewestcountry.co.uk
Sunday
Taunton Star
01823 365151
www.tauntonstar.co.uk
Weekly (Wed)
Taunton Times
01823 250500
www.thisissomerset.co.uk
Weekly free (Thu)
Trader News (West Somerset)
01984 632731
Weekly free (Wed)
Wellington Weekly News
01823 250500
www.thisissomerset.co.uk
Weekly (Wed)
West Somerset Free Press
01984 632731
www.west-somerset-today.co.uk
Weekly (Fri)
Western Daily Press (Bristol)
0117 9343000
www.westpress.co.uk
Daily
Western Gazette
01935 700500
www.westgaz.co.uk
Weekly (Thu)
Weston & Somerset Mercury
01934 422622
www.thewestonmercury.co.uk
Weekly (Fri)
Weston and Worle News
01275 335140
www.thisissomerset.co.uk
Weekly (Thu)

Weston Super Mare Admag
01934 422622
www.thewestonmercury.co.uk
Weekly (Wed)
Yeovil and South Somerset Express
01823 365151
www.thisisthewestcountry.co.uk
Weekly (Thu)
Yeovil Clarion
01935 471764
www.yeovil-clarion-today.co.uk
Weekly free (Fri)
Yeovil Times
01935 700500
Weekly free (Wed)

South Yorkshire

The Star (Sheffield)
York St, Sheffield
South Yorkshire S1 1PU
0114 276 7676
www.sheffieldtoday.net
Daily
Barnsley Chronicle
01226 734734
www.barnsley-chronicle.co.uk
Weekly (Fri)
Barnsley Independent
01226 734734
www.barnsley-chronicle.co.uk
Weekly (Tue)
Dearne Valley Weekender
01709 571111
www.rotherhamadvertiser.com
Weekly (Fri)
Dinnington & Maltby Trader News
01909 550500
Weekly (Thu)
Dinnington & Maltby Guardian
01909 550500
www.dinningtontoday.co.uk
Weekly (Fri)
Doncaster Star
01302 819111
www.doncastertoday.co.uk
Daily
Doncaster Free Press
01302 819111
www.doncastertoday.co.uk
Weekly (Thu)
Epworth Bells & Crowle Advertiser
01427 615323
Weekly (Thu)
Gainsborough News
01427 872202
Weekly free (Fri)
Gainsborough Standard
01427 615323
Weekly (Thu)
The Journal
0114 276 7676
Weekly free (Thu)
Look Local
0114 283 1100
Weekly (Wed)
Profile
0114 276 7676
Monthly

Rotherham & South Yorkshire Advertiser
01709 364721
www.rotherhamadvertiser.com
Weekly (Fri)
Rotherham Record
01709 364721
www.rotherhamadvertiser.com
Weekly (Wed)
Sheffield Journal
0114 276 7676
Weekly free (Thu)
Sheffield Telegraph
0114 276 7676
www.sheffieldtoday.net
Weekly (Fri)
Sheffield Weekly Gazette
0114 276 7676
Weekly (Thu)
Sheffield Mercury
0114 274 6444
Weekly (Fri)

Staffordshire

The Sentinel (Stoke-On-Trent)
Staffordshire Sentinel Newspapers
Sentinel House, Etruria
Stoke-on-Trent
Staffordshire ST1 5SS
01782 602525
www.thesentinel.co.uk
Daily
Sentinel Sunday
Staffordshire Sentinel Newspapers
Sentinel House, Etruria
Stoke-on-Trent
Staffordshire ST1 5SS
01782 602525
www.thesentinel.co.uk
Sunday
The Advertiser
01782 602525
Weekly free (Thu)
Biddulph Chronicle
01260 273737
Weekly (Fri)
Burton & South Derbyshire Advertiser
01283 512345
www.uttoxeteradvertiser.co.uk
Weekly (Wed)
Burton Mail
01283 512345
www.burtonmail.co.uk
Daily
Burton Trader
01283 512000
Weekly (Wed)
Cannock & Rugeley Chronicle
01543 506311
Weekly (Fri)
Cannock & Rugeley Mercury
01827 848535
Weekly (Thu)
Cannock Chase & Burntwood Post
01543 501700
Weekly (Thu)
Cheadle & Tean Times
01538 753162
Weekly (Wed)

Cheadle Post & Times
01538 750011
Weekly (Wed)
Leek Post & Times
01538 399599
Weekly (Wed)
Lichfield and Burntwood Edition Express and Star
01543 414455
www.expressandstar.com
Daily
Lichfield Mercury
01827 848535
Weekly (Thu)
Lichfield Post
01543 258523
Weekly (Thu)
Mid Staffs Edition Express and Star
01543 506311
www.expressandstar.com
Daily
Rugeley Post
01543 258523
Weekly (Thu)
Stafford Post
01543 501700
Weekly (Thu)
Staffordshire Newsletter
01785 257700
www.staffordshirenewsletter.co.uk
Tamworth Herald
01827 848535
www.tamworthherald.co.uk
Weekly (Thu)
Tamworth Times
01827 308000
Weekly (Thu)
Uttoxeter Advertiser
01889 562050
www.uttoxeteradvertiser.co.uk
Weekly (Tue)
Uttoxeter Post & Times
01889 602525
Weekly (Thu)

Suffolk

Beccles & Bungay Journal
01603 628311
www.edp24.co.uk
Weekly (Fri)
Bury Free Press
01284 768911
www.edp24.co.uk
Weekly
Bury St Edmunds Mercury
01473 230023
www.edp24.co.uk
Weekly (Fri)
Citizen (Bury St Edmunds)
01284 768911
Weekly
East Anglian Daily Times
01284 702588
www.eadt.co.uk
Daily
Eastern Counties Telegraph
01788 544121
Weekly (Wed)
Essex Advertiser
01473 611363
www.advertiser-online.co.uk
Weekly (Fri)

Evening Star
01473 230023
www.eveningstar.co.uk
Daily
Haverhill Echo
01440 703456
Weekly (Thu)
Ipswich Advertiser
01473 611363
www.advertiser-online.co.uk
Weekly (Thu)
Lowestoft Journal
01603 628311
www.edp24.co.uk
Weekly (Fri)
Newmarket Journal
01638 668441
Weekly (Thu)
Newmarket Weekly News
01638 660846
Weekly (Wed)
North Essex Advertiser
01473 611363
www.advertiser-online.co.uk
Weekly (Fri)
Sudbury Mercury
01284 702588
www.edp24.co.uk
Weekly (Fri)
Suffolk Advertiser
01473 611363
www.advertiser-online.co.uk
Weekly (Fri)
Suffolk Free Press
01787 375271
www.sudburytoday.co.uk
Weekly (Thu)
Waveney Advertiser
01493 601206
www.advertiser-online.co.uk
Weekly (Fri)

Surrey

Addlestone and Byfleet Review
01483 508700
www.surreyad.co.uk
Weekly (Wed)
Aldershot News
01483 508700
www.aldershot.co.uk
Weekly (Tue s)
Camberley Courier
01252 339760
Weekly free (Wed)
Cranleigh Times
01483 508700
Weekly free (Wed)
Croydon Advertiser
01737 732000
www.iccroydon.co.uk
Weekly (Fri)
Croydon Guardian
020 8646 6336
www.croydonguardian.co.uk
Weekly (Wed)
Dorking Advertiser
01483 741100
www.icsurrey.co.uk
Weekly (Fri)
Elmbridge Guardian
020 8646 6336
Weekly (Thu)

Epsom Guardian
020 8646 6336
www.epsomguardian.co.uk
Weekly (Thu)
Epsom, Ewell & Banstead Post
020 8763 6666
www.icsurrey.co.uk
Weekly (Fri)
Esher News & Mail
01483 508700
www.esher.co.uk
Weekly (Fri)
Farnham Herald
01252 725224
www.farnham-herald-today.co.uk
Weekly (Fri)
Farnham Post
01420 88949
Fortnightly free (Mon)
Godalming Times
01483 508700
Weekly free (Wed)
Guildford Times
01483 508700
www.surreyad.co.uk/news
/guildford-times.html
Weekly free (Wed)
Haslemere Times & Mail
01252 716444
Weekly free (Tue s)
Kingston Guardian
020 8646 6336
www.kingstonguardian.co.uk
Weekly (Thu)
Leatherhead Advertiser
020 8763 4433
www.icsurrey.co.uk
Weekly (Thu)
Leatherhead Guardian
020 8646 6336
Weekly (Thu)
The Messenger (Haslemere)
01428 653999
www.messenger-online.co.uk
Weekly free (Wed)
News & Mail
01483 508900
www.surreyad.co.uk/aboutus.htm
The Post
01738 732000
Weekly (Thu)
Redhill & Reigate Guardian
020 8646 6336
Weekly (Wed)
Reigate, Redhill & Horley Post
020 8763 4433
Weekly (Wed)
Redhill & Reigate Life
020 8645 8888
www.redhillandreigatelife.co.uk
Weekly free (Wed)
Reigate Post
020 8770 7171
Weekly (Thu)
Staines & Ashford News
01932 561111
www.trinitymirrorsouthern.co.uk
Weekly free (Wed)
Staines & Egham News
01932 561111
www.trinitymirrorsouthern.co.uk
Weekly free (Wed)

Staines Guardian
020 8940 6030
www.stainesguardian.co.uk
Weekly (Thu)
Staines Informer
01932 561111
www.trinitymirrorsouthern.co.uk
Weekly free (Thu)
Staines Leader
01932 561111
www.trinitymirrorsouthern.co.uk
Weekly free (Thu)
Surrey & Hants News
01252 716444
Weekly free (Tue s)
Surrey Advertiser
01483 508700
www.surreyad.co.uk
Weekly (Fri)
Surrey and Sussex Telegraph
01895 255661
Weekly free (Wed)
Surrey Comet Series
020 8646 6336
Weekly (Wed)
Surrey Hants Star
01252 316311
www.shstar.co.uk
Weekly free (Thu)
Surrey Herald
01932 561111
Weekly (Wed)
Surrey Mirror
020 8770 7171
www.icsurrey.co.uk
Weekly (Wed)
Sutton Advertiser
020 8763 6666
www.icsurrey.co.uk
Weekly (Fri)
Sutton Guardian
www.suttonguardian.co.uk
Tandridge Chronicle
01959 564766
www.tandridge-today.co.uk
Weekly (Thu)
Tandridge County Border News
01959 564766
www.tandridge-today.co.uk
Weekly (Thu)
Virginia Water Villager
01753 523355
Fortnightly (Thu)
Walton & Weybridge Informer
01932 561111
www.trinitymirrorsouthern.co.uk
Weekly free (Thu)
Weybridge Villager
01753 523355
Fortnightly (Thu)
Wimbledon Guardian
020 8646 6336
www.wimbledonguardian.co.uk
Weekly (Thu)
Woking Informer
01932 561111
www.trinitymirrorsouthern.co.uk
Weekly free (Thu)
Woking News & Mail
01483 755755
www.woking.co.uk

Woking Review
01483 508700
www.surreyad.co.uk
Weekly (Wed)

Tyne and Wear

Evening Chronicle
Groat Market
Newcastle Upon Tyne NE1 1ED
0191 232 7500
www.icnewcastle.co.uk
Daily (Mon –Fri)
The Journal (Newcastle Upon Tyne)
Groat Market
Newcastle Upon Tyne NE1 1ED
0191 232 7500
www.icnewcastle.co.uk
Daily
Citylife
0191 232 8520
www.newcastle.gov.uk/citylife
Monthly (last week of the month)
Gateshead Herald & Post
0191 232 7500
www.icnewcastle.co.uk
Weekly (Wed)
The Gazette (South Shields)
0191 455 4661
www.southtynesidetoday.co.uk
Daily
Houghton Star
0191 501 7208
Weekly free (Thu)
Metro North East
0191 232 7500
www.metronortheast.co.uk
Daily
Newcastle Herald & Post
0191 232 7500
www.icnewcastle.co.uk
Weekly (Wed)
North Shields News Guardian
0191 251 8484
www.northtynesidetoday.co.uk
Weekly free (Wed)
North Tyneside Herald & Post
0191 232 7500
www.icnewcastle.co.uk
Weekly (Wed)
Seaham Star
0191 501 7208
Weekly free (Thu)
South Tyne Star
0191 455 4661
Weekly free (Thu)
South Tyneside Herald & Post
0191 232 7500
www.icnewcastle.co.uk
Weekly (Wed)
Sunday Sun (Newcastle)
0191 232 7500
www.icnewcastle.co.uk
Sunday
Sunderland Echo
0191 501 7208
www.sunderland-echo.co.uk
Daily
Sunderland Star
0191 501 7208
Weekly free (Thu)

Wallsend News Guardian
01670 517171
www.northtynesidetoday.co.uk
Weekly free (Thu)
Washington Star
0191 501 7208
Weekly free (Thu)
Whitley Bay News Guardian
01670 516066
www.northtynesidetoday.co.uk
Weekly free (Thu)

Warwickshire

Bedworth Echo
024 7663 3633
www.iccoventry.co.uk
Weekly (Fri)
Coventry Observer
024 7649 5900
www.coventryobserver.co.uk
Weekly free (Fri)
Daventry Express
01788 535363
www.daventryonline.co.uk
Weekly (Thu)
Heartland Evening News
024 7635 3534
Daily
Hitchen Advertiser
01462 441020
Weekly free (Fri)
Kenilworth Weekly News
01926 457777
www.kenilworthonline.co.uk
Weekly (Fri)
Leamington Spa Courier
01926 457777
www.leamingtononline.co.uk
Weekly (Fri)
**Leamington Spa Observer &
Stratford-upon-Avon Standard**
01926 451900
www.leamington-now.com
Weekly free (Fri)
Leamington Spa Review
01926 457777
www.leamingtonspatoday.co.uk
Weekly (Thu)
Midweek
01789 266261
Weekly (Tue)
Nuneaton Weekly Tribune
024 7663 3633
www.iccoverntry.co.uk
Weekly (Thu)
Rugby Advertiser
01788 535363
www.rugbyadvertiser.co.uk
Weekly (Thu)
Rugby Observer
01788 535147
www.therugbyobserver.co.uk
Weekly free (Fri)
Rugby Review
01788 535363
www.rugbyreviewtoday.co.uk
Weekly (Thu)
Stratford-upon-Avon Journal
01432 274413
www.thisisstratford-upon
   -avon.co.uk
Weekly (Thu)

Stratford-upon-Avon Herald
01789 266261
www.stratford-herald.co.uk
Weekly (Thu)
Stratford-upon-Avon Standard
01789 415717
www.stratfordstandard.co.uk
Weekly free (Fri)
Why Coventry, Nuneaton & Hinckley
01527 588000
Weekly free (Fri)
Why Warwick & Leamington
01527 588000
Weekly free (Fri)

West Midlands

Express & Star
51–53 Queen St, Wolverhampton
West Midlands WV1 1ES
01902 313131
www.expressandstar.com
Daily

Birmingham Evening Mail
Weaman St, Birmingham
West Midlands B4 6AT
0121 236 3366
www.icbirmingham.co.uk
Daily

Coventry Evening Telegraph
Corporation St
Coventry CV1 1FP
024 7663 3633
www.iccoventry.co.uk
Daily

Sunday Mercury
Weaman St. Birmingham
West Midlands B4 6AT
0121 236 3366
www.icbirmingham.co.uk
Sunday

Ad News Willenhall, Wednesbury & Darlaston
01543 501700
Weekly (Wed)
Birmingham News
0121 234 5073
www.icbirmingham.co.uk
Weekly (Thu)
Birmingham Post
0121 236 3366
www.icbirmingham.co.uk
Daily
Black Country Bugle
www.blackcountrybugle.co.uk
01384 567678
Coventry Citizen
024 7663 3633
www.iccoventry.co.uk
Weekly (Thu)
Dudley Chronicle
01384 355355
www.expressandstar.com
Weekly (Fri)
Dudley Edition Express & Star
01384 355355
www.expressandstar.com
Daily

Dudley News
01384 358050
www.dudleynews.co.uk
Weekly (Fri)
Great Barr and Erdington Chronicle
0121 5537171
Weekly free (Wed)
Great Barr Observer
01827 848535
Weekly (Thu)
Halesowen Chronicle
01384 355355
Weekly (Fri)
Halesowen News
01384 358050
www.halesowennews.co.uk
Weekly (Fri)
Metro Birmingham
020 7651 5200
www.metrobirmingham.co.uk
Daily
Sandwell Chronicle
0121 553 7171
Weekly free (Wed)
Solihull News
0121 711 3993
www.icsolihull.co.uk
Weekly (Fri)
Solihull Times
0121 711 3993
www.icsolihull.co.uk
Weekly (Fri)
Stourbridge Chronicle
01384 355355
www.expressandstar.com
Weekly (Fri)
Stourbridge Edition Express and Star
01384 355355
www.expressandstar.com
Daily
Stourbridge News (Incorporating County Express)
01384 358050
www.thisisstourbridge.co.uk
Weekly (Thu)
Sutton Coldfield News
0121 355 7070
Weekly (Fri)
Sutton Coldfield Observer
01827 848535
Weekly (Thu)
Sutton Coldfield Times
0121 202 1171
Fortnightly (Fri)
Walsall Advertiser
01827 848535
Weekly (Thu)
Walsall Express & Star
01922 444444
www.expressandstar.com
Daily
Walsall Observer
01922 636666
www.thisiswalsall.co.uk
Weekly (Fri)
Why Solihull & District
01527 588000
Weekly free (Fri)
Wolverhampton Ad News
01543 501700
Weekly (Wed)

Wolverhampton Chronicle
01902 313131
www.yourchronicle.com
Weekly free (Thu)

West Sussex

Bognor Regis Guardian
01243 532532
www.chichester.co.uk
Weekly free (Wed)
Bognor Regis Observer
01244 532532
www.chichester.co.uk
Weekly (Thu)
Chichester & Selsey Journal
01245 532532
www.chichester.co.uk
Weekly free (Wed)
Chichester Observer
01243 539389
www.chiobserver.co.uk
Weekly (Thu)
Crawley News
020 8763 4433
www.icsurrey.co.uk
Weekly (Wed)
Crawley Observer
01293 562929
www.crawleyobserver.co.uk
Weekly (Wed)
East Grinstead Courier
01892 681000
Weekly (Thu)
East Grinstead Observer
020 8763 4433
www.icsurrey.co.uk
Weekly (Wed)
Friday-Ad
0870 1629999
www.friday-ad.co.uk
Weekly (Fri)
Horsham Advertiser
01403 751200
www.horshamonline.co.uk
Weekly
Littlehampton Gazette
01903 230051
www.littlehamptontoday.co.uk
Daily
Mid Sussex Leader
01273 544544
www.thisismidsussex.co.uk
Weekly (Thu)
Midhurst & Petworth Observer
01246 532532
www.midhurstandpetworth.co.uk
Weekly (Thu)
Mid-Sussex Citizen
01444 452201
www.midsussextimes.co.uk
Weekly free (Wed)
Mid Sussex Times
01444 452201
www.midsussextimes.co.uk
Weekly (Thu)
Shoreham Herald
01903 230051
www.shorehamtoday.co.uk
Weekly free (Wed)

Worthington Herald
01903 230051
www.shorehamtoday.co.uk
Weekly free (Wed)

Weekend Herald (Crawley, Horsham, Horley)
01293 562929
Weekly free (Fri)

West Sussex Gazette
01247 532532
www.chichester.co.uk
Weekly (Wed)

West Sussex County Times
01403 751200
www.horshamonline.co.uk
Weekly

Worthing Advertiser
01903 230051
www.worthingtoday.co.uk
Daily

Worthing Herald
01903 230051
www.worthingtoday.co.uk
Daily

West Yorkshire

Yorkshire Evening Post
PO Box 168, Wellington St
Leeds LS1 1RF
0113 243 2701
www.leedstoday.net
Daily

Yorkshire Post
PO Box 168, Wellington St
Leeds LS1 1RF
0113 243 2701
www.yorkshirepost.co.uk
Daily

Batley News
01924 468282
www.dewsburytoday.co.uk
Weekly (Thu)

Birstall News
01924 468282
www.dewsburytoday.co.uk
Weekly (Thu)

Bradford Target
01274 729511
Weekly (Tue)

Brighouse Echo
01422 260200
www.halifaxtoday.co.uk
Weekly (Fri)

Calderdale News
01422 260200
www.halifaxtoday.co.uk
Weekly free (Wed)

Colne Valley Chronicle
01484 437747
www.ichuddersfield.co.uk
Weekly (Fri)

Dewsbury Reporter
01924 468282
www.dewsburytoday.co.uk
Weekly (Fri)

Halifax Evening Courier
01422 260200
www.halifaxtoday.co.uk
Daily

Hebden Bridge Times
01422 260200
www.halifaxtoday.co.uk
Weekly (Fri)

Heckmondwike Herald
01924 468282
www.dewsburytoday.co.uk
Weekly (Fri)

Hemsworth & South Elmsall Express
01924 375111
www.wakefieldexpress.co.uk
Weekly free (Fri)

Huddersfield Daily Examiner
01484 437747
www.ichuddersfield.co.uk
Daily

Huddersfield District Chronicle
01484 437747
www.ichuddersfield.co.uk
Weekly (Fri)

Huddersfield District News
01484 437747
www.ichuddersfield.co.uk
Weekly free (Tue s)

Ilkley Gazette
01274 729511
www.ilkleygazette.co.uk
Weekly (Wed)

Keighley & Craven Target
01274 729511
Weekly (Tue)

Keighley News
01274 729511
www.keighleynews.co.uk
Weekly (Thu)

Leeds Weekly News
0113 243 2701
Weekly (Thu)

Leeds and Yorkshire Times
01926 431601
Weekly (Fri)

Metro Yorkshire
020 7651 5200
www.metro.co.uk
Daily

Mirfield Reporter
01924 468282
www.dewsburytoday.co.uk
Weekly (Fri)

Morley Advertiser
01924 375111
www.wakefieldexpress.co.uk
Weekly (Wed)

Morley Observer
01924 468282
www.dewsburytoday.co.uk
Weekly (Fri)

Ossett Observer
01924 375111
www.wakefieldexpress.co.uk
Weekly free (Fri)

Pontefract & Castleford Extra
01924 375111
www.wakefieldexpress.co.uk
Weekly free (Fri)

Pontefract and Castleford Express
01924 375111
www.wakefieldexpress.co.uk
Weekly (Thu)

Pudsey Times (Pudsey, Farsley, Bramley, Stanningley)
01943 466750
Weekly (Thu)

Spenborough Guardian
01924 468282
www.dewsburytoday.co.uk
Weekly (Fri)

Telegraph and Argus (Bradford)
01274 729511
www.thisisbradford.co.uk
Daily

Todmorden News & Advertiser
01422 260200
www.halifaxtoday.co.uk
Weekly (Fri)

The Town Crier
01274 729511
Weekly (Thu)

Wakefield Express
01924 375111
www.wakefieldexpress.co.uk
Weekly free (Fri)

Wakefield, Rothwell & Alton Extra
01924 375111
www.wakefieldexpress.co.uk
Weekly free (Thu)

Weekly Advertiser
01924 468282
www.dewsburytoday.co.uk
Weekly free (Fri)

Wharfe Valley Times
01943 466750
Weekly (Thu)

Wharfedale & Airedale Observer
01274 729511
www.wharfedaleobserver.co.uk
Weekly (Wed)

The Yeller
0845 601 0600
2Weekly (Tue, Fri)

Wiltshire

Chippenham, Corsham Advertiser
01225 760945
Weekly (Thu)

Devizes, Melksham and Vale of Pewsey News
01793 528144
Weekly free (Wed)

Evening Advertiser
01793 528144
www.thisisswindon.co.uk
Daily

Melksham Independent News
01225 704761
www.melkshamnews.com
Fortnightly free (Thu)

Salisbury Avon Advertiser
01722 426500
www.thisiswiltshire.co.uk
Weekly (Wed)

Salisbury Journal
01722 426500
www.thisiswiltshire.co.uk
Weekly (Thu)

Scoop Magazine
01793 528144
www.thisisswindon.co.uk
Weekly free (Fri)

Swindon Guardian
024 7655 1796
Daily

Swindon Star
01793 528144
www.thisisswindon.co.uk
Weekly free (Thu)
Trowbridge, Melksham, Bradford-On-Avon Advertiser
01225 760945
Weekly (Thu)
Warminster Journal
01985 213030
Weekly (Fri)
West & North Wilts Star
01225 777292
Weekly free (Thu)
Westbury, Warminster Advertiser
01225 760945
Weekly (Thu)
White Horse News
01225 704761
wiltshirepublications.com
Fortnightly free (Thu)
Wiltshire Gazette and Herald
01793 528144
www.thisisswindon.co.uk
Weekly (Thu)
Wiltshire Times
01225 777292
www.thisiswiltshire.co.uk
Weekly (Fri)

Wales

Western Mail
Thomson House, Havelock St
Cardiff CF10 1XR
029 2058 3583
www.icwales.co.uk
Daily

Wales on Sunday
Thomson House, Havelock St
Cardiff CF10 1XR
029 2058 3583
www.icwales.co.uk
Sunday

North Wales

Abergele Visitor
01492 584321
Weekly (Thu)
Bangor Chronicle
01248 387400
www.northwaleschronicle.co.uk
Weekly (Thu)
Bangor Spectator
028 9127 0270
Weekly (Thu)
Bangor/Anglesey Mail
01286 671111
www.icnorthwales.co.uk
Weekly (Wed)
Buy Sell (Flintshire Edition)
01244 545504
Weekly (Wed)
Buy Sell (Wrexham Edition)
01978 290400
Weekly (Fri)

Caernarfon & Denbigh Herald
01286 671111
www.icnorthwales.co.uk
Weekly (Thu)
Chester Standard (Deeside Edition)
01244 304500
www.chesterstandard.co.uk
Weekly (Thu)
Denbighshire Free Press
01745 813535
www.denbighshirefreepress.co.uk
Weekly (Thu)
Daily Post
01492 574455
www.icnorthwales.co.uk
Daily
Flintshire Chronicle
01244 821911
www.icnorthwales.co.uk
Flintshire Leader & Standard
01352 707707
www.flintshirestandard.co.uk
Weekly (Thu)
Gwynedd Chronicle
01248 387400
www.northwaleschronicle.co.uk
Weekly (Thu)
Holyhead and Anglesey Mail
01286 671111
www.icnorthwales.co.uk
Weekly (Wed)
North Wales Chronicle
01248 387400
www.northwaleschronicle.co.uk
Weekly (Thu)
North Wales Pioneer
01492 531188
www.northwalespioneer.co.uk
Weekly (Thu)
North Wales Weekly News
01492 584321
Weekly (Thu)
Rhyl & Prestatyn Visitor
01745 334144 (Rhyl)
01745 815454 (Denbigh)
www.icnorthwales.co.uk
Weekly free (Wed)
Rhyl Prestatyn & Abergele Journal
01352 707707
Weekly (Thu)
Vale Advertiser
01745 815454
icnorthwales.icnetwork.co.uk/news
/valeadvertiser
Weekly (Fri)
Wrexham Evening Leader
01978 355151
www.eveningleader.co.uk
Daily
Wrexham Leader
01978 355151
www.bigleader.co.uk
Weekly free (Fri)
Wrexham Mail
01244 340151
www.icnorthwales.co.uk
Weekly (Tue)
Y Cymro
01352 707707
www.y-cymro.co.uk
Weekly (Mon)

Ynys Mon Chronicle
01248 387400
www.northwaleschronicle.co.uk
Weekly (Thu)
Yr Herald
01286 671111
www.icnorthwales.co.uk
Weekly (Sat)
Yr Herald
01492 584321
www.icnorthwales.co.uk
Weekly (Sat)

South Wales

South Wales Evening Post
PO Box 14, Adelaide St
Swansea SA1 1QT
01792 510000
www.swep.co.uk
Daily
South Wales Echo
Thomson House, Havelock St
Cardiff CF10 1XR
029 2058 3583
www.icwales.co.uk
Abergavenny Chronicle
01873 852187
www.abergavenny.net/chronicle
Weekly (Thu)
Abergavenny Free Press
01633 810000
www.thisismonmouthshire.co.uk
Weekly (Wed)
Barry Gem
01446 774484
www.barry-today.co.uk
Weekly (Thu)
Barry & District News
01633 810000
www.thisisbarry.co.uk
Weekly (Thu)
Brecon & Radnor Express
01874 610111
www.brecon-radnor.co.uk
Weekly (Wed)
Bridgend & District Recorder
01446 774484
Weekly (Tue)
Cambrian News
01970 611611
www.aberystwyth-today.co.uk
Weekly (Wed)
Campaign Blackwood
01633 810000
Weekly (Fri)
Campaign Caerphilly
01633 810000
Weekly (Fri)
Campaign North Gwent
01633 810000
Weekly (Fri)
Campaign Pontypridd
01633 810000
Weekly (Fri)
Cardiff Advertiser & Property Times
029 203 03900
Weekly (Friday)
Cardigan & Tivyside Advertiser
01239 614343
www.thisistivyside.net
Weekly (Wed)

Carmarthen Herald
01267 227222
Weekly free (Fri)
Carmarthen Journal
01267 227222
www.carmarthenjournal.co.uk
Weekly (Wed)
Chepstow Free Press
01633 810000
www.thisismonmouthshire.co.uk
Weekly (Wed)
County Echo
01348 874445
www.newport-today.co.uk
Weekly (Fri)
County Times & Gazette
01938 553354
www.countytimes.co.uk
Weekly (Thu)
Cowbridge Gem
01446 774484
www.cowbridge-today.co.uk
Weekly (Thu)
Heart of Wales Chronicle
01874 610111
Weekly (Mon)
Llanelli Star
01554 745300
www.thisissouthwales.co.uk
Weekly (Wed, Thu)
Llantwit Major Gem
01446 774484
www.llantwit-major-today.co.uk
Weekly (Thu)
Mid Wales Journal
01952 242424
www.midwalesjournal.co.uk
Weekly (Fri)
Milford & West Wales Mercury
01646 698971
Weekly (Thu)
Monmouth Free Press
01633 810000
www.thisismonmouthshire.co.uk
Weekly (Wed)
Monmouthshire Beacon
01600 712142
www.monmouth-today.co.uk
Weekly (Thu)
Monthly Advertiser
01545 590415
Monthly free (last Mon)
Narbeth & Whitland Observer
01834 843262
Weekly (Fri)
Pontypool Free Press
01633 810000
www.thisismonmouthshire.co.uk
Weekly (Wed)
Port Talbot & Neath Tribune
01639 893722
Monthly free (2nd Wed)
South Wales Argus
01633 810000
www.thisisgwent.co.uk
Daily
South Wales Guardian
01437 763133
www.thisisammanford.co.uk
Weekly (Wed)
South West Wales Publications
01792 510000
Daily

Tenby Observer
01834 843262
www.tenby-today.co.uk
Weekly (Fri)
Tenby Times
01834 843262
www.tenby-today.co.uk
Monthly free (Wed)
Weekly Argus
01633 810000
Weekly (Thu)
Western Telegraph
01437 763133
www.thisispembrokeshire.net
Weekly (Wed)

Scotland

Courier and Advertiser
DC Thomson & Co, 2 Albert Square
Dundee DD1 9QJ
01382 223131
www.thecourier.co.uk
Daily
Daily Record
One Central Quay, Glasgow G3 8DA
0141 309 3000
www.dailyrecord.co.uk
Daily
Edinburgh Evening News
Barclay House, 108 Holyrood Rd
Edinburgh EH8 8AS
0131 620 8620
www.edinburghnews.com
Daily
Glasgow Evening Times
200 Renfield St, Glasgow G2 3QB
0141 302 7000
www.eveningtimes.co.uk
Daily
Glasgow Herald
200 Renfield St,Glasgow G2 3QB
0141 302 7000
www.theherald.co.uk
Daily
Scotland On Sunday
Barclay House, 108 Holyrood Rd
Edinburgh EH8 8AS
0131 620 8620
www.scotlandonsunday.com
Sunday
The Scotsman
Barclay House, 108 Holyrood Rd
Edinburgh EH8 8AS
0131 620 8620
www.scotsman.com
Daily
Sunday Herald
200 Renfield St, Glasgow G2 3QB
0141 302 7800
www.sundayherald.com
Sunday
Sunday Mail
One Central Quay, Glasgow G3 8DA
0141 309 3000
www.sundaymail.co.uk
Sunday

Sunday Post
DC Thomson & Co, 2 Albert Square
Dundee DD1 9QJ
01382 223131
www.thesundaypost.co.uk
Sunday

Other Scottish newspapers

Aberdeen & District Independent
01224 618300
www.aberdeen-indy.co.uk
Weekly (Thu)
Aberdeen Citizen
01224 690222
Daily
Aberdeen Evening Express
01224 690222
Daily
Aberdeen Press and Journal
01224 690222
www.pressandjournal.co.uk
Daily
The Advertiser
0131 561 6600
Weekly (Wed)
Airdrie & Coatbridge Advertiser
01236 748048
www.icScotland.co.uk
Weekly (Fri)
Alloa & Hillfoots Advertiser
01259 214416
www.wee-county-news.co.uk
Weekly (Thu)
Annandale Herald
01461 202078
Weekly (Thu)
Annandale Observer
01461 202078
Weekly (Fri)
Arbroath Herald
01241 872274
www.snpa.org.uk/arbroath.htm
Weekly (Fri)
Ardrossan & Saltcoats Herald
01294 464321
www.threetowners.com
    /Herald/herald_files.htm
Weekly (Fri)
Argyllshire Advertiser
01631 563058
www.argyllshireadvertiser.co.uk
Weekly (Fri)
Arran Banner
01770 302142
www.obantimes.co.uk
Weekly (Sat)
Ayr & District Leader
01292 611666
Weekly (Fri)
Ayr Advertiser
01292 267631
Weekly (Wed)
Ayrshire Post
01563 525115
www.icScotland.co.uk
Weekly (Wed)
Ayrshire World
01294 222288
Weekly free (Wed)
Ayrshire Post
01294 222288
Weekly (Wed)

Banff Gazette
01224 618300
Weekly (Fri)

Banffshire Herald
01542 886262
www.bannfshireherald.com
Weekly (Fri)

Barhead News
0141 887 7055
Weekly (Wed)

Bells Hills Speaker
01698 264611
Weekly (Thu)

Berwick Gazette
01289 306677
Weekly (Thu)

Berwickshire News
01289 306677
www.berwickshiretoday.co.uk
Weekly (Fri)

Blairgowie Adveriser
01738 626211
www.icScotland.co.uk
Weekly (Tue, Fri)

Border Telegraph
01896 758395
www.bordertelegraph.com
Weekly (Tue)

Brechin Advertiser
01356 622767
www.brechinadvertiser.com
Weekly (Thu)

Buchan Observer
01779 472017
www.buchanie.co.uk
Weekly (Tue)

The Buteman
01700 502503
Weekly (Fri)

Caithness Courier
01955 602424
www.caithness-courier.co.uk
Weekly (Wed)

Campbell Time
01631 563058
Weekly (Sat)

Campbeltown Courier & Argyllshire Advertiser
01586 554646
www.campbeltowncourier.co.uk
Weekly (Fri)

Carrick Gazette
01671 402503
Weekly (Thu)

Central Fife Times & Advertiser
01383 728201
Weekly (Wed)

Clyde Post
01475 726511
Weekly free (Wed)

Clyde Weekly News (Clydebank)
01294 222288
Weekly (Wed)

Clydebank Post
0141 952 0565
Weekly (Wed)

Craigmillar Chronicle
0131 661 0791
www.craignet.org.uk/chronicle
Monthly free (1st of month)

Cumbernauld & Kilsyth Advertiser
01236 725578
Weekly (Wed)

Cumbernauld News & Advertiser
01236 725578
Weekly (Fri)

Cumbernauld News & Kilsyth Chronicle
01236 725578
http://www2.falkirktoday.co.uk/inc
/cumbernauld/gbook/default
.asp?offset=70
Weekly (Wed)

Deeside Piper
01330 824955
www.deesidepiper.com
Weekly (Fri)

Donside Piper & Herald
01330 824955
www.donsidepiper.com
Weekly (Fri)

Dumbarton & Vale Of Leven Reporter
01436 673434
Weekly (Tue)

Dumfries & Galloway Standard
01387 253123
www.icScotland.co.uk
Weekly (Wed)

Dumfries and Galloway Today
01387 253123
Weekly (Wed)

Dumfries Courier
01461 202078
Weekly (Fri)

Dunfermline Press & West of Fife Advertiser
01383 728201
http://www.snpa.org.uk
/dunfermline.htm
Weekly (Thu)

Dunoon Observer & Argyllshire Standard
01369 703218
www.dunoon-observer.co.uk
Weekly (Fri)

East End Independent
01698 280000
http://iclanarkshire.icnetwork.co.uk
/news/localnews/eastkilbride
Weekly free (Wed)

East Fife Mail
01592 261451
www.fifenow.co.uk
Weekly free (Wed)

East Kilbride News
01355 265000
www.berwickshire-news.co.uk
Weekly (Wed)

East Kilbride World
01698 283200
Weekly free (Thu)

East Lothian Courier
01620 822451
www.eastlothiancourier.com
Weekly (Fri)

East Lothian Herald
01289 306677
www.berwickshire-news.co.uk
Weekly (Thu)

East Lothian News
0131 561 6600
Weekly (Thu)

East Lothian Times
0131 561 6600
Weekly free (Fri)

Ellon Advertiser
01888 563589
Weekly (Fri)

Ellon Times & East Gordon Advertiser
01779 472017
Weekly (Thu)

Eskdale and Liddesdale Advertiser
01387 380012
Weekly (Thu)

Evening Telegraph
01382 223131
Daily

Falkirk & Grangemouth
01324 624959
Weekly (Wed)

Falkirk Herald
01324 624959
www.falkirktoday.co.uk
Weekly (Thu)

Falkirk, Grangemouth & Linlithgow Advertiser
01324 485028
Weekly (Wed)

Fife & Kinross Extra
01383 728201
Weekly free (Fri)

Fife Free Press
01592 261451
www.fifenow.co.uk
Weekly free (Thu)

Fife Herald
01592 261451
Weekly free (Fri)

Fife Leader
01592 261451
Weekly free (Tue s)

Forfar Dispatch
01307 464899
www.forfardispatch.com
Weekly (Tue)

Forres Gazette
01309 672615
www.forres-gazette.co.uk
Weekly (Wed)

Fraserburgh Herald
01779 472017
Weekly (Fri)

Galloway Gazette
01671 402503
www.gallowaygazette.com
Weekly (Thu)

Galloway News
01387 253123
www.icScotland.co.uk
Weekly (Thu)

Glasgow East News
01324 624959
Weekly (Thu)

Glasgow South & Eastwood Extra
0141 427 7878
Weekly (Thu)

Glaswegian
0141 309 3000
Weekly free

Glenrothes Gazette
01592 261451
www.fifenow.co.uk
Weekly free (Wed)

Gorgie Dalry Gazette
0131 337 2457
Monthly (1st Fri)

Greenock Telegraph
01475 726511
www.greenocktelegraph.co.uk
Weekly (Wed)

Hamilton Advertiser
01698 283200
www.icScotland.co.uk
Weekly (Thu)

Hamilton Extra People
01698 261321
Weekly (Fri)

Hawick News
01289 306677
www.hawicktoday.co.uk
Weekly (Fri)

Helensburgh Advertiser
01436 673434
Weekly (Thu)

Herald & Post Edinburgh
0131 620 8620
Weekly free (Thu)

Huntly Express
01466 793622
Weekly (Fri)

Inverness & Highland News
01463 732222
Daily

Inverness & Nairnshire Herald
01463 732222
Daily

Inverness Courier
01463 233059
www.inverness-courier.co.uk
Weekly (Tue, Fri)

Inverurie Advertiser
01888 563589
Weekly (Fri)

Inverurie Herald
01467 625150
www.inverurieherald.com
Weekly (Thu)

Irvine and North Ayrshire Leader
01292 611666
Weekly (Fri)

Irvine Herald
01294 222288
www.icScotland.co.uk
Weekly (Wed)

Irvine Times
01294 464321
Weekly (Wed)

Ileach (Islay)
01496 810355
www.ileach.co.uk
Weekly (Sat)

John O'Groat Journal
01955 602424
www.johnogroat-journal.co.uk
Weekly (Fri)

Kilmarnock & District Leader
01292 611666
Weekly (Fri)

Kilmarnock Standard
01294 222288
www.icScotland.co.uk
Weekly (Wed)

Kincardineshire Observer
01561 377283
Weekly (Fri)

Kirkintilloch Herald
0141 775 0040
www.kirkintillochtoday.co.uk
Weekly (Wed)

Kirriemuir Herald
01307 464899
www.kirriemuirherald.com
Weekly (Thu)

Lanarkshire World
01698 283200
www.icScotland.co.uk
Weekly (Wed)

Largs & Millport Weekly News
01475 689009
Weekly (Wed)

Lennox Herald
01294 222288
www.icScotland.co.uk
Weekly (Wed)

Linlithgowshire Journal & Gazette
01506 844592
Weekly (Fri)

Lochaber News
01463 732222
www.lochaber-news.co.uk
Weekly (Thu)

Lothian Times East
0131 561 6600
Weekly free (Fri)

Mearns Leader
01569 762139
www.mearnsleader.com
Weekly (Fri)

Metro Scotland
020 7651 5200
www.metroscot.co.uk
Daily

Mid Lothian Times
0131 561 6600
Weekly free (Fri)

Midlothian Advertiser
0131 561 6600
Weekly (Wed)

Milngavie and Bearsden Herald
0141 956 3533
Weekly (Wed)

Milngavie, Bearsden & Glasgow West Extra
0141 427 7878
Weekly (Thu)

Moffat News
01461 202078
Weekly (Thu)

Montrose Review
01674 672605
www.montrosereview.net
Weekly (Thu)

Motherwell Extra
01698 261321
Weekly (Fri)

Musselburgh News
0131 561 6600
Weekly (Thu)

North Edinburgh News
0131 467 3972
www.northedinburghnews.co.uk
Monthly free (2nd Wed)

North Star
01463 732222
www.highland-news.co.uk
Weekly (Thu)

Northern Scot
01343 548777
www.northern-scot.co.uk
Weekly

Northern Times
01408 633993
www.northern-times.co.uk
Weekly (Thu)

North West Highlands Bratach
01641 521227
www.bratach.co.uk
Monthly (1st Thu)

Oban Times
01631 563058
www.obantimes.co.uk
Weekly (Thu)

The Orcadian
01856 879000
www.orcadian.co.uk
Weekly (Thu)

Paisley & District People
0141 887 7055
Weekly free (Fri)

Paisley & Renfrewshire Extra
0141 427 7878
Weekly (Thu)

Paisley and Renfrewshire Gazette
0141 887 7055
Weekly (Wed)

Paisley Daily Express
01698 283200
www.icScotland.co.uk
Weekly (Thu)

Peebles Times
0131 5616600
Weekly free (Fri)

Peeblesshire News
01896 758395
www.peeblesshirenews.com
Weekly (Fri)

Renfrewshire World
01294 222288
Weekly (Wed)

Ross-shire Herald
01463 732222
Weekly (Thus)

Ross-shire Journal
01349 863436
www.rsjournal.co.uk
Weekly (Fri)

Rutherglen Reformer
0141 647 2271
www.icScotland.co.uk
Weekly (Thus)

Selkirk Advertiser
01289 306677
www.selkirktoday.co.uk
Weekly (Fri)

Shetland Life
01595 693622
www.shetlandtoday.co.uk
Monthly (1st Friday)

Shetland News
01806 577332
www.shetland-news.co.uk
Daily

Shetland Times
01595 693622
www.shetlandtoday.co.uk
Weekly

Southern Reporter
01289 306677
www.borderstoday.co.uk
Weekly (Fri)

South West News & Star
01228 612300
www.news-and-star.co.uk
Daily

St Andrews Citizen
01592 261451
www.fifenow.co.uk
Weekly free (Fri)

Strathearn Observer
01738 626211
Weekly (Fri)

Stirling News
01259 214416
Weekly free (Wed)

Stirling Observer
01738 626211
www.icScotland.co.uk
2Weekly free (Wed, Fri)

Stirling/Alloa & Hillfoots Shopper
01738 626211
Weekly (Fri)

Stornoway Gazette and West Coast Advertiser
01851 702687
www.stornowaygazette.co.uk
Weekly (Thu)

Stranraer & Wigtownshire Free Press
01776 702551
www.stranraer.org/freepress
Weekly (Wed)

Strathkelvin Advertiser
0141 775 0040
Weekly (Sat)

Turriff Advertiser
01888 563589
Weekly (Fri)

Wee County News
01259 724724
www.wee-county-news.co.uk
Weekly (Thu)

West Highland Free Press
01471 822464
www.whfp.co.uk
Weekly (Thu)

West Lothian Courier
01506 633544
www.icScotland.co.uk
Weekly (Thus)

West Lothian Herald & Post
0131 620 8620
Weekly free (Thu)

WT (Saturday edition of Evening Times)
0141 302 7000
Weekly (Sat)

Northern Ireland

Belfast Telegraph
124–144 Royal Avenue
Belfast BT1 1EB
028 9026 4000
www.belfasttelegraph.co.uk
Daily

Sunday Life
124–144 Royal Avenue
Belfast BT1 1EB
028 9026 4000
www.sundaylife.co.uk
Sunday

Belfast News
028 9068 0000
www.icnorthernireland.co.uk
Weekly (Thu)

The Daily Mirror
028 9056 8000
Daily

Derry Journal
028 7127 2200
www.icnorthernireland.co.uk
Weekly (Tue & Fri)

Farming Life
028 9068 0000
www.farminglife.com
Weekly (Wed, Sat)

Irish News
028 9032 2226
www.irishnews.com
Daily

News Letter
028 9068 0000
www.icnorthernireland.co.uk
Daily

North Belfast news
028 9058 4444
www.irelandclick.com
Weekly (Fri)

The People (Northern Ireland Editions)
028 9056 8000
Sunday

South Belfast News
028 9024 2411
www.irelandclick.com
Weekly (Fri)

Sunday Mirror
028 9056 8000
www.sundaymirror.co.uk
Sunday

Sunday World (Northern Ireland edition)
00 353 1 490 1980
www.sundayworld.com
Sunday

Antrim

Andersonstown News
028 9061 9000
www.irelandclick.com
Weekly (Mon /Thu)

Antrim Guardian
028 9446 2624
www.ulsternet-ni.co.uk/guardian
/pages/antrim.htm
Weekly (Wed)

Antrim Times
028 3839 3939
Weekly (Wed)

Ballycastle Chronicle
028 7034 3344
www.ulsternet-
ni.co.uk/chronicle/pages
/ballycastle.htm
Weekly (Wed)

Ballymena Chronicle
028 8772 2557
Weekly (Wed)

Ballymena Guardian
028 2564 1221
www.ulsternet-
ni.co.uk/guardian/pages/
ballymena.htm
Weekly (Wed)

Ballymena Times
028 3839 3939
www.ballymenanews.com
Weekly (Wed)

Ballymoney & Coleraine Chronicle
028 7034 3344
www.ulsternet-ni.co.uk/chronicle
/pages/ballymoney.htm
Weekly (Wed)

Ballymoney Times
028 3839 3939
www.ballymoneytimes.com
Weekly (Wed)

Carrick Times
028 3839 3939
www.carricktimes.com
Weekly (Thu)

Carrickfergus Advertiser
028 8772 2274
www.ulsternet-ni.co.uk/carrick
/CPAGES/CMAIN.htm
Weekly (Wed)

East Antrim Advertiser
028 3839 3939
Monthly

East Antrim Guardian
028 2564 1221
www.ulsternet-ni.co.uk/guardian
/pages/eantrim.htm
Weekly (Wed)

Larne Times
028 3839 3939
www.larnetimes.com
Weekly (Thu)

Limavady Chronicle
028 7034 3344
www.ulsternet-ni.co.uk/chronicle
/pages/limavady.htm
Weekly (Wed)

Lisburn Echo
028 3839 3939
Weekly free (Wed)

Magherafelt & Limavady Constitution
028 7034 3344
www.ulsternet-ni.co.uk/ncon/pages
/limavady.htm
Weekly (Wed)

Newtownabbey Times
028 3839 3939
Weekly (Thu)

Valley Icear Gazette
028 8772 2274
Weekly (Wed)

Armagh

Armagh Observer
028 8772 2557
Weekly (Wed)

Craigavon Echo
028 3839 3939
Weekly free (Wed)

Lurgan & Portadown Examiner
028 8772 2557
Weekly (Wed)

Lurgan Mail
028 3839 3939
www.lurganmail.com
Weekly (Thu)

Portadown Times
028 3839 3939
www.portadowntimes.com
Weekly (Fri)

The Ulster Gazette & Armagh Standard
028 3752 2639
www.ulsternet-ni.co.uk/ugazette
/gpages/GMAIN.htm
Weekly (Wed)

Down

Armagh-Down Observer
028 8772 2557
Weekly (Thu)

Banbridge Chronicle
028 4066 2322
Weekly (Wed)
Banbridge Leader
028 4066 2745
www.bambridgeleader.com
Weekly (Wed)
The Down Democrat
028 4461 4400
www.downdemocrat.com
Weekly (Tue)
Down Recorder
028 4461 3711
www.thedownrecorder.com
Weekly (Wed)
Dromore Leader
028 3839 3939
www.dromoreleader.com
Weekly (Wed)
The Leader
028 3839 3939
www.ulsternet-ni.co.uk/leader
/pages/leader.htm
Weekly (Wed)
Mourne Observer & County Down News
028 4372 2666
Weekly (Wed)
Newry Advertiser
028 8772 2557
Monthly free
Newry Democrat
028 3025 1250
www.newrydemocrat.com
Weekly (Tue)
Newtownards Chronicle
028 9127 0270
Weekly (Thu)
Newtownards Spectator
028 9127 0270
Weekly (Thu)
North Down Community Telegraph
028 9026 4000
Weekly (Tue) (Wed) (Thu)
The Outlook
028 4063 0202
www.ulsternet-ni.co.uk/outlook
/outpages/OMAIN.htm
Weekly (Wed)

Fermanagh

Fermanagh News
028 8772 2557
Weekly (Fri)
Impartial Reporter
028 6632 4422
www.impartialreporter.com
Weekly (Thu)
Lakeland Extra
028 6632 4422
Monthly free (3rDailyMon)

Londonderry

City News
028 7127 2200
Weekly (Wed)
Coleraine Constitution
028 7034 3344
www.ulsternet-ni.co.uk/ncon/pages
/coleraine.htm
Weekly (Wed)
Coleraine Times
028 3839 3939
www.colerainetimes.com
Weekly (Wed)

Derry Journal
028 7127 2200
www.icnorthernireland.co.uk
Weekly (Tue & Fri)
Derry News
028 7129 6600
www.derrynews.com
Weekly (Thu)
Dungannon News & Tyrone Courier
028 8772 2271
www.ulsternet-ni.co.uk/courier
/cpages/CMAIN.htm
Weekly (Wed)
Dungannon Observer
028 8772 2557
Weekly (Fri)
Fermanagh Herald
028 8224 3444
www.fermanaghherald.com
Weekly (Wed)
Foyle News
028 7127 2200
http://icderry.icnetwork.co.uk
/ournewspapers/foylenews/
Weekly (Thu)
The Guardian
028 7034 3344
Weekly (Wed)
The Leader (Coleraine)
028 7034 3344
www.ulsternet-ni.co.uk/leader
/pages/leader.htm
Weekly (Mon)
Londonderry Sentinel
028 3839 3939
www.londonderry sentinel.com
Weekly (Wed)
Mid-Ulster Echo
028 3839 3939
Weekly free (Wed)
Mid-Ulster Mail
028 3839 3939
www.midulstermail.com
Weekly (Wed)
Mid-Ulster Observer
028 8772 2557
Weekly (Wed)
North West Echo
028 3839 3939
Weekly free (Wed)
Roe Valley Sentinel
028 3839 3939
www.mortonnewspapers.com
Weekly (Wed)
Strabane Chronicle
028 8224 3444
www.strabanechronicle.com
Weekly (Thu)
Strabane Weekly News
028 8224 2721
www.ulsternet-ni.co.uk/strabane
/spages/SMAIN.htm
Weekly (Thu)
Tyrone Constitution
028 8224 2721
www.ulsternet-ni.co.uk/tcon
/conpages/CMAIN.htm
Weekly (Thu)
Tyrone Times
028 3839 3939
www.tyronetimes.com
Weekly (Fri)
Ulster Herald
028 8224 3444
www.ulsterherald.com
Weekly (Thu)

Main Irish papers

Irish Times
00 353 1 6792022
www.ireland.com
Daily
Irish Independent
00 353 1 7055333
www.independent.ie
Daily
Connacht Tribune
00 353 9 153 6222
www.connacht-tribune.ie
Weekly
Cork Evening Echo
00 353 21 427 2722
www.eecho.ie
Daily
Evening Herald (Dublin)
00 353 1 7055333
www.unison.ie
Daily
Ireland on Sunday
00 353 1 6375800
Sunday
Irish Examiner
00 353 1 6056300
www.examiner.ie
Daily
Kerryman
00 353 6 67145500
www.kerryman.ie
Weekly (Wed)
Leinster Leader
00 353 4 5897302
www.unison.ie/leinster_leader
Weekly (Wed)
Limerick Leader
00 353 6 1214500
www.limerick-leader.ie
Daily
Limerick Post
00 353 6 1413322
www.limerickpost.ie
Weekly (Thu)
Sunday Business Post
00 353 1 6026000
www.sbpost.ie
Weekly (Sat)
Sunday Independent
00 353 1 7055333
www.independent.ie
Sunday
Sunday Tribune
00 353 1 6314300
www.tribune.ie
Sunday
Sunday World
00 353 1 4901980
www.sundayworld.com
Sunday

Main magazine & contract magazine publishers

AMD Brass Tacks
The Mill House, Redcliff Backs
Bristol BS1 6LY
0117 929 7680
enquiry@amdbrasstacks.co.uk
www.amdbrasstacks.co.uk

Brooklands Group
Medway House, Lower Rd
Forest Row, East Sussex RH18 5HE
01342 828700
www.brooklandsgroup.com

BBC Worldwide
Woodlands, 80 Wood Lane
London W12 0TT
020 8433 2000
www.bbcworldwide.com

CBC Media
4–5 Greenwich Quay, Clarence Rd
London SE8 3EY
020 8469 9700
info@cbcomm.co.uk
www.cbcomm.co.uk

Cedar Communications
Pegasus House, 37–43 Sackville St
London W1S 3EH
020 7534 2400
info@cedarcom.co.uk
www.cedarcom.co.uk

Centaur
50 Poland St, London W1F 7AX
020 7970 4000
www.centaur.co.uk

CMP Information
Ludgate House, 245 Blackfriars Rd
London SE1 9UY
020 7921 5000
nmain@cmpinformation.com
www.cmpinformation.com

Condé Nast
Vogue House, Hanover Square
London W1S 1JU
020 7499 9080
www.condenast.co.uk

DC Thomson
185 Fleet St, London EC4A 2HS
020 7400 1030
www.dcthomson.co.uk

Dennis
30 Cleveland St, London W1T 4JD
020 7907 6000
www.dennis.co.uk

Emap
Corporate Office, 40 Bernard St
London WC1N 1LW
020 7278 1452
www.emap.com

Emap Communications
Scriptor Court, 155 Farringdon Rd
London EC1R 3AD
020 7841 6600
www.emap.com

Emap Consumer Media
Endeavour House
189 Shaftesbury Avenue
London WC2H 8JG
020 7437 9011
www.emap.com

Emap Performance
Mappin House, 4 Winsley St
London W1W 9HF
020 7436 1515
www.emap.com

Future
30 Monmouth St, Bath BA1 2BW
01225 442244
www.futurenet.com

H Bauer
Academic House, 24–28 Oval Rd
London NW1 7DT
020 7241 8000
www.bauer.co.uk

Hachette Filipacchi
64 North Row, London W1K 7LL
020 7150 7000
www.hachettefilipacchiuk.co.uk

Haymarket
174 Hammersmith Rd
London W6 7JP
020 8267 5000
hpg@haymarketgroup.com
www.haymarketgroup.co.uk

Haymarket Customer Magazines
38–42 Hampton Rd
Teddington, Middlesex TW11 0JE
020 8267 5000
haycustpub@haynet.com
www.haycustpub.com

Highbury House Communications
1–3 Highbury Station Rd
Islington, London N1 1SE
020 7226 2222
www.hhc.co.uk

IPC Media
King's Reach Tower, Stamford St
London SE1 9LS
0870 444 5000
feedback@ipcmedia.com
www.ipc.co.uk

John Brown Citrus
The New Boathouse
136–142 Bramley Rd
London W10 6SR
020 7565 3000
andrew.hirsch@jbcp.co.uk
www.jbcp.co.uk

Mediamark
11 Kingsway, London WC2B 6PH
020 7212 9000
info@mediamark.co.uk
www.mediamark.co.uk

The National Magazine Company
National Magazine House
72 Broadwick St, London W1F 9EP
020 7439 5000
www.natmags.co.uk

NatMag Contract Publishing
33 Broadwick St, London W1F 0DQ
020 7439 5000
Director:
julian.downing@natmags.co.uk;
editorial and creative director:
carey.sedgwick@natmags.co.uk
www.natmag-contract.co.uk

New Crane Publishing
20 Upper Ground, London SE1 9PD
020 7633 0266
enquiries@newcrane.co.uk
www.newcrane.com

Publicis Blueprint
82 Baker St, London W1U 6AE
020 7830 3803
www.publicis-blueprint.com

Quantum Business Media
Quantum House, 19 Scarbrook Rd
Croydon, Surrey CR9 1LX
020 8565 4200
enquiries@quantumbusinessmedia
.com
www.quantumbusinessmedia.com

Redwood
7 St Martin's Place
London WC2N 4HA
020 7747 0700
infohub@redwoodgroup.net
www.redwoodgroup.net

Reed Business Information
25 Victoria St, London SW1H 0EX
020 8652 3500
www.reedbusiness.com

The River Group
Victory House, Leicester Square
London WC2H 7QH
020 7306 0304
info@riverltd.co.uk
www.therivergroup.co.uk

VNU Business
VNU House, 32–34 Broadwick St
London W1A 2HG
020 7316 9000
feedback@vnunet.com

Adult

Asian Babes
020 7308 5092
Monthly

Escort
020 7292 8000
Monthly

Fiesta
01376 534538
13 pa

Forum
020 7308 5363
13 pa

Knave
01376 534558
Monthly

Mayfair
020 7292 8000
Monthly

Men Only
020 7292 8000
Monthly

Skin Two
020 7498 5533
www.skintwo.com/magazine
4pa

Viz Comic
0191 2414243
www.viz.co.uk
Monthly

Children and teenage

19
020 7261 6320
www.jbmedia.com/19.asp
Monthly

2000 AD
01865 200603
www.2000adonline.com
Weekly

Action Man
01892 500100
www.actionman.com
Monthly

Angel Magazine
020 7250 0750
Monthly

Animal Action
0870 754 0145
Bi-monthly

Aquila Children's Magazine
01323 431313
www.aquila.co.uk
Monthly

Art Attack
01892 500100
www.artattack.co.uk
Monthly

Beano
01382 223131
www.beanotown.com
Weekly

The Best Times
020 8668 2431
9pa

Bliss
020 7208 3791
www.blissmag.co.uk
Monthly

Breakout
01235 553444
Quarterly

Chill Out
01908 651270
2pa

CosmoGirl!
020 7312 3077
www.cosmogirl.com
Monthly

Fresh Magazine
01392 677321
Monthly

Girl Talk
020 8433 3543
www.bbcworldwide.com
/magazines/girltalk
Fortnightly

Guiding
020 7592 1821
Monthly

J-17
020 7208 3408
Monthly

Mizz
020 7261 7358
www.jbmedia.com/mizz.asp
Monthly

Plus/Eagles' Wings
01903 824174
Monthly

Pony
01428 651551
www.horseandridermagazine.co.uk
/PONY
Monthly

Rugrats
0161 624 0414
www.rugratonline.com
14pa

Scouting Magazine
020 8433 7100
www.scoutingmagazine.org
Monthly

Shout Magazine
01382 575774
Fortnightly

Simpsons Comics
020 7620 0200
Monthly

Sindy Magazine
01892 500100
Monthly

Sneak
020 7312 8932
www.sneakmagazine.com
Weekly

Sooty Magazine
01892 500100
Bi-monthly

Spectacular Spiderman
01892 500100
www.dccomics.com
Monthly

Sugar
020 7150 7050
www.sugarmagazine.co.uk
Monthly

Toybox
020 8433 3442
www.bbcworldwide.com/magazines
/toybox
Monthly

Young Scot
0131 313 2488
www.youngscot.org
Monthly

Computing

.net
01225 442244
Monthly

Computer & Video Games
020 7907 6565
www.computerandvideogames.com
Monthly

Computer Music
01225 442244
www.computermusic.co.uk
Monthly

Computer Shopper Magazine
01902 372999
www.computershopper.co.uk
Monthly

Computeractive
020 7316 9000
www.computeractive.co.uk
Fortnightly

Cube
01202 200245
http://www.paragon.co.uk/mags
/cube.html
Monthly

Games Domain
0121 326 0900
www.gamesdomain.com
Website updated daily

Games Master Magazine
01225 442244
www.uniquemagazines.co.uk
13pa

Internet Advisor
01225 442244
www.netadvisor.co.uk
13pa

Internet Made Easy
01202 299900
http://www.paragon.co.uk/mags
/ime.html
Monthly

Internet Magazine
020 7868 7361
www.internet-magazine.com
Monthly

Login Magazine
01702 582895
Monthly

Macworld
020 7831 9252
www.macworld.co.uk
13pa

Max
01225 442244
Monthly

Micro Mart
0121 2338712
www.micromart.co.uk
Weekly

Nintendo Games Cube (NGC)
01225 442244
www.nintendo.com
Monthly

Official Playstation 2 Magazine
01225 442244
Monthly
Official Xbox Magazine
020 7317 2471
www.officialxboxmagazine.co.uk
Monthly
P2
01202 299900
Monthly
PC Adviser
020 7291 5939
www.pcadvisor.co.uk
Monthly
PC Answers
01225 442244
www.pcanswers.co.uk
Monthly
PC Format
01225 442244
www.pcformat.co.uk
Monthly
PC Gamer
01225 442244
www.pcgamer.co.uk
Monthly
PC Gaming World
020 8515 0400
Monthly
PC Home
01202 299900
Monthly
PC Plus
01225 442244
www.pcplus.co.uk
Monthly
PC Pro
020 7907 6260
Monthly
PC Utilities
01625 855086
Monthly
PC Zone
020 7907 6373
www.pczone.co.uk
Monthly
Playstation 1
01225 442244
Monthly
Power Station
01202 200240
www.uniquemagazines.co.uk
Monthly
Practical Internet
01202 299900
http://www.paragon.co.uk/mags
/practicali.html
Monthly
Station Solutions
01392 412458
Monthly
Web Pages Made Easy
01202 200276
http://www.paragon.co.uk/mags
/wpme.html
Web User
020 7261 7294
www.web-user.co.uk
Fortnightly
XBM
01202 200242
www.uniquemagazines.co.uk
Monthly

Current affairs

AFF Families Journal
01980 615517
www.army.mod.uk/aff/Journal
4pa
The American
01297 561147
Monthly
Big Issue
020 7526 3200
www.bigissue.com
Weekly
Big Issue in Scotland
0141 4187000
www.bigissuescotland.com
Weekly
Big Issue in the North
0161 834 6300
www.bigissueinthenorth.com
Weekly
Canada Post
020 7243 4243
www.canadapost.ca
Monthly
The Cat
01403 221936
Bi-monthly
Challenge Newsline
0800 195 7969
Monthly
City News
01273 291039
10pa
Economist
020 7830 7000
www.economistgroup.com
Weekly
Focus on Africa – BBC
020 7557 2906
www.bbc.co.uk/worldservice/africa
/features/focus_magazine
4pa
Glasgow Magazine
0141 287 0901
www.glasgow.gov.uk/html/about
/glasgowmag/glasgowmag.htm
Bi-monthly
Granta
020 7704 9776
www.granta.com
4pa
Haringey People
020 8489 2997
Monthly
Impact International
020 7263 1417
Monthly
Index on Censorship
020 7278 2313
www.indexonline.org
4pa
La Voce Degli Italiani
020 7735 5164
Fortnightly
Liberty
020 7403 3888
www.libertymagazine.org
4pa
Middle East Expatriate
020 8943 3630
www.middleeastexpatonline.com
10pa

New African
020 7713 7711
www.unique
Monthly
New Internationalist
01865 728181
www.uniquemagazines.co.uk
Monthly
New Statesman
020 7730 3444
www.newstatesman.co.uk
Weekly
News Africa
020 7713 8135
Monthly
Newsweek
020 7629 8361
www.newsweek.com
Weekly
Nexus
01342 322854
www.nexus.com
Bi-monthly
Outrage – magazine of Animal Aid
01732 364546
www.animalaid.co.uk
4pa
Party Politics
020 7374 0645
6pa
Private Eye
020 7437 4017
www.private-eye.co.uk
Fortnightly
Prospect
020 7255 1281
www.prospect-magazine.co.uk
Monthly
Report
020 7930 6441
9 to 10pa
Sesame
01908 652451
6pa
The Socialist
020 8988 8782
www.socialistparty.org.uk
/TheSocialistContents.htm
4pa
Socialist Review
020 7538 3308
www.socialistreview.org.uk
Monthly
Spectator
020 7405 1706
www.spectator.co.uk
Weekly
The Sticks Magazine
01462 486810
www.the-sticks.com
4pa
Time
020 7499 4080
www.time.com
Weekly (Mon)
Tribune
020 7433 6410
www.tribune.atfreeweb.com
Weekly
WWF News
01483 426444
www.wwf.org.uk
Quarterly

Your Money, Savings & Investments
020 7404 3123
www.yourmoneydirect.co.uk
Quarterly

Education

Gair Rhydd
029 2078 1434
www.cf.ac.uk/suon/gair
Weekly

London Student
020 7664 2054
www.londonstudent.org.uk

Student Direct
0161 275 2943
www.student-direct.co.uk
Weekly

The MBA Career Guide
020 7554 3350
2 pa

The Lecturer
020 7837 3636
www.natfhe.org.uk
6pa

Higher Education Review
020 8341 1366
3pa

LSE Magazine
020 7955 7582
www.lse.ac.uk
2 pa

Right Start
020 7878 2338
www.rightstartmagazine.co.uk
Bi-monthly

Redbrick
0121 4721841
Weekly

Times Educational Supplement
020 7782 3000
www.tes.co.uk

Entertainment

AN Magazine
0191 241 8000
www.a-n.co.uk
Monthly

BBC Music Magazine
020 8433 3283
www.bbc.co.uk
Monthly

The Big Buzz
028 9020 5050
www.bigbuzzireland.com
Monthly

The Big Cheese
020 7733 0305
www.bigcheesemagazine.com
Monthly

Billboard
020 7420 6003
www.billboard.com
Weekly

The Brighton Source
01273 561617
Monthly

Buzz Magazine
029 2025 6883
www.buzzmag.co.uk
Monthly

Central London Independent
0845 130 6249
4pa

Classic FM – The Magazine
020 8267 5877
Monthly

Classic Rock
01225 442244
www.classicrockmagazine.com
Monthly

Classical Music
020 7333 1742
www.rhinegold.co.uk/classical
_music_magazine.cfm?ord=0
Fortnightly

Country Music People
020 8854 7217
www.countrymusicpeople.com
Monthly

Country Music Round-up
01472 821707
www.cmru.co.uk
Monthly

The Crack
0191 230 3038
http://web.ukonline.co.uk/the.crack/
Monthly

DMC Update
020 7262 6777
www.dmcworld.com/update
Weekly

DVD Monthly
01392 434477
www.predatorpublishing.co.uk
/interact
Monthly

DVD Review
01202 200210
www.dvdreview.net
Monthly

e.p. Magazine
0118 958 1878
Monthly

Early Music Today
020 7333 1744
www.rhinegold.co.uk/early_music
_magazine.cfm?ord=0
Bi-monthly

Echoes
020 7407 5888
Monthly

Edge
01225 442244
www.edge-online.com
Monthly

Empire
020 7437 9011
www.empireonline.co.uk
Monthly

Entertainer
01302 819111
Weekly

Entertainment Sussex
01273 711555
Bi-monthly

Essential Home Cinema
01202 209311
www.paragon.co.uk/mags
/ehomecinema.html
Monthly

Film Review
020 8875 1520
www.visimag.com/filmreview
Monthly

First on Video
020 7608 6789
www.firstonvideo.co.uk
Monthly

The Fly
020 7691 4555
www.fly.co.uk
Monthly

Freetime
01252 621513
www.freetimemag.co.uk
4pa

fRoots
020 8340 9651
www.frootsmag.com
Monthly

Gramophone Magazine
020 8267 5136
www.gramophone.co.uk
Monthly

Guitar Techniques
01225 442244
Monthly

Guitarist
01225 442244
www.guitarist.co.uk
Monthly

Hi-Fi Choice
020 7317 2600
www.hifichoice.co.uk
13 pa

Hi-Fi World
020 7625 3134
www.hi-fiworld.co.uk
Monthly

Hip Hop Connection
01223 210536

The Hollywood Reporter
020 7420 6000
www.hollywoodreporter.com
Weekly

Home Cinema Choice
020 7331 1000
www.homecinemachoice.com
Monthly

Hotdog
01202 299900
www.hotdogmagazine.com
13 pa

Impact
01484 435011
www.martialartsltd.co.uk/impact
Monthly

Inside Soap
020 7150 7570
www.insidesoap.co.uk
Fortnightly

It's Hot
020 8433 3250
www.bbcworldwide.com
/magazines/hot
Monthly

Jazz at Ronnie Scott's
020 7485 9803
www.ronniescotts.co.uk
Bi-monthly

Jazz Guide
01908 312392
Monthly

Jockey Slut
020 7749 1926
www.jockeyslut.com/magazine
Monthly

Kerrang!
020 7436 1515
www.kerrang.com
Weekly
The List
0131 558 1191
www.list.co.uk
Fortnightly
The London Hotel Magazine
020 7373 7282
Bi-monthly
M8
0141 840 5980
www.m8magazine.co.uk
Monthly
Magpie
0870 071 1611
2pa or 3pa
Mixmag
020 7817 8805
www.mixmag.net
Monthly
Mojo
020 7312 8716
www.mojo4music.com
Monthly
Movie Club News
0845 1306249
4pa
The National Gallery Season Guide
020 7747 2836
3pa
Night & Day – Essential Visitors Guide
0121 212 4141
Yearly
NME
020 7261 6472
www.nme.com
Weekly
NW
020 7792 2626
http://sites.ninemsn.com.au/minisite
/NW/default.asp
Monthly
The Official Elvis Presley Fan Club Magazine
0116 253 7271
Bi-monthly
Opera
020 8563 8893
Monthly
Opera Now
020 7333 1740
www.rhinegold.co.uk/opera_now
_magazine.cfm?ord=0
6pa
Piano
020 7333 1724
www.rhinegold.co.uk/piano
_magazine.cfm?ord=0
Bi-monthly
Pub and Club Gazette
01782 860800
Fortnightly
Q
020 7312 8182
www.q4music.com
Monthly
Radio Times
020 8433 3400
www.radiotimes.co.uk
Weekly
Record Buyer
01522 511265
Monthly

Rock Sound
020 7278 5559
www.rock-sound.net
Monthly
Rolling Stone
www.rollingstone.com
Satellite TV Europe
020 7331 1100
www.satellitetvtoday.com
Monthly
SFX
01225 442244
www.sfx.co.uk
Monthly
Shivers
020 8875 1520
www.visimag.com/shivers
Monthly
Sight & Sound
020 7255 1444
www.bfi.org.uk/sightandsound
Monthly
Sky Customer Magazine
020 7565 3000
www.medialive.ie/Magazines/Music
/sky.html
Monthly
Smash Hits
020 7436 1515
www.smashhits.net
Fortnightly
Songlines
01753 865342
www.songlines.co.uk
Bi-monthly
Starburst
020 8875 1520
www.visimag.com/starburst
Monthly
Stardust International
020 8795 5318
Monthly
The Strad
020 7882 1040
www.thestrad.com
4pa
Straight No Chaser
020 8533 9999
www.straightnochaser.co.uk
Bi-monthly
This is London Magazine
020 7434 1281
www.thisislondon.com
Weekly
Time Out
020 7813 3000
www.timeout.co.uk
Weekly
Time Out Student Guide
020 7813 3000
www.timeout.co.uk
Monthly
Top of the Pops Magazine
020 8433 2964
www.bbc.co.uk/totp
Monthly
Top Review
0845 130 6249
Weekly
Total Guitar
01225 442244
www.totalguitar.co.uk
Monthly
TV Choice
020 7241 8403
Weekly

TV Hits!
020 7150 7103
www.tvhits.co.uk
TV Quick
020 7241 8000
www.tpconline.co.uk/website
/tvquick.cfm
Weekly
TV Times
020 7261 7740
www.tvtimes.co.uk
Weekly
Twenty 4-seven
01752 294130
www.twenty4-seven.co.uk
Monthly
Uncut
020 7261 6992
www.uncut.net
Unlimited
0117 927 9009
www.originpublishing.co.uk/custom
/unlimited.htm
What's on in London
020 7278 4393
www.whatsoninlondon.co.uk
Monthly
What's on in the Royal Borough
020 8547 5015
Monthly
What's on TV
020 7261 7535
www.ipc.co.uk/ipc-media-brands
/brandprofiles/whatsontv.html
Weekly
The Wire
020 7422 5010
www.thewire.co.uk
Monthly
Word
020 7520 8625
www.wordmagazine.co.uk
Monthly
The X Files
020 7620 0200
www.thexfiles.com
Monthly
X Ray
020 7729 3773
www.goxray.com
Monthly
Zap
020 7419 8419

Food & drink

Decanter
020 7610 3929
www.decanter.com
Monthly
Food & Travel
020 8332 9090
Monthly
Food Chain
01502 470600
www.foodchain-magazine.com
Monthly
Foodie Magazine
01202 589646
www.foodiemag.com
Italian Wines & Spirits
020 8458 4860
3pa

M&S Magazine
020 7747 0871
www2.marksandspencer.com
/foodmagazine
4pa
Safeway Magazine
020 7470 7000
Monthly
Sainsbury's Magazine
020 7633 0266
www.sainsburysmagazine.co.uk
Monthly
Somerfield Magazine
0117 989 7800
13 pa
Tesco Clubcard Magazine
020 7734 2303
www.tesco.co.uk
4pa
The Vegetarian
0161 925 2000
www.vegsoc.org/vegmag
4pa
Waitrose Food Illustrated
020 7565 3000
www.waitrose.com/wfi
Monthly

Gay and lesbian

see chapter on **Diversity**, page 269

General interest

Al-Jamila
020 7831 8181
www.alkhaleejiahadv.com.sa/srpc
/jamila
Monthly
American in Britain
020 8661 0186
www.americaninbritain.com
4pa
Another Magazine
020 7336 0766
www.anothermag.com
2 pa
Asian Image
01254 298263
www.asianimage.co.uk
Monthly
Buxton Lifestyle Magazine
0161 998 6066
4pa
Caledonia
0131 476 4670
www.caledonia-magazine.com
Monthly
Cheshire Life
01772 722022
www.cheshirelife.co.uk
Monthly
Choice
01733 555123
Monthly
Concord
020 7529 1567
Yearly
Contemporary
020 7740 1704
www.contemporary-magazine.com
Monthly

Der Spiegel
020 7520 6940
www.spiegel.de
Weekly
Derbyshire Life & Countryside
01332 347087
Monthly
DV8
01202 388388
www.dv8online.co.uk
Monthly
Epicurean Life
020 7370 5552
4pa
Essential London
020 7242 5222
Yearly
Expression
01392 263052
2 pa
The Face
020 7295 5000
www.theface.co.uk
Monthly
Focus Magazine
0117 927 9009
Monthly
Folio
0117 942 8491
Monthly
Forward
0118 983 8243
4pa
Freemasonry Today
01284 754155
www.freemasonrytoday.co.uk
4pa
Fresh Direction
020 7424 0400
www.freshdirection.co.uk
3pa every semester
The Green
020 7792 2626
Monthly
Guide Magazine
020 7792 2626
Monthly
Harrods
020 7152 3842
www.harrods.co.uk
2 pa
Harvey Nichols Magazine
020 7747 0700
www.harveynichols.com
4pa
The Hill
020 7792 2626
Monthly
Hot Press
00 353 1 241 1500
www.hotpress.com
i-D
020 7490 9710
www.i-dmagazine.com
Monthly
The Insight
01273 245957
www.theinsight.co.uk
Monthly
Kindred Spirit
01803 866686
www.kindredspirit.co.uk
4pa

kudosmagazine.co.uk
0870 746 1449
www.kudosmagazine.co.uk
online
Learning for Life
020 7375 3092
2 pa
Libas International
020 8452 4387
Bi-monthly
The Lifeboat
01202 663188
4pa
Limited Edition
01689 885661
www.thisislimitededition.co.uk
Monthly
Living South
020 7223 0022
Monthly
Londinium
020 8740 2040
Bi-monthly
Magnet – The Village Communicator
01825 732796
www.magnetpublications.com
Monthly
Majesty
020 7436 4006
www.majestymagazine.com
Monthly
Mayfair and St James's Life
020 7344 9121
Monthly
Mined
020 7434 0110
New Humanist
020 7436 1151
www.newhumanist.org.uk
Bi-monthly
New Scientist
020 7331 2751
www.newscientist.co.uk
Weekly
Nonesuch
0117 928 7778
2pa
North Magazine
020 7250 0750
www.north-magazine.com
Monthly
Occasions
020 7650 2000
www.occasions-mag.com
4pa
The Oldie
020 7436 8801
www.theoldie.co.uk
Monthly
Open Learner
01223 400359
4pa
Oxford Today
01865 280545
www.oxfordtoday.ox.ac.uk
3pa
Password
020 7261 9878
Bi-monthly
Peerage Magazine
020 8747 0385
Yearly
Platform
0115 848 1510
Fortnightly

Prime of Life
01822 855365
Monthly
Quicksilver Magazine
020 7747 9390
www.quicksilver.co.uk
Bi-monthly
Reader's Digest
020 7715 8000
www.readersdigest.co.uk
Monthly
Reform
020 7916 8630
www.urc.org.uk/reform_magazine
/reform_index.htm
Monthly
The Resident
020 7384 9124
Monthly
The Ritz
020 7269 7480
2pa
Royalty
020 8201 9978
www.royalty-magazine.com
Monthly
Saga Magazine
01303 771523
http://holidays.saga.co.uk/magazine
/pages
Monthly
Salvationist
020 7367 4897
http://archive.salvationarmy.org.uk
/salvationist
Weekly
Sayidaty
020 7539 2242
www.uniquemagazines.co.uk
Weekly
Sayidaty Fashion
020 7539 2242
www.uniquemagazines.co.uk
4pa
Scots Magazine
01382 223131 x5867
www.scotsmagazine.com
Monthly
Select
01484 430000
Bi-monthly
Sixer
0114 267 9686
Monthly
Sleazenation
020 7729 8310
www.sleazenation.com
Monthly
The Smoke
020 7911 5000
Fortnightly
Snoop Magazine
020 8571 7700
http://www.alternity.co.uk/snoop.html
Monthly
The Spark
0117 914 3434
www.thespark.co.uk
4pa
Tank
020 7434 0110
www.tankmagazine.com
4pa to 6pa
Trafford Magazine
020 7428 9008
2 pa

The Visitor
01963 351256
4pa
Town & Country News
01692 582287
Monthly
V&A Magazine
020 7942 2272
Monthly
Vivace
01280 829300
Monthly
Vivid
020 7771 7671
2 pa
Vivid Magazine
020 7498 3309
Monthly
Wavelength
01637 878629
www.wavelengthltd.co.uk
Monthly
Weekly News
01382 223131
www.dcthomson.co.uk/mags/weekly
Weekly
Which?
020 7770 7365
www.which.net
Monthly
You Can! Magazine
01242 544873
Monthly
Yours
01733 264666
Monthly

Home and garden

25 Beautiful Homes
020 7261 5718
www.jbmedia.com/25_beautiful
_homes.asp
Monthly
BBC Gardeners' World
020 8433 3593
www.bbcworldwide.com/magazines
/gardenersworld
Monthly
BBC Good Food
020 8433 3777
www.bbcworldwide.com/magazines
/goodfood
Monthly
BBC Good Homes
020 8433 2391
www.bbcworldwide.com/magazines
/goodhomes
Monthly
BBC Homes & Antiques
020 8433 3485
www.bbcworldwide.com/magazines
/homesandantiques
Monthly
Country Homes & Interiors
020 7261 6451
www.jbmedia.com/country_homes
__interio.asp
Monthly
Country Living
020 7439 5000
http://magazines.ivillage.com
/countryliving/
Monthly

Country Market
01273 837807
Monthly
The English Garden
020 7751 4800
www.theenglishgarden.co.uk
Bi-monthly
The English Home
020 7751 4800
www.theenglishhome.co.uk
Bi-monthly
**The Essential Kitchen, Bathroom
& Bedroom Magazine**
01206 851117
Monthly
Essential Water Garden
01206 505977
www.essentialwatergarden.co.uk
Monthly
Fabric
020 7747 0700
Monthly
The Garden
01733 775775
Monthly
Garden News
01733 264666
Weekly
The Gardeners' Atlas
01603 633808
www.gardenersatlas.co.uk
Yearly
Gardening Which?
020 7770 7397
www.which.net/gardeningwhich
10pa
Gardens Illustrated
020 8433 3300
www.bbcworldwide.com/magazines
/gardensillustrated
10pa
Happy Families
0845 130 6249
4pa
HFN Home Furnishing News
020 7240 0420
Monthly
Home
01689 887200
Monthly
Home & Country
020 7731 5777
www.womens-institute.co.uk
/magazine/index.shtml
Monthly
Home & Garden
01522 804330
Monthly
Home Building & Renovating
01527 834400
www.homebuilding.co.uk
Monthly
Home Life Magazine
028 3832 4006
Monthly
Home View
01277 366134
Bi-monthly
Homes & Gardens
020 7261 5000
www.homesandgardens.com
Monthly
Homes & Interiors Scotland
0141 331 2221
www.homesandinteriorsscotland.com
Bi-monthly

69

Homes Overseas
020 7939 9888
www.homesoverseas.co.uk
Monthly
Homes Review
01206 506249
Monthly
HomeStyle
01206 851117
Monthly
House & Garden
020 7499 9080
www.houseandgarden.co.uk
Monthly
House Beautiful
020 7439 5000
www.housebeautiful.co.uk
Housing Association Magazine
0121 682 8881
Bi-monthly
Ideal Home
020 7261 6478
www.jbmedia.com/ideal_home.asp
Monthly
International Homes
01245 358877
www.international-homes.com
Bi-monthly
International Relocation
01295 255177
www.intrel.co.uk
Yearly
Ireland's Homes Interiors & Living
028 9147 3979
Monthly
**KBB – Kitchens, Bedrooms &
Bathrooms Magazine**
020 8515 2000
Monthly
Key
020 7494 3155
2 pa
Lancashire Life & Lake District Life
01772 722022
www.lancashirelife.co.uk
Monthly
Livingetc
020 7261 6603
www.jbmedia.com/living_etc.asp
Monthly
Perfect Home
020 8334 6439
Monthly
Period House
01206 851117
Monthly
Period Ideas
01206 505976
www.periodideas.com
Monthly
Period Living & Traditional Homes
020 7343 8775
www.periodlivingshow.co.uk
      /magazine.html
Monthly
Renovations
020 7384 1985
4pa
Rooms & Living
01206 851117
Monthly
Real Homes Magazine
020 7226 2222
Monthly

Surrey Monocle
01483 425454
Monthly
Traditional Homes & Interiors
01795 599191
Bi-annual
Water Gardener
01707 273999
Monthly
What House?
020 7939 9888
www.whathouse.co.uk
Monthly
World of Interiors
020 7499 9080
www.worldofinteriors.co.uk
Monthly
Your New Home
020 8349 1380
www.yournewhome.co.uk
Bi-monthly

Leisure

Absolute Horse
01473 461515
www.equilinks.co.uk
Monthly
Active Life
01442 289600
Monthly
Adrenalin (International Edition)
020 7345 5066
www.adrenalin.com
4pa
Aeroplane Monthly
020 7261 5849
www.aeroplanemonthly.co.uk
Monthly
Air Enthusiast
01780 755131
www.airenthusiast.com
Bi-monthly
Air Pictorial
01424 720477
www.uniquemagazines.co.uk
      /html/Magazine%20Web
      /AIRPICTORIALMAGAZINE.htm
Monthly
Air Transport World
01628 477775
www.atwonline.com
Monthly
Airliner World
01780 755131
www.airlinerworld.com
Monthly
**Alam Al Youkhout Wal Marakib
(Pan Arab)**
020 7625 8030
www.worldofyachts.com
Bi-monthly
Allotment & Leisure Gardener
01536 266576
www.nsalg.demon.co.uk/
4pa
Animal Life
0870 010 1181
Bi-monthly
Animals Matter
0870 190 4099
4pa
Antique Collecting
01394 389950
Monthly

Antique Dealer & Collectors Guide
020 8691 4820
www.antiquecollectorsguide.co.uk
Bi-monthly
Argos
01732 848499
www.argos.co.uk
2 pa
The Art Book
01323 811759
www.blackwellpublishing.com
      /journal.asp?ref=1368-6267
4pa
The Art Newspaper
020 7735 3331
www.theartnewspaper.co.uk
Monthly
Art Quarterly
020 7225 4818
4pa
Art Review
020 7246 3350
www.art-review.com
Monthly
The Artist
01580 763315
www.theartistmagazine.co.uk
Monthly
Artist's & Illustrator's
020 7700 8500
Monthly
Arts East
01284 701190
Monthly
Asda Magazine
020 7487 4142
Monthly
At Home in Cardiff Bay
029 2045 0532
4pa
Aviation Week & Space Technology
020 7409 1482
www.aviationnow.com/
Weekly
Award Journal
01753 727470
www.theaward.org
3pa
Backtrack
01326 373656
www.trevor-ridley.co.uk/BT.html
Monthly
BBC Wildlife Magazine
0117 973 8402
www.bbc.co.uk/nature/animals/
Monthly
Bird Life
01767 680551
Bi-monthly
Bird Watching Magazine
01733 282605
Monthly
Birds
01767 680551
4pa
Birdwatch Magazine
01580 882039
www.birdwatch.co.uk
Monthly
Black Beauty & Hair
020 7720 2108
www.blackbeautyandhair.com
Bi-monthly

BMFA News
0116 244 0028
www.bmfa.org/news/index.php
Bi-monthly
Boat International
020 8547 2662
www.boatinternational.co.uk/
Monthly
Boats & Yachts for Sale
01243 533394
www.boats-for-sale.com
Monthly
Book & Magazine Collector
020 8579 1082
Monthly
Bridge
020 7388 2404
www.bridgemagazine.co.uk
Bi-monthly
British Horse
0870 120 8880
www.bhs.org.uk/Britishhorse
-magazine.htm
Quarterly
British Naturism
01604 620361
4pa
Budgerigar World
01678 520262
www.tuxford.dabsol.co.uk
Monthly
Buy a Boat (for under £20,000)
01243 533394
Monthly
Cage & Aviary Birds
020 7261 6116
www.countrylife.co.uk/subscriptions
/c&abirds.htm
Weekly
Cakes & Sugarcraft
01252 711749
www.craftstart.co.uk/inf
_magazines.htm
4pa
Camcorder User
020 7331 1000
www.camuser.co.uk
Monthly
Camping & Caravanning
024 7669 4995
Monthly
Camping Magazine
01778 391027
www.campingmagazine.co.uk
Monthly
Canal Boat & Inland Waterways
0118 977 1677
www.canalboatmagazine.com
Monthly
Caravan Club Magazine
01342 336889
www.caravanclubmagazine.co.uk
Monthly
Caravan Life
01778 391165
www.caravanlife.co.uk
Monthly
Caravan Magazine
020 8774 0737
Monthly
Carpworld
0114 258 0812
www.rmcangling.co.uk/carpworld
Monthly

Cat World
01403 711511
www.catworld.co.uk
Monthly
Christmas Cakes – A Design Source
01252 727572
Yearly
Church Music Quarterly
01306 872800
www.rscm.com/cmq/cmq.htm
4pa
Club News
020 8469 9716
7pa
Coin News
01404 44166
Monthly
Coin Yearbook
01404 46972
Yearly
Collect it!
01206 851117
www.collectit.sagenet.co.uk
Monthly
Collections
020 7870 9090
www.bostonhannah.co.uk/mag
/collections.htm
3pa
Collector
020 8740 7020
Bi-monthly
Collector's Gazette
01642 762335
Monthly
Companions Magazine
01952 290999
4pa
Continental Modeller
01297 20580
www.peco-uk.com/cm
/cm_home.htm
Monthly
Country Life
020 7261 7058
www.countrylife.co.uk
Weekly
Country Smallholding
01392 888475
www.countrysmallholding.com
Monthly
The Countryman
01756 701033
www.countrymanmagazine.co.uk
Monthly
The Countryman's Weekly
01822 855281
www.countrymansweekly.co.uk
Weekly
Crafts
020 7806 2538
www.craftscouncil.org.uk/crafts.htm
Bi-monthly
Crafts Beautiful
01206 505975
www.crafts-beautiful.com
Monthly
Crafty Carper
0114 2580812
Monthly
Cross Stitch Collection
01225 442244
www.futurelicensing.com/home
/titles/CSC
Monthly

Cross Stitch Gallery
01227 750215
www.cross-x-stitch.com
Bi-monthly
Cross Stitcher
01225 442244
Monthly
Dalesman
01756 701381
www.dalesman.co.uk
Monthly
Dance Europe
020 8985 7767
www.danceeurope.net
Monthly
Dartmoor Magazine
01822 614899
www.dartmoormagazine.co.uk
4pa
Digital Camera Buyer
01202 299900
Monthly
Digital Photo
01733 264666
Monthly
Digital Photography Made Easy
01202 299900
Monthly
Dog World
01233 621877
www.dogworld.co.uk
Weekly
Dogs Today
01276 858880
Monthly
Dollond & Aitchison Magazine
020 7747 0700
2 pa
Dolls House World
01403 711511
www.dollshouseworld.com
Monthly
Engineering in Miniature
01926 614101
www.fotec.co.uk/mehs/tee
/mags.htm
Monthly
EOS Magazine
01869 331741
www.eos-magazine.com
4pa
The Erotic Review
020 7439 8999
www.theeroticreview.co.uk
Monthly
ESP Magazine
01733 253477
www.espmag.co.uk
Monthly
Evergreen
01242 537900
www.thisengland.co.uk/evmenu.htm
4pa
Everyday Practical Electronics
01202 873872
www.epemag.wimborne.co.uk
Monthly
Families East
020 8694 8694
www.familiesonline.co.uk
Bi-monthly
Families Edinburgh
0131 552 6005
www.familiesonline.co.uk
Bi-monthly

71

Families Liverpool
0151 494 9687
www.familiesonline.co.uk
Bi-monthly
Families North
020 7794 5690
www.familiesonline.co.uk
Bi-monthly
Families Together
01903 821082
www.familiesonline.co.uk
3pa
Families Upon Thames
01932 254584
www.familiesonline.co.uk
Bi-monthly
The Flower Arranger
020 7247 5567
4pa
Fly!
01752 663337
Weekly
Flyer
01225 481440
www.flyer.co.uk
Monthly
Fortean Times
020 7687 7000
www.forteantimes.com
Monthly
Galleries
020 8740 7020
www.artefact.co.uk
Monthly
**Gardens of England & Wales Open
for Charity**
01483 211535
Yearly
Gibbons Stamp Monthly
01425 472363
www.gibbonsstampmonthly.com
Monthly
Goodtimes
020 7431 2259
Advertising Number 01225 465060
www.arp050.org.uk/asp/goodtimes
/index.asp
6pa
Goodwood Magazine
01243 755000
Yearly
Grapevine Age Concern Liverpool
0151 330 5608
4pa
Gulliver's World
01228 404040
4pa
Gun Mart
01702 479724
Monthly
Heritage Magazine
020 7751 4800
www.heritagemagazine.co.uk
Bi-monthly
Hi-Fi News
020 8774 0846
www.hifinews.com
Monthly
Horoscope
01202 873872
www.horoscope.co.uk
Monthly

Jane Greenoff's Cross Stitch
01225 442244
www.futurelicensing.com/home
/titles/JGXS
Bi-monthly
Kew
020 8332 5906
www.griffin.rbgkew.org.uk/friends
/kewmag.html
4pa
Legion – Royal British Legion
020 7296 4200
Bi-monthly
Leisure Painter
01580 763315
www.leisurepainter.co.uk
Monthly
Leisure Scene
01494 888433
www.cssc.co.uk/lscene.htm
3pa
Lifewatch Magazine
020 7449 6241
www.zsl.org/press/pml
_0000001125.html
3pa
London Theatre Guide
020 7557 6700
www.londontheatre.co.uk
Fortnightly
Machine Knitting News
01273 400425
www.machineknittingnews.co.uk
Bi-monthly
Marine Modelling International
01684 595300
www.traplet.com/mmi/index.lasso
Monthly
Military Illustrated Past & Present
020 7692 2900
Monthly
Military Model Craft International
01494 799982
www.modelactivitypress.com
/mmi-monthly.htm
Monthly
Miniature Wargames
01202 297344
www.miniwargames.com
Monthly
MiniWorld Magazine
020 8774 0974
www.miniworld.co.uk
Monthly
Model & Collectors Mart
0121 233 8740
www.modelmart.co.uk
Monthly
Model Collector
020 8774 0600
Monthly
Model Helicopter World
01684 595433
www.modelheliworld.com
Monthly
Motor Boat & Yachting
020 7261 5333
www.mby.com
Monthly
Motor Boats Monthly
020 7261 7256
www.motorboatsmonthly.co.uk
Monthly

Motorcaravan & Camping Mart
01778 391119
www.caravanmart.co.uk
11 pa
Muscle & Fitness
01423 504516
www.muscleandfitness.com
Monthly
Musclemag International
0121 327 7525
www.emusclemag.com
Monthly
The National Trust Magazine
020 7222 9251
3pa
Needlecraft
01225 442244
www.futurenet.com/futureonline/
Monthly
Our Dogs
0870 731 6500
www.ourdogs.co.uk
Weekly
Patchwork & Quilting
01684 595300
www.pandqmagazine.com
Monthly
Paws
020 7622 3626
4pa
The People's Friend
01382 462276
www.dcthomson.co.uk
Weekly
Pilot
01799 544200
www.pilotweb.co.uk
Monthly
Practical Boat Owner
01202 440820
www.pbo.co.uk
Monthly
Practical Caravan
020 8267 5000
www.practicalcaravan.com
Monthly
Practical Fishkeeping
01733 264666
www.practicalfishkeeping.co.uk
Monthly
Practical Photography
01733 264666
www.practicalphotography.co.uk
Monthly
Practical Wireless
01202 659910
www.pwpublishing.ltd.uk/pw
Monthly
Prediction
020 8774 0600
www.predictionmagazine.co.uk
Monthly
Quick & Easy Cross Stitch
01225 442244
www.futurelicensing.com/home
/titles/QES
Monthly
RA Magazine
020 7300 5820
4pa
Radio Control Jet International
01684 594505
www.rcjetinternational.com
Bi-monthly

Radio Control Model Flyer
01525 222573
Monthly
Radio Control Model World
01684 595300
www.rcmodelworld.com
Monthly
Radio Race Car International
01684 595300
www.radioracecar.com
Monthly
Rail Express
01780 470086
Monthly
Railway Modeller
01297 20580
www.peco-uk.com/rm/rm_home.htm
Monthly
The Rambler
020 7339 8500
Quarterly
Raw Vision
01923 856644
www.rawvision.com
4pa
Real Countryside
020 7840 9200
4pa
Reflections Magazine
020 8747 0385
4pa
RIB International
01884 266100
www.ribmagazine.com
Bi-monthly
RYA Magazine
023 8060 4100
4pa
Sailing Today
01489 585225
www.sailingtoday.co.uk
Monthly
Scale Aviation Modeller International
0870 733 3373
www.sampublications.com
Monthly
Scamp's Diary
01628 771232
2 pa
Scotland in Trust
0131 476 4670
3pa
The Searcher
020 8674 5595
Monthly
Sew Bridal
023 9248 9773
Bi-monthly
Sewing With Butterick
023 9248 9773
www.butterick-vogue.co.uk
/magazines.html
4pa
Sewing World
01684 595300
www.sewingworldmagazine.com
Monthly
Short Wave Magazine
01202 659910
www.pwpublishing.ltd.uk/swm
Monthly
Stamp Magazine
020 8774 0772
Monthly

Steam Days
01202 304849
www.steamdaysmag.co.uk
Monthly
Steam Railway
01733 264666
Monthly
Surrey Nature Line
01483 488055
3pa
The Teddy Bear Club International
01206 505979
www.planet-teddybear.com/country
/uk.shtml
4pa
Today Fish Keeper
01673 885352
www.trmg.co.uk
Monthly
Total DVD
020 7331 1000
www.totaldvd.net
Monthly
Treasure Hunting
01376 521900
www.greenlightpublishing.co.uk
/treasure/
Monthly
Trends
020 8340 6868
4pa
Used Bike Guide
01507 525771
www.usedbikeguide.com
Monthly
Vogue Patterns
023 9248 9773
www.butterick-vogue.co.uk
/magazines.html
Bi-monthly
Wag
020 7837 0006
3pa
What Bike?
01733 468000
2 pa
What Camcorder
020 7331 1000
www.whatcamcorder.net
Monthly
What Camera
020 7261 5266
3pa
What Digital Camera
020 7261 7284
www.whatdigitalcamera.com
Monthly
What Hifi Magazine
020 8267 5000
www.whathifi.com
13 pa
What Hi-Fi? Sound & Vision
020 8267 5000
www.whathifi.com
13 pa
What Laptop & Handheld PC
020 8334 1600
www.whatlaptop.co.uk
4pa
What Satellite TV
020 7331 1000
www.wotsat.com
Monthly

What Video & TV
020 7331 1000
www.whatvideotv.com
Monthly
Where London
020 7242 5222
Monthly
Wolverine & Gambit
01892 500100
Monthly
Workbox
01579 340100
www.ebony.co.uk/workbox
Bi-monthly
You & Your Vet
020 7636 6541
4pa
Your Cat
01780 766199
www.yourcat.co.uk
Monthly
Your Dog
01780 766199
www.yourdog.co.uk
Monthly
Lakeland Walker
01778 391126
www.lakelandwalker.co.uk
Bi-monthly
Paddles
01202 735090
Monthly
Time Out Shopping Guide
020 7813 3000
www.timeout.com
Weekly
Toy Soldier & Model Figure
01403 711511
www.toy-soldier.com
Monthly
Waterways
01283 790447
www.waterways.org.uk
Quarterly
Waterways World
01283 742970
Monthly
Wild Times
01767 680551
6pa

Men's interest

Bizarre
020 7687 7000
www.bizarremag.com
Monthly
Boys Toys
01202 735090
Monthly
Dazed & Confused
020 7336 0766
www.confused.co.uk
Monthly
DNR
020 7240 0420
Weekly
Esquire
020 7439 5000
www.esquire.co.uk
Monthly
FHM
020 7436 1515
www.fhm.co.uk
Monthly

FHM Collections
020 7436 1515
Monthly
Front
020 7288 7500
Monthly
GQ
020 7499 9080
www.gq-magazine.co.uk
Monthly
Health & Fitness Magazine
020 7331 1000
www.hfonline.co.uk
Monthly
Jack
020 7687 6000
www.jackmagazine.co.uk
Monthly
Loaded
020 7261 5562
www.uploaded.com
Monthly
Maxim
020 7907 6000
www.maxim-magazine.co.uk
Monthly
Maxim Fashion
020 7907 6410
Quarterly
Men's Fitness
020 7907 6000
www.mensfitnessmagazine.co.uk
10pa
Men's Health
020 7291 6000
www.menshealth.co.uk
10pa
Savile Row
020 7609 5100
2pa to 4pa
Stuff
020 8267 5000
www.stuffmagazine.co.uk
Monthly
T3 – Tomorrow's Technology Today
020 7317 2600
www.t3.co.uk
Monthly
The Veteran
01582 663880
www.pensioneronline.co.uk
    /why_mag.htm
4pa
Wallpaper*
020 7322 1177
www.wallpaper.com
10pa

Money and property

Business Week
020 7491 8985
www.businessweek.com
Weekly
Country Land & Business Magazine
020 7235 0511
Monthly
Countryside La Vie
0116 212 2555
www.countryside-lavie.com
Bi-monthly
The Estate Agent
01926 496800
8pa

Estates Gazette
020 7411 2540
www.reedbusiness.co.uk
Weekly
Euroslot
01622 687031
www.datateam.co.uk/c/euroslot.htm
Monthly
Facilities Management Journal
020 8771 3614
www.fmj.co.uk
Monthly
Facilities Management UK
0161 683 8033
www.worldsfair.co.uk/fmuk
Bi-monthly
Forbes
020 7534 3900
www.forbes.com
Fortnightly
Foresters Magazine
020 8628 3665
2 pa
Fortune
020 7322 1068
www.fortune.com
Fortnightly
ISA Direct
020 7409 1111
2 pa
London Property News
01933 271611
www.londonpropertynews.co.uk
Monthly
Money Observer
020 7713 4188
www.moneyobserver.com
Monthly
Money Week
020 7309 7764
Weekly
Moneywise
020 7715 8303
www.moneywise.co.uk
Monthly
**More Than Magazine from
Royal & Sun Alliance**
020 7565 3377
4pa
Mortgage Advisor & Home Buyer
020 8334 1617
www.homebuyermag.co.uk
Monthly
The Mortgage Edge
020 7404 3123
www.mortgageedge.co.uk
Monthly
Mortgage Matters
020 8301 9311
www.yournewhome.co.uk/2000
    /mortgagematters
Bi-monthly
Negotiator
020 7772 8348
www.negotiator-magazine.co.uk
Fortnightly
New Homes Wales and South West
029 2030 3900
Bi-monthly
**Nottinghamshire Commercial
Property**
0115 910 2102
Weekly
Optima
020 8420 4488
Fortnightly

Party Times
020 7819 1200
Bi-monthly
Pensions & Investments
020 7457 1430
Fortnightly
Pensions Age
020 7426 0101
www.pensions-age.com
Monthly
Personal Finance Confidential
020 7447 4000
Monthly
Personal Finance Magazine
020 7827 5455
www.uniquemagazines.co.uk
Monthly
The Property Magazine
01480 494944
Monthly
Property News
01273 544544
Weekly
Property Paper
01737 732080
Weekly
Property News (NI)
028 3835 5060
Monthly
Retail Property and Development
0161 236 2782
Monthly
Scotland's New Homebuyer
0131 556 9702
www.snhb.co.uk
4pa
Shopping Centre Magazine
01293 610294
www.william-reed.co.uk/magazines
    /s_shop_centre.html
Monthly
Target Property Newspaper
0151 906 3059
Fortnightly
Unlimited
0141 332 3255
www.unlimited-magazine.co.uk
Your Mortgage
020 7404 3123
www.yourmortgage.co.uk
Monthly

Motoring

100% Biker
01244 660044
www.100-biker.co.uk
Monthly
4 x 4
020 8774 0600
www.4x4i.com
Monthly
911 & Porsche World Magazine
01844 260959
www.chpltd.com/911_porsche_world
Monthly
Advanced Driving
01483 230300
www.iam.org.uk/Services
3pa
American Motorcycle Dealer
01892 511516
Monthly

Audi Driver
01525 750500
www.audidrivermag.co.uk
Monthly

Auto Italia
01462 678205
www.auto-italia.co.uk
Monthly

Auto Weekly
01752 765500
www.milestonegroup.co.uk/divisions
/publishing.html
Weekly

Autocar
020 8267 5630
www.autocarmagazine.co.uk
Weekly

The Automobile
01483 268818
Monthly

Autosport
020 8267 5810
www.autosport.com
Weekly

AutoTrader
020 8544 7000
www.autotrader.co.uk

Back St Heroes
020 7772 8300
Monthly

Banzai
01732 748000
www.banzaimagazine.com
Monthly

BBC Top Gear
020 8433 3710
www.topgear.com
Monthly

Car
01733 468379
www.carmagazine.co.uk
Monthly

Car Mechanics
01959 541444
www.carmechanicsmag.co.uk
Monthly

Carbuyer
01420 526994
www.carsupermarkets.co.uk
/car-buyer.asp
Bi-monthly

CarSport Magazine
028 9078 3200
www.carsportmag.net
Monthly

CCC
020 8774 0946
www.linkhouse.co.uk/ccc
Monthly

Classic American
0161 836 4457
www.classic-american.com
Monthly

Classic Bike
01733 468461
Monthly

Classic Car Mart
0121 2338712
www.classic-car-mart.co.uk
Monthly

Classic Car Weekly
01733 347559
www.classic-car-weekly.co.uk
Weekly

Classic Cars
01733 468219
www.classiccarsmagazine.co.uk
Monthly

Classic Ford
01452 317765
www.classicfordmag.co.uk
Monthly

Classic Military Vehicle
01959 541444
www.kelsey.co.uk/magazines/military/
Monthly

Classic Motor Monthly
01204 657212
www.classicmotor.co.uk
Monthly

Classic Motorcycle
01507 525771
www.classicmotorcycle.co.uk
Monthly

Classic Racer
01507 525771
www.classicracer.com

Classics
01689 887276
www.splpublishing.co.uk/publications
/classics.htm
Monthly

Custom Car
01959 541444
www.kelsey.co.uk/magazines
/custom/
Monthly

Enjoying MG
01954 231125
www.mgcars.org.uk
Monthly

Evo
01933 663355
www.evo.co.uk
Monthly

Fast Car
01689 887200
www.fastcar.co.uk
Monthly

Good Motoring
01342 825676
www.roadsafety.org.uk/information
/publish
Quarterly

Jaguar Driver
01582 419332
Monthly

Jaguar World
01959 541444
www.jaguar-world.com
Monthly

Kit Car
01924 469410
www.kit-cars.com
Monthly

Land Rover Enthusiast
01379 890056
www.uniquemagazines.co.uk
Monthly

Land Rover Owner International
01733 468000
www.lro.com
13 pa

Land Rover World
020 8774 0976
www.landroverworld.co.uk
Monthly

Lexus Magazine
020 7324 8000
4pa

LRM Land Rover Monthly
01359 240066
www.lrm.co.uk
Monthly

Max Power
01733 468000
www.maxpower.co.uk
13 pa

MCN
01733 468000
www.motorcyclenews.com

Mercedes
01789 490530
4pa

Mercedes Enthusiast
020 8639 4400
www.mercedesenthusiast.co.uk
Monthly

MG Enthusiast Magazine
01924 499261
www.mgcars.org.uk/mgmag
10pa

Motor Caravanner
01480 496130
www.motorcaravanners.org.uk
Monthly

Motor Cycle News
01733 468000
www.motorcyclenews.com
Weekly

Motor Sport
020 8267 5258
Monthly

Motorcycle Mechanics
01536 507403
www.classicmechanics.com
Monthly

Motorcycle Rider
01652 680060
www.bmf.co.uk/mcrider
4pa

Motorcycle Sport & Leisure
01353 616100
www.motorcyclemag.co.uk
Monthly

Motorhome Monthly
020 8302 6150
www.stoneleisure.com
/MotorhomeMonthly
Monthly

Motoring & Leisure
01273 744759
www.csma.uk.com/news_views
/motoringmag
Monthly

The Motorist
020 8994 3239
Weekly

Performance Bikes
01733 468099
www.emap.com
Monthly

Peugeot Rapport Magazine
0117 9251696
3pa

Porsche Post
01608 652911
Monthly

Post Office Motoring
0191 418 3970
4pa

Rally XS
020 8267 5000
Bi-monthly

Redline
01225 442244
www.uniquemagazines.co.uk/html
/Magazine%20Web/motoring.htm
Monthly
The Renault Magazine
01342 828700
4pa
Revs
01733 468000
Monthly
Safety Fast!
01235 555552
www.mgcars.org.uk/carclub
/sfast.html
Monthly
Scootering
01507 525771
www.scootering.com
Monthly
SuperBike
020 8774 0600
www.superbikemagazine.co.uk
Monthly
Total Car Audio
01452 317773
www.totalcaraudio.co.uk
Bi-monthly
Twist & Go Scooter Magazine
01507 524004
www.twistngo.com
Monthly
VM – Vauxhall
020 7212 9000
buypower.vauxhall.co.uk
/vmmagazine
Quarterly
Volks World
020 8774 0600
www.volksworld.com
Monthly
Volkswagen Driver
01525 750500
www.audidrivermag.co.uk
Monthly
The Volvo Magazine
020 7747 0700
4pa
VW Magazine
01778 391000
Monthly
What Car?
020 8267 5688
www.whatcar.co.uk
Monthly
Which Kit?
01737 222030
www.which-kit.com
Monthly

Puzzles

100 Crosswords
01737 378700
Monthly
Colour Arrowwords
020 7241 8000
Monthly
Pocket Crosswords
01737 378700
13 pa
Puzzle Compendium
01737 378700
10pa

Puzzle Corner Special
01737 378700
10pa
Quizkids
01737 378700
11 pa
Take a Break
020 7241 8000
Weekly

Sport

Ace
020 7605 8002
www.lta.org.uk/ace
Monthly
Ace & British Tennis
020 7605 8000
Monthly
African Soccer Magazine
020 7561 0011
Monthly
Air Gunner
0118 977 1677
www.romseypublishing.net/airgun
/changes/airgunner.html
Monthly
Airgun World
0118 977 1677
www.romseypublishing.net/airgun
/changes/airgunworld.html
Monthly
Angler's Mail
020 7261 5778
Weekly
Angling Times
01733 232600
Weekly
**Athletics Weekly – The Athlete's
Magazine**
01733 898440
www.athletics-weekly.com/
Weekly
Badminton Magazine
020 8866 6517
Quarterly
Bogey
020 7987 6166
www.bogeymag.com
Quarterly
Boxing Monthly
020 8986 4141
www.boxing-monthly.co.uk
Monthly
Boxing News
020 7882 1000
www.newsquestmagazines.co.uk
/magazines/boxingrates.pdf
Weekly
British Homing World
01938 552360
www.pigeonracing.com
Weekly
British Waterskier
01932 570885
Bi-monthly
Bunkered
0141 950 2216
www.bunkered.co.uk
8pa

Calcio Italia
020 7005 2000
www.channel4.com/sport/football
_italia/magazine.html
Monthly
Canoe Focus
0115 982 1100
www.canoefocus.demon.co.uk
Bi-monthly
Carve Surfing Magazine
01637 878074
www.orcasurf.co.uk
Celtic View
0141 551 4218
www.celticfc.co.uk
Weekly
Clay Shooting
01264 889533
www.clay-shooting.com
Monthly
Climber
01778 391117
www.climber.co.uk
Monthly
Coarse Fisherman
0116 251 1277
www.coarse-fisherman.co.uk
Monthly
Combat
0121 344 3737
www.martialartsinprint.com
Monthly
Combat & Survival
01484 435011
www.combatandsurvival.com
Monthly
Corporate Golf Magazine
01273 777994
4pa
Country Walking
01733 264666
www.countrywalking.co.uk
Monthly
Cycle Sport
020 8774 0952
www.countrylife.co.uk/subscriptions
/cyclesport.htm
Monthly
Cycling Plus
01225 442244
Monthly
Cycling Weekly
020 8774 0811
www.countrylife.co.uk/subscriptions
/cycling.htm
Weekly
**Daily Mail Ski & Snowboard
Magazine**
020 8515 2000
www.skiingmail.com
2 pa
Darts Player
020 8650 6580
Darts World
020 8650 6580
www.dartsworld.com
Direct Hit
020 7953 7473
Bi-annual
Dirt Bike Rider
01524 32525
www.dirtbikerider.co.uk
Monthly
Dirt MTB Magazine
01305 251263
Bi-monthly

Distance Running
0141 221 9136
www.inpositionmedia.co.uk
/publishing/drun.html
4pa
DIVE Magazine
020 8332 2709
www.divemagazine.co.uk
Monthly
Diver
020 8943 4288
www.divernet.com
Monthly
Document Snowboard
020 7371 0045
www.uksnowboard.co.uk
/Magazines.htm
Bi-annual
Dog Training Weekly
01348 875011
www.coltriever.org/dtweekly
/dtw-home.html
Weekly
England Rugby
01707 273999
Quarterly
**The Equestrian & Sporting Dog
Journal**
01643 831695
Bi-monthly
Evening Times Wee Red Book
0141 302 6606
Yearly
The Evertonian
0151 472 8437
Monthly
F1 Racing
020 8943 5806
www.autosport.com/f1racing.asp
Monthly
The Fairway Golfing News
01633 666700
Monthly
Fall Line Skiing
020 7371 0045
www.fall-line.co.uk
Bi-annual
The Field
020 7261 5198
www.countrylife.co.uk/thefield
/index.htm
Monthly
First Down
020 7323 1944
Weekly
Fitness First
01202 845000
Quarterly
Fitness First
01932 841450
Quarterly
FitPro
0870 513 3434
www.fitpro.com
Bi-monthly
Flex
01423 504516
www.flexonline.co.uk
Monthly
FourFourTwo
020 8267 5848
442.rivals.net
Monthly

Glory Glory Man United
020 7317 2600
13 pa
Go Tenpin
01502 560445
www.gotenpin.co.uk/publications
.html
Monthly
Going for Golf Magazine
01268 554100
Quarterly
**The Golf Guide: Where to Play/
Where to Stay**
0141 887 0428
Yearly
Golf International
020 7828 3003
www.golfinternationalmag.co.uk
Monthly
Golf Monthly
020 7261 7237
www.golf-monthly.co.uk
Monthly
Golf News
01273 777994
Monthly
Golf Today
01304 615200
www.golftoday.co.uk
Monthly
Golf Weekly
01733 237111
Monthly
Golfing in Britain and Europe
020 8747 0385
Monthly
Good Ski Guide
020 8404 2447
www.goodskiguide.com
4 issues in the winter
Greenside
0870 900 6415
Quarterly
The Gymnast
0116 247 8766
Bi-monthly
High Mountain Sports
0114 236 9296
www.planetfear.com/climbing
/highmountainmag
Monthly
Hoofprint
01565 872107
www.hoofprint.co.uk
Monthly
Horse
020 7261 7969
www.horseandhound.co.uk
/thismonthhorse
Monthly
Horse and Hound
020 7261 6315
www.horseandhound.co.uk
Weekly
Horse & Rider
01428 651551
www.horseandridermagazine.co.uk
Monthly
Improve Your Coarse Fishing
01733 237111
Monthly
In The Know
0870 513 3345
www.itkonline.com
Monthly

The Informer
01923 821909
4pa
International Rugby News
020 7323 1944
Monthly
Ireland's Equestrian Magazine
028 3833 4272
Bi-monthly
Irish Golf Review
0161 683 8000
www.worldsfair.co.uk/media_packs
/documents/irishgolf.pdf
Quarterly
Karting
01689 897123
www.kartingmagazine.com
Monthly
The Kop
0151 285 8412
Monthly
Lady Golfer
01274 851323
Monthly
London Cyclist
020 7928 7220
www.lcc.org.uk/membership
/london_cyclist_magazine.asp
Bi-monthly
Manchester United Magazine
020 7317 2600
14 pa
Martial Arts Illustrated
01484 435011
www.martialartsltd.co.uk/mai
Monthly
Match Angling Plus
01733 465705
Monthly
Mountain Bike Rider
020 8774 0604
www.countrylife.co.uk/subscriptions
/mountainbike.htm
Monthly
Mountain Biking UK
01225 442244
www.mbuk.com
3pa
Muscle & Fitness
01423 504516
www.muscle-fitness-europe.com
Monthly
Muscle & Fitness Hers
01423 504516
www.muscle-fitness-europe.com
Bi-monthly
Musclemag International
0121 327 7525
Monthly
National Club Golfer
01274 851323
Monthly
The Non League Paper
020 7687 7687
www.nonleaguedaily.com
Sunday
**Official Liverpool Matchday
Magazine**
020 8943 5433
Monthly
**The Official Manchester United
Magazine**
020 7317 2600
www.futurelicensing.com/home
/titles/MANU
Monthly

Onside
020 7385 5545
Monthly
Outdoor Pursuits Magazine
01234 853970
Quarterly
Owner
020 7408 0903
Bi-monthly
Pool Industry
01420 563602
Monthly
PQ International
020 7924 2550
www.poloworld.co.uk
4pa
Pull!
01780 754900
www.countrypursuits.co.uk/pll1.html
10pa
Racing Calendar
0870 871 2000
www.bcf.uk.com/communications
     /index.html
Quarterly
Racing Days
020 8534 5303
Quarterly
The Racing Pigeon Weekly
01689 600006
www.racingpigeon.co.uk
Weekly
Racing Post
020 7293 3000
www.racingpost.co.uk
Ride BMX
01305 251263
www.ridebmxmag.co.uk
9pa
Rugby League World
01484 401895
www.totalrugbyleague.com
Monthly
Rugby Leaguer & League Express
01484 401895
www.totalrugbyleague.com
Monthly
The Rugby Times
01484 401895
Monthly
Rugby World
020 7261 6830
www.rugbyworld.com
Monthly
Runners World
020 7291 6000
www.runnersworld.co.uk
Monthly
Running Fitness
01733 347559
Monthly
**Salmon & Trout Association
Newsletter**
020 7283 5838
3pa
Scottish Rugby
0141 3091400
Monthly
Sea Angler
01733 465791
www.nfsa.org.uk/links/seaangler
     /sea_angler.htm
Monthly

Seahorse
01590 671899
www.seahorse.co.uk
Monthly
Shoot Monthly
020 7261 6287
www.shoot.co.uk
Monthly
Shooting & Conservation
01224 573032
Monthly
Shooting Gazette
01780 754900
www.countrypursuits.co.uk/sg1.html
Monthly
Shooting Sports
01206 525697
Monthly
**Shooting Times and Country
Magazine**
020 7261 6180
Monthly
Sidewalk Skateboarding Magazine
01235 536229
www.sidewalkmag.com
Monthly
**The Skier and Snowboarder
Magazine**
0845 310 8303
Snooker Scene
0870 220 2125
Monthly
Speedway Star
020 8335 1100
www.speedwaystar.net
Weekly
SportDiver
01799 544242
www.sportdiver.co.uk
Monthly
Sportvision
020 7401 9998
Monthly
Sporting Gun
01780 481061
www.browning.co.uk/ipc
     /sportinggun.html
Monthly
Spurs Monthly
01708 379877
Monthly
**The Squash Player – England
Squash**
01753 775511
www.squashplayer.co.uk/magazine
     /magazine.htm
Monthly
Summit
0161 445 4747
www.planetfear.com/climbing
     /summit
Quarterly
The Surfer's Path
01288 359636
www.network26.com/path
Monthly
Swimming
01509 618766
www.britishswimming.org/sports
     /swimming_times
Monthly
Swimming Pool News
01353 777656
www.swimmingpoolnews.co.uk

**Taekwondo & Korean Martial Arts
Magazine**
0121 344 3737
www.martialartsinprint.com
Monthly
Target Sports
01905 795564
www.targetsportsmag.com
Monthly
Today's Pilot
01780 755131
www.todayspilot.co.uk
Monthly
Traditional Karate
0121 344 3737
www.martialartsinprint.com
Monthly
Trials & Motorcross News
01524 834029
www.tmxnews.co.uk
Weekly
Trout & Salmon
01733 237111
Monthly
Ultra-Fit
01736 350204
www.ultra-fitmagazine.com
8pa
United
020 7317 2600
Monthly
Unity
01993 811181
www.unitymag.co.uk
10pa
Warren Miller's Snoworld
020 7240 4071
Annually
What Mountain Bike
01225 442244
Monthly
When Saturday Comes
020 7729 1110
www.wsc.co.uk
Monthly
**White Lines Snowboarding
Magazine**
01235 536229
www.whitelines.com
Monthly
Women & Golf
020 7261 7237
www.womandgolf.com
11 pa
World Soccer
020 7261 6397
www.worldsoccer.com
Monthly
Yachting World
020 7261 6800
www.yachting-world.com
Monthly
Yachts & Yachting
01702 582245
www.yachtsandyachting.com
Monthly
Your Horse
01733 264666
4pa

Travel

Activity Wales
01437 766888
www.activitywales.com
Yearly

Adventure Travel
01789 450000
Bi-monthly

Arab Traveller
01621 842745
Bi-monthly

Australian Outlook
01424 223111
Monthly

Be in Spain
020 8740 2040
2 pa

Best of Britain
020 8740 2040
Yearly

Britannia Skyscene Magazine
020 7923 5400
4pa

City to Cities
020 8469 9700
Bi-monthly

Condé Nast Traveller
020 7499 9080
www.cntraveller.co.uk
Monthly

Destination New Zealand
01323 726040
Monthly

The Edinburgh Tourist & Shopping Guide
01506 508001
2 pa

Education Travel Magazine
020 7440 4025
www.hothousemedia.com/etm
Monthly

Enjoy Dorset & Hampshire Magazine
01202 737678
www.enjoydorset.co.uk
Yearly

Ensign
01534 504 800
Yearly

Essentially America
020 7243 6954
Bi-monthly

Essex Life & Countryside
01206 571348
www.essexlife.net
Monthly

Everything France Magazine
01342 828700
www.efmag.co.uk
Monthly

Fly.be Uncovered
020 8649 7233
Bi-monthly

France
01536 747333
www.francemag.com
Monthly

French Property News
020 8543 3113
www.french-property-news.com
Monthly

Go Travel
01245 603334
Weekly

Going USA
01323 726040
Bi-monthly

Holiday & Events Guide
0870 444 2702
4pa

Holiday Which
020 7770 7548
www.holidaywhichfreetrial.co.uk
4pa

Holiday, The RCI Magazine
01536 310101
3pa

Homes Overseas
020 7939 9888
www.homesoverseas.co.uk
Monthly

Illustrated London News
020 7805 5555
www.ilng.co.uk
Bi-monthly/annual/4pa

In Britain
020 7751 4800
www.romseypublishing.net/inbritain
Bi-monthly

Kuoni World Magazine
01306 744247
4pa

LAM – Living Abroad Magazine
020 7005 5000
www.lam-online.co.uk
Monthly

London Planner
020 7751 4800

Mediterranean Life
020 7415 7020
Quarterly

Msafiri-Kenya Airways
01442 875431
www.atta.co.uk/search/member
.asp?m=Msafi
4pa

National Geographic
020 7538 5811
www.nationalgeographic.com
Monthly

Orient-Express Magazine
020 7805 5562
www.ilng.co.uk/clients.htm?list11a
4pa

Overseas
020 7016 6905
4pa

Pride of Britain
020 7739 1434
4pa

The Railway Magazine
020 7261 5533
www.railwaymagazine.co.uk
Monthly

South Africa News
01323 726040
Bi-monthly

Spain
0131 226 7766
www.spainmagazine.co.uk
Monthly

Sunday Times Travel
020 7306 0304
www.sundaytimestravel.co.uk
Bi-monthly

SX Magazine
020 7373 3377
www.sxmagazine.com
Weekly

TNT Magazine
020 7373 3377
www.tntmagazine.com
Weekly

The Travel & Leisure Magazine
020 8554 4456
4pa

Traveller
020 7589 0500
www.travelleronline.com
Quarterly

Travel Australia
01424 223111
2 pa

Travel Bulletin
020 7834 6661
Weekly

Travel GBI
020 7729 4337
Monthly

Triangle
020 8267 5274
2pa

Wanderlust
01753 620426
www.wanderlust.co.uk
Bi-monthly

Welcome to London
020 7231 6772
Bi-monthly

Women and health

Accent Magazine
0191 284 9994
Monthly

Asian Woman
020 8981 6060
4pa

Asthma News
020 7226 2260
4pa

A–Z of Calories
01984 623014
Bi-monthly

B
020 7150 7038
www.hf-uk.com

Baby & You
020 7331 1000
Monthly

Balance
020 7424 1000
Bi-monthly

Be Slim
01984 623014
4pa

Beautiful Brides
0117 934 3742
www.bride-groom.net
4pa

Bella
020 7241 8000
Weekly

Best
020 7312 4142
www.natmags.co.uk

Boots Health and Beauty
020 7747 7272
4pa

Bride & Groom
020 8477 3771
2pa

Brides
020 7499 9080
www.bridesuk.net
Bi-monthly
Caduceus Journal
01926 451897
www.caduceus.info
4pa
Candis
0151 632 3232
www.candis.co.uk
Monthly
Chat
020 7261 6565
www.ipc.co.uk
Weekly
Closer
020 7437 9011
www.emap.com
Company
020 7439 5000
www.company.co.uk
Monthly
Cosmopolitan
020 7439 5000
www.cosmomag.com
Monthly
Cosmopolitan Hair & Beauty
020 7439 5639
Monthly
Elle
020 7150 7000
www.elle.com
Monthly
Essentials
020 7261 6970
www.ipc.co.uk
Monthly
Eve
020 8433 3767
www.bbcworldwide.com
    /magazines/eve/
Monthly
Family Circle
020 7261 6195
www.ipc.co.uk
Monthly
Family Magazine
01200 453000
Bi-monthly
For the Bride
01376 534512
Bi-monthly
For Women
020 7308 5363
9pa
The Glades Magazine
020 8693 9857
4pa
Glamour
020 7499 9080
www.glamourmagazine.co.uk
Monthly
Good Health Magazine
01376 534500
Monthly
Good Housekeeping
020 7439 5000
www.goodhousekeeping.co.uk
Monthly
Hair
020 7261 6975
www.ipc.co.uk
Bi-monthly

Hair & Beauty
020 7436 9766
Bi-monthly
Hair Now
020 7436 9766
Bi-monthly
Hairflair
01376 534540
Bi-monthly
Hairstyles Only
01376 534540
Bi-monthly
Harpers & Queen
020 7439 5000
www.harpersandqueen.co.uk
Monthly
Health
020 7306 0304
Bi-monthly
The Health Store Magazine
0115 955 5255
Bi-monthly
Health Which?
020 7770 7562
www.which.co.uk
Bi-monthly
Health & Fitness
020 7331 1000
www.hfonline.co.uk
Monthly
Healthy Times
020 7819 1111
Bi-monthly
Healthy Times
020 7437 9011
www.emap.com
Hello!
020 7667 8901
www.hellomagazine.com
Hia
020 7539 2270
Monthly
Holistic London Guide
020 8672 7111
3pa
In Style
020 7261 4747
Monthly
Junior
020 7761 8900
www.juniormagazine.co.uk
Monthly
Junior Pregnancy & Baby
020 7761 8900
www.juniormagazine.co.uk
    /pregnancy
Bi-monthly
Ladies First
029 2039 6600
4pa
The Lady
020 7379 4717
www.thelady.co.uk
Weekly
Marie Claire
020 7261 5240
www.marieclaire.com
Monthly
More!
020 7208 3165
Fortnightly
Mother & Baby
020 7347 1869
www.emapmagazines.co.uk
Monthly

MS Matters
020 8438 0755
Bi-monthly
My Weekly
01382 223131
www.dcthomson.co.uk
Weekly
New!
020 7579 2868
Weekly
New Woman
020 7208 3456
www.newwoman.co.uk
Monthly
Now
020 7261 7366
www.nowmagazine.co.uk
Weekly
Now Star Diet & Fitness
020 7261 7366
3pa
Now Star Style
020 7261 7366
3pa
Number Ten
020 7439 9100
www.numberten.co.uk
Yearly
OK!
020 7928 8000
www.ok-magazine.com
Weekly
Parent News UK
020 8337 6337
www.parents-news.co.uk
Monthly
People
020 7322 1134
Weekly
Practical Parenting
020 7261 5058
www.ipc.co.uk
Monthly
Pregnancy and Birth
020 7347 1885
www.emapmagazines.co.uk
Monthly
Pregnancy Magazine
020 7331 1000
Bi-monthly
Pride Magazine
020 7228 3110
Monthly
Prima
020 7439 5000
www.natmags.co.uk
Monthly
Prima Baby
020 7439 5000
www.natmags.co.uk
Monthly
Real
020 7241 8394
Fortnightly
Red
020 7150 7600
www.reddirect.co.uk
**Rosemary Conley Diet
& Fitness Magazine**
01509 620444
www.conley.co.uk/magazine
Bi-monthly
Scottish Home & Country
0131 225 1724
www.swri.org.uk/sh&c.html
Monthly

Select Magazine
0121 212 4141
Monthly
Shape
020 7907 6531
Monthly
She
020 7312 3827
www.she.co.uk
Monthly
Slimmer, Healthier, Fitter
01206 505972
10pa
Slimming Magazine
020 7347 1854
www.emapmagazines.co.uk
Monthly
Slimming World
01773 546360
www.slimming-world.co.uk
/publications/magazine.asp
7pa
Spice Introductions
0870 011 0020
4pa
Spirit of Superdrug
020 7306 0304
www.therivergroup.co.uk
Bi-monthly
That's Life!
020 7241 8000
Weekly
This is Echo Health
01522 820000
Monthly
Top Santé Health & Beauty
020 7437 9011
Monthly
Twins Triplets and More Magazine
01909 500874
3pa
Ulster Bride
028 9068 1371
Bi-monthly
Ulster Tatler
028 9068 1371
www.ulstertatler.com
Monthly
Ultra-Fit
01736 350204
Vanity Fair
020 7499 9080
www.vanityfair.co.uk
Monthly
Vogue
020 7499 9080
www.vogue.co.uk
Monthly
W
020 7240 0420
Monthly
Wave
01273 818160
www.wavemagazine.co.uk
Monthly
Wedding & Home
020 7261 7471
www.ipc.co.uk
Bi-monthly
Wedding Cakes – A Design Source
01252 727572
www.squires-group.co.uk
/c_magazines.shtml
3pa

Wedding Day
020 7761 8980
Bi-monthly
Wedding Journal
028 9045 7457
Quarterly
Weight Watchers
020 8882 2555
8pa
WM
029 2058 3592
Quarterly
Woman
020 7261 5000
Weekly
Woman & Home
020 7261 5176
www.ipc.co.uk
Monthly
Woman 2 Woman
020 7737 7377
Monthly
Woman Alive
01903 821082
www.womanalive.co.uk
Monthly
Woman's Own
020 7261 5550
www.ipc.co.uk
Weekly
Woman's Weekly
020 7261 7023
www.ipc.co.uk
Monthly
WWD Beauty Report International
020 7240 0420
Monthly
Yoga and Health
020 7480 5456
www.yogaandhealthmag.co.uk/
Monthly
You & Your Wedding
020 7439 5000
www.youandyourwedding.co.uk
4pa
Zest
020 7439 5000
www.zest.co.uk
Monthly

Business and trade press

Business and industry

Accountancy
020 8247 1400
www.accountancymagazine.com
Monthly. Editor: Christopher Quick
Accountancy Age
020 7316 9000
www.accountancyage.com
Weekly. Editor: Damian Wild
Accounting and Business
020 7396 5966
www.accaglobal.com
10pa. Editor: John Prosser
Accounting Technician
020 7880 6200
www.accountingtechnician.co.uk
Monthly. Editor: Martin Allen-Smith
CIMA Insider
020 8849 2313
www.cimaglobal.com
Monthly. Editor: Ruth Prickett
Director
020 7766 8950
www.iod.com/director
Monthly. Editor: Joanna Higgins
Euromoney
020 7779 8888
www.euromoney.com
Monthly. Editor: Pete Lee
Financial Adviser
020 7382 8000
www.ftadvisor.com
Weekly. Editor: Hal Austin
Financial Management
020 8849 2313
www.cimaglobal.com
Monthly. Editor: Ruth Prickett
Financial World
01227 818609
www.financialworld.co.uk
Monthly. Editor: Eila Rana
First Voice of Business
01223 477411
www.campublishers.com
Bi-monthly. Editor: Johnathan Wilson
Growing Business
020 8334 1782
www.growingbusinessmag.co.uk
Monthly. Editor: Richard Edwards
**Institutional Investor
– International Edition**
020 7779 8888
www.institutionalinvestor.com
Monthly. Editor: Michael Carroll
The Journal
020 7534 2400
www.cedarcom.co.uk
Bi-monthly. Editor: Martin Baker
Landscape and Amenity Product Update
01952 200809
5pa
Management Today
020 8943 5000
www.clickmt.com
Monthly. Editor: Matthew Gwyther

Money Marketing
020 7970 4000
www.moneymarketing.co.uk
Weekly. Editor: John Lappin
Overseas Trade
020 7368 9600
www.amdgroup.plc.uk
10pa. Editor: Janet Tibble
People Management
020 7880 6200
www.peoplemanagement.co.uk
Fortnightly. Editor: Steve Crabb
Personnel Today
020 8652 3705
www.personneltoday.com
Weekly. Editor: Jane King
Professional Manager
020 7421 2705
www.manager.org.uk
Bi-monthly. Editor: Sue Mann
Real Business
020 7828 0733
www.realbusiness.co.uk
Monthly. Editor: Matthew Rock
Supply Management
020 7880 6249
www.supplymanagement.com
Fortnightly. Editor: Geraint John
Travel Trade Gazette
020 7921 8005
www.ttglive.com
Weekly
What's New In Industry
020 7970 4000
www.wnii.co.uk
Monthly. Editor: David Keighley

Construction and engineering

Building
020 7560 4000
www.building.co.uk
Weekly. Editor: Adrian Barrick
Construction Manager
020 7560 4000
www.thebuildergroup.co.uk
10pa. Editor: Rod Swain
Construction News
020 7505 6600
www.cnplus.co.uk
Weekly. Editor: Aaron Morby
Contract Journal
020 8652 4805
www.contractjournal.com
Weekly. Editor: Rob Willock
The Engineer
020 7970 4000
www.e4engineering.com
Fortnightly. Editor: George Coupe
New Civil Engineer
020 7505 6600
www.nceplus.co.uk
Weekly. Editor: Antony Oliver
Professional Engineering
020 7973 1299
www.proseng.com
Fortnightly. Editor: John Pullin
What's New In Building
01732 364422
www.cmpinformation.com
Monthly. Editor: Mark Pennington

Farming

Arable Farming
01772 203800
18pa. Editor: Dominic Kilburn
British Dairying
01438 716220
Monthly. Editor: Judie Allen
Crops
020 8652 3500
www.fw1.co.uk
Fortnightly. Editor: Charles Abel
Dairy Farmer
01772 203800
Monthly. Editor: Peter Hollinshead
Farmers Guardian
01772 203800
Weekly. Editor: Alan Prosser
Farmers Weekly
020 8652 4911
www.fwi.co.uk
Weekly. Editor: Stephen Howe
Tractor & Machinery
01959 541444
Monthly
NFU Horticulture
020 7331 7200
3pa

Health and social care

Ambulance Today
0151 708 8864
www.ambulance_today.co.uk
Quarterly. Editor: Declan Henethan
Care and Health Magazine
0870 901 7773
www.careandhealth.com
Fortnightly. Editor: Marcia White
Community Care
020 8652 3500
www.communitycare.co.uk
Weekly. Editor: Polly Neate
Doctor
020 8652 3500
www.doctorupdate.net
Weekly
GP
020 8276 5000
www.gponline.com
Weekly. Editor: Editor: Colin Cooper
Hospital Doctor
020 8652 3500
Weekly. Editor: Mike Broad
Medeconomics
020 8943 5000
Monthly/Editor: Julian Tyndale-Biscoe
Mims
020 8943 5000
www.emims.net
Monthly. Editor: Colin Duncan
NHS Journal of Healthcare Professionals
020 8455 1166
www.cyworksdirect.co.uk
Bi-monthly. Editor: Toni Nickson
NHS Magazine
01904 613702
www.nhs.uk/nhsmagazine
10pa. Editor: Richard Spencer

Nursing Standard
020 8423 1066
www.nursing-standard.co.uk
Weekly. Editor: Jean Gray
Nursing Times
020 7874 0500
www.nursingtimes.net
Weekly. Editor: Rachel Downey
The Pharmaceutical Journal
020 7572 2420
www.pjonline.com
Weekly. Editor: Olivia Timbs
The Practitioner
020 7921 8113
www.practitioner-i.co.uk
Monthly. Editor: Gavin Atkin
Pulse
020 7921 8102
www.pulse-i.co.uk
Weekly. Editor: Phil Johnson
RCN Bulletin
020 8423 1066
www.nursing-standard.co.uk
Weekly. Editor: Ken Edwards
Update
020 8652 8878
www.doctorupdate.net
Fortnightly. Editor: Andrew Baxter

Law

Law Society Gazette
020 7320 5820
www.lawgazette.co.uk
Weekly. Editor: Jonathan Ames
The Lawyer
020 7970 4000
www.thelawyer.com
Weekly. Editor: Catrin Griffiths
Media Lawyer
020 7963 7000
Bi-monthly. Editor: Tom Welsh

Retail and catering

Asian Trader
020 7928 1234
www.gg2.net
Fortnightly. Editor: Kalpesh Solanki
Caterer and Hotelkeeper
020 8652 3500
www.caterer.com
Weekly. Editor: Forbes Mutch
Catering Update
020 8652 3500
www.caterer.com
Monthly. Editor: Kathy Bowry
Convenience Store
01293 613400
www.foodanddrink.co.uk
Fortnightly. Editor: Sonia Young
The Grocer
01293 613400
www.grocertoday.co.uk
Weekly. Editor: Julian Hunt
Independent Retail News
01322 660070
www.irn-talkingshop.co.uk
Fortnightly. Editor: Richard Siddle

The Pub Business
020 8302 4024
Monthly. Editor: Tim Palmer
Publican
020 8565 4200
www.thepublican.com
Weekly. Editor: Lorna Harrison
The Restaurant Business
020 8302 4024
Monthly. Editor: David Foad

Journalism trade press

Best Sellers
Newtrade Publishing, 11 Angel Gate
City Rd, London EC1V 2SD
020 7689 0600
sanjeev.khaira@newtrade.co.uk
2pa, Consumer magazine data.
Editor: Catriona Dean
CPU News
Commonwealth Press Union
17 Fleet St, London EC4Y 1AA
020 7583 7733
cpu@cpu.org.uk
www.cpu.org.uk
6pa. Editor: Jeremy Scott-Joynt
The Journal
The Chartered Institute of Journalists
2 Dock Offices, Surrey Quays Rd
London SE16 2XU
020 7252 1187
memberservices@ioj.co.uk
www.ioj.co.uk
Quarterly. Editor: Andy Smith
The Journalist
National Union of Journalists
Acorn House, 308–312 Gray's Inn Rd
London WC1X 8DP
020 7278 7916
journalist@nuj.org.uk
www.nuj.org.uk
10pa. Editor: Tim Gopsill
Magazine Retailer
Newtrade Publishing, 11 Angel Gate
City Rd, London EC1V 2SD
020 7689 0600
sanjeev.khaira@newtrade.co.uk
2pa. Editor: Catriona Dean
Magazine World
FIPP, Queens House
55–56 Lincoln's Inn Field
London WC2A 3LJ
020 7404 4169
info@fipp.com
www.fipp.com
Quarterly. Editor: Arif Durrani
News from NewstrAid
NewstrAid Benelovent Society
PO Box 306
Great Dunmow CM6 1HY
01371 874198
oldben@newstraid.demon.co.uk
www.newstraid.org.uk
Annual. Charity for the newspaper industry

Press Gazette
Quantum Business Media
Quantum House, 19 Scarbrook Rd
Croydon CR9 1LX
020 8565 4448
pg@pressgazette.co.uk
www.pressgazette.co.uk
Weekly. Editor: Ian Reeves
Ulrich's Periodical Directory
Bowker
3rd Floor, 19 Thomas More St
Faringdon House, Wood St
East Grinstead RH19 1UZ
01342 310450
sales@bowker.co.uk
www.ulrichsweb.com
Quarterly. International directory

Useful associations

Association of American Correspondents in London
c/o Time Magazine
Brettenham House
Lancaster Place
London WC2E 7TL
020 7499 4080
elizabeth_lea@timemagazine.com
Association of British Science Writers (ABSW)
23 Savile Row, London W1S 2EZ
020 7439 1205
absw@absw.org.uk
www.absw.org.uk
Association of Freelance Writers
Sevendale House, 7 Dale St
Manchester M1 1JB
0161 228 2362
Audit Bureau of Circulations (ABC)
Saxon House, 211 High St
Berkhamsted
Hertfordshire HP4 1AD
01442 870800
marketing@abc.org.uk
www.abc.org.uk
Authors' Club
40 Dover St, London W1S 4NP
020 7499 8581
circles@author.co.uk
www.author.co.uk
British Copyright Council
Copyright House
29–33 Berners St
London W1T 3AB
01986 788122
copyright@bcc2.demon.co.uk
British Equestrian Writers' Association
Priory House, Station Rd
Swavesey, Cambridge CB4 5QJ
01954 232084
gnewsumn@aol.com
British Guild of Beer Writers
68A Elmwood Rd
London SE24 9NR
020 8853 8585
peterhaydon@onetel.net.uk
www.beerguild.com
British Guild of Travel Writers
51B Askew Cresent
London W12 9DN
020 8749 1128
charlotte@virtualnecessities.com
www.bgtw.org
British Newspaper Library
The British Library
Newspaper Library
Colindale Avenue
London NW9 5HE
020 7412 7353
newspaper@bl.uk
www.bl.uk/catalogues/newspapers
.html

British Society of Magazine Editors (BSME)
137 Hale Lane, Edgware
Middlesex HA8 9QP
020 8906 4664
admin@bsme.com
www.bsme.com

Broadcasting Press Guild
Tiverton, The Ridge, Woking
Surrey GU22 7EQ
01483 764895
torin.douglas@bbc.co.uk

Bureau of Freelance Photographers
Focus House, 497 Green Lanes
London N13 4BP
020 8882 3315
info@thebfp.com
www.thebfp.com

Campaign for Press and Broadcasting Freedom
Second Floor, 23 Orford Rd
Walthamstow, London E17 9NL
020 8521 5932
freepress@cpbf.org.uk
www.cpbf.org.uk

Caravan Writers' Guild
2 Harbury Field Cottage
Harbury, Leamington Spa
Warwickshire CV33 9JN
01926 613186
caratesters@hotmail.com

Chartered Institute of Journalists
2 Dock Offices, Surrey Quays Rd
London SE16 2XU
020 7252 1187
memberservices@ioj.co.uk
www.ioj.co.uk

Critics' Circle
c/o Catherine Cooper
69 Marylebone Lane
London W1U 2PH
020 7224 1410
www.criticscircle.org.uk

Foreign Press Association in London
11 Carlton House Terrace
London SW1Y 5AJ
020 7930 0445
secretariat@foreign-press.org.uk
www.foreign-press.org.uk

Garden Writers' Guild
c/o Institute of Horticulture
14/15 Belgrave Square
London SW1X 8PS
020 7245 6943
gwg@horticulture.org.uk
www.gardenwriters.co.uk

Guild of Agricultural Journalists
Charmwood, 47 Court Meadow
Rotherfield, East Sussex TN6 3LQ
01892 853187
don.gomery@farmline.com
www.gaj.org.uk

Guild of Food Writers
48 Crabtree Lane, London SW6 6LW
020 7610 1180
guild@gfw.co.uk
www.gfw.co.uk

Guild of Motoring Writers
39 Beswick Avenue
Bournemouth BH10 4EY
01202 518808
gensec@gomw.co.uk
www.newspress.co.uk/guild

Medical Writers' Group
The Society of Authors
84 Drayton Gardens
London SW10 9SB
020 7373 6642
info@societyofauthors.org
www.societyofauthors.org

National Union of Journalists
Headland House, 308 Gray's Inn Rd
London WC1X 8DP
020 7278 7916
acorn.house@nuj.org.uk
www.nuj.org.uk

Newspaper Marketing Agency
Berkeley Square House
Berkeley Square, London W1J 6BD
020 7887 1931
enquiries@nmauk.co.uk
www.nmauk.co.uk

Newspaper Society
Bloomsbury House
74–77 Great Russell St
London WC1B 3DA
020 7636 7014
ns@newspapersoc.org.uk
www.newspapersoc.org.uk

Outdoor Writers' Guild
PO Box 520, Bamber Bridge
Preston, Lancashire PR5 8LF
01772 696732
info@owg.org.uk
www.owg.org.uk

Periodical Publishers Association (PPA)
Queens House, 28 Kingsway
London WC2B 6JR
020 7404 4166
info1@ppa.co.uk
www.ppa.co.uk

The Picture Research Association
Head Office, 2 Culver Drive
Oxted, Surrey RH8 9HP
01883 730123
pra@lippmann.co.uk
www.picture-research.org.uk

Press Complaints Commission
1 Salisbury Square
London EC4Y 8JB
020 7353 1248
complaints@pcc.org.uk
www.pcc.org.uk

Publishers Publicity Circle
65 Airedale Avenue
London W4 2NN
020 8994 1881
ppc-@lineone.net
www.publisherspublicitycircle.co.uk

Scottish Newspaper Publishers Association
48 Palmerston Place
Edinburgh EH12 5DE
0131 220 4353
info@snpa.org.uk
www.snpa.org.uk

Scottish Print Employers Federation
48 Palmerston Place
Edinburgh EH12 5DE
0131 220 4353
info@spef.org.uk
www.spef.org.uk

Society of Editors
University Centre, Granta Place
Mill Lane, Cambridge CB2 1RU
01223 304080
info@societyofeditors.org
www.societyofeditors.org

Society of Women Writers & Journalists
Calvers Farm, Thelveton Diss
Norfolk IP21 4NG
01379 740550
zoe@zoeking.com
www.swwj.com

Sports Writers' Association of Great Britain
c/o Sport England External Affairs
16 Upper Woburn Place
London WC1H 0QP
020 7273 1589
petta.naylor@sportengland.org
www.sportswriters.org.uk

Note: press agencies, page 296

TV

Television remains the number one leisure activity in the UK. A Mori/Radio Times survey in 2001 showed that 54% of the population – around 26 million people – would be lonely without the television; but then, 67% said they thought there was often nothing worth watching. Whatever the truth, British television is now a multi-billion pound industry employing around 24,000 people and contributing around £12bn to the economy.

The nation's main public service broadcaster is the BBC. The corporation is controlled by 12 crown-appointed governors, who in turn appointed the director general, Greg Dyke. Funded primarily by the licence fee, it runs the two national terrestrial channels, BBC1 and BBC2. It also runs two free-to-air digital channels, BBC3 and BBC4; a rolling news service, BBC News 24; and other specialist channels such as BBC Parliament. The BBC's director of television is Jana Bennett.

There are three national terrestrial broadcasters. ITV is made up of 15 regional companies, 12 of which are owned by media giants Carlton and Granada; there is also a national commercial breakfast-time service, GMTV. The semi-public Channel 4 – together with S4C, the fourth channel in Wales – was created in 1982 to provide distinctive programming; its chief executive is Mark Thompson. Five, a more downmarket national channel launched in 1997, is ultimately owned by German media giant Bertelsmann; its chief executive, Dawn Airey, joined BSkyB in January 2003, to be replaced by Jane Lighting.

There are now hundreds of channels available on satellite and cable, and 35 channels available on digital terrestrial. The market leader in the multichannel market is BSkyB, the Murdoch-owned satellite broadcaster, which in June 2003 had 6.6 million subscribers in the UK, from a total of almost 12 million who had access to multichannel TV. In all multichannel homes, non-terrestrial TV accounted for 41.5% of viewing.

British commercial television advertising rose 4.3% in 2002 to £3.7bn, of which the lion's share was earned by ITV1. Long-term, ITV1 is losing advertisers to the increased competition from newcomers, particularly cable and satellite. Nevertheless, it continues to charge premium rates for its advertising, as it is the only commercial channel to consistently command the very highest audience figures at peak time.

Television audiences, for their part, are measured by Barb, the Broadcasters Audience Research Board. The board lost the confidence of advertisers and broadcasters at the beginning of 2002, as a relaunch failed to bed in, but under Nigel Walmsley, the former Carlton boss parachuted in to resolve the situation, the controversy has died down.

The two main broadcasting regulators, the ITC and broadcasting standards commission, are both due to fall under the umbrella of super-regulator Ofcom from December 2003.

WHAT'S ON THE OTHER SIDE ?

THE GOVERNMENT.

BBC NEWS

BBC

It was a tumultuous year for the BBC. Its royal charter is due for renewal in 2006; amid debate over where the corporation's public service duties end and its commercial activities begin, the culture secretary, Tessa Jowell, promised a review of its funding beyond that date. The BBC, accordingly, began gearing up to justify the licence fee. Against that background came increasing Downing Street pressure on the BBC over its reporting of war in Iraq, culminating in the row over a story by Radio 4 correspondent Andrew Gilligan: when Gilligan quoted an unnamed MoD official, saying the government had made its dossier on Iraq's weapons capability "sexier", the government tried to shoot the story down – and finally confirmed the source to be David Kelly, a senior scientific adviser. The public row culminated in Dr Kelly's death and a public inquiry (Iraq: the media war, page 1).

A television licence cost £116 from April 2003, an above-inflation rise on 2002 which gave the corporation about £100m in extra revenue. According to the BBC's annual report in July 2003, £2.7bn of the BBC's £3.5bn income came from TV licences, of which most of the rest (£627m) came from commercial enterprises. In the same year director-general Greg Dyke received £96,000 in bonuses and benefits on top of his £368,000 salary, while director of television Jana Bennett received £228,000 in bonuses and benefits, including relocation costs, on top of a £216,000 salary.

BBC1 extended its ratings lead over ITV1 in the year to June 2003, as the commercial channel came under increased competition from the multichannel sector in a slow advertising market: its overall audience share was 26.3%, compared with 24% for ITV. EastEnders was its most popular show, but its ratings success was built on good performance during the day as ITV1 pipped it in peak-time. A slow-burning success was Fame Academy, the talent show produced by Endemol, which started poorly in the ratings but pulled in more than 8.2 million viewers at its climax in December 2002; viewers cast nearly seven million telephone and internet votes. BBC2 stayed just ahead of Channel 4 and Five in the ratings: the Great Britons poll, for which 1.2 million people voted on the phone and the internet, was a particular success.

BBC News 24 came in for some criticism early in the year, as former Financial Times editor Richard Lambert concluded in a report that it should be both better and more accountable; it also came a distant second to Sky News in the ratings throughout the war in Iraq. But Roger Mosey, the BBC's head of television news, pointed out that the channel supplied an average of five hours of output each day to other BBC channels during the war.

In sport, the BBC celebrated the return of Match of the Day, paying £105m for Premiership highlights for three years from 2004. It also won live rights to all home England internationals and three FA Cup matches per round, for four years from the same season.

The BBC's digital future has continued to attract headlines. The BBC joined BSkyB in launching Freeview, a commercial free-to-air digital terrestrial service that successfully bid for ITV Digital's broadcast licences; the service originally cost a one-off £99 per television for a set-top box, a price which fell to £60 in summer 2003.

Freeview will be instrumental in meeting the government's stated aim of switching off the analogue transmission system by 2010; but it is also the kind of move that led Channel 4 chief executive Mark Thompson to call on the BBC in January to set out the limits of its public service ambitions, saying there was a widespread perception of BBC "mission creep". Jana Bennett, the BBC's director of television, responded by saying the BBC was a "highly creative organisation, pushing people's horizons, offering things that surprise and broaden people's lives".

February 2003 saw the launch of BBC3, a digital entertainment channel aimed at people in their twenties and thirties. Initial ratings were poor, as audience share hovered at about 0.6% for the first few months; which was at least better than the highbrow BBC4, whose share was stuck at around the 0.1% mark (although BBC3's launch budget was more than three times higher). The figures will arouse mixed feelings among BBC executives: low audiences will at least deflect the argument that the BBC is competing unfairly with its commercial rivals, as BBC4 controller Roly Keating, appointed with Charles Constable to head the campaign to retain the licence fee, will no doubt testify. Meanwhile David Edmonds, Ofcom board member and former director general of Oftel, said cross-promotion of BBC digital services on BBC1 and BBC2 was an activity he might be asking the corporation to explain.

In April the BBC decided to abandon the satellite encryption service it had been buying from BSkyB, and switch its eight digital channels to its own satellite – allowing viewers to watch its channels without a viewing card. BSkyB threatened to relegate BBC channels from the top of its electronic programme guide – but after a public stand-off, a compromise was reached. As a result of the deal, however, many satellite viewers without a Sky subscription were left unable to watch ITV, Channel 4 or Five without switching back to terrestrial.

BBC executive committee and remuneration, 2002–03

		Salary £k	bonus £k	benefits £k	2003 £k	2002 £k
Greg Dyke	director-general	368	88	8	464	469
Jenny Abramsky	radio and music	211	45	18	274	273
Jana Bennett	television (appointed April 2002)	216	47	181*	444	–
Glenwyn Benson	factual and learning**	185	37	16	238	226
Mark Byford	world service	235	54	17	306	294
Stephen Dando	human resources	221	49	2	272	222
Andy Duncan	marketing	231	55	15	301	235
Carolyn Fairbairn	strategy and distribution	122†	32	15	169	248
Roger Flynn	BBC Ventures	231	65	18	314	243
Rupert Gavin	BBC Worldwide	278	62	22	362	339
Ashley Highfield	new media	230	45	19	294	294
Pat Loughrey	nations and regions	191	41	48	280	259
Peter Salmon	sport	205	46	28	279	273
Richard Sambrook	news	222	49	16	287	260
John Smith	finance, property, business affairs	227	47	26	300	311
Michael Stevenson	factual and learning (resigned Jan 2003)	151	–	24	175	233
Caroline Thomson	policy and legal	179	35	22	236	226
Alan Yentob	drama, entertainment and children	228	67	26	321	302
Total		**3,931**	**864**	**521**	**5,316**	**4,707**

* includes £167,000 relocation package
** became controller of factual television in February 2003; replaced by John Willis
† includes period of unpaid leave

The BBC has a statutory obligation to ensure that 25% of its commissioned programme hours are made by independent producers – a target it missed in 2001–02 for the second successive year, leading to the promise of an investigation by the office of fair trading.

ITV

ITV has had a dreadful couple of years, losing both audience share and advertising revenue amid uncertainty over a proposed merger of media giants Carlton and Granada.

Between January 1999 and June 2003, ITV1's share of total viewing in terrestrial homes slipped sharply from 33% to 24%, according to Barb (and to below 20% in multichannel homes); this continued a long-term slide roughly mirroring the rise in audience share of multichannel TV. The second half of 2002 did see a recovery in ITV's advertising revenue after a severe slump earlier in the year; but in 2003, as the war in Iraq played havoc with the schedules, advertisers deferred spending, leaving the network holding out for only slight gains. Amid the bleak news, ITV scored a notable entertainment coup with Pop Idol, which attracted huge viewing figures and critical acclaim.

The major proposed change for ITV was the planned merger of **Carlton** and **Granada**. In September 2002, and after much speculation, these two media giants – who between them already control all the ITV franchises in England and Wales, plus Border in Scotland – announced their intention to merge, which would lead to a united ITV in England commanding more than 50% of the terrestrial advertising market. But the competition commission began an inquiry: advertisers are concerned that a single advertising sales department would be anti-competitive, and the commission may demand that they sell their sales houses – a plan the Granada chairman, Charles Allen, sees as a deal-breaker. In a last-ditch attempt to save the merger, Carlton and Granada offered to change the way they sell advertising space.

The ITC, in its last report before being subsumed into super-regulator Ofcom, criticised the channel for its "patchy performance" in 2002: ITV, it said, was too dependent on soaps, after it introduced a fifth weekly instalment of Coronation Street (four nights with a double bill on Mondays) in addition to five editions of Emmerdale. But the dependence is understandable: Coronation Street is a perennial feature at the top of audience share tables, and so a major source of advertising. ITV was praised, though, for producing a "good range and volume of drama", with new adaptations of the Forsyte Saga and Dr Zhivago seen as "landmark" programmes.

ITV1's decision to move its evening news to 9pm during the Iraq war was a ratings success, pulling an average 1.4 million more viewers than BBC1's 10 O'Clock News in the first two weeks of the military campaign.

The other ITV companies are **Scottish Media Group**, which controls Scottish TV and Grampian; **Ulster TV**; and **Channel TV** (see panel). Of these, Ulster outperformed the network, with advertising revenues growing by 4.7% in 2002.

TV has eaten itself **Janine Gibson**

The announcement that television had eaten itself was relatively low-key when it finally came on an otherwise unremarkable Thursday in June 2003. Many might indeed have missed the significance of the story tucked away in the trade press. After all, there are few programming announcements from Five which augur a seismic shift in broadcasting itself.

This one, though, was a cracker. Five had ordered a "champions league" reality show in which the winners of past hits would be locked in a house to compete for a prize. It's surely the ultimate reality TV nightmare and one that only Five would dream up? Well, no. Channel 4 had been developing the idea of Big Brother Gold for some months before deciding finally not to take the idea further.

Five's venture into meta-textual commentary (I'm assuming that director of programmes Kevin Lygo, who is no fool, has planned the whole thing as a commentary on the state of British television rather than simply chucking some money at another reality format) might actually turn out to be good news for those stick-in-the-mud viewers who yearn for some proper programmes rather than the almost unedited ramblings of a bunch of no-marks in a room/jungle/fame academy.

There is a point with all ubiquitous TV formats when critical mass appears. It happened with Changing Rooms, it happened with docu-soaps and it happened with domestic-based sitcoms. Usually about six months after every viewer becomes thoroughly fed up with the whole thing, an ambitious TV commissioner will announce they've had enough with the whole genre, and suddenly no one with a folder marked "new make-over ideas" can get a meeting for a year. This turning point is generally prefigured by Five or Sky One entering the genre, so on those grounds reality TV is just about dead.

And the same surely goes for property shows, any programme that involves downshifting or changing your life and those shows on BBC 2 and Channel 4 where someone you've never heard of who works for a magazine and is best confined to that job appears in a member of the public's house and shouts at them about their personal hygiene/table manners/dress sense. As for programmes that follow a bunch of pissed holiday reps round some of Europe's least salubrious hot-spots, those were over last year (except, obviously, on Sky One).

The funny thing is that the channel controllers, the commissioners and even the producers all know this. In their heart of hearts, they all know property's over. They all know that reality's on its last legs. They just haven't the faintest clue what's next. All over the swankiest restaurants in London, conversations are taking place about what might be the next big thing. And while they can't figure out what to do next, they'll just have to commission some more of the same.

For those viewers rather miserably sat at home wondering whatever happened to drama, comedy and documentaries, the key three words to cling on to are "BBC charter renewal". This process – which seems to take roughly three years to complete – means that until 2006, when the corporation basically gets its lease renewed for another 10 years, BBC1 has to pretend to be a bit too grown-up to mud-wrestle with the commercial hoi polloi. I confidently predict a spate of quality drama, more peaktime arts programmes along the lines of Alan Yentob's Leonardo da Vinci and, unfortunately, several more attempts to engage young people with political affairs.

Make the most of it.

Janine Gibson is editor-in-chief of MediaGuardian

Major fraud

The crown court hosted a royal farce last spring, as Major Charles Ingram, his wife Diana and accomplice Tecwen Whittock were convicted of cheating their way to the £1m top prize on Who Wants to Be a Millionaire?

The major, 39, of the Royal Engineers, answered all 15 multiple-choice questions correctly in the show, but jurors decided he was guided by Whittock's strategic coughing from the studio floor.

At a comical trial at Southwark crown court – in which jurors watched tapes of the quiz show, were treated to an appearance from host Chris Tarrant, and even saw the trial suspended once due to, of all things, a coughing fit – the three were convicted and given suspended jail sentences of between 12 and 18 months.

After trial by jury, trial by media. ITV announced on the day of the verdict that it planned to screen the footage of the cheating major on its Tonight programme, in a co-production by Granada and Millionaire makers Celador. The gripping 90-minute documentary, which showed the major appearing to change his mind several times after each question as Whittock's coughs directed him, attracted 16.7 million viewers at its peak.

After the programme, Ingram continued to protest his innocence, telling BBC television that the Granada show had been "one of the greatest TV editing con tricks" – a charge denied by Granada.

But it seems the programme-makers aren't doing badly out of the saga: barely a few weeks later, programme-makers Celador announced their intention to turn the drama into a Hollywood film.

The Major's questions

For £100: On which would you air laundry?
a) *Clothes dog*
b) *Clothes horse*
c) *Clothes rabbit*
d) *Clothes pig*

£200: What name is given to a person who is against increasing the powers of the European Union?
a) *Eurosceptic*
b) *Eurostar*
c) *Eurotrash*
d) *Eurovision*

£300: What is Butterscotch?
a) *Shortbread*
b) *A pavement game*
c) *A garden flower*
d) *Brittle toffee*

£500: Which of these is a nickname for a famous Scottish army regiment?
a) *Black Cat*
b) *Black Widow*
c) *Black Sea*
d) *Black Watch*

£1,000: The Normans who invaded and conquered England in 1066 spoke which language?
a) *German*
b) *Norwegian*
c) *French*
d) *Danish*

£2,000: In Coronation Street, who is Audrey's daughter?
a) *Janice*
b) *Gail*
c) *Linda*
d) *Sally*

£4,000: The River Foyle is found in which part of the UK?
a) *England*
b) *Scotland*
c) *Northern Ireland*
d) *Wales*

£8,000: Who was the second husband of Jacqueline Kennedy?
a) *Adnan Khashoggi*
b) *Ronald Reagan*
c) *Aristotle Onassis*
d) *Rupert Murdoch*

£16,000: Emmenthal is a cheese from which country?
a) *France*
b) *Italy*
c) *The Netherlands*
d) *Switzerland*

£32,000: Who had a hit UK album with Born To Do It, released in 2000?
a) *Coldplay*
b) *Toploader*
c) *A1*
d) *Craig David*

£64,000: Gentlemen versus Players was an annual match between amateurs and professionals of which sport?
a) *Lawn tennis*
b) *Rugby Union*
c) *Polo*
d) *Cricket*

£125,000: The Ambassadors in the National Gallery is a painting by which artist?
a) *Van Eyck*
b) *Holbein*
c) *Michelangelo*
d) *Rembrandt*

£250,000: What type of garment is an Anthony Eden?
a) *Overcoat*
b) *Hat*
c) *Shoe*
d) *Tie*

£500,000: Baron Haussman is best known for the planning of which city?
a) *Rome*
b) *Paris*
c) *Berlin*
d) *Athens*

£1m: A number one followed by 100 zeroes is known by what name?
a) *Googol*
b) *Megatron*
c) *Gigabit*
d) *Nanomole*

■ The million-pound question

TARRANT: "A number one followed by 100 zeros is known by what name? A googol, a megatron, a gigabit or a nanomole?"

MAJOR INGRAM: "I am not sure."

TARRANT: "Charles, you've not been sure since question number two."

MAJOR INGRAM: "The doubt is multiplied. I think it is nanomole but it could be a gigabit, but I am not sure. I do not think I can do this one. I do not think it is a megatron. I do not think I have heard of a googol."

Cough.

MAJOR INGRAM: "Googol, googol, googol. By a process of elimination I have to think it's a googol but I do not know what a googol is. I do not think it's a gigabit, nanomole, and I do not think it's a megatron. I really do think it's a googol."

TARRANT: "But you think it's a nanomole. You have never heard of a googol."

MAJOR INGRAM: "It has to be a googol."

Charles Ingram: convicted of £1m deception

TARRANT: "It's also the only chance you will have to lose £468,000. You are going for the one you have never heard of."

MAJOR INGRAM: "I do not mind taking the odd risk now and again. My strategy has been direct so far – take it by the bit and go for it. I've been very positive, I think. I do not think it's a gigabit, I do not think it's a nanomole or megatron. I am sure it's a googol."

Cough.

MAJOR INGRAM: "Surely, surely."

TARRANT: "You lose £468,000 if you are wrong."

MAJOR INGRAM: "No, it's a googol. God, is it a googol? Yes, it's a googol. Yes, yes, it's a googol."

Cough.

MAJOR INGRAM: "I am going to play googol."

TARRANT (*after a break*): "He initially went for nanomole, he then went through the various options again. He then went for googol because he had never heard of it and he had heard of the other three. You've just won £1m."

The Guardian/Graham Turner

Answers: £100: b. £200: a. £300: d. £500: d. £1,000: c. £2,000: b. £4,000: c. £8,000: c. £16,000: d. £32,000: d. £64,000: d. £125,000: b. £250,000: b. £500,000: b. £1m: a.

Channel 4

"One of our jobs is to be a kind of subversive, disruptive element in Britain's cultural life in a way that, in the end, the BBC doesn't try and do." So said the Channel 4 chief executive Mark Thompson in March, in a Financial Times interview marking his first year in charge; but after a year marked by large-scale job losses and the closure of the respected film production company, FilmFour, most of the disruption so far has been internal.

The channel had a troubled 2002, shedding one-fifth of its workforce in the biggest restructuring in its 20-year history: 122 jobs were lost from its core Channel 4 operation, plus 48 from both the channel and its multichannel arm 4Ventures, and a further 50 at FilmFour. Added to 45 earlier job losses, the channel was left employing just 850 people. The reason for the cuts: a £28m loss for 2001 across the channel and its associated businesses, and the threat of increasing competition from Five. Nevertheless, Thompson remained optimistic, promising to put "every penny" saved in job losses toward a £430m investment in programming, in an effort to meet the channel's remit to foster diversity and innovation. The channel's multichannel share slipped slightly to 9.6% in the year to June 2003, but thanks to the savings, it returned a £16.5m profit in 2002.

> "They look fantastic on the outside, but are a little bit grey on the inside"
>
> John Yorke, new Channel 4 head of drama, on the channel's buildings (June 2003)

The past few years have seen Channel 4 battle to hang on to its top talent – after the influential Kevin Lygo left in 2001 to join Five, he was followed to the same channel by Andrew Newman, Dan Chambers and Sue Murphy; while Sara Ramsden, head of factual, jumped ship in 2002 to become controller of Sky One. But in July 2003 Lygo returned, to replace Tim Gardam as director of television. "I had only one person in mind when it came to replacing Tim," Thompson later said.

The signs, at least, are that Channel 4 is now attempting to do better what it does best: attracting the 16- to 34-year-olds who watch it and thus allow it to command premium rates from advertisers. (Channel 4 had a 12.8% peak-time share of 16- to 34-year-olds in 2002.) The axing of Brookside, the long-running soap that had lost its ratings pull after the days of Anna Friel and Ricky Tomlinson, complemented this strategy; this left space for off-beat contemporary dramas such as 40, starring Eddie Izzard, and 20 Things to Do Before You're 30, neither of which particularly excited the critics. Boys and Girls, a Saturday-night entertainment show devised by Chris Evans, flopped in the ratings and was moved to a 10.30pm slot.

The demise of the FilmFour production company was a major PR blow. FilmFour had delivered box office hits such as Trainspotting and East is East, but its latest venture, Charlotte Gray, the most expensive

Terrestrial net advertising revenue 2002 (£m)	
ITV	1,686
Channel 4	632
Five	237
S4C	9
GMTV	58
Total	2,622
Sponsorship	56
Total	**2,678**
Source: ITC	

Analogue terrestrial ownership		
BBC	BBC1, BBC2	publicly owned; board of governors answerable to government
ITV	Anglia, Border, Granada, LWT, Meridian, Tyne Tees, Yorkshire	Granada Group
	Carlton, Central, HTV, Westcountry	Carlton
	Grampian, Scottish	Scottish Media Group
Ulster	Ulster TV	
Channel	Channel TV	
Channel 4	Channel 4, S4C	independent
Channel 5	Five	RTL, owned by Bertelsmann

independent film ever made in Britain, barely covered its costs. In 2001–02 the company lost £5m. When the decision came to close it, its £30m budget was cut to £10m for television-only films, made by the Channel 4 drama department.

Elsewhere, Channel 4 renewed its contract with ITN for Channel 4 News, in a deal that will guarantee the relationship for another five years; and planned to launch new digital channels to make use of its space on Freeview.

Five

One question remains about Five: can it expand in its present form – or will it sell? The channel's audience share reached 6.4% in 2002 and 2003, making it a serious competitor for Channel 4; but its largest shareholder, the Bertelsmann-owned RTL, has set a target of 10%. Both analysts and advertisers have said it needs to invest further in programming if that is to be achieved.

But with the departures of chief executive Dawn Airey (to BSkyB) and programme director Kevin Lygo (to Channel 4), speculation about a possible sale intensified. The Communications Act removes Britain's restrictions on both cross-media and foreign ownership of television channels, legislation which could clear the way for the purchase of Five by Rupert Murdoch's NewsCorp (if, that is, he clears a "public interest" test imposed by Lord Puttnam). Gerhard Zeiler, the chief executive of RTL who replaced Didier Bellens in March 2003, has said he would not sell Five, and Murdoch himself ruled out an acquisition in November, saying his pay TV group is "not interested" in terrestrial broadcasters. But Murdoch also said he had no plans to buy US satellite platform DirecTV, and then proceeded to purchase a controlling stake in April 2003.

Five's share of the advertising market reached 7.5% in 2002, and the channel has set a target for 8.5% for 2003 under new chief executive Jane Lighting.

BSkyB and satellite

Almost 7 million homes in the UK receive satellite television; of these, almost all are subscribers to BSkyB, the dominant force in the UK multi-channel market. In June 2003, Sky increased its subscriber base to 6.8 million customers (including 286,000 in Ireland) – more than double the number of customers taking pay TV through cable.

BSkyB is a "vertically integrated" business: that is, it both broadcasts and controls the satellite platform, setting the price at which rival channels can access it. There are more than 375 channels on BSkyB's digital satellite, of which 16, at the latest count, are Sky own-brand channels and spin-off channels. It has 96 different subscription packages, ranging from £12.50 to £38 a month the annual average revenue per subscriber was £366 in the second quarter of 2003.

BSkyB also charges other digital platforms to carry its channels on their networks. This was the subject of a three-year investigation by the office of fair trading, ending in December 2002, in which rivals such as ITV Digital said BSkyB charged so much to carry its channels on their networks that it was impossible for them to make a profit. The regulator indicated in 2001 that it would probably find the broadcaster guilty of breaking competition law, at which ITV Digital suggested it would sue; but in a bizarre reversal, the OFT concluded a year later that there was "not enough evidence" to support the charges. ITV Digital, for its part, had been out of business for seven months.

BSkyB added to its team in January by recruiting Dawn Airey, former chief executive at Five, as managing director of Sky Networks, where (reporting to chief executive Tony Ball) she takes control of all the own-brand channels bar sport. Sky channels had slipped slightly in 2002 ratings, to below 12.8% of multichannel share; particular attention will fall on Sky One, where Airey is expected to invest in programming to drive the channel upmarket, much as she did with Five. The appointment of Sara Ramsden, former head of factual at Channel 4, as Sky One controller seemed to support the strategy.

Three new music channels were also launched just after Airey's arrival, to compete with MTV and Emap's music programming: they are called Scuzz, Flaunt and the Amp.

BSkyB has retained the rights to all live Premiership games, paying just over £1bn for 138 games a season for three years from August 2004. But the deal could be threatened: the European commission pledged to investigate the tendering process amid fears that it could be anti-competitive.

Within BSkyB, there has been something of a battle among shareholders to secure directors' independence from NewsCorp, the majority owner controlled by Rupert Murdoch. Legally, eight of the 15 board members of BSkyB must be independent non-executive directors; these include Gail Rebuck, the chief executive of publisher Random House, and Jacques Nasser, the former boss of Ford. Such appointees may have worried Rupert Murdoch, as his son James was voted on to the board as non-executive director in February 2003.

In summer 2003, meanwhile, there were plans to relaunch Live TV – the channel that featured the news bunny, topless darts and bouncing weather dwarfs – on Sky Digital.

Cable

Cable television is a subscription-based service, usually offered in conjunction with telephone or internet, all broadcast through an underground analogue or digital cable into the home. More than 3.3 million people in the country subscribed in March 2003, mostly in urban areas. NTL, which broadcasts to homes in Oxford, Cambridge, Surrey, Hampshire and Teesside, had 2 million subscribers, down slightly on the previous quarter; while Telewest, which broadcasts to London and the south-east, the Midlands and parts of northern England and Scotland, had 1.3 million.

But these are difficult times for cable. Both companies reported heavy losses in 2002, as they tried to convert customers from analogue to digital services; and they were forced to delay proposals for a possible merger. NTL lost £589m, down from £6bn the previous year, while Telewest lost £2.2bn, and in 2003 was in the process of restructuring £3.5bn debts.

Digital terrestrial: Freeview

The government wants to switch off the analogue transmission system by 2010 and replace it with digital terrestrial television. With that aim in mind, it has set up six digital terrestrial "multiplexes" or networks, each of which could carry five channels plus interactive services such as home shopping. After the collapse of ITV Digital in 2002, licences for three of

Key contact

Freeview
2nd Floor
85 Tottenham Court Road
London W1T 4DU
020 7765 1149
www.freeview.co.uk
General manager: Matthew
Seaman. DTT Platform for
Crown Castle, BBC and BSkyB

these multiplexes were awarded to the BBC and transmission firm Crown Castle – which, in association with BSkyB, now markets the entire digital terrestrial service, and its maximum 30 TV and radio channels, on a free-to-air basis under the brand name Freeview.

Freeview is not entirely "free"; users without digital-compatible televisions must part with up to £60 for a set-top box. But, since its launch in December 2002, it has been something of a success. More than 650,000 set-top boxes had been sold by March 2003, taking the total number of digital terrestrial homes to nearly 1.6 million. The BBC hopes that millions more people turn to digital terrestrial TV, making its investment in digital television (see section on the BBC) seem more in tune with its public service remit. Nevertheless, according to audience research body Barb, digital channels accounted for just 17% of all viewing in Freeview homes during March.

Challenges remain for the government's digital terrestrial strategy. Freeview still only covered 70% of the UK in March 2003, and did not work with older TV aerials; the government has promised that all viewers who can receive analogue television now (99.4%) must be able to receive the main free-to-air channels digitally, and 95% of people must be able to afford it. Estimates put the total cost of the switchover to digital TV in infrastructure, marketing and equipment at between £15bn and £20bn.

BSkyB is thought to be pursuing a canny strategy by buying into digital terrestrial TV, even though regulars have so far banned it from running a multiplex. Three of its own-brand channels – Sky News, Sky Sports News and Sky Travel – are available on Freeview.

The last rites of **ITV Digital**, Carlton and Granada's pay-TV platform which collapsed in 2002 with the loss of 1,500 jobs, were administered in April 2003. Liquidator Grant Thornton wrote to over 200,000 creditors offering just 2p in the pound for the total £1.3bn they were owed when the company folded. Ironically, Carlton and Granada received the biggest settlement – £804,000 – because they were the biggest creditors. Some 150 former employees later won £2,000 each at an employment tribunal, after it ruled they were made redundant without proper consultation.

Interactive

TV's interactive services stuttered in 2002. Sky's interactive revenues fell over the year, and little was heard of its commitment to make £50 per subscriber from interactive services by 2005. In April, Carlton and Granada formed a combined interactive TV division, ITV Interactive, headed by Jane Marshall, the former chief executive of Carlton's interactive service, Carlton Active. The previous month, Carlton Active had been axed along with its 24 staff.

Multichannel TV: the options			
	Main operators	**Connected homes**	**Comments**
Satellite	Sky Digital	6.8m* (June 03)	subscription (also available: satellite free-to-air)
Cable	NTL, Telewest	3.3m (Mar 03)	subscription, usually including phone or internet
Digital terrestrial	Freeview	1.6m (Mar 03)	free-to-view; requires digital-compatible TV or set-top box

*includes 286,000 homes in Republic of Ireland

Independent TV production

There are 1,000 independent TV producers in the UK, most of whom are members of Pact, the producers' alliance for cinema and television. Of these, only 20 or 30 companies have the resources to compete regularly for the major budgets; but between them, they have nevertheless produced some of the biggest hits of 2002 and 2003. Pop Idol (19TV), Big Brother (Endemol), Faking It (RDF) and Jamie's Kitchen (Talkback/Fresh One), to name but a few of the successes, won both large audiences and industry awards. Televisual magazine (see panel) conducts an annual peer poll of the most successful production companies.

But 2002 and 2003 were challenging years. Reduced advertising means reduced programming budgets, and increased pressure on production companies to produce cheaper programmes that hit advertisers' target demographics. Terrestrial broadcasters are in theory supposed to commission at least a quarter of their programming hours from independents; but in practice, said the ITC programme supply report, the quota is seen by some as a "ceiling, not a floor". The BBC in particular missed its 25% target in both 2000-01 and 2001-02. The same report said that broadcasters, rather than the producers who had thought of them, were too often cashing in on the success of their hit shows.

The Communications Act, however, is a success story for the independent production sector. A total of 61 amendments were made to the draft bill as a direct consequence of the ITC's intervention in an effort to safeguard the industry. In particular, producers will retain rights to their programmes unless they negotiate otherwise, while broadcasters and their distributors (for example, the BBC and its commercial arm BBC Worldwide) are required to act at "arms' length" from each other. Broadcasters' 25% quotas will also in future apply to each individual channel,

"Is it really our job to make large numbers of independent producers extremely rich?"

BBC director-general Greg Dyke
(June 2002)

Top 20 independent production companies

	Company	Credits
1=	Endemol	Big Brother (C4)
1=	TWI	British Empire in Colour (ITV)
3	Chrysalis	Richard and Judy (C4)
4	TV Corporation	Robot Wars (BBC), Today at the Test (C4)
5	Thames/Talkback	Pop Idol (BBC)
6	RDF	Faking It (C4)
7	Tiger Aspect	Teachers (C4)
8	Lion	Castaway 2000 (BBC)
9	Princess	Rise (C4), Wright Stuff (Five)
10	Wall to Wall	1940s House (C4)
11=	Ideal World	Location, Location, Location (C4)
11=	Prospect	Ruby's Health Quest (BBC)
11=	Ragdoll	Teletubbies (C4)
14	Zenith	2000 Acres of Sky (ITV)
15=	Celador	Who Wants to Be a Millionaire? (ITV1)
15=	September	Greece on the Beach (Sky One)
17	Optomen	Naked Chef (BBC)
18	Two Four	The City Gardener (C4)
19	Hat Trick	The Kumars At Number 42 (BBC)
20	Diverse	Girls on Tour (C4)

Source: Production 100 survey, October 2002, Televisual monthly magazine (www.televisual.com). Survey takes into account industry peer poll.

rather than to broadcasters as a whole, preventing broadcasters such as the BBC from, say, commissioning much more than its quota on a little-watched digital channel and much less at peak time on BBC1.

The result is that, more than ever, the holy grail for the independent producer is the "returnable format" – the programme that, like Faking It or Who Wants to be a Millionaire?, can be sold internationally as well as to the UK.

Channel 4 remains the broadcaster with the closest relationship with independent production companies; but Channel 5 and Sky One are both expected to invest further in programming in 2004, which will increase the "shopping market" available to independents.

In July 2003, Chrysalis – one of the biggest independent television production companies – agreed to sell its television production business to a group led by former Granada chief executive Steve Morrison.

Further reading

■ **Press**

MediaGuardian
media.guardian.co.uk/broadcast

Broadcast: weekly trade magazine
www.broadcastnow.co.uk

Screen International: film trade magazine
www.screendaily.com

Televisual: monthly trade magazine
www.televisual.com

■ **Web only**

Digital Spy
www.digitalspy.co.uk

■ **Books**

Strange Places, Questionable People
JOHN SIMPSON; PAN 1999 Autobiography of the ubiquitous BBC television journalist

Life On Air DAVID ATTENBOROUGH; BBC 2002
Autobiography of the ubiquitous BBC television naturalist

Broadcast Journalism ANDREW BOYD; FOCAL PRESS 2000
Widely recommended guide.

John Birt: the Harder Path TIME WARNER PAPERBACKS
2003 Autobiography of a director-general.

■ **Other resources**

Barb
www.barb.co.uk

British Film Institute
www.bfi.org.uk

Digital television (government site)
www.digitaltelevision.gov.uk

Ofcom
www.ofcom.gov.uk

Pact
www.pact.co.uk

Award-winning programmes

Baftas

- *Drama series:* Spooks (Kudos, BBC1)
- *Drama serial:* Shackleton (Firstsight, Channel 4)
- *Feature:* Faking It (RDF, Channel 4)
- *Entertainment:* I'm a Celebrity, Get Me Out of Here! (LWT, ITV1)
- *Situation comedy:* The Office (BBC2)
- *Soap:* Coronation Street (Granada, ITV1)

Broadcast awards

- *Best light entertainment programme:* Pop Idol (19 TV, ITV1)
- *Best news programme:* 10 O'Clock News (BBC1)
- *Best comedy:* The Office (BBC2)
- *Best drama series:* Spooks (Kudos, BBC1)
- *Best independent production company:* Ideal World

National TV awards

- *Most popular entertainment programme:* Pop Idol (19 TV, ITV1)
- *Most popular serial drama:* EastEnders (BBC1)
- *Most popular drama:* Auf Wiedersehen, Pet (Ziji, BBC1)
- *Most popular comedy:* Cold Feet (Granada, ITV1)
- *Most popular factual programme:* Big Brother (Endemol, Channel 4)

Broadcasting Press Guild awards

- *Best single drama:* The Gathering Storm (BBC2)
- *Best drama series/serial:* Daniel Deronda (BBC1)
- *Best documentary series:* Jamie's Kitchen (Talkback and Fresh One, Channel 4)
- *Best single documentary:* Faking It: Drag Queen (RDF, Channel 4)
- *Best entertainment:* Bremner, Bird & Fortune: At Her Majesty's Pleasure (Vera, Channel 4)

▶ Media awards, page 307

Multichannel audience share, year to June

	2002–03	2002 §	2000–01	1999–2000	1998–99
Animal Planet	0.1	0.1	0.1	0.1	–
At the Races	0.1	–	–	–	–
BBC3	0.1	–	–	–	–
BBC4	0.1	–	–	–	–
BBC Choice	0.1	0.3	0.4	0.1	–
BBC News 24	0.4	0.3	0.2	0.1	0.1
Bid-Up TV	0.1	–	–	–	–
Biography Channel	0.1	0.1	–	–	–
Boomerang	0.4	0.3	0.2	–	–
The Box	0.2	0.2	0.3	0.2	0.1
Bravo	0.2	0.3	0.2	0.2	0.2
Cartoon Network	0.3	0.4	0.7	0.7	0.8
Cartoon Network Plus	0.1	0.1	–	–	–
CBBC	0.1	–	–	–	–
CBeebies	0.7	0.4	–	–	–
Challenge TV	0.3	0.2	0.3	0.2	0.2
CNN	0.1	†	†	0.1	0.1
CNX	0.1	–	–	–	–
Discovery	0.3	0.4	0.3	0.3	0.3
Discovery Health	0.1	0.1	–	–	–
Disney Channel	0.3	0.3	0.4	0.4	0.4
Disney Playhouse	0.1	0.1	0.1	–	–
Disney Toon	0.1	0.1	–	–	–
E4	0.7	0.9	0.2	–	–
Eurosport	0.2	0.3	0.3	0.3	0.3
Fox Kids Network	0.2	0.2	0.2	0.2	0.1
Granada Men & Motors	0.1	0.1	0.1	0.1	–
Granada Plus	0.4	0.4	0.3	0.3	0.3
Hallmark	0.4	0.3	0.1	–	–
The History Channel	0.1	0.1	0.2	0.1	0.1
The Hits	0.1	–	–	–	–
Home and Leisure	0.3	0.3	0.2	0.2	0.2
ITN News	0.1	0.1	–	–	–
ITV2	0.7	0.5	0.1	0.1	–
Kerrang	0.1	0.1	–	–	–
Kiss TV	0.1	0.1	0.1	–	–
Living	0.6	0.6*	0.5	0.6	0.6
Magic TV	0.1	0.1	–	–	–
MTV	0.2	0.2	0.3	0.4	0.4
MTV Base	0.1	0.1	0.1	–	–
MTV Hits	0.1	0.1	0.1**	–	–
MTV2	0.1	0.1	–	–	–
National Geographic	0.1	0.1	0.1	0.1	0.1

* previously UK Living   ** MTV Extra renamed MTV Hits on May 1, 2001

	2002–03	2002 §	2000–01	1999–2000	1998–99
Network 2	0.1	0.1	0.1	0.1	0.1
Nickelodeon	0.5	0.4	0.7	0.7	0.7
Nick Jr	0.2	0.2	0.2	0.1	–
Nick Toons	0.1	–	–	–	–
The Paramount Channel	0.3	0.3	0.2	0.1	0.1
QVC	0.1	0.1	0.2	0.2	0.2
Reality TV	0.1	–	–	–	–
RTE1	0.1	0.1	0.1	0.1	0.1
The Sci-Fi Channel	0.3	0.3	0.3	0.2	0.2
Sky Box Office	0.1	0.1	†	0.1	–
Sky Cinema	0.1	0.1	0.2	0.2	0.2
Sky Cinema 2	0.1	0.1	0.1	–	–
Sky Moviemax	0.2	0.3	0.4	0.5	0.5
Sky Moviemax 2	0.1	0.1	0.1	–	–
Sky Moviemax 3	0.1	0.1	0.1	–	–
Sky Moviemax 4	0.1	0.1	0.1	–	–
Sky Moviemax 5	0.1	0.1	0.1	–	–
Sky News	0.7	0.3	0.3	0.3	0.4
Sky One	1.7	2.1	1.8	1.7	1.5
Sky One Mix	0.1	–	–	–	–
Sky Premier	0.4	0.4	0.6	0.7	0.8
Sky Premier 2	0.2	0.3	0.2	0.1	–
Sky Premier 3	0.2	0.2	0.2	0.1	–
Sky Premier 4	0.2	0.2	0.2	0.1	–
Sky Premier Widescreen	0.1	0.1	0.1	–	–
Sky Sports 1	1.0	0.8	0.9	0.8	0.8
Sky Sports 2	0.3	0.4	0.5	0.6	0.6
Sky Sports 3	0.2	0.1	0.2	0.2	0.3
Sky Sports Extra	0.1	0.1	0.1	–	–
Sky Sports News	0.2	0.2	0.1	0.1	–
Smash Hits	0.1	0.1	–	–	–
TCM	0.2	0.2	0.1	–	–
TMF	0.1	–	–	–	–
Trouble	0.2	0.2	0.2	0.2	0.2
UK Food	0.1	0.1	–	–	–
UK Gold	0.9	0.9	1.2	1.0	0.8
UK Gold 2	0.1	0.1	–	–	–
UK History	0.1	–	–	–	–
UK Horizons	0.2	0.3	0.1	0.1	0.1
UK Style	0.6	0.6	0.3	0.1	0.1
VH-1	0.1	0.1	0.2	0.2	0.3
VH-1 Classic	0.1	0.1	0.1	–	–
Zee TV	0.1	0.1	†	0.2	0.2

† figures unavailable   § figures cover six months to June 2002   Source: ITC

% of viewing (individuals): terrestrial channels/other

	BBC1	BBC2	ITV	CH4	CH5	OTHERS (Cable/Sat/RTÉ)
1982	38.0	12.0	50.0	–	–	–
1987	38.0	12.0	42.0	8.0	–	–
1992	34.0	10.0	41.0	10.0	–	5.0
1997	30.8	11.6	32.9	10.6	2.3	11.8
2002	26.2	11.4	24.1	10.0	6.3	22.1

Source: Barb

Terrestrial audience share, year to June					
	2002–03	2002 §	2000–01	1999–2000	1998–99
BBC1	26.3	26.4	26.6	27.8	28.7
BBC2	11.3	11.3	10.9	10.6	11.2
ITV	24.0	24.6	28.2	30.2	31.4
Anglia	1.4	1.4	1.8	1.8	1.9
Border	0.3	0.4	0.5	0.4	0.5
Carlton	2.1	2.2	2.5	2.8	2.9
Central	3.5	3.4	4.2	4.5	4.7
GMTV	1.5	1.6	1.4	1.5	1.6
Granada Television	2.9	2.9	3.4	3.7	3.9
HTV Wales	1.1 ⎫	1.9	2.1	2.2	2.3
HTV West	0.8 ⎭				
LWT	1.5	1.6	1.9	2.0	2.0
Meridian	1.9	1.9	2.1	2.3	2.4
Tyne Tees	1.2	1.2	1.4	1.5	1.5
Scottish & Grampian	2.1	2.2	2.3	2.4	2.5
Ulster	0.7	0.7	0.8	1.0	1.0
Westcountry	0.6	0.6	0.8	0.8	0.8
Yorkshire	2.4	2.4	3.0	3.2	3.3
Channel Four	9.6	9.9	9.9	10.1	9.9
Five	6.4	6.4	5.6	5.7	4.9
S4C Wales	0.2	0.3	0.3	0.3	0.3

Source: ITC   § figures cover six months to June 2002

Top 20 programmes, 2002		
	Programme	Audience
1	Only Fools and Horses, BBC1	16.3m
2	EastEnders, BBC1	16.0m
3	Coronation Street, ITV1	15.0m
4	Pop Idol Final, ITV1	13.3m
5	Jubilee 2000: Party at the Palace, BBC1	12.5m
6	World Cup: England v Brazil, BBC1	12.5m
7	World Cup: England v Denmark, BBC1	12.5m
8	Auf Wiedersehen, Pet, BBC1	12.4m
9	A Touch of Frost, ITV1	12.4m
10	World Cup: England v Sweden, ITV1	12.2m
11	Heartbeat, ITV1	12.1m
12	World Cup: England v Argentina, BBC	12.0m
13	Who wants to Be a Millionaire?, ITV1	11.6m
14	Emmerdale, ITV1	11.3m
15	I'm a Celebrity... Get me Out of Here!, ITV1	11.0m
16	Christmas Day News, BBC1	10.8m
17	World Cup: Germany v Brazil, BBC1	10.8m
18	The Mummy, BBC1	10.7m
19	Indiana Jones: The Last Crusade, BBC1	10.3m
20	Indiana Jones: Temple of Doom, BBC1	10.1m

Source: Barb

"Bouncing weather dwarfs were a major milestone in British TV"

Kelvin MacKenzie on talk of a Live TV revival (May 2003)

TV Contacts

Office of Communications (Ofcom)
Riverside House
2A Southwark Bridge Road
London
SE1 9HA
020 7981 3000
www.ofcom.gov.uk

BBC

BBC Television
Television Centre, Wood Lane
London W12 7RJ
020 8743 8000
press.office@bbc.co.uk
www.bbc.co.uk

BBC Television Scotland
Broadcasting House
Queen Margaret Drive
Glasgow G12 8DG
0141 338 2000
press.office@bbc.co.uk
www.bbc.co.uk/scotland/
Controller: John McCormick

BBC Wales Television
Broadcasting House
Llantrisant Road, Llandaff
Cardiff CF5 2YQ
029 2032 2000
press.office@bbc.co.uk
www.bbc.co.uk/wales
Controller: Menna Richards

BBC Northern Ireland
Broadcasting House
Ormeau Avenue, Belfast BT2 8HQ
028 9033 8000
press.office@bbc.co.uk
www.bbc.co.uk/northernireland
Controller: Anna Karragher

BBCi
Television Centre, Wood Lane
London W12 7RJ
www.bbc.co.uk

BBC Television News
Room 1502, Television Centre
Wood Lane, London W12 7RJ
020 8624 9043
http://news.bbc.co.uk

BBC Monitoring
Marketing Unit, Caversham Park
Reading RG4 8TZ
0118 948 6289
csu@mon.bbc.co.uk
www.bbcmonitoringonline.com and
www.monitor.bbc.co.uk
Monitors world media

BBC Research Central
Broadcasting House
Portland Place, London W1A 1AA
020 7557 2452
research-central@bbc.co.uk
www.bbcresearchcentral.com
*Senior researchers: Helen Turner,
Huw Martin, Guy Watkins, Angie
Francis, Kyla Thorogood, Richard
Jeffery, Jacqueline Faulkner,
Michael Paige
Information, footage, pronunciation,
radio and photo research services*

BBC regions

BBC East
The Forum, Millennium Plain
Norwich NR2 1BH
01603 619331
look.east@bbc.co.uk
www.bbc.co.uk/england/lookeast
*Head of regional and local
programmes: Tim Bishop*

BBC East Midlands
London Road, Nottingham NG2 4UU
0115 955 0500
emt@bbc.co.uk
www.bbc.co.uk/england
/eastmidlandstoday
*Head of regional and local
programmes: Alison Ford*

BBC London
35c Marylebone High Street
London W1U 4QA
020 7224 2424
yourlondon@bbc.co.uk
www.bbc.co.uk/london
*Head of regional and local
programmes: Michael MacFarlane*

BBC North
Broadcasting Centre
Woodhouse Lane, Leeds LS2 9PX
0113 244 1188
look.north@bbc.co.uk
www.bbc.co.uk/england
/looknorthyorkslincs
*Head of regional and local
programmes: Colin Philpott*

BBC North East and Cumbria
Broadcasting Centre, Barrack Rd
Newcastle upon Tyne NE99 2NE
0191 232 1313
look.north.northeast.cumbria@
bbc.co.uk
www.bbc.co.uk/england
/looknorthnecumbria
*Head of regional and local
programmes: Wendy Pilmer*

BBC North West
New Broadcasting House
PO Box 27, Oxford Road
Manchester M60 1SJ
0161 200 2020
nwt@bbc.co.uk
www.bbc.co.uk/manchester
*Head of regional and local
programmes: Martin Brooks*

BBC South
Havelock Road
Southampton SO14 7PU
023 8022 6201
south.today@bbc.co.uk
www.bbc.co.uk/england/southtoday
*Head of regional and local
programmes: Eve Turner*

BBC South East
The Great Hall
Mount Pleasant Road
Tunbridge Wells TN1 1QQ
01892 670000
southeasttoday@bbc.co.uk
www.bbc.co.uk/england
/southeasttoday
*Head of regional and local
programmes: Laura Ellis*

BBC South West
Broadcasting House
Seymour Road, Mannamead
Plymouth PL3 5BD
01752 229201
spotlight@bbc.co.uk
www.bbc.co.uk/england/spotlight
*Head of regional and local
programmes: Leo Devine*

BBC West
Broadcasting House
Whiteladies Road, Bristol BS8 2LR
0117 973 2211
pointswest@bbc.co.uk
www.bbc.co.uk/england/pointswest
Head of regional and local
programmes: Andrew Wilson

BBC West Midlands
BBC Pebble Mill
Birmingham B5 7QQ
0121 432 8888
midlands.today@bbc.co.uk
www.bbc.co.uk/birmingham
Head of regional and local
programmes: David Holdsworth
Moving late 2003 to: The Mailbox,
Royal Mail Street, Birmingham,
B1 1XL; Tel: 0121 567 6767

BBC channels

BBC One
Television Centre, Wood Lane
London W12 7RJ
020 8743 8000
www.bbc.co.uk/bbcone
Controller: Lorraine Heggessey

BBC Two
Television Centre
020 8743 8000
www.bbc.co.uk/bbctwo
Controller: Jane Root

BBC Three
Television Centre
020 8743 8000
bbcthreefeedback@bbc.co.uk
www.bbc.co.uk/bbcthree
Controller: Stuart Murphy

BBC Four
Room 6239, Television Centre
020 8576 3193
linda.hall@bbc.co.uk
www.bbc.co.uk/bbcfour
Managing editor: Nick Ware;
controller: Roly Keating

CBBC
Television Centre
020 8743 8000
cbbc.online@bbc.co.uk
www.bbc.co.uk/cbbc
Controller: Dorothy Prior

Cbeebies
Television Centre
020 8743 8000
www.bbc.co.uk/cbeebies
Controller: Dorothy Prior

Ceefax
Television Centre
020 8225 7022

BBC America
7475 Wisconsin Avenue, 11th Floor
Bethesda, USA   MD 20814
001 301 347 2222 or 020 8576 3992
bbcamerica@bbc.co.uk
Business Development Manager:
jennifer_bennett@discovery.com
www.bbcamerica.com
Programme executive: Alison
Fredericks

BBC Canada
121 Bloor Street East, Suite 200
Toronto, Ontario, Canada M4W 3M5
00 416 934 7800
feedback@bbccanada.com
www.bbccanada.com

BBC Food
PO Box 5054, London W12 0ZY
020 8433 2221
goodfoodlive@ukfood.tv and
bbcfood@bbc.co.uk
www.bbcfood.com
Editor: David Weiland,
david.weiland@bbc.co.uk

BBC News 24
Television Centre
020 8743 8000
bbcnews24@bbc.co.uk
www.bbc.co.uk/bbcnews24

BBC Parliament
4 Millbank, London SW1P 3JA
020 7973 6216
parliament@bbc.co.uk
www.bbc.co.uk/bbcparliament

BBC Prime
PO Box 5054, London W12 0ZY
020 8433 2221
bbcprime@bbc.co.uk
www.bbcprime.com
Editor: David Weiland,
david.weiland@bbc.co.uk

BBC World
Television Centre
020 8743 8000
bbcworld@bbc.co.uk
www.bbcworld.com
Global programming business
manager: Raymond Marshall,
raymond.marshall.01@bbc.co.uk;
regional commissioning editor:
Narendhra Morar,
narendhra.morar@bbc.co.uk

Lifestyle channels (UK Style, UK Food, UK Bright Ideas)
UKTV, 2nd Floor, Flextech Building
160 Great Portland Street
London W1W 5QA
020 7765 1974
Head of lifestyle: Nick Thorogood;
commissioning executive, UK Style:
Chantal Rutherford-Browne;
commissioning executive, UK Food:
Gareth Williams

Factual channels (UK Horizons, UK History)
UKTV, 2nd Floor, Flextech Building
160 Great Portland Street
London W1W 5QA
020 7765 2043
Head of factual: Charlotte Ashton;
commissioning manager: Andy
Whitman

Entertainment and drama channels (UK Gold, UK Drama)
UKTV, 2nd Floor, Flextech Building
160 Great Portland Street
London W1W 5QA
020 7765 0440
Head of entertainment and drama:
Matt Tombs; channel editor, UK Gold
and UK Drama: Katie Barnard

Commercial ventures

BBC Worldwide
Woodlands, 80 Wood Lane
London W12 0TT
020 8433 2000
www.bbcworldwide.com
Commercial arm: businesses include
distribution, TV channels, magazines,
books, videos, spoken word, music,
DVDs, licensed products, CD-ROMs,
English language teaching, videos for
education and training, interactive
telephony, co-production, library
footage sales, magazine subscription
exhibitions, live events, film and
media monitoring

BBC Ventures Group
020 7765 2938
bbcventuresgroup@bbc.co.uk
Commercial director: David Moody;
head of Press and PR: Alison Jeremy
Wholly owned commercial subsidiary,
comprising BBC Vecta, BBC Broadcast,
BBC Resources and BBC Technology

BBC Resources
08700 100883
bbcresources@bbc.co.uk
www.bbcresources.com
Managing director: Mike Southgate
Production facilities

BBC Costume and Wigs
Victoria Road, London W3 6UL
020 8576 1761
costume@bbc.co.uk;
wigs@bbc.co.uk
www.bbcresources.com

BBC Studios
Television Centre, Wood Lane
London W12 7RJ
020 8576 7666
tvstudio.sales@bbc.co.uk
www.bbcresources.com

BBC Post Production
Television Centre
020 8225 7702
postproduction@bbc.co.uk
www.bbcresources.com

BBC Post Production Bristol
Broadcasting House
White Ladies Road, Bristol BS8 2LR
0117 974 6666
postproduction@bbc.co.uk
www.bbcresources.com

BBC Post Production Birmingham
BBC Pebble Mill
Birmingham B5 7QQ
0121 432 8621
postproduction@bbc.co.uk
www.bbcresources.com

BBC Outside Broadcasts
Kendal Avenue, London W3 0RP
020 8993 9333
ob@bbc.co.uk
www.bbcresources.com

BBC Broadcast
Television Centre
020 8225 6666
bbcbroadcast@bbc.co.uk
www.bbcbroadcast.com
Managing director: Pam Masters
Offers range of play-out and channel
management services across multiple
media platforms; planning to move in
2004 to: Media Village, BBC White
City, 201 Wood Lane, London

BBC Technology
3rd Floor, Brock House
19 Langham Street
London W1 1AA
020 7765 4748
bbctechnology-sales@bbc.co.uk
www.bbctechnology.com
Managing director: Ann Wilson
Offers solutions in media, broadcast
and interactive applications to the
BBC and other companies

BBC Vecta
The Studio, 1 Mortimer Street
London W1T 3JA
020 7765 0850
amanda.harris@bbc.co.uk
www.bbcvecta.com
Managing director: Mark Popkiewicz;
Communications Manager:
Amanda Harris
Represents BBC in commercial
exploitation of rights; works with BBC
Research and Development to bring
developments to market

BBC International Unit
020 8576 1963
international.unit@bbc.co.uk
www.bbc.co.uk/international
Manager: Peter James
Supplies TV facilities to overseas
broadcasters transmitting from UK

BBC Training and Development
35 Marylebone High Street
London W1U 4PX
0870 122 0216
training@bbc.co.uk
www.bbctraining.co.uk
Press contact: Louise Findlay-Wilson;
01993 823011, louise@energypr.co.uk
Training solutions in programme-
making, broadcasting and new media

BBC Training and Development
BBC Elstree, Clarendon Road
Borehamwood, Herts WD6 1JF
0870 122 0216
training@bbc.co.uk
www.bbctraining.co.uk

BBC Training and Development
BBC Wood Norton Training Centre
Evesham, Worcestershire WR11 4YB
0870 122 0216
training@bbc.co.uk
www.bbctraining.co.uk

Advisory bodies

Broadcasting Council for Scotland
The Secretary, Broadcasting House
Queen Margaret Drive
Glasgow G12 8DG

Broadcasting Council for Wales
The Secretary, Broadcasting House
Llandaff, Cardiff CF5 2YQ

Broadcasting Council for Northern Ireland
Head of Public Affairs and Secretary,
Broadcasting House
Ormeau Avenue, Belfast BT2 8HQ

English National Forum
Head of Press and Public Affairs
English Regions
BBC Broadcasting Centre
Pebble Mill Road
Birmingham B5 7QQ

Governors' World Service Consultative Group
World Service, Bush House, Strand
London WC2B 4PH

Central Religious Advisory Committee
The Secretary
Broadcasting House
London W1A 1AA

Television

Controller of daytime:
Alison Sharman
Room 3560, BBC White City
201 Wood Lane
London W12 7TS
daytime.proposals@bbc.co.uk
*Daytime drama, factual and
entertainment on BBC1 and BBC2*

Head of interactive TV
programmes: Scott Gronmark
6th Floor, Bush House, Strand
London WC2B 4PH
020 7557 3064
scott.gronmark@bbc.co.uk
Does not accept proposals

Controller, programme acquisition:
George McGhee

Controller, English regions:
Andy Griffee

Factual and learning

Director of factual and learning:
John Willis

Controller, factual TV:
Glenwyn Benson

Development executive:
Michelle Matherson
Room 3559, BBC White City
201 Wood Lane, London W12 7TS
020 8752 5766
genfact.proposals@bbc.co.uk
*All areas of documentaries and
contemporary factual*

Executive editor, children's
education: Karen Johnson
Room 3416, BBC White City
020 8752 5241

Head of current affairs:
Peter Horrocks
Room 1172, BBC White City
020 8752 7005
peter.horrocks@bbc.co.uk

Head of independent
commissioning, specialist factual,
current affairs and arts:
Adam Kemp
Room 4631, BBC White City
020 8752 6764
specfact.proposals@bbc.co.uk

Head of Lifeskills TV: Seetha Kumar
Room 2308, BBC White City
020 8752 4574
seetha.kumar@bbc.co.uk

Series editor, documentaries:
Todd Austin
Room 5503, BBC White City
020 8752 6608
todd.austin@bbc.co.uk
*Responsible for new BBC1
documentary strand*

Series editor, Arena: Anthony Wall
Room 2168, BBC White City
020 8752 5172

Editor, Correspondent:
Karen O'Connor
Room 1362, BBC White City

Creative director, Everyman
(strand): Ruth Pitt
Room 5048, BBC Manchester
Broadcasting House, Oxford Road
Manchester M60 1SJ
0161 244 3321
ruth.pitt@bbc.co.uk

Editor, Horizon: Matthew Barrett
Room 4523, BBC White City
020 8752 6134
horizon@bbc.co.uk

Executive producer of arts, editor of
Imagine strand: Claire Lewis
Arts Department, 2nd Floor
BBC White City
020 8752 4092
claire.lewis.02@bbc.co.uk

Editor, The Natural World:
Mike Gunton
BBC Natural History Unit
Broadcasting House
Whiteladies Road, Bristol BS8 2LR
0117 974 2413

Editor, Panorama: Mike Robinson
Room 1118, BBC White City
020 8752 7152
mike.robinson@bbc.co.uk

Executive producer, Money
programme: Clive Edwards
Room 4116, BBC White City
020 8752 7400

Commissioning editor, Storyville:
Nick Fraser
Room 201, 1 Mortimer Street
London W1T 3JA
020 7765 5211
storyville@bbc.co.uk

Editor, Timewatch: John Farren
Room 3150, BBC White City
020 8752 7079

Executive editor, Wild (strand):
Fiona Pitcher
BBC Natural History Unit
Broadcasting House
Whiteladies Road, Bristol BS8 2LR
0117 974 7403

Editor, Wildlife on One: Sara Ford
BBC Natural History Unit
Broadcasting House
Whiteladies Road, Bristol BS8 2LR
0117 974 6696

*Factual and learning: Scotland,
Wales and Northern Ireland*

Editor, education, Scotland:
Moira Scott
Room 230, BBC Scotland
Queen Margaret Drive
Glasgow G12 8DG
0141 338 1507
moira.scott@bbc.co.uk

Head of factual programmes,
Wales: Adrian Davies
Room 4020, BBC Wales
Broadcasting House,
Llantrisant Road, Cardiff CF5 2YQ
02920 322976

Head of arts, Wales:
Paul Islwyn Thomas
Room 4001, BBC Wales
Broadcasting House
Llantrisant Road, Cardiff CF5 2YQ
02920 322943
paul.islwyn.thomas@bbc.co.uk

Head of education and learning,
Wales: Dr Eleri Wyn Lewis
Room E3106, BBC Wales
Broadcasting House
Llantrisant Road, Cardiff CF5 2YQ
02920 322834

106

Editor, network factual, NI:
Eamon Hardy
Room C402, Centre House
56 Wood Lane, London W12 7SB
020 8576 7045
eamon.hardy@bbc.co.uk

Editor, learning, NI: Kieran Hegarty
Education Unit, First Floor
BBC Northern Ireland
Broadcasting House
Ormeau Avenue, Belfast BT2 8HQ
02890 338445
kieran.hegarty@bbc.co.uk

Head of factual and learning, NI:
Bruce Batten
2nd Floor, BBC Northern Ireland
Broadcasting House
Ormeau Avenue, Belfast BT2 8HQ
02890 338207

Drama and entertainment

Director of drama, entertainment
and CBBC:
Alan Yentob

Controller, commissioning, drama:
Jane Tranter

Controller, commissioning,
entertainment:
Jane Lush

Head of drama commissioning:
Gareth Neame
Room D313, Centre House
56 Wood Lane, London W12 7SB
020 8576 4935
Responsible for peak-time drama from
independent production companies/
writers, all channels

Executive producer and head of
development: Tracey Scoffield
BBC Films
1 Mortimer Street, London W1T 3JA
020 7765 0475
Responsible for BBC films

Head of BBC Films: David Thompson
BBC Films
1 Mortimer Street, London W1T 3JA
020 7765 0251
Responsible for BBC films

Head of television, classical music
and performance: Peter Maniura
Room EG09, BBC TV Centre
Wood Lane, London W12 7RJ
020 8895 6541
Responsible for classical music and
performance (incl BBC 4 performance)

Head of comedy and entertainment,
Scotland: Mike Bolland
Room 3167, BBC Scotland
Queen Margaret Drive
Glasgow G12 8DG
0141 338 2370
Responsible for Scotland (comedy and
entertainment)

Head of television drama, Scotland:
Barbara McKissack
Room 2170, BBC Scotland
Queen Margaret Drive
Glasgow G12 8DG
0141 338 2517
Responsible for Scotland (drama and
films)

Head of factual programmes,
Scotland: Andrea Miller
Room 3178, BBC Scotland
Queen Margaret Drive
Glasgow G12 8DG
0141 338 3646
andrea.miller.01@bbc.co.uk
Responsible for Scotland (factual)

Head of music, Wales:
David Jackson
Room E4113, BBC Wales
Broadcasting House
Llantrisant Road, Cardiff CF5 2YQ
02920 322111
davidm.jackson@bbc.co.uk
Responsible for classical music/
Performance outside M25 and Wales
(entertainment)

Head of drama, Wales:
Julie Gardner
Room E2106, BBC Wales
Broadcasting House
Llantrisant Road, Cardiff CF5 2YQ
02920 322935
Responsible for Wales (drama and
films)

Head of entertainment, events and
sport, NI: Mike Edgar
Room 229, BBC Northern Ireland
Broadcasting House
Ormeau Avenue, Belfast BT2 8HQ
02890 338375
mike.edgar@bbc.co.uk
Responsible for Northern Ireland
(entertainment and events)

Head of drama, NI: Robert Cooper
Room C403, Centre House
56 Wood Lane, London W12 7SB
020 8576 1664
Responsible for Northern Ireland
(drama and films)

CBBC

Head of CBBC drama:
Elaine Sperber
Room T210, Threshold House
65–69 Shepherds Bush Green
London W12 8TX
020 8576 8245
Responsible for CBBC drama

Head of entertainment, CBBC:
Anne Gilchrist
Room T508, Threshold House
65–69 Shepherds Bush Green
London W12 8TX
020 8225 9269
Responsible for CBBC entertainment

Head of CBBC news and factual
programmes: Roy Milani
Room E111, BBC TV Centre
Wood Lane, London W12 7RJ
020 8576 3118
Responsible for CBBC news and
factual programmes

Head of pre-school, CBBC:
Clare Elstow
Room N105, Neptune House
BBC Elstree, Clarendon Road
Borehamwood, Herts WD6 1JF
020 8228 7072
Responsible for CBBC pre-school

Head of acquisitions and
co-productions, CBBC:
Theresa Plummer Andrews
Room 360 DB, BBC TV Centre
Wood Lane, London W12 7RJ
020 8576 1105
Responsible for CBBC animation and
live action acquisitions

Head of CBBC Scotland:
Claire Mundell
Room 4177, BBC Scotland
Queen Margaret Drive
Glasgow G12 8DG
0141 338 2007
claire.mundell@bbc.co.uk
Responsible for CBBC Scotland

Nations and regions

Network development, nations and
regions: Colin Cameron
Room 3187, BBC Scotland
Queen Margaret Drive
Glasgow G12 8DG
0141 338 2424
colin.cameron@bbc.co.uk
All genres in Northern Ireland,
Scotland and Wales supplying
programmes to network television

Sport

Head of new media, sports
news and development:
Andrew Thompson
Room 5060, BBC TV Centre
Wood Lane, London W12 7RJ
020 8225 8400
andrew.thompson.01@bbc.co.uk
Responsible for live and highlight
sport event coverage

ITV

200 Grays Inn Road
London WC1X 8HF
020 7843 8000
info@itv.com
www.itv.com

*Director of programmes: Nigel
Pickard; director of programme
strategy, ITV1 and ITV2: David Bergg;
controller of news, current affairs, arts
and religion: Steve Anderson;
controller, factual: Bridget Boseley;
controller, daytime: Liam Hamilton;
controller, network children's and
youth programmes: Steven Andrew;
head of CITV programming: Estelle
Hughes; controller, network drama:
Nick Elliot; controller, network
acquisitions: Jeremy Boulton;
controller, network entertainment:
Claudia Rosencrantz; controller,
comedy: Sioned Wiliam; controller,
sport: Brian Barwick; head of
programmes, ITV2: Daniela
Neumann*

ITV Press Office

200 Grays Inn Road
London WC1X 8HF
020 7843 8218
caroline_heap@itv.co.uk

ITV Interactive

200 Grays Inn Road
London WC1X 8HF
020 7843 8000
*ITV Interactive controller: Jane
Marshall; head of creative and
content: Andrew Kearney; head of
technology: Clive Malcher*

ITV2

200 Grays Inn Road
London WC1X 8HF
020 7843 8000
dutyoffice2@itv2.co.uk
www.itv.com/itv2

ITV News

200 Grays Inn Road
London WC1X 8XZ
020 7833 3000
itvplanning@itn.co.uk
www.itv.com/news

Anglia Television

Anglia House, Norwich NR1 3JG
01603 615151
anglianews@angliatv.com
www.angliatv.com
*Managing director: Graham
Creelman; controller of programmes:
Neil Thompson; head of network
factual programmes: Andrea Cornes;
head of news: Guy Adams
Granada Enterprises Channels (East),
address as above;
Tel: 020 7396 6393*

Border Television

The Television Centre
Carlisle, Cumbria CA1 3NT
01228 525101
btv@granadamedia.com
www.border-tv.com
*Managing director: Douglas Merrall;
controller of programmes: Neil
Robinson; head of news: Ian
Proniewicz
Granada Enterprises Channels
(Border), address as above,
tel: 01228 829213; email:
peter.fergusson@granadamedia.com*

Carlton content

35–38 Portman Square
London W1H 6NU
020 7486 6688
dutyoffice@carltontv.co.uk
*Chief executive: Rupert Dilnott-
Cooper; director of programmes: Steve
Hewlett; director of drama and co-
production: Jonathan Powell; director
of factual programmes: Richard
Clemmow; controller of light
entertainment: Mark Wells; controller
of factual entertainment: Nick Bullen;
controller of children's and young
people's programmes: David Mercer;
controller of sport: Gary Newbon*

Carlton Television London

101 St Martins Lane
London WC2N 4AZ
020 7240 4000
dutyoffice@carltontv.co.uk
www.carltontv.co.uk
*Managing director: Coleena Reid;
head of regional programmes: Emma
Barker
Carlton UK Sales, 101 St Martins
Lane, London, WC2N 4RF;
tel: 020 7240 4000; email:
gary.digby@carltontv.co.uk*

Carlton Television Central

Central Court, Gas Street
Birmingham B1 2JT
0121 643 9898
dutyoffice@carltontv.co.uk
www.carltontv.co.uk
*Managing director: Ian Squires; head
of regional programmes: Duncan
Rycroft
Carlton Sales (east, west and south
Midlands), address as above;
tel: 0121 643 9898; email:
denver.logan@carltontv.co.uk*

Carlton Television Westcountry

Langage Science Park, Plymouth
Devon PL7 5BQ
01752 333333
dutyoffice@carltontv.co.uk
www.carltontv.co.uk
*Managing director: Mark Haskell;
director of programmes: Jane
McCloskey; controller of features and
programme development: Caroline
Righton; controller of news: Phil
Carrodus
Carlton Sales (South-west), address as
above; Tel: 01752 333311, email:
andy.smallwood@carltontv.co.uk*

Channel Television

Television Centre
La Pouquelaye Road, St Helier
Jersey JE1 3ZD
01534 816816
broadcast@channeltv.co.uk
www.channeltv.co.uk
*Managing director: Michael Lucas;
director of programmes: Karen
Rankine; news editor: Allan Watts
Channel TV, address as above;
Tel: 01534 816777; email:
airtimesales@channeltv.co.uk*

Grampian Television

Queens Cross, Aberdeen AB15 4XJ
01224 848848
grampian.newsroom@smg.plc.uk
www.grampiantv.co.uk
*Managing director and controller
of programmes: Derrick Thomson;
news editor: Henry Eagles;
head of sport: Tyrone Smith
Carlton Media Sales (Grampian),
address as above; Tel: 01224 848848;
email: gavin.fairweather@smg.plc.uk*

Granada Television

Quay Street, Manchester M60 9EA
0161 832 7211
Granadainfo@granadamedia.com
www.granadatv.com
*Managing director: Brenda Smith;
director of regional affairs: Jane Luca
David Croft, address as above;
Tel: 0161 827 2227; email:
david.croft@granadamedia.com*

GMTV

Television Centre, London SE1 9TT
020 7827 7000
talk2us@gmtv.co.uk
www.gm.tv
*Managing director: Paul Corley;
director of programmes: Peter
McHugh
GMTV, address as above;
Tel: 020 7827 7000;
email: brook.saunders@gmtv.co.uk*

HTVCymru/Wales

TV Centre, Culverhouse Cross
Cardiff CF5 6XJ
02920 590590
news@itvwales.com
www.htvwales.com
*Controller: Owen Elis; head of factual:
Bruce Kennedy; head of news: John G
Williams
Carlton Media Sales (Cardiff), address
as above; Tel: 02920 590294; email:
gareth.stockdale@htv-wales.co.uk*

HTV West

Television Centre, Bath Road
Bristol BS4 3HG
0117 972 2722
htvnews@htv-west.co.uk
www.htv-west.co.uk
*Controller of programmes: Jane
McCloskey; head of features and
current affairs: James Garrett;
head of news: Steve Egginton
Carlton Media Sales, address as above;
contact: Jeremy Payne*

London Weekend Television
London Television Centre
London SE1 9LT
020 7620 1620
www.lwt.co.uk
Managing director: Christy Swords;
deputy director of broadcasting:
Geraldine Woods; director of factual:
Jim Allen; project director of
operations: Max Graesser
Granada Enterprises Channels,
200 Grays Inn Road, London,
WC1X 8XZ; Tel: 020 7396 6000;
email:
andy.farwell@granadamedia.com

Meridian Television
Television Centre, Southampton
Hants SO14 OPZ
02380 222555
news@meridiantv.com
www.meridian.tv.co.uk
Managing director: Lindsay
Charlton; controller of news: Andy
Cooper; controller of regional
programmes: Mark Southgate
Granada Enterprises Channels
(Southampton), address as above;
Tel: 02380 712012; email:
charlotte.bell@granadamedia.com

Scottish Television
200 Renfield Street
Glasgow G2 3PR
0141 300 3000
scotlandtoday@smg.plc.uk
www.scottishtv.co.uk
Chief executive: Donald Emslie;
Managing director: Sandy Ross; head
of factual: Agnes Wilkie; head of news:
Paul McKinney; head of sport: Andrea
Brownlie; head of PR: Nik McHugh
Carlton UK Sales, 101 St Martins
Lane, London, WC2N 4RF;
tel: 020 7240 4000; email:
gary.digby@carltontv.co.uk

Tyne Tees Television
Television Centre, City Road
Newcastle Upon Tyne NE1 2AL
0191 261 0181
tyne.tees@granadamedia.com
www.tynetees.tv
Managing director: Margaret Fay;
controller of programmes: Graeme
Thomson; managing editor, news:
Graham Marples
Granada Enterprises Channels
(North East), address as above;
Tel: 0191 269 3888; email:
alastair.gibson@granadamedia.com

Ulster Television (UTV)
Ormeau Road, Belfast BT7 1EB
02890 328122
newsroom@utvplc.com
www.u.tv
Group chief executive: John McCann;
head of news and current affairs: Rob
Morrison; director of television: Alan
Bremner
Granada Enterprises Channels,
200 Grays Inn Road, London,
WC1X 8XZ; Tel: 020 7396 6393;
email:
andy.farwell@granadamedia.com

Yorkshire Television
TV Centre, Kirkstall Road
Leeds LS3 1JS
0113 243 8283
calendar@yorkshiretv.com
www.yorkshiretv.com
Managing director: David Croft;
controller of programmes: Clare
Morrow; head of factual: Jeff
Anderson; head of news: Will Venters
Granada Enterprises Channels
(Yorkshire), address as above;
Tel: 0113 2228312; email:
jane.webster@granadamedia.com

Channel 4

Channel 4
124 Horseferry Road
London SW1P 2TX
020 7306 8333
www.channel4.com

Director of programmes: Kevin Lygo;
head of documentaries: Peter Dale;
editor, independent film and video:
Jess Search; head of drama:
John Yorke; head of programmes,
E4: Andrew Newman; head of
entertainment, controller of E4:
Danielle Lux; head of entertainment:
John McHugh; head of comedy
and comedy films: Caroline Leddy;
head of daytime: Jo McGrath;
head of FilmFour: Tessa Ross;
managing director, 4Learning:
Heather Rabbatts; managing editor,
interactive: Andy Grumbridge;
head of news and current affairs:
Dorothy Byrne; controller of
programme acquisition: June
Dromgoole; head of series
(C4 and E4): Jay Kandola;
head of sport: David Kerr
Channel 4, address as above;
Tel: 020 7306 5491

Press office
124 Horseferry Road
London SW1P 2TX
020 7396 4444
press-front-desk@channel4.co.uk
www.channel4.com

Channel 4 News
200 Grays Inn Road
London WC1X 8XZ
020 7833 3000
C4home@itn.co.uk
www.channel4.com/news

S4C
Parc Ty Glas, Llanishen
Cardiff CF14 5DU
029 2074 7444
hotline@s4c.co.uk
www.s4c.co.uk
Director of programmes: Iona Jones;
director of channel management:
Emlyn Penny Jones; director of
animation: Chris Grace;
commissioning editor, factual
programmes: Cenwyn Edwards

S4C
Parc Ty Glas, Llanishen
Cardiff CF14 5DU
Press: 029 2074 1451
hannah.thomas@s4c.co.uk
contact: Hannah Thomas

E4
124 Horseferry Road
London SW1P 2TX
Press: 020 7396 4444
dot4@channel4.co.uk;
customer.service@e4.com
www.channel4.com/e4
Head of programming: Murray
Boland

FilmFour
124 Horseferry Road
London SW1P 2TX
020 7396 4444
editorialissues@filmfour.com
www.filmfour.com
Head of film: Tessa Ross

Five

five
22 Long Acre, London WC2E 9LY
020 7550 5555
dutyoffice@five.tv
www.five.tv

*Controller of factual: Dan Chambers;
controller of sport: Robert Charles;
controller of drama: Corinne
Hollinworth; controller of
entertainment: Andrew Newman;
controller of children's programmes:
Nick Wilson; controller of factual
entertainment: Sue Murphy;
controller of daytime, arts and
religion: Kim Peat; director of
broadcasting: Ashley Hill; head of
planning and acquisitions: Jane
Dorman; controller of broadcast
services: David Burge; head of
broadcast strategy: Paul Mortimer;
director of acquisitions: Jeff Ford;
senior programme controller, news
and current affairs: Chris Shaw;
controller of interactive, youth and
music: Sham Sandhu
Five, address as above; Tel: 020 7550
5551; head of sales: Nick Milligan;
email: nick.milligan@five.tv*

five news
ITN, 200 Gray's Inn Road
London WC1X
020 7430 4100
simon.fordham@itn.co.uk
News editor: Simon Fordham

five press office
22 Long Acre, London WC2E 9LY
020 7550 5558
paul.leather@five.tv
Head of press: Paul Leather

five Interactive
22 Long Acre, London WC2E 9LY
020 7550 5532
elin.parry@five.tv
Online manager: Elin Parry

ITN

ITN
200 Grays Inn Road
London WC1X 8XZ
020 7833 3000
editor@itn.co.uk
www.itn.co.uk

*Chief executive: Mark Wood;
editor, ITV News: David Mannion;
Editor, Channel 4 News: Jim Gray;
editor, five news: Gary Rogers;
chief editor, ITN radio: Nicholas
Wheeler
produces news and factual
programmes for television, radio
and new media platforms, both in
Britain and overseas; jointly owned
by Carlton Communications,
Granada, Daily Mail and General
Trust, United Business Media and
Reuters; provides news for ITV,
the ITV News Channel, Channel 4,
five, and Independent Radio News
(IRN); manages the ITN Archive*

RTÉ

Radio Telefís Éireann
New Library Building
Donnybrook, Dublin 4
Ireland
00 353 1 208 3111
info@rte.ie
www.rte.ie
Irish national broadcaster

Satellite

Multichannel

BSkyB
British Sky Broadcasting Group
Grant Way, Isleworth TW7 5QD
020 7705 3000
www.sky.com
*Chief executive: Tony Ball; chief
financial officer: Martin Stewart;
managing director, Sky Networks:
Dawn Airey; managing director,
Sky Interactive and director, sales and
marketing: Jon Florsheim; chief
operating officer: Richard
Freudenstein; director of
communications and corporate
affairs: Julian Eccles*

Sky Interactive
skydigital@sky.com
www.sky.com
*Operations and design director:
Gerry O'Sullivan*

Sky channels

The Amp
020 7705 3000
skydigital@sky.com
www.sky.com

Sky Bet
020 7705 3000
help@skybet.com
www.skybet.com
Managing director, Sky Bet: Nick Rust

Sky One
020 7705 3000
skydigital@sky.com
www.skyone.co.uk
Controller: Sara Ramsden

Sky News
020 7705 3000
skydigital@sky.com
www.skynews.co.uk
Head of Sky News: Nick Pollard

Sky Travel
020 7705 3000
skydigital@sky.com
www.skytravel.co.uk
*General manager, Sky Travel:
Delia Bushell*

Sky Sports 1, 2, 3, Extra
020 7705 3000
skydigital@sky.com
www.skysports.com
*Managing director, Sky Sports:
Vic Wakeling*

Sky Movies Premier (x5)
020 7705 3000
skydigital@sky.com
www.skymovies.com
*Director of film channels and
acquisitions: Sophie Turner Laing*

Flaunt
020 7705 3000
skydigital@sky.com
www.sky.com

Scuzz
020 7705 3000
skydigital@sky.com
www.sky.com

Cable
- -

NTL UK
NTL House
Bartley Wood Business Park,
Bartley Way, Hook
Hampshire RG27 9UP
01256 752000
www.ntl.com
Managing director, NTL Home: Aizad Hussain; managing director, NTL Business: Tom Bennie

NTL Corporate Press Office
NTL House
Bartley Wood Business Park,
Bartley Way, Hook
Hampshire RG27 9UP
020 7746 4096
contact: Justine Parrish

NTL Broadcast
Crawley Court, Winchester
Hampshire SO21 2QA
01962 822400
www.ntlbroadcast.com
Managing director: Peter Douglas

NTL Broadcast Press Office
Crawley Court, Winchester
Hampshire SO21 2QA
01962 822582
Bruce Randall

Telewest Communications
Genesis Business Park
Albert Drive, Woking
Surrey GU21 5RW
01483 750900;
press office: 020 7299 5888,
        01483 582716;
investor relations: 020 7299 5571
www.telewest.co.uk
Managing director: Charles Burdick; director of corporate communications: Jane Hardman

Cablecom Investments
Surtees House, The Market Place
Mildenhall IP28 7EF
01345 222532
customer@cablecom.co.uk
www.cablecom.co.uk
Managing director Charles Tompkins

Elmsdale Media (Yes Television)
16 Grosvenor Street
Mayfair, London W1K 4QF
020 7907 5600
www.yestelevision.com
contact: Graeme Leversedge

Omne Telecommunications
Centenary Road
Riverside Business Park
Irvine, North Ayrshire KA11 5DP
01294 230000
contact: Alex Jennings

Stockwhiz
c/o Ashurst Morris Crisp
Broadwalk House, 5 Appold House
London EC2A 2HA
020 7972 7310
contact: Tony Ghee

Video Networks
205 Holland Park Avenue
London W11 4XB
020 7348 4000
info@videonetworks.com
www.videonetworks.com/
contact: Andy Swann

WightCable
56 Love Lane, Cowes
Isle of Wight PO31 7EU
01983 242424
enquiries@wightcable.com
www.iowctc.co.uk
Chief operating officer: Sandra Ayres; installation/construction Manager: Malcolm Anley; network operations manager: Peter Williams

Digital terrestrial

Freeview
2nd Floor, 85 Tottenham Court Road
London W1T 4DU
020 7765 1149
www.freeview.co.uk
General manager: Matthew Seaman. DTT Platform for Crown Castle, BBC and BSkyB

Crown Castle UK
PO Box 98, Warwick CV34 6TN
01926 416211
MarketingUK@crowncastle.com;
Communications.Department@
        crowncastle.com
www.crowncastle.com
Aims to set technical standards for implementation of digital terrestrial television

The Digital Television Group
7 Old Lodge Place, St Margarets
Twickenham TW1 1RQ
020 8891 1830
office@dtg.org.uk
www.dtg.org.uk
International industry-led consortium

The Digital Video Broadcasting Project (DVB)
Project Office, 17a Ancienne Route
CH-1218 Grand Saconnex, Geneva
Switzerland
+41 22 717 2719
dvb@dvb.org
www.dvb.org
Not-for-profit international association

DigiTAG (Digital Terrestrial Television Action Group)
17a Ancienne Route
CH-1218 Grand Saconnex, Geneva
Switzerland
+41 22 717 2716
projectoffice@digitag.org
www.digitag.org

Department for Culture, Media and Sport
2–4 Cockspur Street
London SW1Y 5DH
020 7215 5974/1/8
enquiries@culture.gov.uk;
broadcasting@culture.gov.uk;
digitaltelevision@culture.gov.uk
www.digitaltelevision.gov.uk and
www.culture.gov.uk/broadcasting

Department for Trade and Industry
151 Buckingham Palace Road
London SW1W 9SS
020 7215 5974/1/8
dti.enquiries@dti.gsi.gov.uk;
digitaltelevision@culture.gov.uk
www.digitaltelevision.gov.uk and
www.dti.gov.uk/industries
        /broadcasting
David Fuhr, Digital Television; Anthony Segal, Broadcasting Policy; Ian Dixon, Broadcasting Technology Joint venture between BBC, Crown Castle and BSkyB

TV channels

Adventure One
Grant Way, Isleworth TW7 5QD
020 7705 3000
www.nationalgeographic.co.uk
General manager UK operations:
Jane Larner; head of operations:
Stephanie Holm

Afro-Caribbean Channel
28 Lawrence Road
London N15 4EG
020 8809 7700
vernon.king@btinternet.com

The Amp
Grant Way, Isleworth TW7 5QD
020 7705 3000
skydigital@sky.com
www.sky.com
Managing director, Sky Networks:
Dawn Airey

Apna TV
42 Theobalds Road
London WC1X 8NW
020 7831 2525
info@apnatv.freeserve.co.uk
www.apnatv.com

Artsworld
80 Silverthorne Road
London SW8 3XA
020 7819 1160
info@artsworld.com and
press@artsworld.com
www.artsworld.com
Managing director: John Hambley;
Programme controller: Alison Martin

Asia Net
24–28 Fournier Street
London E1 6QE
020 7247 2202
karamjitasianet@netscapeonline.co.uk

At The Races
11–13 Charlotte Street
London W17 1RH
0870 7871000
team@attheraces.co.uk
www.attheraces.co.uk
Managing director: Sir Iain Hogg;
Head of betting: David Stewart

B4U
Transputec House
19 Heather Park Drive
Wembley HA0 1SS
020 8795 7171
b4u@b4unetwork.com
www.b4utv.com

B4U Music
Transputec House
19 Heather Park Drive
Wembley HA0 1SS
020 8795 7171
sajnit@b4unetwork.com
www.b4utv.com

BBC Choice
Room 2021, Television Centre
Wood Lane, London W12 7RJ
020 8743 8000
gabriel.campbell@bbc.co.uk
www.bbc.co.uk

BBC Four
Room 6239, Television Centre
Wood Lane, London W12 7RJ
020 8576 3193
linda.hall@bbc.co.uk
www.bbc.co.uk/bbcfour

BBC News 24
Television Centre, Wood Lane
London W12 7RJ
020 8743 8000
bbcnews24@bbc.co.uk
www.bbc.co.uk/bbcnews24

BBC One
Television Centre, Wood Lane
London W12 7RJ
020 8743 8000
www.bbc.co.uk/bbcone

BBC Parliament
4 Millbank, London SW1P 3JA
020 7973 6216
parliament@bbc.co.uk
www.bbc.co.uk/bbcparliament

BBC Three
Television Centre, Wood Lane
London W12 7RJ
020 8743 8000
bbcthreefeedback@bbc.co.uk
www.bbc.co.uk/bbcthree

BBC Two
Television Centre, Wood Lane
London W12 7RJ
020 8743 8000
www.bbc.co.uk/bbctwo

BBC World
Television Centre, Wood Lane
London W12 7RJ
020 8743 8000
newsdesk: 020 8624 9003
bbcworld@bbc.co.uk
www.bbcworld.com
Global programming business
manager: Raymond Marshall,
raymond.marshall.01@bbc.co.uk;
regional commissioning editor:
Narendhra Morar,
narendhra.morar@bbc.co.uk

Biography Channel
Grant Way, Isleworth TW7 5QD
0870 240 3000
contact@thebiographychannel.co.uk
www.thebiographychannel.co.uk
Managing director: Geoff Metzger;
head of on air: Terry Yetton; head of
programming: Richard Melman

Bloomberg Television
City Gate House
39–45 Finsbury Square
London EC2A 1PQ
020 7330 7797
www.bloomberg.co.uk/tv

Boomerang
Turner House
16 Great Marlborough Street
London W1F 7HS
020 7693 1000
toon.pressoffice@turner.com
www.cartoonnetwork.co.uk

The Box
Mappin House, 4 Winsley Street
London W1W 8HF
020 7436 1515
Kkirsty.lawrence@emap.com
www.emap.com

Bravo
Flextech Television
160 Great Portland Street
London W1W 5QA
020 7299 5000
jaqueline_lewis@flextech.co.uk
www.bravo.co.uk

British Eurosport
Lacon House, 84 Theobalds Road
London WC1X 8RW
020 7468 7777
mguy@eurosport.co.uk
www.eurosport.co.uk

Cartoon Network
Turner Broadcasting System Europe
  Ltd, 16 Great Marlborough Street
London W1F 7HP
020 7693 1000
toon.pressoffice@turner.com
www.cartoonnetwork.co.uk

CBBC
Television Centre, Wood Lane
London W12 7RJ
020 8743 8000
cbbc.online@bbc.co.uk
www.bbc.co.uk/cbeebies

Cbeebies
Television Centre, Wood Lane
London W12 7RJ
020 8743 8000
www.bbc.co.uk/cbbc

Challenge
Flextech Television
160 Great Portland Street
London W1W 5QA
020 7299 5000
jess_alder@flextech
www.challengetv.co.uk

Channel Health
6th Floor 10 Wardour Street
Swiss Centre, London W1D 6QF
020 7758 3200
cwalsh@channelhealth.tv
www.channelhealth.tv

Chelsea TV
Stamford Bridge, Fulham Road
London SW6 1HS
020 7915 1980
chelseatv@chelseafc.com
www.chelseafc.com
Managing director: Chris Tate

Chinese Channel
Teddington Studios, Broom Road
Teddington TW11 9NT
020 8614 8364
editor@news.chinese-channel.co.uk
www.chinese-channel.co.uk

CNBC Europe
10 Fleet Place, London EC4M 7QS
020 7653 9300
CBlenkinsop@cnbceurope.com
www.cnbceurope.com

CNN
Turner Broadcasting System Europe
    Ltd, Turner House
16 Great Marlborough Street
London W1F 7HS
020 7693 0942
suki.johal@turner.com
http:edition.cnn.com

CNN
One CNN Center, Atlanta GA 30348
USA
+1 404 827 1500
cnn@cnn.com
www.cnn.com
News network.

The Community Channel
3–7 Euston Centre
Regent's Place, London NW1 3JG
020 7874 7626
planningdesk@
    communitychannel.org
www.communitychannel.org

Discovery Animal Planet
160 Great Portland Street
London W1W 5QA
020 7462 3600
becky_weathers@
    discovery-europe.com
www.discoverychannel.co.uk

Discovery Channel
160 Great Portland Street
London W1W 5QA
020 7462 3600
lee_hobbs@discovery-eurpope.com
www.discoverychannel.co.uk

Discovery Civilisation
160 Great Portland Street
London W1W 5QA
020 7462 3600
jo_march@discovery-europe.com
www.discoverychannel.co.uk

Discovery Health
160 Great Portland Street
London W1N 5QA
020 7462 3600
clare_howdle@
    discovery-europe.com
www.discoverychannel.co.uk

Discovery Home and Leisure
160 Great Portland Street
London W1N 5QA
020 7462 3600
penny_crook@
    discovery-europe.com
www.discoverychannel.co.uk

Discovery Kids
160 Great Portland Street
London W1N 5QA
020 7462 3600
jo_march@discoveryeurope.com
www.discoverychannel.co.uk

Discovery Science
160 Great Portland Street
London W1N 5QA
020 7462 3600
becky_weathers@
    discovery-europe.com
www.discoverychannel.co.uk

Discovery Travel and Adventure
160 Great Portland Street
London W1N 5QA
020 7462 3600
jo_march@discovery-europe.com
www.discoverychannel.co.uk

Discovery Wings
160 Great Portland Street
London W1N 5QA
020 7462 3600
becky_weathers@
    discovery-europe.com
www.discoverychannel.co.uk

Disney Channel
Beaumont House, Avonmore Road
London W14 8TS
020 7605 2401
tdc_talk@studio.disney.com
www.disneychannel.co.uk

E4
124 Horseferry Road
London SW1P 2TX
020 7396 4444
dot4@channel4.co.uk;
customer.service@e4.com
www.channel4.com/e4
*Head of programming: Murray
Boland*

Einstein TV
The Picture House, 4 Lower Park Row
Bristol BS1 5BJ
0117 927 7473
zena.howard@einstein.tv
www.einstein.tv

Eurosport
Lacon House, 84 Theobalds Road
London WC1X 8RW
020 7468 7777
comheadoffice@eurosport.co.uk
www.eurosport.co.uk

Eurosportnews
Lacon House, 84 Theobalds Road
London WC1X 8RW
020 7468 7777
comheadoffice@eurosport.co.uk
www.eurosport.co.uk

Extreme Sports Channel
131–151 Titchfield Street
London W1W 5BB
020 7886 0770
info@extremeinternational.com
www.extreme.com

Fantasy Channel
Suite 14 Burlington House
Saviours Road, St Helier
Jersey JE2 4LA
01534 703700
pfarrell@nasnet.je

Filmfour
124 Horseferry Road
London SW1P 2TX
020 7396 4444
editorialissues@filmfour.com
www.filmfour.com
Head of film: Tessa Ross

Flaunt
Grant Way, Isleworth TW7 5QD
020 7705 3000
skydigital@sky.com
www.sky.com
*Managing director, Sky Networks:
Dawn Airey
Launched in April 2003, this music
channel features a mix of chart music,
fashion, celebrities and gossip aimed
at a core audience of streetwise, fashion
conscious girls aged 13–16*

FTN
160 Great Portland Street
London W1W 5QA
0870 043 4141
enquiries@ftn.tv
www.ftn.tv

God digital
Crown House, Borough Road
Sunderland SR1 1HW
0191 568 0800
info@god.tv
www.GOD.tv.

Granada Men and Motors
Franciscan Court, 16 Hatfields
London SE1 8DJ
020 7578 4040
sophia.ellis@gsb.co.uk
www.menandmotors.co.uk
*Director of programming: Gary
Shoefield*

Granada Plus
Franciscan Court, 16 Hatfields
London SE1 8DJ
020 7578 4040/ 4218
sophia.ellis@gsb.co.uk
www.plustv.co.uk
*Director of programming: Gary
Shoefield*

Hallmark
234a Kings Road, London SW3 5UA
020 7368 9100
info@hallmarkchannel.co.uk
www.hallmarkchannel.co.uk

The History Channel
Grant Way, Isleworth TW7 5QD
020 7705 3000
feedback@thehistorychannel.co.uk
www.thehistorychannel.co.uk
General manager: Geoff Metzger

Hits Channel
Mappin House, 4 Winsley Street
London W1W 8HF
020 7436 1515
david_young@thebox.co.uk
www.emap.com

ITV2
200 Grays Inn Road
London WC1X 8HF
020 7843 8000
dutyoffice2@itv2.co.uk
www.itv.com/itv2

ITV News
200 Grays Inn Road
London WC1X 8XZ
020 7833 3000
itvplanning@itn.co.uk
www.itv.com/news

Kerrang TV
Mappin House, 4 Winsley Street
London W1W 8HF
020 7436 1515
david_young@thebox.co.uk
www.emap.com

Kiss TV
Mappin House, 4 Winsley Street
London W1W 8HF
020 7476 1313
david_young@thebox.co.uk

Living
160 Great Portland Street
London W1W 5QA
020 7299 5000
julie_wells@flextech.co.uk
www.livingtv.co.uk

Magic TV
Mappin House, 4 Winsley Street
London W1W 8HP
020 7436 1515
david_young@thebox.co.uk
www.emap.com

MTV Dance
17–29 Hawley Crescent
London NW1 8TT
020 7284 6348
curlewis.samantha@mtvne.com
www.mtv.co.uk/dance

MTV Networks Europe
180 Oxford Street
London W1D 1DS
020 7284 7777
pressinfo@mtvne.com
http://mtv-europe.com

MTV2
17–29 Hawley Crescent
London NW1 8TT
020 7284 6348
curlewis.samantha@mtvne.com
www.mtv2europe.co.uk

Music Choice Europe
Fleet House
57–61 Clerkenwell Road
London EC1M 5AR
020 7014 8700
feedback@musicchoice.co.uk
www.musicchoice.co.uk
*Managing director: Margo Daly;
director of music and marketing:
Simon George*

Muslim Television Ahmadiyya International
16 Gressenhall Road
London SW18 5QL
020 8870 0922
info@mtaintl.org
www.aislam.org/mta

MUTV
4th Floor, 274 Deansgate
Manchester M3 4JB
0161 834 1111
mutv@mutv.com
www.manutd.com/mutv
*Managing director: Peter Brooks;
editor-in-chief: Barbara Farrer*

National Geographic Channel
Grant Way, Isleworth TW7 5QD
020 7705 3000
www.nationalgeographic.co.uk
*General manager, UK operations:
Jane Larner; head of operations:
Stephanie Holm*

Nick Jr
Nickelodeon House
15–18 Rathbone Place
London W1T 1HU
020 7462 1000
www.nickjr.co.uk
*Managing director: Nicky Parkinson;
director of programming: Howard
Litton*

Nickelodeon
Nickelodeon House
15–18 Rathbone Place
London W1T 1HU
020 7462 1000
www.nick.co.uk
*Managing director: Nicky Parkinson;
director of programming: Howard
Litton*

Nicktoons TV
Nickelodeon House
15–18 Rathbone Place
London W1T 1HU
020 7462 1000
www.nick.co.uk/toons
*Managing director: Nicky Parkinson;
Director of Programming: Howard
Litton*

Paramount Comedy
3–5 Rathbone Place
London W1T 1HJ
020 7478 5300
www.paramountcomedy.co.uk

Performance Arts Channel
New Pathe House
57 Jamestown Road
London NW1 7XX
020 7424 3688
info@performancetv.co.uk
www.performance-channel.co.uk

Plus
Franciscan Court, 16 Hatfields
London SE1 8DJ
020 7578 4040
plus@gsb.co.uk
www.plustv.co.uk

Pub Channel
6 Centaurs Business Park
Grant Way, Isleworth TW7 5QD
020 7705 3000
almudena.rodriguez@bskyb.com
www.pubchannel.com

Q TV
Mappin House, 4 Winsley Street
London W1W 8HP
020 7436 1515
david_young@thebox.co.uk
www.emap.com

QVC
Marco Polo House,
346 Queenstown Road
Chelsea Bridge, London SW8 4NQ
020 7705 5600
www.qvcuk.com
*Chief executive: Mark Suckle;
Production Director: Brian Farrelly*

Revelation TV
91–93 Cleveland Street
London W1T 6PL
020 7631 4446
info@revelationtv.com
www.revelationtv.com

Sci-Fi
Universal Studios Networks Ltd
PO Box 4276, London W1A 7YE
020 7535 3517
mail@scifiUK.com
http://uk.scifi.com/

Scuzz
Grant Way, Isleworth TW7 5QD
020 7705 3000
skydigital@sky.com
www.sky.com
*Managing director, Sky Networks:
Dawn Airey
launched in April 2003, this is
marketed as the natural viewing home
for disruptive rock fans and targets a
core audience of 15- to 19-year-old men*

Setanta Sport Europe
52 The Haymarket, St James's
London SW1Y 4RP
020 7930 8926
setantauk@setanta.com
www.setanta.com

Sky Bet
Grant Way, Isleworth TW7 5QD
020 7705 3000
help@skybet.com
www.skybet.com
Managing director, Sky Bet: Nick Rust

Sky Movies Premier (x5)
Grant Way, Isleworth TW7 5QD
020 7705 3000
skydigital@sky.com
www.skymovies.com/
*Director of film channels and
acquisitions: Sophie Turner Laing*

Sky News
Grant Way, Isleworth TW7 5QD
020 7705 3000
skydigital@sky.com
www.skynews.co.uk/
Head of Sky News: Nick Pollard

Sky One
Grant Way, Isleworth TW7 5QD
020 7705 3000
skydigital@sky.com
www.skyone.co.uk
Controller: Sara Ramsden

Sky Sports 1, 2, 3, Extra
Grant Way, Isleworth TW7 5QD
020 7705 3000
skydigital@sky.com
www.skysports.com/
Managing director, Sky Sports: Vic Wakeling

Sky Travel
Grant Way, Isleworth TW7 5QD
020 7705 3000
skydigital@sky.com
www.skytravel.co.uk/
General manager, Sky Travel: Delia Bushell

Smash Hits Channel
Mappin House, 4 Winsley Street
London W1W 8HF
020 7436 1515
simon.sadler@emap.com
www.smashhits.net

Sony Entertainment TV Asia
34 Foubert's Place
London W1V 2BH
020 7534 7575
ash_jaswal@spe.sony.com
www.setindia.com

Star News
Grant Way, Isleworth TW7 5QD
020 7705 3000
suruchi.sthalekar@bskyb.com
www.startv.com

Star TV
Great West House, Great West Road
Brentford TW8 9DF
020 7805 2326
rinku.devgun@bskyb.com
http://staruk.indya.com

Studio
5–7 Mandeville Place
London W1U 3AR
020 7535 3500
rebecca.edwards@unistudios.com
www.thestudio.com

TMF The Music Factory
17–29 Hawley Crescent
London NW1 8TT
020 7284 6348
bisoni.maddy@mtvne.com

Travel Channel
66 Newman Street
London W1T 3EQ
020 7636 5401
petra@travelchannel.co.uk
www.travelchannel.co.uk

Trouble
160 Great Portland Street
London W1W 5QA
020 7299 5000
suzy_lambert@flextech.co.uk
www.trouble.co.uk

Turner Classic Movies
Turner House
16 Great Marlborough Street
London W1F 7HS
020 7693 1000
tcmeurope@turner.com
www.tcmonline.co.uk

TV Jobshop
1–4 Archers Court, 48 Masons Hill
Bromley BR2 9JG
020 8461 8461
georgie.palmer@tvjobshop.com
http://tv-jobshops.com

UK Bright Ideas
UKTV, 2nd Floor, Flextech Building
160 Great Portland Street
London W1W 5QA
020 7765 1974
ukbrightideas@bbc.co.uk
www.ukbrightideas.tv

UK Drama
UKTV, 2nd Floor, Flextech Building
160 Great Portland Street
London W1W 5QA
020 7765 0440
ukdrama@bbc.co.uk

UK Food
UKTV, 2nd Floor, Flextech Building
160 Great Portland Street
London W1W 5QA
020 7765 1974
ukfood@bbc.co.uk

UK Gold
UKTV, 2nd Floor, Flextech Building
160 Great Portland Street
London W1W 5QA
020 7765 0440
ukgold@bbc.co.uk

UK History
UKTV, 2nd Floor, Flextech Building
160 Great Portland Street
London W1W 5QA
020 7765 2043
ukhistory@bbc.co.uk

UK Horizons
UKTV, 2nd Floor, Flextech Building
160 Great Portland Street
London W1W 5QA
020 7765 2043
ukhorizons@bbc.co.uk

UK Style
UKTV, 2nd Floor, Flextech Building
160 Great Portland Street
London W1W 5QA
020 7765 1974
ukstyle@bbc.co.uk
www.ukstyle.tv

VH1
17–29 Hawley Crescent
London NW1 8TT
020 7284 6348
bisoni.maddy@mtvne.com
www.vh1.co.uk

VH1 Classic
Zee Tv, 64 Newman Street
London NW1 8TT
020 7284 6348
bisonimaddy@mtvne.com
www.vh1.co.uk

Zee TV News
Zee News, 64 Newman Street
London W1T 3ES
020 7637 4502
zeenews@zeetv.co.uk
www.zeetelevision.com

Data services

Teletext
Building 10, Chiswick Park
566 Chiswick High Road
London W4 5TS
0870 731 3000
editor@teletext.co.uk
www.teletext.co.uk
Has a licence to use spare capacity within the Channel 3 (ITV) signal

Data Broadcasting International (DBI)
Allen House, Station Road
Egham, Surrey TW20 9NT
01784 471515
sales@databroadcast.co.uk
www.databroadcast2.co.uk

Other broadcasters

BFBS Forces Radio and TV
01494 878290
pearl.mina@ssvc.com
www.ssvc.com

Bloomsbury Television (BTV)
020 7387 3827
jonathan_i_abraham@hotmail.com
www.homepages.ucl.ac.uk
/~uczxbts/

The Box
020 7436 1515
kirsty.lawrence@emap.com
www.emap.com

BVTV
0870 3672888
info@bvtv.co.uk
http://bvtv.co.uk

C4TV
07734 533068
c4tv@cant.ac.uk

Caledonia Television
01463 790310
george.cocker@tvaye.co.uk
www.tvaye.co.uk

Capital TV (Wales)
02920 488500
capitaltv@newsnet.co.uk
www.newsnet.co.uk

Carlisle TV
01565 751100

Channel One Liverpool
0151 4722701

Fawley
023 8023 2400
michael.finlason@btinternet.com
www.mytvnetwork.com

Glasgow University Student Television (GUST)
0141 341 6216
gust@src.gla.ac.uk
www.src.gla.ac.uk/gust

Glasgow's Own Television Channel Limited
0141 331 0077
rockettvf@aol.com

Guild Television (GTV)
0212 472 1841 x2249
www.bugs.bham.ac.uk/gtv/

Leeds University Union TV (LUUTV)
0113 244 8518
nick.smith@luutv.co.uk
www.luutv.co.uk/

Loughborough Students Union TV (LSUTV)
01509 635045
manager@lsutv.co.uk
www.lsutv.co.uk/

Channel M
0161 211 2366
info@channelM.co.uk
www.channelm.co.uk

Middlesex Broadcasting Corporation (MATV Channel 6)
0116 253 2288
info@matv.co.uk
www.matv.co.uk/

Midlands Cable TV (Dallington)
01604 682000
general@northantstv.co.uk

Midlands Cable TV (Northampton)
01604 682000
general@northantstv.co.uk

EBS New Media
01992 500 016
ben@newmedia.co.uk

MyTV Network
023 8023 2400
feedback@southamptontv.co.uk
www.southamptontv.co.uk

MyTV Network (Portsmouth Television)
023 8023 2400
enquiries@portsmouthtv.co.uk
www.portsmouthtv.co.uk

Nerve TV
01202 595774
sucptomms@bournemouth.ac.uk
www.subu.org.uk/nerve

Nexus UTV
01603 456161
sunexus@uea.ac.uk
www.uea.ac.uk/~sunexus/

North West Television Services (Channel 9 – Coleraine)
028 7131 4400
info@c9tv.tv
www.c9tv.tv

North West Television Services (Channel 9 – Limavady)
028 7131 4400
info@c9tv.tv
www.c9tv.tv

North West Television Services (Channel 9 – Londonderry/Derry)
028 7131 4400
info@c9tv.tv
www.c9tv.tv

Northants TV
01604 682000
general@northantstv.co.uk

Northern Visions
028 9024 5495

Oxford Broadcasting (Six TV)
01865 557000
admin@oxfordchnnel.com
www.oxfordchannel.com

Radio Enterprises (Chichester)
01962 713134

Red TV
01223 722722
tarba@dawemedia.co.uk
www.redtv.co.uk

Solent TV (Isle of Wight)
01983 522344
info@solent.tv
www.solent.tv

STOIC Student Television of Imperial College
020 7594 8104
james@stoictv.com
www.stoictv.com

Thistle Technology Group (Lanarkshire Television)
01698 833773
lanarkshiretv@btinternet.com
www.lanarkshiretv.com

Thistle TV
01698 833773
gordony@tfmplc.com

TV Norwich
01508 570970
www.ebecustv.co.uk

XTV
01392 673598
gareth@xtv.org.uk
www.xtv.org.uk

YCTV Youth Cable Television
020 8964 4646
info@yctv.org
www.yctv.org

York University Student Television (YSTV)
01904 430000
http://ystv.york.ac.uk

TV and film studios

3 Mills Studios
Three Mill Lane
London E3 3DU
020 7363 3336
info@3mills.com
www.3mills.com

Access Studios
8–10 Creekside
London SE8 3DX
020 7231 6185
inof@accessstudios.com
www.accessstudios.com

After Image
32 Acre Lane
London SW2 5SG
020 7737 7300
jane@arc.co.uk
www.after.arc.co.uk

Ardmore Studios Ltd
Herbert Road
Bray, Co. Wicklow
Ireland
00 353 1 2862971
film@ardmore.ie
www.ardmore.ie

BBC Elstree Centre
Clarendon Road
Borehamwood
Herts WD6 1JF
020 8576 7666

BBC TV Centre Studios
BBC TV Centre
Wood Lane, Shepherds Bush
London W12 7RJ
020 8576 7666
bbcresources@bbc.co.uk
www.bbcresources.co.uk

Black Island Studios
9–11 Alliance Road
Acton
London W3 0RA
020 8752 1700
blackisland@compuserve.com
www.blackislandstudios.co.uk

Box Studios
15 Mandela Street
London NW1 0DU
020 7388 0020
mail@boxstudios.co.uk
www.boxstudios.co.uk

Bray Studios
Down Place
Windsor Road, Water Oakley
Windsor, Berks SL4 5UG
01628 622111

Broadley Studios
Broadley House,
48 Broadley Terrace
London NW1 6LG
020 7258 0324
markfrench@broadleystudios.com
www.broadleystudios.com

Capital Studios
13 Wandsworth Plain
London SW18 1ET
020 8877 1234
louise.prior@capitalstudios.co.uk
www.capitalstudios.co.uk

Central Studios
The Old Drill Hall
Old Market Street
Bristol BS2 0EN
0117 9081220
info@centralstudios.co.uk
www.centralstudios.co.uk

Corinthian Television Facilities
Chiswick Park, Building 12
London W4 5AN
020 8100 1000
annaliese.landa@ctv.co.uk
www.ctv.co.uk

**CTS and Lansdowne Recording
Studios**
Lansdowne House
Lansdowne Road
London W11 3LP
020 7727 0041
info@cts-lansdowne.co.uk
www.cts-lansdowne.co.uk

Dukes Island Studios
2 Dukes Road
Acton
London W3 0SL
020 8956 5600
info@islandstudios.net
www.islandstudios.net

Ealing Studios
Ealing Green
London W5 5EP
020 8567 6655
info@ealingstudios.com
www.ealingstudios.com

East Side Studios
40A River Road
Barking
Essex IG11 0DW
020 8507 7572
info@eastsidestudios.com
www.eastsidestudios.com

Elstree Film and Television Studios
Shenley Road
Borehamwood, Herts WD6 1JG
020 8953 1600
info@elstreefilmtv.com
www.elstreefilmtv.com

Enfys
Unit 31 Portanmoor Road,
East Moors
Cardiff, South Glamorgan
Wales CF2 2HB
029 2049 9988
mail@enfys.tv
www.enfys.tv

Fountain TV Studios
128 Wembley Park Drive
Wembley
Middlesex HA9 8HQ
020 8900 5800
wembley@ftv.co.uk
www.ftv.co.uk

Greenford Studios
5–11 Taunton Road, Metropolitan
Centre
Greenford
Middlesex UB6 0LE
020 8587 2382

Hillside
Merry Hill Road
Bushey, Herts WD23 1DR
020 8950 7919
dave.hillier@hillside-studios.co.uk
www.hillside-studios.co.uk

Holborn Studios
49/50 Eagle Wharf Road
London N1 7ED
020 7490 4099
studiomanager@
    holborn-studios.co.uk
www.holborn-studios.co.uk

Leavesden Studios
South Way, Leavesden
Watford
Herts WD2 7LT
01932 685060

London Studios
London Television Centre
Upper Ground Floor
London SE1 9LT
020 7737 8888
sales@londonstudios.co.uk
www.londonstudios.co.uk

Magic Eye Film Studios
20 Lydden Road
London SW18 4LR
020 8877 0800
info@magiceye.co.uk
www.magiceye.co.uk
Currently non-operational

Park Royal Studios
1 Barretts Green Road
London NW10 7AE
020 8965 9778
info@parkroyalstudios.com
www.parkroyalstudios.com

Pinewood Studios
Pinewood Road
Iver Heath
Slough, Bucks SL0 0NH
01753 651700
suzanne_garton@
    pinewood-studios.co.uk
www.pinewood-studios.co.uk

Riverside Studios
Crisp Road
Hammersmith
London W6 9RL
020 8237 1000
online@riversidestudios.co.uk
www.riversidestudios.co.uk

Sands Films Studios
Grices Wharf
119 Rotherhithe Street
London SE16 4NF
020 7231 2209
OStockman@sandsfilms.co.uk
www.sandsfilms.co.uk

Shepperton Studios
Studios Road
Shepperton, Middlesex TW17 0QD
01932 562611
suzanne_garton@
    pinewood-studios.co.uk
www.sheppertonstudios.co.uk

stu-dio
Cabul Road
London SW11 2PR
020 7228 5228
info@the-studio.co.uk
www.the-studio.co.uk

Teddington Studios
Broom Road
Teddington, Middlesex TW11 9NT
020 8977 3252
sales@teddington.tv
www.teddington.co.uk

Twickenham Studios
The Barons, St Margarets
Twickenham
Middlesex TW1 2AW
020 8607 8888
caroline@twickenhamfilmstudios.com
www.twickenhamstudios.com/

Waterfall Studios
2 Silver Road
Wood Lane
London W12 7SG
020 8746 2000
enquiries@waterfall-studios.com
www.waterfall-studios.com

The Worx
10 Heathmans Road
Fulham
London SW6 4TJ
020 7371 9777
enquiries@theworx.co.uk
www.the-worx.co.uk

MediaGuardian Edinburgh International Television Festival

1st floor, 17–21 Emerald Street
London WC1N 3QN
020 7430 1333

info@mgeitf.co.uk
www.mgeitf.co.uk

Britain's biggest international forum for the TV industry. Held over the English August bank holiday, August 27–29 2004.

MGEITF also organises some evening events in London.

Independent production companies

12 Yard Productions
020 7432 2929
mike.beale@12yard.com
www.12yard.com
In It To Win It, Without Prejudice?, Double Cross, EggHeads, Here Comes The Sun, Three's A Crowd

1A Productions
01360 620855
langshot@nildram.co.uk
Tales From the Madhouse, Man Dancin', The Rock (in development 2003); The Power

3BM Television
020 7251 2512
3bmtv@3bmtv.co.uk
www.3bmtv.co.uk
Desert Rats; The Age of Terror; Auntie – the Inside Story of the BBC

The 400 Company
020 8746 1400
info@the400.co.uk
www.the400.co.uk

A Works TV
01256 698353
adrian@aworks.tv
www.aworks.tv
Sergeant Stripes (BBC)

Triple A Multimedia Group
01622 880599
gmcstudio@triple-a.uk.com
www.triple-a.uk.com
The Management, Act Now

Absolutely Productions
020 7930 3113
info@absolutely-uk.com
www.absolutely-uk.com
Stressed Eric, Trigger Happy TV

Acacia Productions
020 8341 9392
projects@acaciaproductions.co.uk
www.acaciaproductions.co.uk
Documentary and news, environment, current affairs and human rights

Accomplice Television
00 353 1660 3235
office@accomplice-tv.com
www.iftn.ie/productions
Bachelors Walk Series 3 (RTE)

Addictive Television
020 7700 0333
mail@addictive.com
www.addictive.com
The Web Review, Mixmasters (ITV1), Visual Stings (Magnetic Channel)

Aimimage Camera Company
020 7482 4340
cameras@aimimage.com
www.aimimage.com

Alibi Communications/Alibi Productions/Alibi Films International
020 7845 0400
rebekahdeboo@alibifilms.co.uk
www.alibifilms.co.uk
Goodbye Mr Steadman

Amirani Fillms
020 7328 7057
info@amiranifilms.co.uk

angel eye film and television
020 7437 0082
office@angeleye.co.uk
www.angeleye.co.uk

Antelope
01243 370806
mick.csaky@antelope.co.uk
www.antelope.co.uk
31 Willow Road, London NW3 1TL
Docs: Mozart in Turkey; Rebel Music: The Bob Marley Story; Geiko Girl, Africa Live; Epic Journey; 13-part series about Kyoto

APT Films
020 7284 1695
admin@aptfilms.com
www.aptfilms.com
Wondrous Oblivion (feature); Solomon and Gaenor (Oscar nomination, best foreign film); The Chosen Ones, Solo One, When I Lived in Modern Times

At It Productions
020 8964 2122
enquiries@atitproductions.com
www.atitproductions.com
Popworld; 25 Years of Smash Hits

Atlantic Productions
020 7371 3200
films@atlanpro.demon.co.uk
www.atlanticproductions.tv
The Conquistadors; The Search for Atlantis; 20,000 Leagues under the Sea

Big Bear Films
020 7229 5982
office@bigbearfilms.co.uk
www.bigbearfilms.co.uk
My Hero (BBC1), Strange (with BBC1); Agatha Raisin; Hairy Bikers Cookbook

Big Heart Media
020 7608 0352
info@bigheartmedia.com
www.bigheartmedia.com

Big Umbrella Media
01225 817500
production@bigumbrellamedia.co.uk
www.bigumbrellamedia.co.uk
Third Floor, 37 Foley Street
London W1W 7TN
Tel: 020 7631 2050
Executive produced: programmes for C4, BBC3, BBC4

Big Wave Productions
01243 532531
info@bigwavetv.com
www.bigwavetv.com

Black Coral Productions
020 8520 2881
bcp@coralmedia.co.uk
www.m4media.net
Killing Time, Phil's Job. Factual documentaries: Surviving the Hero, Rewind, Whose the Hero. Drama: Which Witch is Which

Blackwatch Productions
0141 222 2640
info@blackwatchtv.com
www.blackwatchtv.com

Blakeway Producations
020 8743 2040
admin@blakeway.co.uk
www.blakeway.co.uk
*Prince William; Winston's War;
The Major Years*

Blast! Films
020 7267 4260
blast@blastfilms.co.uk
www.blastfilms.co.uk
*Tales from Pleasure Beach; Tina Takes
a Break; Lifters*

**Blue Egg Television/Blue Egg
Studios**
0870 765 0007
info@blueegg.tv
www.blueegg.tv

Brechin Productions
020 8876 4333
clive@brechin.com
www.brechin.com

Brian Waddell Productions
028 9042 7646
strand@bwpltv.co.uk
www.bwpltv.co.uk
*Chasing Time In... (13-part travel
series, National Geographic);
Ulster Fly; Boffins (6×30')*

Brighter Pictures
020 7733 7333
info@brighter.co.uk
www.brighter.co.uk
*Take the Mike; Bombay Blush;
Diet Another Day*

Brighter Pictures Scotland
0141 572 0861
scotland@brighter.co.uk
www.brighter.co.uk
*Get A New Life (BBC2), Tabloid Tales
(BBC1), Nick Nairn and the Dinner
Ladies (BBC Scotland)*

Brighton Films
01273 224260
sally@brightonfilms.co.uk
www.brightonfilms.co.uk

Brook Lapping Productions
020 7428 3100
info@tenalps.com
www.brooklapping.com
*Avenging Terror; Before the Booker;
I met Adolf Eichmann*

Cactus TV
202 7091 4900
touch.us@cactustv.co.uk
www.cactustv.co.uk
*Richard & Judy; The British Soap
Awards*

Caledonia, Sterne And Wyld
0141 564 9100
info@caledonia-tv.com
www.caledonia-tv.com
The Real Tartan Army

Carnival (Films and Theatre)
020 8968 0968
info@carnival-films.co.uk
www.carnival-films.co.uk
As If; Poirot; Rosemary and Thyme

Catalyst Television
020 7603 7030
info@catalyst-films-tv.com or
info@catalyst-tv.com
Kings Heath Park House
Vicarage Road
Birmingham B14 7TQ
Tel: 0121 444 8777

Celador Productions
020 7845 6999
www.celador.co.uk
*Who Wants to be a Millionaire?;
Winning Lines; Britain's Brainiest*

Chrysalis
020 7502 6000
www.chrysalis.co.uk
*Chrysalis TV unit sold to MBI Group
and venture capital firm Bridgepoint
in July 2003*

CHX Productions
020 7428 3999
info@chxp.co.uk
www.chxp.co.uk
*Reeves & Mortimer; Date That;
Popetown*

Cicada Films
020 7266 4646
cicada@cicadafilms.com
www.cicadafilms.com
The Abyss; Beyond Pompeii; Bikini

Circle Multimedia
01243 601482/01628 509501
circlemultimedia@hotmail.com
www.circlemultimedia.com
*Wire in the Blood; Alchemist's Cat
(feature film), Afterlife (feature film),
Conqueror (feature film),
The Cloak (TV-DVD)*

Clearcut Communications
0161 427 3052
info@clearcut.freeserve.co.uk
*On the Edge (Granada); Sense of Place
(BBC1); Shanghai'd (BBC2); Proof
Positive (pilot for Discovery America)*

Clerkenwell Films
020 7608 2726
andy@clerkenwellfilms.com
*Dr Jekyll and Mr Hyde (Universal TV);
Indepxtor Rebus, Parlablane (ITV1)*

Collinwood O'Hare Entertainment
020 8993 3666
info@crownstreet.co.uk
www.collingwoodohare.com
*Animal Stories, Eddy and the Bear, The
King's Beard, Yoko! Jakamoko! Toto!*

COLOUR Television
0141 222 2442
mail@colour-tv.com
www.colour-tv.com

The Comedy Unit
0141 305 6666
comedyunit@comedyunit.co.uk
www.comedyunit.co.uk
*Still Game; The Karen Dunbar Show;
Offside; Yo! Diary!; Taxi for Cowan
Spanish Special; New Year specials:
Chewin' The Fat; Only An Excuse?*

Company Pictures
020 7380 3900
enquiries@companypictures.co.uk
www.companypictures.co.uk
Forty; White Teeth; Anna Karenina

Cosgrove Hall Films
0161 882 2500
animation@chf.co.uk
www.chf.co.uk
*Dangermouse; Duckula;
Chorlton & the Wheelies*

CTVC
020 8950 4426
ctvc@ctvc.co.uk
www.ctvc.co.uk
*Bethlehem Year Zero; John Meets
Paul: A Mediterranean Journey;
Understanding Islam*

Dai4Films
01570 47163
dai4films@aol.com
www.dai4films.com
Raw Spice; Dirty Streets

Dan Films
020 7916 4771
office@danfilms.com
www.danfilms.com

Darlow Smithson Productions
020 7482 7027
mail@darlowsmithson.com
www.darlowsmithson.com

Darrall Macqueen
020 7407 2322
billy@darrallmacqueen.com
www.darrallmacqueen.com
*Smile series 2, BBC2; U Get Me series
3, CBBC*

Dazed Film and TV
020 7549 6840
laura@confused.co.uk
Untold Beauty, BBC3

Diverse
020 7603 4567
info@diverse.tv
www.diverse.tv
*The House of War; The Real George V;
The Truth About Gay Animals*

DLT Entertainment UK
020 7631 1184
jbartlett@dltentertainment.co.uk
*My Family, BBC1; Meet My Folks,
BBC1*

DNA Films
020 7291 8010
info@dnafilms.com
www.dnafilms.com

Double Exposure
020 7490 2499
reception@doublex.com
www.doublex.com
The House; Culloden; Pleasure Beach

Eagle and Eagle
020 8995 1884
producer@eagletv.co.uk
www.eagletv.co.uk
*The Nuclear Boy Scout (C4);
Robo Sapiens (Discovery/TLC);
Big Questions (C4 Learning)*

Eagle Films
01372 844484
eagle.films@virgin.net
www.eaglefilms.co.uk
*Shorts: Black Mark, Let's do Lunch;
features: It Started with a Kiss, Road
to Somewhere*

East Wind Films
01603 628728
averilbrennan@
    oldrectory44.freeserve.co.uk
*Dramas: Deep Sleep (ITV); A Clear
Conscience (ITV); Shadow Play (ITV);
Trial By Fire (ITV). Drama series:
Flaxborough; SSI (pilot)*

ECM Productions
020 7727 5752
ecmproductions@ecm-group.co.uk
www.ecminternational.com

Ecosse Films
020 7371 0290
webmail@ecossefilms.com
www.ecossefilms.com
*Monarch of the Glen; Ambassador;
McCready & Daughter*

**Educational Broadcasting Services
Trust**
020 7613 5082
enquiries@ebst.co.uk
www.ebst.co.uk

Einstein Group
0117 927 7473
www.einstein.tv

Electric Sky
01273 224240
info@electricsky.com
www.electricsky.com
Live Forever; Be a Grand Prix Driver

The Elstree Production Company
01932 572680
enquiries@elsprod.com
www.elsprod.com

Endemol UK
0870 333 1700
info@endemoluk.com
www.endemoluk.com
*Big Brother, Fame Academy, Orange
British Academy Films Awards,
Ground Force, Changing Rooms, Party
in the Park, Restoration, The Salon 2,
National Celebrity Games*

Extreme Production
028 9080 9050
dmalone@extremeproduction.com
www.extremeproduction.com
*Clash of the Celtic Giants;
Ballykissanything; Country Practice*

FACE Television
01256 350022
tv@face.demon.co.uk
www.facetv.co.uk

Faction Films
020 7690 4446
faction@factionfilms.co.uk
www.factionfilms.co.uk
*Love for Sale (BBC); Resistencia (SBS,
YLE, SVT, Maori TV); Cinematic
Orchestra (C4); Sonic Revolution
(C4/Levi's); Point Annihilation
(surf drama)*

The Farnham Film Company
01252 710313
info@farnfilm.com
www.farnfilm.com
Mona the Vampire, The Druid's Tune

Festival Film and TV
020 8297 9999
info@festivalfilm.com
Feature films: Man Dancin', The Colour

Fettis Films
020 7241 3459
fettis.films@virgin.net
www.fettisfilms.com

Film and Music Entertainment
020 7636 9292
info@fame.uk.com
www.fame.uk.com

Fireside Favourites
020 7439 6110
info@firesidefavourites.co.uk
www.firesidefavourites.co.uk

Flame Television
020 7713 6868
contact@flametv.co.uk
www.theflamegroup.co.uk
*Discovery Health 2 bulletins; Cage
Combat (Carlton); Crime Team (C4);
Square Planet (Discovery Europe);
Roadies 2 (UK Horizons); ANN
Summers Uncovered (Carlton);
Dim Crims (Five); Jane Goldman
investigates (Living TV);
Wild Prince (C4)*

Flashback Television
020 7490 8996
mailbox@flashbacktv.co.uk or
bristol@flashbacktv.co.uk
www.flashbacktv.co.uk or
wwwflashbacktv.co.uk
1–2 Fitzroy Terrace
Lower Redland Road
Bristol BS6 6TF
Tel: 0117 973 8755

Flick Features
020 7855 3636
info@flickfeatures.com
www.flickfeatures.co.uk
*Feature film: Conspiracy of Silence,
Pictures of Anna (in development)*

Flying Elephant Films
020 8230 6920
info@flyingelephant.co.uk
www.flyingelephant.co.uk

Focus Productions
0117 904 6292
martinweitz@focusproductions.co.uk
    or
maddern@focusproductions.co.uk
www.focusproductions.co.uk
PO Box 173
Stratford-upon-Avon CV37 7ZA
Tel:01789 298948
*Pharaoh's Holy Treasure (BBC2),
This Sceptred Isle, The Jewish Journey
(BBC R4). Winner Sony Gold Award.
Projects 2003: Witness on saint-
making (C4), The Godfather of the
Blues (BBC4), The Human Computer
(C5 film). The Silver Cigarette Case
(History Channel/BBC film)*

Footstep Productions
020 7836 9990
footstepproductions@
    compuserve.com
www.footstepsproductions.com

Free@Last TV
020 7242 4333
barry@freeatlasttv.co.uk
www.freeatlasttv.co.uk
*The Spiderman Story (C5);
Making Of Jackass The Movie (C5);
Rock N Roll Myths (C4);
Blackadder@20 (UKTV); Projects
2003: Adored:The Stone Roses Story;
Mobo Unsung (C4); Dr Who@40
(UKTV)*

Fresh One Productions
020 7359 1000
simon@freshone.tv

Fulcrum TV
020 7253 0353
info@fulcrumtv.com
www.fulcrumtv.com

Genesis Media Group
029 2066 6007
alan@genesis-media.co.uk
www.genesis-media.co.uk
*Corporate and government projects
plus travel, arts, music and docs for TV*

Ginger Television
020 7663 2300
production@ginger.com
www.ginger.com
*Don't Drop the Coffin (ITV),
Timewatch – Enzo Ferrari (BBC2)*

Glasshead
020 8740 0024
media@glasshead.co.uk
www.glasshead.co.uk

Green Bay Media
029 2078 6607
lowri-jones@green-bay.tv
www.green-bay.tv
The Story of Welsh

Green Umbrella
0117 973 1729
postmaster@umbrella.co.uk
www.umbrella.co.uk

Greenlit Productions
020 7287 3545
info@greenlit.co.uk
www.greenlit.co.uk
*Event' television dramas such as
Foyle's War, The Swap and Menace*

Greenpoint Films
020 7240 7066
info@greenpointfilms.com
www.greenpointfilms.co.uk
*Cold Enough for Snow; Eskimo Bay;
Bye Bye Columbus*

Grosvenor Park Productions
020 7529 2500
chris.chrisafis@grosvenorpark.com
www.grosvenorpark.com

Gruber Films
0870 366 9313
office@gruberfilms.com
www.gruberfilms.com
*Shooting Fish, Waking Ned, The
Abduction Club. Development slate
supported by Momentum and UK
Film Council*

Hand Pict Productions
0131 346 1111
ask@handpict.com
www.handpict.com

Hanrahan Media
01789 450182
info@hanrahanmedia.com
www.hanrahanmedia.com
*Star Lives (ITV); World's Biggest
Ghost Hunt; Most Haunted Live;
(LivingTV); Men's Health (Bravo)*

Harry Nash Film Productions
020 7025 7500
info@harrynash.co.uk
www.harrynash.co.uk

Hasan Shah Films
020 7722 2419
hsfilms@blueyonder.co.uk
*Short: Art Of The Critic. Feature in
development 2003: A Little Scary*

Hat Trick Productions
020 7434 2451
info@hattrick.com
www.hattrick.com
*Room 101; The Kumars at No 42;
Father Ted; Jeffrey Archer – The Truth;
Underworld; Drop the Dead Donkey*

Sally Head Productions
020 8607 8730
admin@shpl.demon.co.uk
*Tipping The Velvet (BBC2), The Cry
(ITV), Mayor of Casterbridge (ITV);
The Return (ITV)*

Hewland International
020 7916 2266
www.hewland.co.uk

hopscotch films
0141 334 5576
info@hopscotchfilms.co.uk
www.hopscotchfilms.co.uk

Hotbed Media
0121 248 3900
mail@hotbedmedia.co.uk
www.hotbedmedia.co.uk
*100 Worst Britons (C4), Everything
Must Go (ITV1). 100 Worst Pop
Records (C4 2004); Star Portraits with
Rolf Harris (BBC1 2004)*

Hot Shot Films
028 9031 3332
info@hotshotfilms.com
www.hotshotfilms.com
*Seven Days That Shook United (C4),
Front Line (BBC)*

Hourglass Pictures
020 8540 8786
pictures@hourglass.co.uk
www.hourglass.co.uk

HRTV
020 7494 3011
lesley@hrtv-online.com
www.hrtv-online.com

Hyphen Films
020 7734 0632
nmk@hyphenfilms.com
*Spotlights and Saris (Omnibus, BBC1),
Bollywood Dancing (BBC4),
Bollywood Women – Intros (C4),
Bismillah of Benaras (BBC4),
Bollywood Celebrities (C4),
Bollywood 2004 (C4)*

Icon Films
0117 924 8535
info@iconfilms.co.uk
www.iconfilms.co.uk

Ideal World Productions
0141 353 3222
islai@idealglasgow.com
www.idealworldproductions.com
*Location, Location, Location;
The Planman; The Changemakers;
Who Killed Jill Dando?*

Illumina Digital
020 8600 9300
info@illumina.co.uk
www.illumina.co.uk

Illuminations Films
020 7288 8400
griff@illumin.co.uk
www.illumin.co.uk

Images Of War
020 7267 9198
derek@dircon.co.uk
www.warfootage.com
Footage for Hitler's Britain (C4)

Imago Productions
01603 727600
mail@imagoproductions.tv
www.imagoroductions.tv
*Swimming Lions (Discovery/Animal
Planet), Mistresses (ITV1), Look of
Lurve (ITV), Tasting History (Anglia)*

Independent Image
01883 654867
info@indimage.com
www.indimage.com

Infinite Pictures
01752 830000
info@infinitepictures.com
www.infinitepictures.com

Infonation
020 7370 1082
www.infonation.org.uk

Intelfax
020 7928 2727
billskirrow@intelfax.co.uk
www.intelfax.co.uk

**Intermedia Film and Video
(Nottingham)**
0115 955 6909
info@intermedianotts.co.uk
www.intermedianotts.co.uk
*One For The Road (Filmfour/Film
Council/EMMI), Slot Art (C4),
Shifting Units (BFI/Filmfour), The
Entertainer (Comedy Lab C4); DV
Shorts (Film Council/EMMI), First
Cut (Carlton/EMMI), First Light
(Film Council)*

**International Media Productions
(IMP)**
0191 245 1000
improductions@aol.com
www.improductions.co.uk

**International News Productions
(INP)**
020 7963 7474
info@inptvnews.com
www.inptvnews.com

ITN Factual
itn.factual@itn.co.uk
www.itn.co.uk
*Hunt for The Hood/Bismarck,
Leonardo's Dream Machines, Sars –
Global Killer, Are Your Kids on Drugs?*

The Jim Henson Company
020 7428 4000
fanmail@henson.com
www.henson.com

Just Television
020 7916 6200
info@justtv.co.uk
www.justabout.tv

Keo Films
020 7490 3580
www.keofilms.com

The Kilroy Television Company
020 7893 7900
info@kilroy.co.uk

Landmark Films
01865 427301
info@landmarkfilms.com
www.landmarkfilms.com

Landseer Productions
020 7485 7333
mail@landseerfilms.com
www.landseerfilms.com

Leopard Films
0870 420 4232
mail@leopardfilms.com
www.leopardfilms.com
*Cash in the Attic (BBC1); Thunder
Races (Discovery/C4), Elvis Mob
(BBC1)*

Liberty Bell Productions
0191 222 1200
fahima.chowdhury@libertybell.tv
www.libertybell.tv

Libra Television
0161 236 5599
hq@libratelevision.com
www.libratelevision.com
*Citizen Power (C4); How to be a Bully
(BBC); Copycat Kids (CiTV);
History Busters (Discovery Kids);
Gross! (Discovery Kids)*

Lion Television
020 8846 2000
mail@liontv.co.uk
www.liontv.co.uk
*Britain's Finest (Channel 5), Castles
(C4), Royal Deaths and Diseases (C4),
Passport to the Sun (BBC1)*

Little Bird
00 353 1 613 1710
info@littlebird.ie
www.littlebird.ie

Loose Moose
020 7287 3821
info@loosemoose.net
www.loosemoose.net
Animated commercials

Lupus Films
020 7419 0997
info@lupusfilms.net
www.lupusfilms.net
*Little Wolf's Book of Badness (C4);
Wilde Stories; Little Wolf's Adventure
Academy; Mia, Cool Hunter*

Macmillan Media
08703 502150
info@macmillanmedia.co.uk
www.macmillanmedia.co.uk
Live broadcasting services

Malachite
01790 763538
info@malachite.co.uk
www.malachite.co.uk

Maverick Television
0121 771 1812
mail@mavericktv.co.uk
www.mavericktv.co.uk
London office:
4th Floor, 15 Berners Street
London W1T 3LJ
Tel: 020 7631 1062

Maya Vision International
020 7836 1113
info@mayavisionint.com
www.mayavisionint.com
*Hitler's Search for the Holy Grail
(C4/PBS), Conquistadors (BBC/PBS),
In Search of Shakespeare (BBC/PBS),
Two Moons (feature), Michael Wood
projects tba*

Mentorn
020 7258 6800
mentorn@mentorn.co.uk
www.mentorn.co.uk

Midlantic Films
020 8455 4481
susan@midlantic.co.uk

Mint Productions
028 9024 0555
info@mint.ie
www.mint.ie
1 Kengar Mews, Rathgar Avenue
Dublin 6, Ireland
*Abu Hamza, Two Day Coup, De
Lorean, Workers Strike (BBC), Crash,
'Emmet, All the Queen's Men (RTÉ),
Shergar (C4/RTÉ)*

Monkey
020 7250 0000
info@monkeykingdom.com
www.monkeykingdom.com

MousePower Productions
01225 817600
enquiries@
    mousepowerproductions.com
www.mousepowerproductions.com

Multi Media Arts
0161 374 5566
info@mmarts.com
www.mmarts.com

mykindofshow.com
020 7916 8394
mail@blueonline.tv
www.mykindofshow.com
105 The Custard Factory
Gibb Street, Birmingham B9 4AA
Tel: 0121 693 1894

Nexus Productions
020 7749 7500
info@nexusproductions.com
www.nexusproductions.com
*Catch Me If You Can (titles);
Goldfrapp, Erasure (music videos);
Nike (Run London campaign), T-
Mobile, Aiwa (campaigns); Monkey
Dust (sketch show)*

North West Vision
0151 291 9197
lucye@northwestvision.co.uk
www.northwestvision.co.uk

October Films
020 7284 6868
info@octoberfilms.co.uk
www.octoberfilms.co.uk

Octopus Television
020 7531 8612
www.octopus-television.tv,
www.octopus-publishing.co.uk

Open Mind Productions
020 7437 0624
enquiries@openmind.co.uk
www.openmind.co.uk

Open Road Films
020 7813 4333
info@openroadfilms.co.uk
www.ashesandsand.com

Optomen Television
020 7967 1234
otv@optomen.com
www.optomen.com
*Jump London; Red Gold; Tyler's
Ultimate; Role Reversal; The Naked
Chef; It's a Girl Thing; Police, Camera,
Action*

ORTV (ORMEDIA)
020 8987 1000
info@ormedia.co.uk
www.ormedia.co.uk

Otmoor Productions
01865 744844
otmoorproductions@
    compuserve.com
*Everyman: Our Father the Serial
Killer; docs in development*

Oxford Film And Television
020 7483 3637
email@oftv.co.uk
www.oftv.co.uk
*Philip Larkin: Love and Death in
Hull; Lionheart: the Crusade; Second
Generation (all C4); Superfly, Terry
Jones' Medieval Tales, National Trust
(BBC)*

Paladin Invision
020 7371 2123
pitv@pitv.com
www.pitv.com

Pathé Pictures
020 7323 5151
susanna.wyatt@pathe-uk.com
www.pathe.co.uk
Theatrical feature films

Pepper's Ghost Productions
020 8546 4900
enquiries@peppersghost.com
www.peppersghost.com
Tiny Planets

Pesky
020 7430 0200
hodge@pesky.com
www.pesky.com
*Stress Maniacs (C4 pilot); Amazing
Adrenalini Brothers (award-winning
cartoon shorts, CBBC); Thingamijig
(preschool, in development 2003);
I Could Murder A Curry (adult,
in development 2003)*

Pilot Film and TV Productions
020 8960 2721
info@pilotguides.com
www.pilot.co.uk

Pioneer Productions
020 8748 0888
pioneer@pioneertv.com
www.pioneertv.com

Planet 24 Productions
020 7612 0671
www.planet24.com

Planet Wild
0161 233 3090
office@planetwild.co.uk
www.planetwild.co.uk

Pozzitive
020 773 3258
pozzitive@pozzitive.demon.co.uk

Presentable
029 2057 5729
all@presentable.co.uk
www.presentable.co.uk

The Press Association
020 7963 7474
broadcasting.info@pa.press.net
www.pa.press.net
*A network of reporters, camera crews
and editing facilities across the UK
and Ireland*

Princess Productions
020 7243 5100
reception@princess.uk.com
www.princess.uk.com
Rise; The Wright Stuff

Principle Films
020 7928 9287
group@principalmedia.com
www.principalmedia.com

Prism Entertainment
020 8969 1212
info@prism-e.com
www.prismentertainment.co.uk

Prospect Pictures
020 7222 1234
www.prospect-uk.com
*Ruby's Health Quest; Health UK; The
BBC Diet Programme; Fight Cancer;
Ulster Unearthed*

Quality Time Television
020 7846 1855
qtvmoir@aol.com
Regional office:
Foxhills Farm House, Chapel End
Swerford, Oxon OX7 4BQ
*Death (C4), Bafta award-winner and
RTS nominee; Shattered (C4)*

Ragdoll
01753 631800
pinewood@ragdoll.co.uk
www.ragdoll.co.uk
*Rosie and Jim, Tots TV, Brum,
Teletubbies, Teletubbies Everywhere,
Boohbah*

Raw Charm
029 2064 1511
pam@rawcharm.co.uk
www.rawcharm.tv
*War Stories (BBC Wales), Grave
Detectives (HTV West), Simon Weston's
War Heroes (BBC)*

RDF Media
020 7013 4000
contactus@rdfmedia.com
www.rdfmedia.com
*Faking It 4, Wife Swap & Celebrity
Wife Swap, Scrapheap Challenge
5, Century of the Self, Wreck Detectives,
Trust Me I'm a Teenager, Holiday
Showdown, Dream Holiday Homes 2,
Masters and Servants, Spitfire,
Carthage*

Real Life Media Productions
0113 234 7271
info@reallife.co.uk
www.reallife.co.uk

Red Fig
020 7944 0500
info@redfig.com
www.redfig.com
*I'm A Celebrity... Get Me Out Of Here!,
Popstars: The Rivals (Granada), Wild
In Your Garden, The Big Conversation
(BBC); Heaven and Earth, Asylum
Day, Darkhouse (BBC), Justin
Timberlake Karaoke Line (WFX)*

Red Green and Blue Company
020 8746 0616
max@rgbco.com
www.rgbco.com
Production office:
1 Underwood Row, London N1 7LZ
Tel: 020 7490 1788
DVD science and reference

Red Kite Productions
0131 554 0060
info@redkite-animation.com
www.redkite-animation.com

Red Production Company
0161 827 2530
www.redproductioncompany.com

Reef Television
020 7287 7877
mail@reeftv.com
www.reef.tv

Reel Life Television
020 7713 1585
enquiries@reel-life-tv.co.uk
www.reel-life-tv.co.uk

renting eyeballs entertainment
020 7437 4417
malcolm.rasala@rentingeyeballs.com
www.rentingeyeballs.com
*Commercials, promos, brand
television, motion pictures*

Resource Base
023 8023 6806
post@resource-base.co.uk
www.resource-base.co.uk
*VEE-TV, Without You, World of
Difference (C4), Lion Mountain, Who
Cares? (BBC),*

Richmond Films and Television
020 7722 6464
mail@richmondfilms.com
PO Box 33154, London NW3 4AZ

Ricochet Films
020 7251 6966
mail@ricochet.co.uk
www.ricochet.co.uk

Ronin Entertainment
020 7734 3884
mail@ronintv.com
www.ronintv.com

RS Productions
0191 224 4301
info@rsproductions.co.uk
www.rsproductions.co.uk

Samson Films
00 353 1667 0533
info@samsonfilms.com
www.iftn.ie/productions
*Co-producer: Blind Flight (Parallax),
Honeymooners (Utah), Abduction
Club (Gruber), Most Fertile Man in
Ireland (Sky Pictures). Feature
development: Mir Friends, Immortal,
Havoc*

Scream Films
020 8995 8255
info@screamfilms.com
www.screamfilms.com

Screenhouse Productions
0113 266 8881
info@screenhouse.co.uk
www.screenhouse.co.uk

September Films
020 8563 9393
september@septemberfilms.com
www.septemberfilms.com
*Making It; Cosmetic Surgery;
Hopelessly Rich; The Bottom Line;
Bridezillas; Greece on the Beach;
Hollywood Real Estate*

Seventh Art Productions
01273 777678
info@seventh-art.com
www.seventh-art.com
*Easter in Art (Five); Pelé – World Cup
Hero (BBC); Great Artists II (Five);
Boy who plays on the Buddhas of
Bamiyan*

Shed Productions
020 8215 3387
shed@shedproductions.com
www.shedproductions.com

Shine
020 7313 8000
info@shinelimited.com
www.shinelimited.com

Silver Light
01865 744451
mail@silverlightmedia.com
www.silverlightmedia.com

SMG TV Productions
0141 300 3000
elizabeth.partyka@smg.plc.uk
*Taggart, Club Reps: The Workers,
Good Bye Mr Chips, Medics of the Glen,
Squeak!, How 2*

Smith And Watson Productions
01803 863033
info@smith-watson.demon.co.uk
www.smithandwatson.com
57A Jamestown Road
London NW1 7DB

Smoking Dogs Films
020 7249 6644
info@smokingdogsfilms.com
*Stan Tracey – Godfather of British Jazz
(BBC4), Mariah Carey – a profile (C4)*

So Television
020 7960 2000
info@sotelevision.co.uk
www.sotelevision.co.uk
V Graham Norton (Channel 4)

Specific Films
020 7580 7476
info@specificfilms.com
*Last Seduction II, Paws, Mr Reliable,
Priscilla, Queen of the Desert*

Spire Films
01865 371979
mail@spirefilms.co.uk
Fact or Fiction

**Straight Forward Film and
Television Productions**
028 9042 6298
enquiries@straightforwardltd.co.uk

Sunset + Vine
020 7478 7300
reception@sunsetvine.co.uk
www.sunsetvine.co.uk

Sunset + Vine North
0113 284 2495
nicklord@sunsetvine.co.uk
www.sunsetvine.co.uk

Sunstone Films
020 7431 0535
sunstone@sunstonefilms.co.uk
www.sunstonefilms.co.uk

Synchronicity Productions Ltd
01273 746201
info@synchronicity-tv.co.uk
www.synchronicity-tv.co.uk
*Documentaries for eg BBC Flextech,
ITV. Factual and drama programmes
for radio and corporate, promotional
and training films*

Talent Television
020 7659 2017
entertainment@talenttv.com
www.talenttv.com
*Test the Nation (BBC1);
The Villa – Series 4 (Sky One);
TV Scrabble – Series 3 (Challenge)*

Talisman Films
020 7603 7474
info@talismanfilms.com
www.talismanfilms.com

Talkback Productions
020 7861 8060
reception@talkback.co.uk
www.talkback.co.uk
Bo Sielecta; I'm Alan Partridge; Smack the Pony; Jamie's Kitchen; Property Ladder; Perfect Strangers

Telemagination
020 7434 1551
mail@tmation.co.uk
www.telemagination.co.uk
Pongwiffy (ITV), Little Ghosts (ITV and ZDF), Something Else (ZDF and Family Channel); Metalheads, Cramp Twins (BBC), Heidi (theatrical release)

The Television Corporation
020 7478 7300
tvcorp@tvcorp.co.uk
www.televisioncorporation.co.uk
Robot Wars; Britain's Worst Driver; Techno Games; Botham's Ashes; Gillette World Sport; Hitler's Legacy; Club Culture; Question Time; The Fall of the Iron Lady; The Real Monty

Television Junction
0121 248 4466
info@televisionjunction.co.uk
www.televisionjunction.co.uk
Education

Tell-Tale Productions
020 8324 2308
info@tell-tale.co.uk
www.tell-tale.co.uk

Tern Television
0224 211123
www.terntv.com
73 Crown Street
Aberdeen AB11 6EX
Tel: 01224 211123

Thrilanfere
01287 626988
thrilanfere@onetel.net.uk
Apartment 12, 5 Bewley Street
London SW19 1XF
020 8543 0284 and 07810 344 644
Live action thrillers and animation for teenage market

Tiara Productions
01564 742520

Tiger Aspect Productions
020 7434 6700
general@tigeraspect.co.uk
www.tigeraspect.co.uk
Comedy, drama, entertainment, factual and animation programming Teachers; Murphy's Law; Fat Friends; Streetmate; Gimme Gimme Gimme

Tigress Productions
020 7434 4411
general@tigressproductions.co.uk
   or
general@tigressbristol.co.uk
www.tigressproductions.co.uk
2 St Paul's Road
Clifton, Bristol BS8 1LT.
Tel: 0117 933 5600

Tinopolis
020 8743 9255
info@tinopolis.com
www.tinopolis.com
Park Street, Llanelli
Carmarthenshire SA15 3YE
Tel: 01554 880880

Torpedo
029 2076 6117
info@torpedoltd.co.uk
www.torpedoltd.co.uk

Touch Productions
01747 828030
enquiries@touchproductions.co.uk
www.touchproductions.co.uk

TransAtlantic Films
020 8735 0505
mail@transatlanticfilms.com
www.transatlanticfilms.com
Cabalva
Whitney-On-Wye
Hereford HR3 6EX
Tel: 01497 831800

Turn On Television
0161 247 7700
mail@turnontv.co.uk
www.turnontv.co.uk

TV6
020 7610 0266
tv6mail@aol.com
www.tv6.co.uk

TWI (Trans World International)
www.imgworld.com
Wimbledon; The Olympics; Premier League; PGA European Tour; Colour of War

Twofour Productions
01752 333900
enq@twofour.co.uk
www.twofour.co.uk
20–24 Kirby Street
London EC1N 8TS
Tel: 0207 2424 007
The City Gardener; The Ideal Home Show

Uden Associates
020 7351 1255
www.uden.com

Unique Communications Group
020 7605 1200
ucg@uniquegroup.co.uk or
info@uniquecomms.com
www.uniquecomms.com
Laser House, Waterfront Quay
Salford Quays M50 3XW
Tel: 0161 874 5700
British Comedy Awards 2002 (ITV); Plastic Surgery Story (Five/TLC); Deepcut: Perfect Place for Murder? (Five) British Comedy Awards 2003 (ITV); Stars Behind Bars (Five); Harley Street (Living TV); I'm the Answer (ITV)

Vera Productions
020 7436 6116
siobhan@vera.co.uk
The Big Impression (BBC1); Between Iraq and A Hard Place (C4); Bremner Bird and Fortune (C4)

Visual Voodoo Films
020 7430 4466
omar.njie@visualvoodoo.co.uk
www.visualvoodoo.co.uk

Vivum Intelligent Media
020 7729 2749
nick@vivum.net
www.vivum.net
World Trade Centre series (PBS); documentary in Russia (BBC4); high-brow factual content

Venner TV
020 7478 7300
www.televisioncorporation.co.uk

Wag TV
020 7688 1711
post@wagtv.com
www.wagtv.com
Gods in the Sky, C4; The Naked Pilgrim, Five; Extreme Ironing, C4; Get me to the Church on Time, Sky One

Wall To Wall
020 7485 7424
mail@walltowall.co.uk
www.walltowall.co.uk
George Orwell: A Life in Pictures; The Day Britain Stopped; The Tournament; The World's First Predator; Spymaster

Wark Clements and Company
0141 429 1750
info@warkclements.co.uk
www.warkclements.co.uk
Jeopardy (Children's best drama Bafta 2002), First World War (C4)

Wild Dream Films
01273 236168
mail@wild-dream.com
www.wild-dream.com

Wild Rover Productions
028 9050 0980
enquiries@wild-rover.com
www.wild-rover.com

Wilton Films
020 7749 7282
paul@wiltonfilms.com
www.wiltonfilms.com

Windfall Films
020 7251 7676
postmaster@windfall-films.co.uk
www.windfall.dircon.co.uk

World Of Wonder
020 7349 9000
wow@worldofwonder.co.uk
www.worldofwonder.net

World Wide Pictures
020 7434 1121
info@worldwidegroup.ltd.uk
www.worldwidegroup.ltd.uk

World's End Productions
020 7751 9880
info@wordsendproductions.com
www.wordsendproductions.com

Zeal Television
020 8780 4600
tv.sales@zealtv.net
www.zealtv.net
Resistance (BBC3), Demolition (Five/Bravo), Superhuman (C4), Sushi TV (Challenge)

Zebra Film Productions
0117 970 6026
info@zebrafilms.co.uk

Zenith Entertainment
020 7224 2440
general@zenith-entertainment.co.uk
www.zenith-entertainment.co.uk
Byker Grove, 2000 Acres of Sky (BBC),
CD:UK (ITV); RE-Covered (BBC3);
Headliners (C4);Garden Rivals, Room
Rivals (UK Style); Safari Chef (UK
Food), Brian's Boyfriends (ITV),
Murder Most Foul (Westcountry TV)

Zeppotron
0870 333 1700
contact@zeppotron.com
www.zeppotron.com

Zig Zag Productions
020 7353 7799
production@zigzag.uk.com
www.zigzagproductions.tv
The John Leslie Scandal, Wayne's
World, When Football Managers Go
Mad, Football Years Series 2 (Sky
One); Real Texas Chainsaw Massacre
(C4); Crime Business (Bravo); From
Merton to Enfield (Carlton); Extreme…
Animal Attacks, Holiday Disasters etc
(Five)

TV associations

Bafta (British Academy of Film and Television Arts)
195 Piccadilly, London W1J 9LN
020 7734 0022
www.bafta.org
Awards, training and education

Barb (Broadcasters' Audience Research Board)
18 Dering Street, London W1S 1AQ
020 7529 5531
www.barb.co.uk
Industry-owned audience data

British Film Council International
10 Little Portland Street
London W1W 7JG
020 7861 7860
internationalinfo@ukfilmcouncil.org.uk
www.bfc.co.uk
Promotes UK as production centre

British Film Institute
21 Stephen Street, London W1T 1LN
020 7255 1444
publishing@bfi.org.uk
www.bfi.org.uk
Education, exhibitions and resources

British Universities Film and Video Council
77 Wells Street, London W1T 3QJ
020 7393 1500
ask@bufvc.ac.uk
www.bufvc.ac.uk/

Broadcasting Press Guild
Tiverton, The Ridge
Woking, Surrey GU22 7EQ
01483 764895
torin.douglas@bbc.co.uk

Bectu (Broadcasting, Entertainment, Cinematograph and Theatre Union)
020 7346 0900
www.bectu.org.uk

Cinema and Television Benevolent Fund
22 Golden Square
London W1F 9AD
020 7437 6567
charity@ctbf.co.uk
www.ctbf.co.uk
Trade charity

Drama Association of Wales
The Old Library Building
Singleton Road, Splott
Cardiff CF24 2ET
029 2045 2200
aled.daw@virgin.net

Equity
Guild House, Upper St Martins Lane
London WC2H 9EG
020 7379 6000
info@equity.org.uk
www.equity.org.uk
Actors' union

Fact (Federation Against Copyright Theft)
Unit 7, Victory Business Centre
Worton Road, Isleworth
Middlesex TW7 6DB
020 8568 6646
bc@fact-uk.org.uk
Industry-funded

Federation of Entertainment Unions
1 Highfield, Twyford, Nr Winchester
Hampshire SO21 1QR
01962 713134
harris@interalpha.co.uk

Film Council
10 Little Portland Street
London W1W 7JG
020 7861 7861
info@filmcouncil.org.uk
www.filmcouncil.org.uk

Focal International
Pentax House, South Hill Avenue
South Harrow HA2 0DU
020 8423 5853
info@focalint.org
www.focalint.org
Trade association for libraries and
researchers

IVCA (International Visual Communication Association)
19 Pepper Street, Glengall Bridge
London E14 9RP
020 7512 0571
info@ivca.org
www.ivca.org

Musicians Union
60–62 Clapham Road
London SW9 0JJ
020 7582 5566
webmaster@musiciansunion.org.uk
www.musiciansunion.org.uk

Nasta (National Student Television Association)
c/o Glasgow University Student
Television, John McIntyre Building
University Avenue
Glasgow G12 8OO
0141 339 8541 x30
http://80.71.2.74/~nasta/index.html
Consists of 11 student-run TV stations

National Film Theatre
Belvedere Road, South Bank
Waterloo, London SE1 8XT
020 7928 3535
nft@bfi.org.uk
www.bfi.org.uk/nft

New Producers Alliance (NPA)
9 Bourlet Close, London W1W 7BP
020 7580 2480
queries@npa.org.uk
www.newproducer.co.uk

Northern Ireland Film and Television Commission
Third Floor, Alfred House
21 Alfred Street, Belfast
Northern Ireland BT2 8ED
028 9023 2444
info@niftc.co.uk
www.niftc.co.uk

Pact (Producers Alliance for Cinema and Television)
45 Mortimer Street
London W1W 8HJ
020 7331 6000
enquiries@pact.co.uk
www.pact.co.uk
Trade association for independent
production companies

Performing Right Society
29–33 Berners Street
London W1T 3AB
020 7580 5544
www.prs.co.uk
Collects and distributes music royalties

Picture Research Association
Head Office, 2 Culver Drive
Oxted, Surrey RH8 9HP
01883 730123
pra@lippmann.co.uk
www.picture-research.org.uk
Professional body for supply of visual material to media

Royal Television Society
Holborn Hall, 100 Gray's Inn Road
London WC1X 8AL
020 7430 1000
info@rts.org.uk
www.rts.org.uk

Scottish Screen
Second Floor
249 West George Street
Glasgow G2 4QE
0141 302 1700
info@scottishscreen.com
www.scottishscreen.com

Screenwriters' Workshop
Suffolk House, 1–8 Whitfield Place
London W1T 5JV
020 7387 5511
screenoffice@tiscali.co.uk
www.lsw.org.uk

Sgrin, Media Agency for Wales
The Bank, 10 Mount Stuart Square
Cardiff Bay, Cardiff CF10 5EE
029 20 333300
sgrin@sgrin.co.uk
www.sgrin.co.uk

Spoken Word Publishing Association (SWPA)
c/o Macmillan Audio
20 New Wharf Road
London N1 9RR
020 7014 6041
z.howes@macmillan.co.uk
www.swpa.co.uk

Voice of the Listener and Viewer (VLV)
101 Kings Drive, Gravesend
Kent DA12 5BQ
01474 352835
vlv@btinternet.com
www.vlv.org.uk

Writernet
Cabin V, Clarendon Buildings
25 Horsell Road, Highbury
London N5 1XL
020 7609 7474
writernet@btinternet.com
www.writernet.org.uk
Writing for live and recorded performance

Broadcasting trade press

Audio Media
IMAS Publishing UK
Atlantica House, 11 Station Road
St Ives, Cambs PE27 5BH
01480 461555
pr@audiomedia.com
www.audiomedia.com
Monthly. Editor: Paul Mac

BFI Film and Television Handbook
The British Film Institute
21 Stephen Street, London W1T 1LN
020 7255 1444
eddie.dyja@bfi.org.uk
www.bfi.org.uk/handbook
Annual. Editor: Eddie Dyja

Broadcast
Emap Media
33–39 Bowling Green Lane
London EC1R 0DA
020 7505 8000
bcletters@media.Emap.com
www.broadcastnow.co.uk
Weekly. Editor: Conor Dignam

Broadcast Hardware International
Hardware Creations
48 The Broadway, Maidenhead
Berks SL6 1PW
01628 773935
cathy@hardwarecreations.tv
www.broadcast-hardware.com
10pa. Editor: David Sparks

Cable and Satellite International
Perspective Publishing
402 The Fruit and Wool Exchange
Brushfield Street, London E1 6EP
020 7426 0101
john.moulding@
    perspectivepublishing.com
www.cable-satellite.com
6pa. Editor: John Moulding

Commonwealth Broadcaster
Commonwealth Broadcasting
Association
17 Fleet Street, London EC4Y 1AA
020 7583 5550
cba@cba.org.uk
www.cba.org.uk
Quarterly. Editor: Elizabeth Smith

Contacts
The Spotlight, 7 Leicester Place
London WC2H 7RJ
020 7437 7631
info@spotlightcd.com
www.spotlightcd.com
Annual. Contacts for stage, film, tv and radio. Editor: Kate Poynton

Crewfinder
Adleader Publications
15 Chartwell Park, Belfast BT8 6NG
028 9079 7902
mail@adleader.co.uk
www.crewfinderwales.co.uk
Annual. Wales' film, tv and video directory

FilmBang
Marianne Mellin, 43 Hyndland Road
Glasgow G12 9UX
0141 334 2456
info@filmbang.com
www.filmbang.com
Annual. Scotland's film and video directory. Editor: Marianne Mellin

Filmscan
Adleader Publications
15 Chartwell Park, Belfast BT8 6NG
028 9079 7902
mail@adleader.co.uk
http://filmscan.ie
Annual. Ireland's film, tv and video directory

Kemps Film, TV, Video Handbook (UK edition)
Reed Business Information
Windsor Court
East Grinstead House
East Grinstead
West Sussex RH19 1XA
01342 332038
www.kftb.com
Annual. Guide to international production. Editor: Pat Huwson

The Knowledge
CMP Information
Riverbank House, Angel Lane
Tonbridge, Kent TN9 1SE
01732 377591
knowledge@cmpinformation.com
www.theknowledgeonline.com
Annual. Production directory

Line Up
Line Up Publications
The Hawthornes
4 Conference Grove
Crowle WR7 4SF
01905 381725
editorlineup@cix.co.uk
www.ibs.org.uk
6pa. Journal of the Institute of Broadcast Sound. Editor: Hugh Robjohns

Multichannel News
Chilton Company, 37 The Towers
Lower Mortlake Road
Richmond TW9 2JR
020 8948 8561
chrisforrester@compuserve.com
www.multichannel.com
Weekly. Editor: Chris Forester

Pact Directory of Independent Producers
Producers Alliance for Cinema and
Television (PACT)
45 Mortimer Street
London W1W 8HJ
020 7331 6000
enquiries@pact.co.uk
www.pact.co.uk
Annual. Editor: Louise Bateman

The Producer
Small World Publishing
26 Carnarvon Road, Redland
Bristol BS6 7DU
0117 942 6977
cda@blueyonder.co.uk
3pa. Editor: Chris Dickinson

The Production Guide
Emap Information
33–39 Bowling Green Lane
London EC1R ODA
020 7505 8000
theproductionguide@Emap.com
www.productionguideonline.com
Annual. Editor: Mei Mei Rogers

Radcom
Radio Society of Great Britain
Lambda House, Cranbourne Road
Potters Bar EN6 3JE
01707 659015
radcom@rsgb.org.uk
www.rsgb.org
Monthly. Editor: Steve Telenius-Lowe

Satellite Finance
Thompson Stanley Publishers
1–3 Leonard Street
London EC2A 4AQ
020 7251 2967
oliver.cann@satellitefinance.com
www.telecomfinance.com
11pa. Editor: Oliver Cann

Screen Digest
Screen Digest, Lymehouse Studios
38 Georgiana Street
London NW1 OEB
020 7424 2820
editorial@screendigest.com
www.screendigest.com
Monthly. Editor: David Fisher

Screen International
Emap Media
33–39 Bowling Green Lane
London EC1R ODA
020 7505 8080
screeninternational@hotmail.com
www.screendaily.com
Weekly. Editor: Colin Brown

Sports TV Yearbook
Perspective Media
PO Box 22499, London W6 9YS
020 7401 9998
pnicholson@sportsvisionnews.com
www.sportsvisionnews.com
Annual. Editor: Jay Stuart

Stage Screen and Radio
Bectu
373–377 Clapham Road
London SW9 9BT
020 7346 0900
janice@stagescreenandradio.org.uk
www.bectu.org.uk
10pa. Editor: Janice Turner

Televisual
Centaur Communications
St Giles House, 50 Poland Street
London W1F 7AX
020 7970 6666
televisual@centaur.co.uk
www.mad.co.uk
Monthly. Editor: Mundy Ellis

TV International Daily
Informa Media and Telecoms
Mortimer House
37–41 Mortimer Street
London W1T 3JH
020 7017 4269
toby.scott@informa.com
www.informamedia.com
260pa. Editor: Toby Scott

TV Technology and Production
IMAS Publishing UK
Atlantica House, 11 Station Road
St Ives, Cambs PE27 5BH
01480 461555
www.imaspub.com
*6pa. Broadcasting and production
technology. Editor: Mark Hallinger*

TVB Europe
CMP Information
8th Floor Ludgate House
245 Blackfriars Road
London SE1 9UX
020 7921 8307
sgrice@cmpinformation.com
www.tvbeurope.com
*Monthly. Broadcasting innovation
and technology. Editor: Fergal
Ringrose*

Variety
Reed Business Information
84 Theobalds Road
London WC1X 8RR
020 7611 4580
www.variety.com
Weekly. Editor: Steve Gaydos

VLV Bulletin
Voice of the Listener and Viewer
101 Kings Drive
Gravesend DA12 5BQ
01474 352835
vlv@btinternet.com
www.vlv.org.uk
Quarterly. Editor: Jocelyn Hay

Zerb
The Deeson Group, Sunnyside
Church Street, Charlbury
Chipping Norton OX7 3PR
01608 810954
alichap@mac.com
www.gtc.org.uk
*2pa. Aimed at cameramen and
managers. Editor: Alison Chapman*

Radio

Key contact

Radio Joint Audience Research (Rajar)
Gainsborough House
81 Oxford Street
London W1D 2EU
info@rajar.co.uk
www.rajar.co.uk

Britons devote around a third of their "media time" listening to radio – making it the second most popular medium behind TV, and the most popular until the early evening each day. The industry is growing at an unprecedented rate: new radio stations are launching all the time as the radio authority – now subsumed into super-regulator Ofcom – advertises new local analogue and digital licences at the rate of about one of each a month. There are now more than 250 analogue and more than 300 digital stations in the UK, although many of these overlap.

Radio listening figures are calculated by **Rajar**, an independent company. According to its latest figures, the BBC remains slightly bigger than the commercial sector: almost 32 million people listened to a BBC radio station for at least five minutes a week in the last quarter of 2002; 31.5 million listened to a commercial station in the same period. This statistic is known as a station's "reach". BBC stations dominate in the national market, with a reach of 28 million to commercial's 12 million; but commercial stations dominate locally, with a reach of 27 million to the BBC's 10 million.

In 2003 Rajar rejected calls to convert to an electronic system of audience measurement. It trialled two systems, one of which was an electronic wristwatch commissioned by the Wireless Group, owners of TalkSport, whose chairman is former Sun editor Kelvin MacKenzie. The system, which records everything participants listen to including in cars and shops, showed much higher audiences for speech stations than in Rajars. MacKenzie, who has been campaigning for nearly three years against the existing pen-and-paper system, threatened to take Rajar to court.

A new third tier of radio stations began broadcasting in March 2002. **Access radio**, a not-for-profit community radio scheme run by the radio authority, was deemed a success and will now survive on a combination of public funding and advertising. Stations will normally be permitted to receive up to half their income from advertising sales and sponsorship, as long as their coverage areas have no more than a five-kilometre radius and they comply with other rules designed to minimise competition with the local commercial sector.

In April 2003 the Radio Academy launched its **hall of fame**: its list of 25 people who in its opinion have made an outstanding contribution to the radio industry. See the panel (page 134) for the full list.

"I have done more radio shows hung over than not hung over"
Chris Evans at the high court (March 2003)

DOES IT TELL LIES WHEN MR BLAIR IS TALKING?

Awards

BBC

BBC radio has five national analogue stations: Radio 1, for popular and chart music; Radio 2, for slightly older music listeners; Radio 3, for classical, world music and arts; Radio 4, the speech station with flagship news programmes such as Today; and Five Live, for rolling news and sport. The BBC also broadcasts the World Service, the international news station funded separately by the Foreign Office. On digital, it broadcasts all these stations plus five digital-only stations: 6music, for modern music; 1xtra, for new black music; the Asian Network, for British Asians; BBC7, for comedy and drama; and Five Live Sports Extra.

The last few years have seen a marked change in the fortunes of Britain's two most popular stations, Radio 1 and Radio 2. As recently as 1999, Radio 1 held the top spot: it reached 11.3 million listeners in the third quarter of that year, almost 2 million ahead of Radio 2. Then Radio 2 signed Jonathan Ross and Steve Wright to complement irreplaceable favourites such as Terry Wogan, and in the fourth quarter of 2002, it rose to a record reach of 13.3 million, while in the second quarter of 2003 Radio 1 plunged below 10 million for the first time in its history.

In an attempt to reverse the long-term slide, Radio 1 pledged to revamp. It killed off the Britpop-inspired Evening Session, and poached Xfm's Zane Lowe to present the show that replaced it. It tinkered with the Sunday Top 40 chart show, bringing in affable DJ "Wes" to replace Mark Goodier. In August 2002, Sara Cox signed a new £1m deal to present the breakfast show; but into 2003 her show continued to shed listeners.

At Radio 2, meanwhile, controller Jim Moir thanked newspapers for helping to make the station "cool". "If the Daily Mirror and the Sun say you're cool, that's worth more than the entire length of the M1 covered in advertising hoardings."

Radio 4's audience grew as international affairs dominated the agenda: its reach was a huge 10 million a week in the first quarter of 2003, making it almost as popular as Radio 1, although it slipped back slightly in the following quarter. The rise followed controversy in October 2002 when Rod Liddle, editor of the Today programme, resigned after rightwing accusations of political bias; the final straw came when he wrote in the Guardian that the Countryside Alliance march reminded voters why they had voted Labour. He left his job rather than stop writing the column. Kevin Marsh became Today editor, and Richard Clark later took over Marsh's old job at The World at One.

Five Live also grew in popularity, with a reach of 6.4 million in the first quarter of 2003 – though this slipped back to 5.8 million in the three months to June. Radio 3 remained stable with a reach of about 2 million.

"The truth prevailed
and everyone can get
on with the job"

Paul Jackson of Virgin,
on the Evans case (June 2003)

Commercial radio

The radio advertising industry is recovering slowly. According to the Advertising Association, ad spend declined in real terms in 2002, growing just 0.8% overall to £491m (£563m according to industry figures); while in the first quarter of 2003, it grew 2.1% year on year – though this was again a below-inflation rise. GWR, though, recorded a 3.9% overall fall in revenues in the same quarter, warning that it saw "no sign" of recovery; while Capital said the market remained "challenging".

In 2003, commercial radio owners celebrated the relaxation of media ownership rules in the **Communications Act**. Companies may now broadcast to 55% (previously 15%) of potential listeners in any one region, or 45% if they own more than half the local newspaper market; but in any one area there must be at least two independent radio stations plus the BBC. A series of mergers and acquisitions in the commercial sector is expected, and there has been speculation that Clear Channel or another international broadcaster could move into the British radio market – as long as it meets the public interest test. But the competition commission fired a warning shot when it ruled that GWR's £12.5m plan to merge its Vibe brand with Chrysalis-owned Galaxy in Bristol was "against the public interest".

The government also applied a last-minute "localness test" to local radio content. MPs had warned that the draft bill could stifle the diversity of music played on British radio stations, unless stations were forced to play songs by local musicians.

Top tale from the water-cooler in 2003 was the court battle between **Chris Evans** and SMG, owners of Virgin Radio. The DJ was sacked in 2001 when he skipped work for almost a week and holed up in the Nag's Head in Belgravia in full view of the tabloid press. Evans said he was unfairly dismissed and that the company withheld £8.6m in shares to which he was entitled; but a high court judge threw out the claim, calling Evans a "liar" and a "prima donna". In a settlement in July 2003, Evans agreed to pay SMG costs and damages totalling £7m.

Capital Radio remained the largest commercial radio group in 2002; its DJ Chris Tarrant remained number one in the London breakfast show wars, despite losing listeners in 2002 and claiming the station had "lost the plot" with its music policy. But rumours persisted that Tarrant would be leaving Capital by the end of 2003; Radio 2 DJ Jonathan Ross's agent, Addison Cresswell, said his client had been approached "on three or four occasions".

In April 2003 Capital poached Emma Forbes, whose Heart 106.2 breakfast show had grown by 11% in the previous year, to present a weekend programme. But Chrysalis, owner of Heart, bucked trends by outperforming its rivals on revenue: it reported a 17% rise in advertising revenues between September and November 2002.

Commercial radio ownership	
	Main stations
Capital Radio	Capital, Capital Gold, XFM, Century, BRMB (Birmingham)
Emap Radio	Kiss 100, Key 103, Magic
Chrysalis	Heart, Galaxy, LBC, News Direct
GWR	Classic FM
Wireless Group	TalkSport

Digital radio

Digital radio underwent a significant expansion in 2002 and 2003. Four years after the launch of the first digital radio service, there are now more than 300 digital radio stations, according to the digital radio development bureau, which markets the technology. UK consumers had bought 135,000 digital radio sets by the end of 2002, a figure which could hit 500,000 by January 2004. There are two national digital multiplexes, or networks, in the UK: the BBC network and Digital One, a commercial venture backed by GWR and NTL; plus almost 50 local multiplexes, added at the rate at about one a month since 1999. But the number of adults listening to the radio via the television grew 24% in 2002 to 7.9 million; Sky Digital subscribers have access to 62 digital stations, and Freeview customers have access to 16.

Listeners in most major towns in the UK can already receive between 30 and 50 radio stations with a digital radio, which in many cases is more than double what is available on analogue; because digital radio uses the radio spectrum more efficiently than analogue, it is possible to broadcast more channels using the same frequency. Digital radio also delivers improved sound quality: the technology eliminates the "hissing" of some medium-wave stations.

The BBC signal is expected to cover 85% of the population by 2004, with some commercial operators reaching the same target this year.

In March 2003, the culture secretary, Tessa Jowell, ordered the BBC and communications super-regulator Ofcom to conduct a review into the progress of digital radio. The review will cover the BBC's six national digital radio services and more than 100 national, regional and local commercial digital stations.

Some digital radio stations are in fact only available as audio channels on Freeview – in other words, digital TV.

Further reading

■ **Press**
MediaGuardian
media.guardian.co.uk/radio

■ **Books**
Travels with My Radio
FI GLOVER, EBURY PRESS 2002
Insightful radio travelogue

Local Radio Journalism
PAUL CHANTLER AND SIM HARRIS,
FOCAL PRESS 1997 Useful guide

■ **Other resources**
Radio Academy
www.radioacademy.org
World Radio Network
www.wrn.org
Digital radio development bureau
www.drdb.org

Making waves **Julia Day**

Radio

The Communications Act, the advent of digital radio and the emergence of the BBC as a potent commercial force are among the factors conspiring to radically change the UK radio market.

The Act allows greater freedom for radio companies to take each other over, and lets foreign groups buy British radio stations for the first time. America's largest radio group, Clear Channel, may be among the first to grab a slice of the UK radio market.

But Emap, Capital Radio and Daily Mail & General Trust – Classic FM-owner GWR's biggest shareholder – are the British radio groups that look most able to take advantage of the relaxed ownership rules.

Yet the feeding frenzy at the table of UK radio that was originally predicted may turn out to be more of a measured, long-term realignment as British groups try to steady their balance sheets after the ravages of a deep advertising downturn and unclear recovery timescale.

Listenership to some digital radio stations has started to be measured by Rajar for the first time as sales of digital sets finally take off, having been much slower to ignite the public imagination than digital TV.

But, helped no doubt by the millions ploughed in to promoting its services, digital radio is beginning to establish itself as a viable medium and an affordable one, with the price of sets dipping below the £100 mark.

However, the culture secretary, Tessa Jowell, has ordered a review of digital radio – including the BBC's seven stations and the 100-plus national, regional and local stations – describing 2003 as a "crucial year" for the medium.

She said the review would: "take stock – to measure performance to date and consider what more needs to be done."

The establishment of the media super-regulator Ofcom has renewed the age-old BBC versus commercial broadcaster power struggle in the radio industry just as much as within the television companies.

The commercial radio companies have campaigned for the BBC to be brought under Ofcom's regulation, but the BBC has wasted no time in firing a warning shot across the bows of the regulator, calling for its radio content to be left free of heavy-handed regulation.

But the big four commercial radio groups – GWR, Capital, Emap and Chrysalis – are not only fighting it out with the BBC but among themselves on several fronts.

The battle for London's breakfast show audience has neared obsessive levels. Indecision over the future of Capital Radio's Chris Tarrant, and falling audience figures for his most successful of London shows, sparked a succession war.

One half of Tarrant's closest rival breakfast team – Emma Forbes, left her on-air partner Jono Coleman at Chrysalis Radio's Heart 105.2 for Capital.

Capital and BBC Radio 1 were among the stations revamping their music policy in an attempt to keep up with the rapidly evolving tastes of listeners. Less pop, more specialist shows – R&B, rock, new unsigned bands – seems to be the consensus way forward.

Another battleground has emerged with the launch of a third chart show – Emap's Smash Hits Chart, which broke away from the one existing commercial chart, the Hit 40 UK (previously the Pepsi Chart).

Radio 1 also revamped its 50-year-old Official UK Top 40, axing its 41-year old presenter Mark Goodier in favour of 23-year-old virtual unknown Wes Butters as part of a more widespread attempt to connect with its young listeners.

BBC Radio 2 needs no such make-over these days, having gone from strength to strength, piling on millions of listeners to become the nation's most listened-to station.

However, Virgin Radio – owned by Scottish Media Group – is still trying to come to terms with life after maverick presenter and one-time owner Chris Evans. Nothing could have highlighted the station's irrevocable split with the ginger-haired millionaire more than the 2002 high court face-off over the events that led to his sacking.

Julia Day is radio correspondent for
MediaGuardian.co.uk

National digital radio

On BBC network and Freeview:

BBC Radio 1*

BBC Radio 2*

BBC Radio 3*

BBC Radio 4*

BBC Radio Five Live*

BBC Five Live Sports Extra

BBC 6Music

BBC 7

BBC World Service

BBC 1Xtra

BBC Asian Network

On Digital One and Freeview

Oneword

On Digital One only

Primetime Radio

Talksport*

Virgin Radio*

Core

Planet Rock

Classic FM*

Life

On Freeview only

The Hits

Jazz FM*

Kerrang!

Kiss*

Magic*

Q

Smash Hits

*also available on analogue

Listening figures, second quarter 2003

Rajars, second quarter 2003

National stations	Reach (m)	Reach (%)	Share (%)
BBC Radio 2	13.0	27	16.3
BBC Radio 1	9.9	20	7.6
BBC Radio 4	9.7	20	11.4
Classic FM	6.6	14	4.5
BBC Radio Five Live	5.8	12	4.4
Virgin*	2.8	6	1.6
Kiss*	2.6	5	1.3
BBC Radio 3	2.0	4	1.1
BBC World service	1.5	3	0.7
Jazz*	1.4	3	0.7
Smash Hits	0.9	2	0.3
TalkSport	0.8	2	1.6
Kerrang!	0.8	2	0.3
XFM*	0.6	1	0.3
BBC Asian Network	0.4	1	0.3
Mean Country	0.1	–	0.1
Oneword	0.1	–	–
All BBC national	**27.8**	**57**	**40.8**
All commercial national	**11.6**	**24**	**8.4**

Source: Rajar   *Total networks

Top 20 local and regional stations by reach

		Reach (m)	Reach (%)	Share (%)
95.8 Capital FM	London	2.6	25	8.9
Heart 106.2 FM	London	1.9	18	6.7
Kiss 100 FM	London	1.6	15	4.6
Magic 105.4	London	1.4	13	4.4
Capital Gold	London	1.1	10	2.7
Galaxy 105	Leeds	1.0	25	7.8
BBC Radio Scotland		1.0	24	9.2
100.7 Heart FM	Birmingham	0.9	26	11.7
105.4 Century FM	Manchester	0.7	15	5.6
Jazz FM	London	0.7	7	2.0
Key 103	Manchester	0.7	26	9.0
Clyde 1 FM	Glasgow	0.7	37	17.6
Real Radio	Scotland	0.6	23	12.2
Radio City 96.7	Liverpool	0.6	33	15.4
BBC Radio Wales/Cymru		0.6	25	14.5
96.4FM BRMB	Birmingham	0.6	29	9.8
Galaxy 105–106	North-east	0.5	26	11.2
Metro Radio	North-east	0.5	38	17.6
LBC 97.3	London	0.5	5	2.7
100–102 Century	North-east	0.5	23	10.0
All BBC local		**10.1**	**21**	**11.3**
All commercial local		**26.7**	**55**	**36.7**
Other listening		**2.9**	**6**	**2.1**

Source: Rajar, second quarter 2003

Radio Contacts

Office of Communications (Ofcom)
Riverside House
2A Southwark Bridge Road
London SE1 9HA
020 7981 3000
mediaoffice@ofcom.org.uk
www.ofcom.gov.uk

Key contact

BBC radio stations

BBC Radio 1
Broadcasting House
Portland Place, London W1A 4DJ
08700 100100
info@bbc.co.uk
www.bbc.co.uk/radio1
Controller: Andy Parfitt

BBC Radio 2
Broadcasting House
Portland Place, London W1A 4WW
08700 100200
info@bbc.co.uk
www.bbc.co.uk/radio2
Controller: James Moir

BBC Radio 3
Broadcasting House
Portland Place, London W1A 1AA
08700 100300
radio3.website@bbc.co.uk
www.bbc.co.uk/radio3
Controller: Roger Wright

BBC Radio 4
Broadcasting House
Portland Place, London W1A 1AA
08700 100400
info@bbc.co.uk
www.bbc.co.uk/radio4
Controller: Helen Boaden

BBC Radio Five Live
News centre, Television Centre
Wood Lane, London W12 7RJ
08700 100500
info@bbc.co.uk
www.bbc.co.uk/fivelive
Controller: Bob Shennan

BBC Radio Five Live Sports Extra
News centre, Television Centre
Wood Lane, London W12 7RJ
08700 100500
info@bbc.co.uk
www.bbc.co.uk/fivelive
Controller: Bob Shennan

BBC 1Xtra
Yalding House
152–156 Great Portland Street
London W1N 6AJ
08700 100222
1xtra@bbc.co.uk
www.bbc.co.uk/1xtra
Controller: Andy Parfitt

BBC 6 Music
Broadcasting House
Portland Place, London W1A 1AA
08700 100222
info@bbc.co.uk
www.bbc.co.uk/6music
Controller: Helen Boaden

BBC Asian Network
Epic House, Charles Street
Leicester LE1 3SH
08700 100222
info@bbc.co.uk
www.bbc.co.uk/asiannetwork
Controller: Bijay Sharma

BBC 7
Broadcasting House
Portland Place, London W1A 1AA
08700 100222
info@bbc.co.uk
www2.thny.bbc.co.uk/bbc7
Controller: Helen Boaden

BBC World Service
Bush House, Strand
London WC2B 4PH
020 7557 2941
worldservicepress@bbc.co.uk
www.bbc.co.uk/worldservice
Director, World Service: Mark Byford

BBC local radio

BBC Radio Berkshire
PO Box 1044, Reading RG4 8FH
0118 946 4200
radio.berkshire@bbc.co.uk
www.bbc.co.uk/berkshire
Editor: Marianne Bell

BBC Radio Bristol and Somerset Sound
PO Box 194, Bristol BS99 7QT
01179 741111
radio.bristol@bbc.co.uk
www.bbc.co.uk/radiobristol and
www.bbc.co.uk/bristol
Managing editor, Bristol: Jenny Lacey; assistant editor, Bristol: Dawn Trevett. Somerset Sound: assistant editor: Simon Clifford

BBC Radio Cambridgeshire
PO Box 96, 104 Hills Road
Cambridge CB2 1LD
01223 259696
cambs@bbc.co.uk
www.bbc.co.uk/cambridgeshire
Editor: David Martin

BBC Radio Cleveland
PO Box 95FM, Newport Road
Middlesbrough TS1 5DG
01642 225211
bbcradiocleveland@bbc.co.uk
www.bbc.co.uk/tees
Editor: Andrew Glover

BBC Radio Cornwall
Phoenix Wharf, Truro
Cornwall TR1 1UA
01872 275421
radio.cornwall@bbc.co.uk
www.bbc.co.uk/cornwall
Editor: Pauline Causey

BBC Radio Cumbria
Annetwell Street, Carlisle CA3 8BB
01228 592444
radio.cumbria@bbc.co.uk
www.bbc.co.uk/radiocumbria
Editor: Nigel Dyson

BBC Radio Derby
PO Box 104.5, Derby DE1 3HL
01332 361111
radio.derby@bbc.co.uk
www.bbc.co.uk/radioderby
Editor: Simon Cornes

BBC Radio Devon
PO Box 1034, Plymouth PL3 4BD
01752 260323
radio.devon@bbc.co.uk
www.bbc.co.uk/devon
Editor: John Lilley

BBC Essex
198 New London Road
Chelmsford, Essex CM2 9XB
01245 616000
essex@bbc.co.uk
www.bbc.co.uk/essex
News editor: Alison Hodgkins-Brown

BBC Radio Gloucestershire
London Road, Gloucester GL1 1SW
01452 308585
radio.gloucestershire@bbc.co.uk
www.bbc.co.uk/gloucestershire
Editor: Mark Hurrell

BBC GMR
PO Box 951, Oxford Road
Manchester M60 1SD
0161 200 2000
gmr.newsdesk@bbc.co.uk
www.bbc.co.uk/england/gmr
GMR editor: Steve Taylor; Radio
Lancashire editor: John Clayton

BBC Radio Guernsey
Bulwer Avenue, St Sampsons
Guernsey GY2 4LA
01481 200600
radio.guernsey@bbc.co.uk
www.bbc.co.uk/guernsey
Editor: Rod Holmes

BBC Hereford and Worcester
Hylton Road, Worcester WR2 5WW
01905 748485
bbchw@bbc.co.uk
www.bbc.co.uk
/worcester or hereford
Editor: James Coghill

BBC Radio Humberside and
BBCi Hull
9 Chapel Street, Hull HU1 3NU
01482 323232
radio.humberside@bbc.co.uk
www.bbc.co.uk/humber
Editor: Simon Pattern
(moving February 2004 to
Queens Court, Queens Gardens, Hull
HU1 3NP)

BBC Radio Jersey
18 Parade Road, St Helier
Jersey JE2 3PL
01534 870000
radio.jersey@bbc.co.uk and
denzil.dudley01@bbc.co.uk
www.bbc.co.uk/jersey
Editor: Denzil Dudley

BBC Radio Kent
The Great Hall, Mount Pleasant Road
Tunbridge Wells, Kent TN1 1QQ
01892 670000
radio.kent@bbc.co.uk
www.bbc.co.uk/kent
Editor: Robert Wallace

BBC Radio Lancashire and BBC
Open Centre
26 Darwen Street, Blackburn
Lancs BB2 2EA
01254 262411
radio.lancashire@bbc.co.uk
www.bbc.co.uk/lancashire
Editor: John Clayton

BBC Radio Leeds
Broadcasting Centre
Woodhouse Lane, Leeds LS2 9PN
0113 244 2131
radio.leeds@bbc.co.uk
www.bbc.co.uk/leeds
Managing editor: Richard Whitaker

BBC Radio Leicester
Epic House, Charles Street
Leicester LE1 3SH
0116 251 6688
radio.leicester@bbc.co.uk
www.bbc.co.uk/leicester
Editor: Liam McCarthy

BBC Radio Lincolnshire
PO Box 219, Newport
Lincoln LN1 3XY
01522 511411
radio.lincolnshire@bbc.co.uk
www.bbc.co.uk/lincolnshire
Managing editor: Charlie Partridge

BBC London 94.9
35 Marylebone High Street
London W1U 4QA
0207 224 2424
yourlondon@bbc.co.uk
www.bbc.co.uk/london
Editor: David Robey

BBC Radio Merseyside and BBC
Open Centre
55 Paradise Street
Liverpool L1 3BP
0151 708 5500
radio.merseyside@bbc.co.uk
www.bbc.co.uk/liverpool
Editor: Mick Ord

BBC Radio Newcastle
Broadcasting Centre, Barrack Road
Newcastle upon Tyne NE99 1RN
0191 232 4141
radio.newcastle@bbc.co.uk
www.bbc.co.uk/england
/radionewcastle
Editor: Sarah Drummond

BBC Radio Norfolk
The Forum, Millennium Plain
Norwich NR2 1BH
01603 617411
radionorfolk@bbc.co.uk
www.bbc.co.uk/norfolk
Editor: David Clayton

BBC Radio Northampton
Broadcasting House
Abington Street
Northampton NN1 2BH
01604 239100
northampton@bbc.co.uk
www.bbc.co.uk/northamptonshire
Managing editor: David Clargo

BBC Radio Nottingham
London Road
Nottingham NG2 4UU
0115 955 0500
radio.nottingham@bbc.co.uk
www.bbc.co.uk/notttingham
Editor: Mike Bettison

BBC Radio Oxford
PO Box 95.2, Oxford OX2 7YL
01865 311444
radio.oxford@bbc.co.uk
www.bbc.co.uk/radiooxford
Editor: Phil Ashworth

BBC Radio Sheffield and
BBC Open Centre
54 Shoreham Street
Sheffield S1 4RS
0114 273 1177
radio.sheffield@bbc.co.uk
www.bbc.co.uk/england
/radiosheffield
Editor: Angus Moorat

BBC Radio Shropshire
2–4 Boscobel Drive
Shrewsbury SY1 3TT
01743 248484
radio.shropshire@bbc.co.uk
www.bbc.co.uk/shropshire
Editor: Tim Pemberton

BBC Radio Solent
Broadcasting House
Havelock Road
Southampton SO14 7PW
02380 631311
solent@bbc.co.uk
www.bbc.co.uk/radiosolent
Editor: Mia Costello

BBC Southern Counties Radio
Broadcasting Centre
Guildford GU2 5AP
01483 306306
southern.counties.radio@bbc.co.uk
www.bbc.co.uk/southerncounties
Editor: Mike Hapgood

BBC Radio Stoke and
BBC Open Centre
Cheapside, Hanley
Stoke on Trent ST1 1JJ
01782 208080
radio.stoke@bbc.co.uk
www.bbc.co.uk/stoke
Editor: Sue Owen

BBC Radio Suffolk
Broadcasting House
St Matthew's Street, Ipswich
Suffolk IP1 3EP
01473 250000
radiosuffolk@bbc.co.uk
www.bbc.co.uk/suffolk
Managing editor: Gerald Main

BBC Radio Swindon
PO Box 1234, Swindon SN1 3RW
01793 513626
radio.swindon@bbc.co.uk
www.bbc.co.uk/wiltshire
Editor: Tony Worgan

BBC Three Counties Radio
PO Box 3CR, Luton
Bedfordshire LU1 5XL
01582 637400
3cr@bbc.co.uk
www.bbc.co.uk/threecounties
Editor: Mark Norman

BBC Radio Wiltshire
PO Box 1234, Swindon SN1 3RW
01793 513626
radio.wiltshire@bbc.co.uk
www.bbc.co.uk/wiltshire
Editor: Tony Worgan

BBC WM (Birmingham)
PO Box 206, Birmingham B5 7SD
0121 432 9000
radio.wm@bbc.co.uk
www.bbc.co.uk/birmingham or
htttp://www.bbc.co.uk/blackcountry
Editor: Keith Beech
(moving early 2004 to The Mailbox,
Royal Mail Street Birmingham B1 1XL
Tel. 0121 567 6000)

BBC WM (Coventry)
1 Holt Court, Greyfriars Road
Coventry CV1 2WR
02476 860086
coventry.warwickshire@bbc.co.uk
www.bbc.co.uk/coventry
Editor: Keith Beech
(moving late 2004 or early 2005,
address as yet unknown)

BBC North Yorkshire – Radio York
20 Bootham Row, York YO30 7BR
01904 641351
northyorkshire.news@bbc.co.uk
www.bbc.co.uk/northyorkshire
Editor: Matt Youdale

BBC radio resources

Outside Broadcasts Bookings
Brock House, Langham street
London W1A 1AA
020 7765 4889
duncan.smith@bbc.co.uk
Senior Operations Manager: Duncan
Smith

The Radio Theatre
Broadcasting House
Portland Place, London W1A 1AA
Event Services: 020 7765 5100
rr-events-team@bbc.co.uk
www.bbcradioresources.com
Events manager: Mark Diamond
Presently closed. Earliest re-opening
2005.

Maida Vale Studios
1–129 Delaware Road
London W9 2LG
Event Services: 020 7765 5100
rr-events-team@bbc.co.uk
www.bbcradioresources.com
Events manager: Mark Diamond

Broadcasting House
Portland Place, London W1A 1AA
Event Services: 020 7765 5100
rr-events-team@bbc.co.uk
www.bbcradioresources.com
Events manager: Mark Diamond

Birmingham Studios
Pebble Mill, Pebble Mill Road
Edgbaston, Birmingham
West Midlands B5 7QQ
Bookings – Studios and Studio
Managers: 0121 432 8126
www.bbcradioresources.com
Operations co-ordinator: Liz Treacher

Bristol Broadcasting House
Whiteladies Road, Bristol BS8 2LR
Bookings – Studios and Studio
Managers: 0117 974 2167
www.bbcradioresources.com
Operations co-ordinator: Maria
Clutterbuck

Manchester Studios
New Broadcasting House
PO Box 27, Oxford Road
Manchester M60 1SJ
Bookings – Studios and Studio
Managers: 0161 244 4607
www.bbcradioresources.com
Operations co-ordinator: Lilian
O'Callaghan

Commercial radio

Commercial Radio Companies Association
77 Shaftesbury Avenue
London W1D 5DU
020 7306 2603
info@crca.co.uk
www.crca.co.uk

Main commercial radio groups

CN Group
Dalston Road
Carlisle, Cumbria CA2 5UA
01228 612600
news@cumbrian-newspapers.co.uk
www.cumbria-online.co.uk
Chief executive: Robin Burgess;
general manager: Christopher Bisco

Capital Radio
30 Leicester Square
London WC2H 7LA
020 7766 6000
www.capitalradio.plc.uk
Chairman: Ian Irvins; chief executive:
David Mansfield; operations director:
Paul Davies

Chrysalis Radio Group
The Chrysalis Building
13 Bramley Road, London W10 6SP
020 7221 2213
enquiries@chrysalis.com
www.chrysalis.com
Chief executive: Phil Riley; group
programme director: Jim Hicks;
group commercial director: Don
Thomson; strategy and development
director: Daniel Owen; technical
director: Bruce Davidson

Classic Gold Digital
Network Centre, Chiltern Road
Dunstable LU6 1HQ
01582 676200
www.classicgolddigital.com
Chairman: Tim Blackmore;
managing director: Colin Wilsher;
programme controller: Don Douglas

Emap Performance Network
Mappin House, 4 Winsley Street
London W1W 8HF
020 7436 1515
www.emap.com
Chief executive: Tim Schoonmaker;
group managing director: Dee Ford;
MD performance north: Michelle
Surrell; advertising director: Dave
King; programme director: Phil Roberts

Forever Broadcasting
7 Diamond Court, Kingston Park
Newcastle Upon Tyne NE3 2EN
0191 286 0000
mail@foreverbroadcasting.com
www.foreverbroadcasting.com
Chairman: John Josephs

GWR Group
Chiseldon House, Stonehill Green
Westlea, Swindon SN5 7HB
0118 928 4313
www.gwrgroup.musicradio.com
Executive chairman: Ralph Barnard;
group operations director UK: Steve
Orchard

Lincs FM
Witham Park, Waterside South
Lincoln LN5 7JN
01522 549900
enquiries@lincsfm.co.uk
www.lincsfm.co.uk
Chief executive: Michael Betton;
director of programming: Jane Hill;
director of sales: Jeff Harwood

SMG
200 Renfield Street
Glasgow G2 3PR
0141 300 3300
www.smg.plc.uk
Chief executive: Andrew Flanagan;
chief executive SMG Radio: John
Pearson; business development
director (radio): Bobby Hain

Scottish Radio Holdings
Clydebank Business Park
Clydebank, Glasgow G81 2RX
0141 565 2200
www.srhplc.com
Chairman: Lord Gordon of
Strathblane CBE; chief executive:
Richard Findlay; MD radio: David
Goode; MD Score Digital: Grae Allan

The Wireless Group
18 Hatfields, London SE1 8DJ
020 7959 7800
www.talksport.net
Chairman and chief executive:
Kelvin MacKenzie; MD ILRS:
Ashley MacKenzie; group programme
director: Paul Chantler

Tindle Radio Holdings
Weaver's Yard, 6 West Street
Farnham, Surrey GU9 7DN
01252 735667
Chairman: Sir Ray Tindle;
deputy chairman: Robert Stiby;
directors: Colin Christmas,
Kevin Stewart

UKRD Group
Cam Brea Studios, Wilson Way
Redruth, Cornwall TR15 3XX
01209 310435
www.ukrd.com
Chairman: James St Aubyn; chief
executive: Mike Powell; development
director: David Bruce; sales and
commercial director: Rob van Pooss;
programme director: Phil Angell

National commercial radio: Digital One and Freeview

Digital One
20 Southampton Street
London WC2E 7QH
020 7288 4600
press 07813 783181
info@digitalone.co.uk
www.ukdigitalradio.com
Joint venture backed by GWR and NTL

Freeview
2nd floor, 85 Tottenham Court Road
London W1T 4DU
020 7755 1149
www.freeview.co.uk
General manager: Matthew Seaman

Stations

Capital Disney
30 Leicester Square
London WC2H 7LA
020 7766 6000
kevin.palmer@capitalradiogroup.com
www.capitaldisney.co.uk
*Head of communications group radio:
Elly Smith
Digital One*

Classic FM
7 Swallow Place, Oxford Circus
London W1B 2AG
020 7343 9000
www.classicfm.com
*Editorial contact: Rob Weinberg
Digital One; 99.9–101.9 FM*

Core
PO Box 2269, London W1A 5UQ
GWR Group
020 7911 7300
fresh@corefreshhits.com
www.corefreshhits.com
*Digital content manager: Nick Piggott
Digital One*

The Hits
Castle Quay, Castlefields
Manchester M15 4PR
0161 288 5000
studio@thehitsradio.com
www.thehitsradio.com
*Station manager: Phil Poole
Freeview; DAB Digital Radio:
Greater London*

Jazz FM
26–27 Castlereagh Street
London W1H 5DL
020 7706 4100
jazzinfo@jazzfm.com
www.jazzfm.com
*Managing director: Carter Tanner
Freeview; DAB Digital Radio: Central
Scotland; Greater London; South
Wales and Severn Estuary; West
Midlands; 102.2 FM*

Kerrang!
900 Herries Road, Sheffield S6 1RH
0114 209 1034; 020 7347 9350
natalie.johnson@emap.com
www.Emapdigitalradio.com
Freeview

Kiss
Mappin House, 4 Winsley Street
London W1W 8HF
Emap Performance Network
020 7975 8100
firstname.lastname@kiss100.com
www.kiss100.com
*Programme director: Simon Long
100 FM; Greater London; Freeview*

Life
30 Leicester Square
London WC2H 7LA
020 7766 6000
studio@listentolife.com
*Programme manager: Kevin Palmer
Digital One*

Magic
900 Herries Road, Sheffield S6 1RH
0114 209 1034; 020 7347 9350
natalie.johnson@emap.com
www.Emapdigitalradio.com
Freeview

Oneword Radio
Landseer House
19 Charing Cross Road
London WC2H OES
020 7976 3030
info@oneword.co.uk
www.oneword.co.uk
*Managing director: Ben Budworth;
Programme manager: Christina
Captieux
Digital One; Freeview*

Planet Rock
PO Box 2269, London W1A 5UQ
GWR Group
020 7911 7300
joinus@planetrock.com
www.planetrock.com
*Digital content manager: Nick Piggott
Digital One*

Q Radio
Mappin House, 4 Winsley Street
London W1W 8HF
020 7436 1515
www.q4music.com
Freeview

Primetime Radio
PO Box 5050, London SW1E 6ZR
0870 050 5050
david.atkey@primetimeradio.org
www.primetimeradio.org
*Managing director: Ron Coles;
operations director: David Atkey
Digital One*

Smash! Hits
900 Herries Road, Sheffield S6 1RH
0114 209 1034; 020 7347 9350
natalie.johnson@emap.com
www.Emapdigitalradio.com
Freeview

Talksport
18 Hatfields, London SE1 8DJ
The Wireless Group
020 7959 7800
www.talksport.net
*Managing director: Jason Bryant;
programme director: Mike Parry
Digital One; 1107 AM; 1053 AM;
1071 AM; 1089 AM*

Virgin Radio
No 1 Golden Square
London W1F 9DJ
020 7434 1215
reception@virginradio.co.uk
www.virginradio.co.uk
*Station manager: Steve Taylor;
programme director: Paul Jackson
Digital One; 1197 AM; 1215 AM;
1233 AM; 1242 AM; 1260 AM*

News services

ITN Radio
200 Grays Inn Road
London WC1X 8XZ
radio@itn.co.uk
www.itn.co.uk
*Provides news service for Independent
Radio News (IRN), plus other feeds*

Independent Radio News (IRN)
200 Grays Inn Road
London WC1X 8XZ
020 7430 4090
news@irn.co.uk
www.irn.co.uk

Commercial local radio

London

95.8 Capital FM
Greater London
020 7766 6000
info@capitalradio.com
www.capitalfm.com
*Managing director for 95.8 FM:
Keith Pringle
95.8 FM. Owner: Capital Radio*

Capital Gold (1548)
Greater London
020 7766 6000
info@capitalradio.com
www.capitalgold.com
*Programme director: Andy Turner
1548 FM. Owner: Capital Radio*

Choice FM
Brixton
020 7378 3969
info@choicefm.com
www.choicefm.com
*Programme controller: Ivor Etienne
96.9 FM*

Choice 107.1 FM
North London
020 7378 3969
info@choicefm.com
www.choicefm.com
*Programme controller: Ivor Etienne
107.1 FM*

Fusion 107.3
South East London
020 8691 9202
www.fusion1073.com
*Station director: Steve Ramsey
107.3 FM. Owner: Fusion Radio
Group*

Heart 106.2
Greater London
020 7468 1062
www.heart1062.co.uk
Programme controller: Francis Currie
106.2 FM. Owner: Chrysalis Radio

Jazz FM 102.2
Greater London
020 7706 4100
jazzinfo@jazzfm.com
www.jazzfm.com
Programme director: Mark Walker
102.2
Owner: Guardian Media Group Radio

Kiss 100 FM
Greater London
020 7975 8100
firstname.lastname@kiss100.com
www.kiss100.com
Programme director: Simon Long
100 FM
Owner: Emap Performance Network

LBC 97.3
Greater London
020 7314 7300
firstname.lastname.lbc.co.uk
www.lbc.co.uk
Programme director: Steve Kyte
97.3 FM. Owner: Chrysalis Radio

LBC News 1152
Greater London
020 7314 7309
newsroom@lbc.co.uk
www.lbc.co.uk
Editorial director: Jonathan Richards
1152 AM. Owner: Chrysalis Radio

London Greek Radio LGR
North London
0871 288 1000
www.lgr.co.uk
Programme controller: G. Gregoriou
103.3 FM

London Turkish Radio LTR
North London
020 8881 0606
ltr1584am@aol.com
www.londonturkishradio.com
Programme controller: Umit Dandul
1584 AM

Magic 105.4 FM
Greater London
020 7955 1054
firstname.lastname@emap.com
Programming director: Trevor White
105.4 FM
Owner: Emap Performance Network

Mean Country 1035AM
Greater London
020 8795 1035
email@meancountry.com
www.meancountry.com
Programme controller: Neil Bob Herd
1035 AM
Owner: Mean Fiddler Music Group

Premier Christian Radio
Greater London
020 7316 1300
premier@premier.org.uk
www.premier.org.uk
Programme controller: Charmaine
Noble-Mclean
1413 AM; 1305 AM; 1413 AM; 1332 AM

Spectrum Radio
Greater London
020 7627 4433
name@spectrumradio.net
www.spectrumradio.net
General manager: Paul Hogan
558 AM

Sunrise Radio
Greater London
020 8574 6666
www.sunriseradio.com
Managing director (London):
Dr Avtar Lit; Managing director
(Midlands): Andrew Housley
1458 AM

Time FM
Thamesmead, Greater London
020 8311 3112
sramsay@time1068.com
www.1068.com
Station director: Steve Ramsey
106.8 FM
Owner: Fusion Radio Holdings

Virgin 105.8
Greater London
020 7434 1215
reception@virginradio.co.uk
www.virginradio.co.uk
Programme director: Paul Jackson
105.8 FM. Owner: SMG

Xfm
Greater London
020 7766 6600
www.xfm.co.uk
Programme controller: Andrew Phillips
104.9 FM. Owner: Capital Radio

South-east

107.4 The Quay
Portsmouth
023 9236 4141
mail@quayradio.com
www.quayradio.com
Programme controller: Paul Owen
107.4 FM. Owner: Radio Investments

107.5 Sovereign Radio
Eastbourne
01323 442700
info@1075sovereignradio.co.uk
www.1075sovereignradio.co.uk
Programme controller: Mike Buxton
107.5 FM. Owner: Radio Investments

107.6 Kestrel FM
Basingstoke
01256 694000
kestrelfm@kestrelfm.com
www.kestrelfm.com
Programme manager: Paul Allen
107.6 FM

107.8 Arrow FM
Hastings
01424 461177
info@arrowfm.co.uk
www.arrowfm.co.uk
Programme controller: Mike Buxton
107.8 FM. Owner: Radio Investments

107.8 SouthCity FM
Southampton
023 8022 0020
info@southcityfm.co.uk
www.southcityfm.co.uk
Programme director: Stuart McGinley
107.8 FM

2-Ten FM
Reading, Basingstoke, Newbury
and Andover
0118 945 4400
tim.parker@creation.com
www.musicradio.com
Programme controller: Tim Parker
103.4 FM; 97 FM; 102.9 FM
Owner: GWR Group

96.4 The Eagle
Guildford
01483 300964
onair@964eagle.co.uk
www.964eagle.co.uk
Programme director: Peter Gordon
96.4 FM. Owner: UKRD Group

Bright 106.4
Burgess Hill and Haywards Heath
01444 248127
info@bright1064.com
www.bright1064.com
Programme director: Mark Chapple
106.4 FM

Capital Gold (1170 and 1557)
South Hampshire
020 7766 6000
info@capitalgold.com
www.capitalgold.com
Programme director: Andy Turner
1557 AM; 1170 AM
Owner: Capital Radio

Capital Gold (1242 and 603)
Maidstone, Medway and East Kent
020 7766 6000
info@invictaradio.co.uk
www.capitalgold.com
Programme director: Andy Turner
603 AM; 1242 AM
Owner: Capital Radio

Capital Gold (1323 and 945)
Brighton, Eastbourne and Hastings
020 7766 6000
info@capitalgold.co.uk
www.capitalgold.com
Programme director: Andy Turner
945 AM; 1323 AM
Owner: Capital Radio

Classic Gold 1431/1485
Reading, Basingstoke and Andover
0118 945 4400
firstname.surname@
    classicgolddigital.com
www.classicgolddigital.com
Programme controller: Don Douglas
1431 AM; 1485 AM
Owner: Classic Gold Digital

Classic Gold 1521
Reigate and Crawley
01293 519161
studio@mercuryfm.co.uk
www.mercuryfm.co.uk
Programme controller: Don Douglas
1521 AM. Owner: Classic Gold Digital

County Sound Radio 1566 AM
Guildford
01483 300964
onair@countysound.co.uk
www.ukrd.com
Programme director: Peter Gordon
1566 AM. Owner: UKRD Group

Delta FM
Alton Hampshire
01428 651971
studio@deltafm.freeserve.co.uk
www.deltaradio.co.uk
Managing director: David Way
101.6 FM; 102 FM; 97.1 FM; 101.6 FM
Owner: UKRD Group

FM 103 Horizon
Milton Keynes
01908 269111
reception@horizon.musicradio.com
www.musicradio.com
Programme controller: Trevor Marshall
103.3 FM. Owner: GWR Group

Invicta FM
Maidstone, Medway and East Kent
01227 772004
info@invictaradio.co.uk
www.invictafm.com
Programme controller:
Rebecca Trbojevich
95.9 FM; 102.8 FM; 96.1 FM; 97 FM;
103.1 FM. Owner: Capital Radio

Isle of Wight Radio
Isle of Wight
01983 822557
admin@iwradio.co.uk
www.iwradio.co.uk
Programme controller: Tom Stroud
102 FM; 107 FM
Owner: Radio Investments

Juice107.2
Brighton
01273 386107
info@nonstopjuice.com
www.nonstopjuice.com
Programme controller: David Harber
107.2 FM
Owner: Forever Broadcasting

Kick FM
Newbury
01635 841600
mail@kickfm.com
www.kickfm.com
Managing director: Junie Lewis
105.6 FM; 107.4 FM

KMFM Canterbury 106
Canterbury
01227 789106
Tdibbon@kmfm.co.uk
www.kentonline.co.uk/kmfm
Group programme controller:
Mike Osborne
106 FM. Owner: KM Radio

KM-FM for Folkestone and Dover
Dover and Folkestone
01303 220303
Scork@kmfm.co.uk
www.kentonline/kmfm
Group programme controller:
Mike Osborne
106.8 FM; 96.4 FM. Owner: KM Radio

Medway's KM-FM
Medway Towns
01634 841111
pcarter@kmfm.co.uk
www.kentonline.co.uk/kmfm
Group programme controller:
Mike Osborne
100.4 FM; 107.9 FM.
Owner: KM Radio

Mercury FM
Reigate and Crawley
01293 519161
tim.parker@musicradio.com
www.musicradio.com
Programme controller: Tim Parker
97.5 FM; 102.7 FM
Owner: GWR Group

Mix 96
Aylesbury
01296 399396
info@mix96.co.uk
www.mix96.co.uk
Programme controller: Nathan Cooper
96.2 FM. Owner: Radio Investments

Ocean FM
South Hampshire
01489 589911
info@oceanfm.co.uk
www.oceanfm.com
Programme controller: Stuart Ellis
96.7 FM; 97.5 FM
Owner: Capital Radio

Reading 107 FM
Reading
0118 986 2555
firstname@reading107fm.com
www.reading107fm.com
Programme controller: Tim Grundy
107 FM

Soul City 107.5
Havering
0870 607 1075
info@soulcity1075.com
www.soulcity1075.com
Programme director: Chris Slack
107.5 FM

Southern FM
Brighton/Eastbourne and Hastings
01273 430111
news@southernfm.co.uk
www.Southernfm.com
Programme controller: Tony Aldridge
103.5 FM; 96.9 FM; 102.4 FM; 102 FM
Owner: Capital Radio

Spirit FM
Chichester, Bognor Regis,
Littlehampton
01243 773600
info@spiritfm.net
www.spiritfm.net
Programme controller: Duncan Barkes
102.3 FM; 96.6 FM

Star 106.6
Slough, Maidenhead, Windsor
01753 551066
onair@1066starfm.co.uk
www.star1066.co.uk
Programme controller: Ian Downs
106.6 FM. Owner: UKRD Group

Swan FM
High Wycombe
01494 446611
www.swanfm.co.uk
Programme director: Andy Muir
107.4 FM; 107.7 FM
Owner: Radio Investments

Thames 107.8
Kingston Upon Thames
020 8288 1300
info@thamesradio.com
www.thamesradio.com
Programme director: Dave Owen
107.8 FM

Thanet's KM-FM
Thanet
01843 220222
pwillson@kmfm.co.uk
www.kentonline.co.uk/kmfm
Group programme controller:
Mike Osborne
107.2 FM. Owner: KM Radio

Wave 105 FM
Solent
01489 481057
martin.ball@wave105.com
www.wave105.com
Programme controller: John Dash
105.2 FM; 105.8 FM
Owner: ScottishRadio Holdings

West Kent's KM-FM
Tunbridge Wells and Sevenoaks
01732 369200
bhayward@kmfm.co.uk
www.kentonline.co.uk/kmfm
Group programme controller:
Mike Osborne
96.2 FM; 101.6 FM. Owner: KM Radio

Win 107.2
Winchester
01962 841071
jo@winfm.co.uk
www.winfm.co.uk
Station manager: Jo Talbot
107.2 FM. Owner: Radio Investments

South-west

102.4 Severn Sound FM
Gloucester/Cheltenham
01452 313200
reception@
    severnsound.musicradio.com
www.musicradio.com
Programme controller: Russ Wilcox
103 FM; 102.4 FM
Owner: GWR Group

104.7 Island FM
Guernsey
01481 242000
firstname@islandfm.guernsey.net
www.islandfm.guernsey.net
Programme controller: Gary Burgess
104.7 FM; 93.7 FM
Owner: Tindle Radio

107.5 3TR FM
Warminster
01985 211111
admin@3trfm.com
www.3trfm.com
Station manager: James Moran
107.5 FM. Owner: Radio Investments

2CR FM
Bournemouth
01202 259259
www.musicradio.com
Programme controller: Craig Morris
102.3 FM. Owner: GWR Group

97 FM Plymouth Sound
Plymouth
01752 275600
mail@
    plymouthsound.musicradio.com
www.musicradio.com
Programme controller: Gavin Marshall
97 FM; 96.6 FM. Owner: GWR Group

97.4 Vale FM
Shaftesbury
01747 855711
studio@valefm.co.uk
www.valefm.co.uk
Programme controller: Martin Lee
97.4 FM; 96.6 FM
Owner: Radio Investments

Bath FM
Bath
01225 471571
news@bath.fm
www.bath.fm
Programme controller: Faye Dicker
107.9 FM

BCRfm
Bridgwater
01278 727701
studio@bcrfm.co.uk
www.bcrfm.co.uk
Programme controller:
David Englefield
107.4 FM

Channel 103 FM
Jersey
01534 888103
firstname@channel103.com
www.channel103.com
Programme director: Matt Howells
103.7 FM. Owner: Tindle Radio

Classic Gold 1152 AM
Plymouth
01752 275600
Peter.Greig@musicradio.com
www.classicgolddigital.com
Programme controller: Don Douglas
1152 AM. Owner: GWR Group

Classic Gold 1260
Bristol and Bath
0117 984 3200
firstname.surname@
    classicgolddigital.com
www.classicgolddigital.com
Programme controller: Don Douglas
1260 AM. Owner: GWR Group

Classic Gold 666/954
Exeter/Torbay
01392 444444
colin.slade@musicradio.com
www.musicradio.com
Programme controller: Colin Slade
954 AM; 666 AM. Owner: GWR Group

Classic Gold 774
Gloucester/Cheltenham
01452 313200
reception@severnfm.musicradio.com
www.classicgolddigital.com
Programme controller: Russel Wilcox
774 AM. Owner: Classic Gold Digital

Classic Gold 828
Bournemouth
01202 259259
www.classicgold.co.uk
Programme controller: Don Douglas
828 AM. Owner: Classic Gold Digital

Classic Gold 936/1161 AM
Swindon
0117 984 3200
reception@musicradio.com
www.musicradio.com
Programme controller: Sue Carter
936 AM; 1161 AM
Owner: Classic Gold Digital

Fire 107.6FM
Bournemouth and Poole
01202 318100
firstname@fire1076.com
www.fire1076.com
Programme controller: Max Hailey
107.6 FM. Owner: Radio Investments

Gemini FM
Exeter/Torbay
01392 444444
gemini@geminifm.musicradio.com
www.musicradio.com
Programme controller: Collin Slade
97 FM; 103 FM; 96.4 FM
Owner: GWR Group

GWR FM
Swindon and West Wiltshire
01793 842600
reception@musicradio.com
www.musicradio.com
Programme controller: Sue Carter
102.2 FM; 96.5 FM; 97.2 FM
Owner: GWR Group

GWR FM (Bristol and Bath)
Bristol and Bath
0117 984 3200
reception@gwrfm.musicradio.com
www.musicradio.com
Programme controller: Paul Andrew
103 FM; 96.3 FM. Owner: GWR Group

Lantern FM
Barnstable
01271 340340
jim.trevelyan@creation.com
www.musicradio.com
Programme controller: Paul Hopper
97.3 FM; 96.2 FM. Owner: GWR Group

Pirate FM102
Cornwall
01209 314400
enquiries@piratefm102.co.uk
www.piratefm102.co.uk
Programme director: Bob McCreadie
102.2 FM; 102.8 FM
Owner: UKRD Group

Quay West Radio
West Somerset
01984 634900
studio@quaywest.fm
Programme director: David Mortimer
102.4 FM

South Hams Radio
South Hams
01548 854595
southams@musicradio.com
Station manager: David Fitzgerald
101.9 FM; 100.8 FM; 100.5 FM;
101.2 FM. Owner: GWR Group

Spire FM
Salisbury
01722 416644
admin@spirefm.co.uk
www.spirefm.co.uk
Programme controller: Matt Rogers
102 FM. Owner: Radio Investments

Star 107
Stroud
01453 767369
studio@star107.co.uk
www.star107.co.uk
Programme controller: Ben Williams
107.2 FM; 107.9 FM
Owner: UKRD Group

Star 107.5
Cheltenham
01242 699555
studio@star1075.co.uk
www.star1075.co.uk
Programme manager: Ian Timms
102 FM. Owner: UKRD Group

Star 107.7 FM
Weston Super Mare
01934 624455
name@star1077.co.uk
www.star1077.co.uk
Programme controller: Scott Temple
107.7 FM; 107.1 FM; 106.5 FM
Owner: UKRD Group

Vibe 101
Severn Estuary
0117 901 0101
info@vibe101.co.uk
www.vibe101.co.uk
Programme controller: Jason Staveley
97.2 FM; 101 FM
Scotish Radio Holdings

Wessex FM
Weymouth and Dorchester
01305 250333
admin@wessexfm.co.uk
www.wessexfm.com
Programme controller: Stewart Smith
97.2 FM; 96 FM
Owner: Radio Investments

Eastern England

Chiltern FM
Bedford
01234 272400
simon.marshall@musicradio.com
www.musicradio.com
96.9 FM. Owner: GWR Group

Chiltern FM
Herts/Beds/Bucks
01582 676200
ian.walker@musicradio.com
www.musicradio.com
Programme controller: Ian Walker
97.6 FM. Owner: GWR Group

Classic Gold 1332 AM
Peterborough
01733 460460
don.douglas@classicgolddigital.com
www.classicgolddigital.com
Programme controller: Don Douglas
1332 AM. Owner: OPUS Group.
Classic Gold Digital

Classic Gold 792/828
Luton/Bedford
01582 676200
don.douglas@classicgolddigital.com
www.classicgolddigital.com
Programme controller: Don Douglas
792 AM; 828 AM. Owner: OPUS
Group. Classic Gold Digital

Classic Gold Amber
Norwich
01603 630621
Paul.Baker@classicgolddigital.com
www.classicgolddigital.com
Programme controller: Paul Baker
1152 AM . Owner: OPUS Group.
Classic Gold Digital

Classic Gold Amber (Suffolk)
Ipswich and Bury St Edmunds
01473 461000
paul.baker@classicgolddigital.com
www.classicgolddigital.com
Programme controller: Paul Baker
1251 AM; 1170 AM. Owner: OPUS
Group. Classic Gold Digital

Classic Gold Breeze
Southend and Chelmsford
01702 333711
paul.baker@classicgolddigital.com
www.classicgolddigital.com
Programme controller: Paul Baker
1359 AM; 1431 AM. Owner: OPUS
Group. Classic Gold Digital

Dream 100 FM
North Essex/South Suffolk
01206 764466
jonathan.hemmings@dream100.com
www.dream100.com
Programme controller:
Jonathan Hemmings
100.2 FM. Owner: Tindle Radio

Essex FM
Southend and Chelmsford
01702 333711
tracy.cooper@musicradio.com
www.musicradio.com
Programme manager and News editor:
Tracy Cooper
102.6 FM; 96.3 FM; 97.5 FM
Owner: GWR Group

Hereward FM
Greater Peterborough
01733 460460
paul.green@musicradio.com
www.musicradio.com
Programme controller: Paul Green
102.7 FM. Owner: GWR Group

Hertbeat FM
Hertfordshire
01438 810900
info@hertbeat.com
www.hertbeat.com
Programme controller: Robert Owen
106.9 FM; 106.7 FM

KL.FM 96.7
Kings Lynn and West Norfolk
01553 772777
admin@klfmradio.co.uk
www.klfm967.co.uk
Programme controller: Steve Bradley
96.7 FM. Owner: UKRD Group

Lite FM
Peterborough
01733 898106
rob@litefm.co.uk
www.litefm.co.uk
Programme manager: Rob Jones
106.8 FM
Owner: Forward Media Group

Norfolk and Suffolk's Broadland 102
Nofolk and North Suffolk
01603 630621
chris.marston@musicradio.com
www.musicradio.com
Programme controller: Chris Marston
102.4 FM. Owner: GWR Group

Q103 FM
Cambridge and Newmarket
01223 235255
reception@q103.musicradio.com
www.musicradio.com
Area programme controller:
Siobhan Burke
97.4 FM; 103 FM. Owner: GWR Group

SGR Colchester
Colchester
01206 575859
www.musicradio.com
Programme controller: Paul Morris
96.1 FM. Owner: GWR Group

SGR FM
Suffolk
01473 461000
tracy.cooper@musicradio.com
www.musicradio.com
Programme controller: Tracy Cooper
96.4 FM; 97.1 FM. Owner: GWR Group

Star 107.9
Cambridge
01223 722300
reception@star1079.co.uk
www.star1079.co.uk
Programme controller: James Keen
107.9 FM. Owner: UKRD Group

Ten 17
East Herts/West Essex
01279 431017
jill.admin@musicradio.com
www.musicradio.com
Programme director: Jeff O'Brien;
Programme manager: John White
101.7 FM. Owner: GWR Group

The Beach
Great Yarmouth and Lowestoft
0845 345 1035
sue.taylor@thebeach.com
www.thebeach.co.uk
103.4 FM. Owner: Tindle Radio

Vibe FM
East of England
01473 467500
general@vibefm.co.uk
www.vibefm.co.uk
Programme controller: Paul Saunders
105–108FM. Owner: ScottishRadio

East Midlands

106 Century FM
East Midlands
0115 910 6100
www.106centuryfm.com
Brand programme director:
Giles Squire
106 FM. Owner: Capital Radio

96 Trent FM
Nottinghamshire
0115 952 7000
dick.stone@musicradio.com
www.musicradio.com
Programme controller: Dick Stone
96.2 FM. Owner: GWR Group

Centre FM
South East Staffordshire
01827 318000
centrefm@centrefm.com
www.centre.fm
Programme manager: Mike Vitti
101.6 FM; 102.4 FM. Owner: CN Group

Classic Gold 1557
Northampton
01604 795600
reception@
    Northants96.musicradio.com
www.northamptonshire.co.uk/1557/
Programme controller: Dong Griff
1557 AM. Owner: Classic Gold Digital

Classic Gold 954/1530
Hereford and Worcester
01905 740600 / 01432 360246
james.hilton@classicgolddigital.fm
www.themagicam.com
Programme controller: James Hilton
954 AM; 1530 AM
Owner: Murfin Media International

Classic Gold GEM
Nottingham/Derby
0115 952 7000
don.douglas@classicgolddigital.com
www.classicgolddigital.com
Programme controller: Don Douglas
999 AM 945 AM
Owner: Classic Gold Digital

Connect FM
Kettering, Corby, Wellingborough
01536 412413
info@connectfm.com
www.connectfm.com
Programme manager: Danny Gibson
107.4 FM; 97.2 FM
Owner: Forward Media Group

Derby's RAM FM
Derby
01332 205599
ramfm@musicradio.com
www.musicradio.com
Programme controller: James Daniels
102.8 FM. Owner: GWR Group

Fosseway Radio
Hinckley/Nuneaton
01455 614151
enquiries@fossewayradio.co.uk
www.fossewayradio.co.uk
Programme manager: Ian Ison
107.9 FM. Owner: Lincs FM

Leicester Sound
Leicester
0116 256 1300
reception@
    leicesterfm.musicradio.com
www.musicradio.com
Programme controller: Craig Boddy
105.4 FM. Owner: GWR Group

Lincs FM
Lincoln
01522 549900
enquiries@lincsfm.co.uk
www.lincsfm.co.uk
Programme manager: John Marshall
102..2 FM; 97.6 FM; 96.7 FM
Owner: Lincs FM

Mansfield 103.2
Mansfield and District
01623 646666
info@mansfield103.co.uk
www.mansfield103.co.uk
Head of news: Katie Trinder
103.2 FM

Oak 107
Charnwood/NW Leicestershire
01509 211711
studio@oak107.co.uk
www.oak107.co.uk
Programme manager: Mike Vitti
107 FM. Owner: CN Group

Peak 107 FM
Chesterfield/N. Derbyshire/S.
Sheffield/Peak District
01246 269107
info@peak107.com
www.peak107.com
Group programme controller:
Steve King
102 FM; 107.4 FM
Owner: Forever Broadcasting

Rutland Radio
Rutland and Stamford
01572 757868
enquiries@rutlandradio.co.uk
www.rutlandradio.co.uk
Programme manager: Ian Ison
97.4 FM; 107.2 FM. Owner: Lincs FM

Sabras Radio
Leicester
0116 261 0666
info@sabrasradio.com
www.sabrasradio.com
Managing director and programme
controller: Don Kotak
1260 FM

Saga 106.6 FM
East Midlands
0115 986 1066
reception@saga1066fm.co.uk
www.saga1066fm.co.uk
Programme director: Paul Robey
101.4 FM; 106.6 FM. Saga Group

Signal 1
Stoke on Trent
01782 441300
info@signalradio.com
www.signal1.co.uk
Group programme director:
John Evington
96.4 FM; 102.6 FM; 96.9 FM
Owner: The Wireless Group

Signal Two
Stoke on Trent
01782 441300
info@signalradio.com
www.signal1.co.uk
ILR group programme director:
Kevin Howard
1170 FM. Owner: The Wireless Group

Trax FM
Bassetlaw
01909 500611
enquiries@traxfm.co.uk
www.traxfm.co.uk
Programme controller: Rob Wagstaff
107.9 FM. Owner: Lincs FM

West Midlands

100.7 Heart FM
West Midlands
0121 695 0000
news@heartfm.co.uk
www.heartfm.co.uk
Programme director: Alan Carruthers
100.7 FM. Owner: Chrysalis Radio

107.1 Rugby FM
Rugby
01788 541100
mail@rugbyfm.co.uk
www.rugbyfm.co.uk
Head of news: Lesley Cowper
107.1 FM; 107.5 FM
Owner: Milestone Radio Group

107.4 Telford FM
Telford
01952 280011
staff@telfordfm.co.uk
www.telfordfm.co.uk
Programme director: Pete Wagstaff
107.4 FM

107.7 The Wolf
Wolverhampton
01902 571070
firstname@thewolf.co.uk
www.thewolf.co.uk
Group programme director: Steve King
107.7 FM. Owner: Forever Broadcasting

96.4 FM BRMB
Birmingham
0121 245 5000
info@brmb.co.uk
www.brmb.co.uk
Programme controller: Adam Bridge
96.4 FM. Owner: Capital Radio

Beacon FM
Wolverhampton
01902 461300
firstname.surname@creation.com
www.musicradio.com
Programme director: Chris Pegg
97.2 FM; 103.1 FM
Owner: GWR Group

Capital Gold (1152)
Birmingham
020 7766 6000
info@capitalgold.co.uk
www.capitalgold.com
Programme director: Andy Turner
1152 AM. Owner: Capital Radio

Classic Gold 1359
Coventry
024 7686 8200
firstname.surname@
    classicgolddigital.com
www.classicgolddigital.com
Programme controller: Luis Clark
1359 AM. Owner: Classic Gold Digital

Classic Gold WABC
Wolverhampton, Shrewsbury
and Telford
01902 461300
firstname.surname@
    classicgolddigital.com
www.classicalgolddigital.com
Programme controller: Don Douglas
990 AM; 1017 AM
Owner: Classic Gold Digital

FM 102 – The Bear
Stratford Upon Avon
01789 262636
info@thebear.co.uk
www.thebear.co.uk
Programme manager: Mike Vitti
102 FM. Owner: CN Group

Galaxy 102.2
Birmingham
0121 695 0000
galaxy1022@galaxy1022.co.uk
www.galaxy1022.co.uk
Programme director: Neil Greenslade
102.2 FM. Owner: Chrysalis Radio

Kix 96
Coventry
024 7652 5656
firstname.surname@kix.fm
www.kix.fm
Programme manager: Mike Vitti
96.2 FM. Owner: CN Group

Mercia FM
Coventry
024 7686 8200
merciafm@musicradio.com
www.musicradio.com
Programme controller: Luis Clark
102.9 FM; 97 FM. Owner: GWR Group

Radio XL 1296 AM
Birmingham
0121 753 5353
arun@radioxl.net
www.radioxl.net
Sukjoinder Ghataore
1296 AM

Saga 105.7 FM Radio
West Midlands
0121 452 1057
onair@saga1057fm.co.uk
www.saga1057fm.co.uk
Programme director: Brian Savin
105.7 FM. Owner: Saga Group

Wyvern FM
Hereford and Worcester
01905 612212
simon.monk@creation.com
www.musicradio.com
Programme controller: Simon Monk
102.8 FM; 97.6 FM; 96.7 FM
Owner: GWR Group

North-east

Alpha 103.2
Darlington
01325 255552
alpha1032news@aol.com
www.alpha1032.com
Programme manager: Ricky Durkin
103.2 FM. Owner: Radio Investments

Century Radio
North East England
0191 477 6666
info@centuryfm.co.uk
www.100centuryfm.com
Programme controller: Paul Drogan
96.2 FM; 96.4 FM; 100.7 FM; 101.8 FM
Owner: Capital Radio

Galaxy 105–106
North East England
0191 206 8000
matt.mcclure@galaxy1056.co.uk
www.galaxy1056.co.uk
Programme director: Matt McClure
105.3 FM; 105.6 FM; 105.8 FM;
106.4 FM. Owner: Chrysalis Radio

Magic 1152
Tyne and Wear
0191 420 0971
tony.mckenzie@metroandmagic.com
www.magic1152.co.uk
Programme director: Tony McKenzie
1152 AM
Owner: Emap Performance Network

Magic 1170
Teesside
01642 888222
colin.paterson@tfmradio.com
www.tfmradio.co.uk
Programme director: Colin Paterson
1170 AM
Owner: Emap Performance Network

Metro Radio
Tyne and Wear
0191 420 0971
tony.mckenzie@metroandmagic.com
www.magic1152.co.uk
Programme director: Tony McKenzie
97.1 FM; 102.6 FM; 103 FM; 103.2 FM
Owner: Emap Performance Network

Sun FM
Sunderland
0191 548 1034
progs@sun-fm.com
www.sun-fm.com
Programme controller: Ricky Durkin
103.4 FM. Owner: Radio Investments

TFM
Teesside
01642 888222
colin.paterson@tfmradio.com
www.tfmradio.co.uk
Programme director: Colin Paterson
96.6 FM
Owner: Emap Performance Network

Yorkshire and Humberside

96.3 Radio Aire
Leeds
0113 283 5500
firstname.lastname@radioaire.com
www.radioaire.co.uk
Programme director Stuart Baldwin
96.3 FM
Owner: Emap Performance Network

96.9 Viking FM
Harrogate
01423 522972
mail@972strayfm.co.uk
www.972strayfm.co.uk
Programme director: Ray Stroud
97.2 FM. Owner: Radio Investments

97.2 Stray FM
Harrogate
01423 522972
mail@972strayfm.co.uk
www.strayfm.com/
Programme director: Ray Stroud
97.2 FM. Owner: Radio Investments

Classic Gold 1278/1530 AM
Bradford, Halifax and Huddersfield
01274 203040
general@pulse.co.uk
www.pulse.co.uk
ILR group programme director:
John Evington
1278 AM; 1530 AM
Owner: The Wireless Group

Compass FM
Grimsby
01472 346666
enquiries@compassfm.co.uk
www.compassfm.co.uk
Programme manager: Andy Marsh
96.4 FM. Owner: Lincs FM

Fresh Radio
Yorkshire Dales with Skipton
01756 799991
info@freshradio.co.uk
www.freshradio.co.uk
News editor: James Wilson
1431 MW; 1413 MW; 936 MW

Galaxy 105
Yorkshire
0113 213 0105
mail@galaxy105.co.uk
www.galaxy105.co.uk
Programme director: Mike Cass
105.8 FM; 105.6 FM; 105.1 FM;
105.6 FM. Owner: Chrysalis Radio

Hallam FM
South Yorkshire
0114 209 1000
programmes@hallamfm.co.uk
www.hallamfm.co.uk
Programme director: Anthony Gay
102.9 FM; 103.4 FM; 97.4 FM
Owner: Emap Performance Network

Home 107.9
Huddersfield
01484 321107
info@home1079.com
www.home1079.com
Programme controller: Nick Hancock
107.9 FM. Owner: Radio Investments

Magic 1161 AM
Humberside (East Yorkshire
and North Lincolnshire)
01482 593067
reception@magic1161.co.uk
www.magic1161.co.uk
Programme director:
Darrell Woodman
1161 AM
Owner: Emap Performance Network

Magic 828
Leeds
0113 283 5500
firstname.lastname@radioaire.com
www.radioaire.co.uk
Programme director: Stuart Baldwin
828 AM
Owner: Emap Performance Network

Magic AM
South Yorkshire
0114 209 1000
programmes@magicam.co.uk
www.magicam.co.uk
Programme director: Anthony Gay
990 AM; 10305 AM; 1548 AM
Owner: Emap Performance Network

Minster FM
York
01904 488888
general@minsterfm.co.uk
www.minsterfm.co.uk
Programme controller: Ed Bretton
104.7 FM; 102.3 FM
Owner: Radio Investments

The Pulse
Bradford, Huddersfield and Halifax
01274 203040
general@pulse.co.uk
www.pulse.co.uk
ILR group programme director:
John Evington
102.5 FM; 97.5 FM
Owner: The Wireless Group

Real Radio (Yorkshire)
South and West Yorkshire
0113 238 1114
info@realradiofm.com
www.realradiofm.com
Programme director: Terry Underhill
107.6 FM; 106.2 FM; 107.7 FM
Owner: Guardian Media Group Radio

Ridings FM
Wakefield
01924 367177
enquiries@ridingsfm.co.uk
www.ridingsfm.co.uk
Programme manager: Phil Butler
106.8 FM. Owner: Lincs FM

Sunrise FM
Bradford
01274 735043
usha@sunriseradio.fm
www.sunriseradio.fm
Programme controller: Usha Parmar
103.2 FM

Trax FM
Doncaster
01302 341166
events@traxfm.co.uk
www.traxfm.co.uk
Programme controller: Rob Wagstaff
107.1 FM;
Owner: Lincs FM

Yorkshire Coast Radio
Scarborough
01723 500962
www.yorkshirecoastradio.com
Programme controller: Chris Sigsworth
96.2 FM; 103.1 FM
Owner: Radio Investments

Yorkshire Coast Radio
Bridlington's Best
Bridlington
01262 404400
www.yorkshirecoastradio.com
Programme controller: Chris Sigsworth
102.4 FM. Owner: Radio Investments

North-west

102.4 Wish FM
Wigan
01942 761024
studio@wish_fm.com
ILR group programme director:
John Evington
102.4 FM. Owner: The Wireless Group

106.9 Silk FM
Macclesfield
01625 268000
mail@silkfm.com
www.silkfm.com
Programme manager: Andy Clewes
106.9 FM. Owner: Radio Investments

107.2 Wire FM
Warrington
01925 445545
info@wirefm.com
www.wirefm.com
ILR group programme director:
John Evington
107.2 FM. Owner: The Wireless Group

2BR
Burnley
01282 690000
info@2br.co.uk
www.2br.co.uk
Managing director: Mark Matthews
99.8 FM

96.2 The Revolution
Oldham
0161 621 6500
info@therevolution.uk.com
www.revolutiononline.co.uk
Programme controller: Chris Gregg
96.2 FM

97.4 Rock FM
Preston and Blackpool
01772 477700
firstname.lastname@rockfm.co.uk
www.rockfm.co.uk
Programme director: Brian Paige
97.4 FM
Owner: Emap Performance Network

Asian Sound Radio
East Lancashire
0161 288 1000
info@asiansoundradio.co.uk
www.asiansoundradio.co.uk
Programme director: Shujat Ali
963 AM 1377 AM

Capital Gold 1548 AM
Manchester
020 7766 6000
info@capitalgold.com
www.capitalgold.com
Programme director: Andy Turner
1458AM. Owner: Capital Radio

Century 105
North West England
0161 400 0105
info1054@centuryfm.co.uk
www.1054centuryfm.com
Brand programme director:
Giles Squire
105.4 FM. Owner: Capital Radio

Classic Gold Marcher 1260 AM
Wrexham and Chester
01978 752202
firstname.surname@
    classicgolddigital.com
www.classicgolddigital.com
Programme controller: Don Douglas
1260 AM. Owner: Classic Gold Digital

Dee 106.3
Chester
01244 391000
info@dee1063.com
www.dee1063.com
Head of news: Faye Ruscoe
106.3 FM

Dune FM
Southport
01704 502500
firstname.lastname@dunefm.co.uk
www.dunefm.co.uk
Programme manager: Jonathan Dean
107.9 FM

Galaxy 102
Manchester
0161 279 0300
mail@galaxy102.co.uk
www.galaxy102.co.uk
Programme director: Vaughan Hobbs
102 FM; 107.4 FM
Owner: Chrysalis Radio

Imagine FM
Stockport
0161 609 1400
info@imaginefm.com
www.imaginefm.co.uk
ILR group programme director:
John Evington
104.9 FM. Owner: The Wireless Group

Jazz FM 100.4
North West England
0161 877 1004
jazzinfo@jazzfm.com
www.jazzfm.com
Programming director: Steve Collins
100.4 FM
Owner: Guardian Media Group Radio

Juice 107.6
Liverpool
0151 707 3107
mail@juiceliverpool.com
www.juice.fm
Programme director:
Grainne Landowski
107.6 FM. Owner: Forever Broadcasting

KCR 106.7
Knowsley
0151 290 1501
kcrsales@btconnect.com
www.kcr.fm
Programme controller: Ray Ferguson
106.7 FM

Key 103
Manchester
0161 288 5000
first.name@piccradio.com
www.key103.com
Programme director: Andrew Robson
103 FM
Owner: Emap Performance Network

Lakeland Radio
Kendal and Windermere
01539 737380
info@lakelandradio.co.uk
www.lakelandradio.co.uk
Programme manager: Lindsey Kerr
100.8 FM

Magic 1548
Liverpool
0151 472 6800
firstname@magic1548.com
www.radiocity.co.uk
Programme director: Richard Maddock
1548 AM
Owner: Emap Performance Network

Magic 999
Preston and Blackpool
01772 477700
name.surname@magic999.co.uk
www.magic999.co.uk
Programme director: Brian Page
999 AM
Owner: Emap Performance Network

Manchester's Magic 1152
Manchester
0161 288 5000
first.lastname@picradio.com
www.key103.co.uk
Programme director: Andrew Robson
1152 AM
Owner: Emap Performance Network

MFM 103.4
Wrexham and Chester
01978 752202
sarah.smithard@musicradio.com
www.mfmradio.co.uk
Area programme director:
Graham Ledger
103.4 FM. Owner: GWR Group

Radio City 96.7
Liverpool
0151 472 6800
firstname.surname@
   radiocity967.com
www.radiocity.co.uk
Programme director: Richard Maddock
96.7 FM
Owner: Emap Performance Network

Radio Wave
Blackpool
01253 304965
any@the wavefm.co.uk
www.thewavefm.co.uk
Station director: Mel Booth
96.5 FM. Owner: The Wireless Group

The Bay
Morecambe Bay
01524 848747
information@thebay.fm
www.thebay.fm
102.3 FM 96.9 FM. Owner: CN Group

Tower FM
Bolton and Bury
01204 387000
info@towerfm.co.uk
www.towerfm.co.uk
Programme director: Gary Stein
107.4 FM. Owner: Forever Broadcasting

Wirral's Buzz 97.1
Wirral
0151 650 1700
sarah.smithard@musicradio.com
www.wirralsbuzz.com
Area programme controller:
Graham Ledger
97.1 FM. Owner: GWR Group

Wales

102.5 Radio Pembrokeshire
Pembrokeshire/
West Carmarthenshire
01834 869384
enquiries@radiopembrokeshire.com
www.radiopembrokeshire.com
News editor: Anna Wilson
102.5 FM; 107.5 FM

106.3 Bridge FM
Bridgend
01656 647777
firstname.surname@bridge.fm
www.bridge.fm
Programme controller: Lee Thomas
106.3 FM. Owner: Tindle Radio

96.4 FM The Wave
Swansea
01792 511964
info@thewave.co.uk
www.thewave.co.uk
ILR group programme director:
John Evington
96.4 FM. Owner: The Wireless Group

Capital Gold (1305 and 1359)
Cardiff and Newport
020 7766 6000
first.surname@capitalgold.com
www.capitalgold.com
Programme director: Andy Turner
1305 AM; 1359 AM
Owner: Capital Radio

Champion FM
Caenafon
01248 671888
sarah.smithard@musicradio.com
www.champion103.com
Area programme controller:
Graham Ledger
103 FM. Owner: GWR Group

Coast FM
North Wales Coast.
01248 673272
sion.pritchard@musicradio.com
www.coastfm.co.uk
Area programme controller:
Graham Ledger
96.3 FM. Owner: GWR Group

Radio Ceredigion
Ceredigion
01970 627999
admin@ceredigionradio.co.uk
www.ceredigionradio.co.uk
Programme controller: Mark Simon
97.4 FM; 103.3 FM; 96.6 FM

Radio Maldwyn
Montgomeryshire
01686 623555
radio.maldwyn@ukonline.co.uk
www.magic756.net
Operations Director: Austin Powell
756 AM
Owner: Murfin Media International

Real Radio (South Wales)
South Wales Regional
02920 315100
info@realradiofm.com
www.realradiofm.com
Programme director: Sarah Graham
105.9 FM; 106 FM; 105.2 FM 105.4 FM
Owner: Guardian Media Group Radio

Red Dragon FM
Cardiff and Newport
029 2066 2066
mail@reddragonfm.co.uk
www.reddragonfm.co.uk
Programme controller: David Rees
103.2 FM; 97.4 FM
Owner: Capital Radio

Star 107.3
Bristol
0117 910 6600
frontdesk@star1073.co.uk
www.star1073.co.uk
Station manager: Dev Chakraborty
107.3 FM. Owner: UKRD Group

Sunshine 855
Ludlow
01584 873795
sunshine855@ukonline.co.uk
www.sunshine855.com
Managing director Ginny Murfin
855 AM
Owner: Murfin Media International

Swansea Sound
Swansea
01792 511170
info@swanseasound.co.uk
www.swanseasound.co.uk
ILR group programme director:
John Evington
1170 AM. Owner: The Wireless Group

Valleys Radio
Heads of South Wales Valleys
01495 301116
admin@valleysradio.co.uk
www.valleysradio.co.uk
ILR group programme director:
John Evington
1116 AM; 999 AM
Owner: The Wireless Group

Scotland

96.3 QFM
Paisley
0141 429 9430
sales@q-fm.com
www.q96.net
ILR group programme director:
John Evington
96.3 FM. Owner: The Wireless Group

Argyll FM
Kintyre, Islay and Jura
01586 551800
argyllradio@hotmail.com
Programme controller: Kenny Johnson
107.7 FM; 107.1 FM; 106.5 FM

Beat 106
Central Scotland
0141 566 6106
info@beat106.com
www.beat106.com
Programme controller: Claire Pattenden
106.1 FM; 105.7 FM
Owner: Capital Radio

Castle Rock FM 103
Dumbarton
01389 734422
info@castlerockfm.com
www.castlerockfm.com
Programme director: Jack Bennie
103 FM

Central FM
Stirling and Falkirk
01324 611164
mail@centralfm.co.uk
www.centralfm.co.uk
Programme controller: Tom Bell
103.1 FM. Owner: Radio Investments

CFM (Carlisle)
Carlisle
01228 818964
reception@cfmradio.com
www.cfmradio.com
Programme controller: David Bain
96.4 FM; 102.5 FM
Owner: Scottish Radio Holdings

CFM (West Cumbria)
West Cumbria
01228 818964
reception@cfmradio.com
www.cfmradio.com
Programme controller: David Bain
103.4 FM; 102.2 FM
Owner: Scottish Radio Holdings

Clan FM
North Lanarkshire
01698 733107
firstname.lastname@clanfm.com
www.clanfm.com
Head of news: Andrew Thompson
107.9 FM; 107.5 FM
Owner: UKRD Group

Clyde 1 FM
Glasgow
0141 565 2200
info@clyde1.com
www.clyde1.com
Programme controller: Ross Macfadyen
97 FM; 103.3 FM; 102.5 FM
Owner: Scottish Radio Holdings

Clyde 2
Glasgow
0141 565 2200
info@clyde2.com
www.clyde2.com
Programme controller: Ross Macfadyen
1152 AM
Owner: Scottish Radio Holdings

Forth 2
Edinburgh
0131 556 9255
info@forth2.com
www.forth2.com
Programme controller: Nik Goodman
1548 AM
Owner: Scottish Radio Holdings

Forth One
Edinburgh
0131 556 9255
info@forthone.com
www.forthone.com
Programme controller: Nik Goodman
97.6 FM; 102.2 FM; 97.3 FM
Owner: Scottish Radio Holdings

Heartland FM
Pitlochry and Aberfeldy
01796 474040
mailbox@heartlandfm.co.uk
Programme controller: Peter Ramsden
97.5 FM; 102.7 FM

Isles FM
Western Isles
01851 703333
studio@isles.fm
www.isles.fm
Director of operations: David Morrison
103 FM

Kingdom FM
Fife
01592 753753
info@kingdomfm.co.uk
www.kingdomfm.co.uk
Programme director: Kevin Brady
95.2 FM; 105.4 FM; 96.6 FM;
106.3 FM; 96.1 FM

Moray Firth Radio (MFR)
Inverness
01463 224433
mfr@mfr.co.uk
www.mfr.co.uk
Managing director: Gary Robinson
96.6 FM; 96.7 FM; 97.4 FM;
102.5 FM; 102.8 FM
Owner: Scottish Radio Holdings

Moray Firth Radio (MFR)
Inverness
01463 224433
mfr@mfr.co.uk
www.mfr.co.uk
Managing director Gary Robinson
96.7 FM; 96.6 FM; 102.5 FM;
97.4 FM; 102.8 FM
Owner: Scottish Radio Holdings

NECR
Inverurie
01467 632909
necrradio102.1fmsales@supanet.com
Programme controller: John Dean
102.1 FM; 102.6 FM; 97.1 FM; 103.2 FM

Nevis Radio
Fort Williamand parts of Lochaber
01397 700007
studio@nevisradio.co.uk
www.nevisradio.co.uk
Programme controller: Willie Cameron
96.6 FM; 102.4 FM; 97 FM; 102.3 FM

Northsound One
Aberdeen
01224 337000
northsound@srh.co.uk
www.northsound1.co.uk
Programme controller: Fiona Stalker
96.9 FM; 97.6 FM; 103 FM
Owner: Scottish Radio Holdings

Northsound Two
Aberdeen
01224 337000
northsound@srh.co.uk
www.northsound2.co.uk
Programme controller: Fiona Stalker
1035 AM
Owner: Scottish Radio Holdings

Oban FM
Oban
01631 570057
obanfmradio@btconnect.com
Programme director: Coll MacDougall
103.3 FM

Radio Borders
The Borders
01896 759444
programming@radioborders.com
www.radioborders.com
Programme controller:
Danny Gallagher
96.8 FM; 103.1 FM; 103.4 FM; 97.5 FM
Owner: Scottish Radio Holdings

Real Radio (Scotland)
Central Scotland
0141 781 1011
contact.name@realradiofm.com
www.realradiofm.com
Programme director: Jay Crawford
100.3 FM; 101.1 FM
Owner: Guardian Media Group Radio

SIBC
Shetland
01595 695299
info@sibc.co.uk
www.sibc.co.uk
Programme controller: Inga Walterson
96.2 FM; 102.2 FM

South West Sound
Dumfries and Galloway
01387 250999
info@westsound.co.uk
www.westsound.co.uk
Programme director: Alan Toomey
96.5 FM; 97 FM; 103 FM
Owner: Scottish Radio Holdings

Tay AM
Dundee/ Perth
01382 200800
tayam@radiotay.co.uk
www.radiotay.co.uk
Programme director: Arthur Ballingail
1584 AM; 1161 AM
Owner: Scottish Radio Holdings

Tay FM
Dundee/ Perth
01382 200800
tayam@radiotay.co.uk
www.radiotay.co.uk
Programme director: Arthur Ballingail
102.8 FM; 96.4 FM
Owner: Scottish Radio Holdings

Wave 102
Dundee
01382 901000
studio@wave102.co.uk
www.wave102.co.uk
ILR group programme director:
John Evington
102 FM. Owner: The Wireless Group

Waves Radio Peterhead
Peterhead
01779 491012
waves@radiophd.freeserve.co.uk
www.wavesfm.com
Programme controller: Norman Spence
101.2 FM

West FM
Ayr
01292 283662
info@westfm.co.uk
www.westfmonline.com
Programme director: Alan Toomey
97.5FM; 96.7 FM
Owner: Scottish Radio Holdings

West Sound AM
Ayr
01292 283662
info@westsound.co.uk
www.west-sound.co.uk
Programme director: Alan Toomey
1035 AM
Owner: Scottish Radio Holdings

Northern Ireland

102.9 FM
Londonderry
02871 344449
manager@102.fm
www.q102.fm
Programme controller:
Frank McLaughlin
102.9 FM

City Beat 96.7
Belfast
028 9020 5967
misic@citybeat.co.uk
www.citybeat.co.uk
Station director: John Rosborough
96.7 FM
Owner: CN Group

Cool FM
Northern Ireland
028 9181 7181
music@coolfm.co.uk
www.coolfm.co.uk
Programme controller:
David Sloan MBE
97.4 FM
Owner: Scottish Radio Holdings

Downtown Radio
Northern Ireland
028 9181 5555
programmes@downtown.co.uk
www.downtown.co.uk
Programme controller:
David Sloan MBE
97.1 FM;103.1 FM;103.4 FM;
102.4 FM; 1026 AM; 96.6 FM;
102.3 FM; 96.4 FM
Owner: Scottish Radio Holdings

Mid 106
Mid-Ulster
02886 758696
firstnamelastname@midfm106.co.uk
www.mid106fm.co.uk
Station director: Neil McLeod Berriskell
106 FM. Owner: CN Group

Q101.2 FM West
Omagh and Enniskillen
028 8224 5777
manager@q101west.fm
www.q101west.fm
Programme controller:
Frank McLaughlin
101.2 FM

Q97.2 Causeway Coast Radio
Coleraine
028 7035 9100
manager@q972.fm
www.q972.fm
Programme controller:
Frank McLaughlin
97.2 FM

Access radio

ALL FM
Manchester
Radio Regen
0161 273 4072
info@allfm.org
www.allfm.org
Programme organiser: Dave Lenaghan
96.9 FM

Angel Community Radio
Havant
02392 481988
angelradio@37.com
Managing director: Tony Smith
101.1 FM

Awaz FM
Glasgow
0141 427 2266
javed@radioawaz.com
www.radioawaz.com
Project manager: Javed Sattar
107.2 FM

BCB 96.7 FM
Bradford
01274 771677
info@bcb.yorks.com
www.bcb.yorks.com
Programmes Director: Mary Dowson
96.7 FM

Cross Rhythms City Radio
Stoke on Trent
0870 011 8008
admin@crossrhythms.co.uk
www.crossrhythms.co.uk
Programmes Controller: Steve Perry
101.8 FM. Digital satellite channel 876

Desi Radio
Southall
020 8574 9591
info@desiradio.org.uk
www.desiradio.org.uk
Chair of the trustees: Amarjit Khera
1602 AM

Forest Of Dean Radio
Gloucester
01594 820722
contactus@fodradio.org
www.fodradio.org
Project co-ordinator: Amanda Smith
1503 AM; 1521 AM

GTFM
Pontypridd
01443 406111
news@gtfm.fsnet.co.uk
www.gtfm.co.uk
Manager: Andrew Jones
106.9 FM

New Style Radio
Birmingham
0121 456 3826
c_r_t@lineone.net
www.newstyleradio.co.uk
Manager: Barbara Richards
98.7 FM

Northern Visions Radio
Belfast
028 9024 5495
info@northernvisions.org
www.northernvisions.org/
Community media development
officer: David Hyndman
100.6 FM

Radio Faza
Nottingham
0115 844 0047
radiofaza@hotmail.com
Media co-ordinator: Kathleen Ahmed
97.1 FM

Resonance 104.4 FM
London
020 7836 3664
resonancefm@easynet.co.uk
www.resonancefm.com
Studio manager: Knut Aufermann;
Programmer: Ed Baxter
104.4 FM

Shine FM
Bainbridge, Northern Ireland
028 4062 8406
admin@shinefm.org.uk
www.shinefm.org.uk
Annmarie Asiimwe
106.1 FM; 105.7 FM

Sound Radio
Hackney, East London
020 8533 8899
lol@svt.org.uk
www.svt.org.uk
Chief executive: Lol Gellor
1503 AM

Takeover Radio
Leicester
0116 299 9600
grahamcoley@takeoverradio.com
www.takeoverradio.com
Station manager: Graham Coley
103.2 FM

Wythenshawe FM
Manchester
Radio Regen
0161 499 7982
info@wfmradio.org
www.wfmradio.org
Programme organiser: Jason Kenyon
97.2 FM

Hospital, student and sporting event radio

1287 AM Insanity
01784 486309
sridhar@su.rhul.ac.uk
www.su.rhul.ac.uk
1287 kHz

1503 AM Radio Diamonds
01933 652000
1503 kHz. Matchday service for
Rushden and Diamonds FC

Acorn FM
01272 338152
87.7 MHz

Bailrigg FM
01524 593902
87.7 MHz

Basildon Hospital Radio
01268 282828
1287 kHz

BFBS
02892 266688
bfbsni@bfbs.com
www.bfbs.com
1287 kHz

Blast 1386
0118 967 5068
blast1386@reading-college.ac.uk
www.blast1386.com
1386 kHz

Bridge FM
01382 423000 x 25151
87.7 MHz

Bridge FM
01382 423000 x 25151
87.7 MHz

Bridge FM
01382 496333
87.7 MHz

C4 Radio
01227 782424
999 kHz

Canterbury Hospital Radio
01227 457967
945 kHz

Carillion Radio
01509 838671
1386 kHz

Chichester Radio
01243 788122 x 3000
1431 kHz

City Hospital Radio
01727 832204
1287 kHz

Crush
01707 285005
uhsu.comms@herts.ac.uk
www.uhsu.herts.ac.uk
1278 kHz

CUR
07968 305128
1350 kHz

Dorton Radio Station
01732 592600
1350kHz

Frequency
01772 513200
surecreation@uclan.ac.uk
www.yourunion.co.uk
1350 kHz

Gara Sound
01623 464220
1386 kHz

Garrison Radio
01748 830050
hq@garrisonradio.com
www.garrison.com
1287 kHz; 1350 kHz

Garrison Radio
01748 830050
hq@garrisonradio.com
www.garrison.com
1287 kHz; 1350 kHz

Garrison Radio
01748 830050
hq@garrisonradio.com
www.garrison.com
1287 kHz; 1350 kHz

Garrison Radio
01748 830050
hq@garrisonradio.com
www.garrison.com
1287 kHz; 1350 kHz

GU2
01483 689980
1350 kHz

Hemel Hospital Radio
01727 832204
1350 kHz

Hospital Radio Basingstoke
01256 313521
945 kHz

Hospital Radio Crawley
01293 534859
1287 kHz

Hospital Radio Gwendolen
0116 256 1686
1287 kHz

Hospital Radio Plymouth
01752 763441
87.7 MHz

Hospital Radio Pulse
01384 263852
1350 kHz

Hospital Radio Reading
0118 950 7420
945 kHz

Hospital Radio Rossendale
01706 233334
945 kHz

Hospital Radio Yare
01493 842613
Chairman: Lorraine Whitpen
1350 kHz. James Paget, Northgate,
Lowestoft Hospitals

IC Radio
020 7594 8100
manager@icradio.com
www.icradio.com
999 kHz
Imperial College Halls of Residence

Jam 1575
01482 466289
1575 kHz

Junction 11
0118 931 8698
1287 kHz

Kingstown Radio
01482 327711
onair@kingstownradio.com
www.kingstownradio.co.uk
1350 kHz

Kool AM
020 8373 1072
pfmnews@email.com
www.koolam.co.uk
1134 kHz

Livewire
01603 592512
1350 kHz

Loughborough Campus Radio
01509 632027
1350 kHz

Manchester United Radio
0161 868 8133
Contact: Kenneth Ramsden
1413 kHz
Manchester United matchday service

Mid-Downs Hospital Radio
01444 441350
studio@ndr.org.uk
1350 kHz

Nevill Hall Sound
07771 722738
1287 kHz

Newbold Radio
01344 454607
mpearson@newbold.ac.uk
www.newbold.ac.uk
1350 kHz

Oakwell 1575 AM
01226 215753
oakwell.studio@virgin.net
Contact: Stuart Cocker
1575 kHz
Matchday service for Barnsley FC

Oldchurch Radio
01708 738700
846 kHz

Palace Radio
020 8653 5799
info@cpfc.co.uk
Communications manager:
Terry Byfield
1278 AM
Matchday service for Crystal Palace FC

Portsmouth Hospital Broadcasting
01705 286299
945 kHz

RKI FM
01691 773671
87.7 MHz

Radio Airthrey
01786 467180
1350 kHz

Radio Branwen
01766 781911
radiobranwen@yahoo.co.uk
87.7 MHz

Radio Brockley
020 8954 6591
studio@radiobrockley.org
www.radiobrockley.org
Contact: the trustees
999 kHz. The wards within the RNOH

Radio Bronglas
01970 635363
87.8 MHz

Radio Brunel
01895 462238
999 kHz

Radio Castle Combe
0870 011 8850
anthony.ynn@arb-teamwork.com
Contact: Anthony Lynn
1602 kHz. Motor racing

Radio Cavell
0161 620 3033
1350 kHz

Radio Donnington
01869 336200
enquiries@event-tech.biz
www.event-tech.biz
(Contact for Temporary Electric Hire):
Diane Smith
1602 kHz. Motor racing

Radio Glangwili
01267 227504
87.7 MHz

Radio Gosh
020 7405 9200
999 kHz

Radio Heatherwood
01344 625818
999 kHz

Radio Hotspot
01473 326200
www.royalhospitalschool.org
Contact: Don Topley
1287 kHz

Radio Kings
020 7346 3152
999 kHz

Radio Knockhill
01796 473074
aardvark@pitlochry.org
Contact: Garry Stagg
1602 kHz. Motor racing

Radio Lonsdale
01229 467261
87.7 MHz

Radio Nightingale
01709 304244
1350 kHz

Radio Nightingale
01709 304244
945 kHz

Radio North Angus
01382 424095
87.7 MHz

Radio North Angus
01382 660111 x 33430
87.7 MHz

Radio North Angus
01382 424095
info@radionorthangus.co.uk
87.7 MHz

Radio Northwick Park
020 8869 3959
945 kHz

Radio Rainbow
01224 681818
945 kHz

Radio Redhill
01737 768511
studio@radioredhill.co.uk
www.radioredhill.co.uk
Contact: Nigel Gray
1287 kHz

Radio Rockingham
01869 336200
enquiries@event-tech.biz
www.event-tech.biz
(contact for temporary electric hire):
Diane Smith
1602 kHz
Rockinham speedway commentary

Radio Rovers
01254 261413
alan.yardley@creatv.co.uk
Contact: Alan Yardley
1404 kHz
Blackburn Rovers matchday service

Radio Silverstone
01869 336200
enquiries@event-tech.biz
www.event-tech.biz
(contact for temporary electric hire):
Diane Smith
1602 kHz. Motor racing

Radio Southlands
01273 446084
846 kHz

Radio Stortford
07950 190221
1350 kHz

Radio Thruxton
01869 336200
enquiries@event-tech.biz
www.event-tech.biz
(contact for temporary electric hire):
Diane Smith
1602 kHz. Motor racing

Radio Tyneside
0191 273 6970
1575 kHz

Radio Warwick
024 7657 3077
1251 kHz

Radio West Suffolk
01284 713403
www.radiowestsuffolk.co.uk
Vice chairman: P Owen
1350 kHz. West Suffolk Hospital

Radio Wexham
01753 570033
945 kHz

Radio ysbty Glan Clwyd
01745 584229
1287 kHz

Ram Air
01274 233267
exec@ramairfm.com
www.ramairfm.co.uk
Station manager: Mark Pickering
1350 kHz

Range Radio
0161 861 9727
rap@whalleyrange.manchester
.sch.uk
www.whalleyrange.manchester
.sch.uk
Contact: Roy Appleby
1350 kHz

RED
01206 863211
red@essex.ac.uk
www.essexstudent.com
1404 kHz

Rookwood Sound Hospital Radio
029 2031 3796
945 kHz

Royal 945 AM
0151 706 2125
945 kHz

Rugby Ref!Link
01225 835553
ppd@reflink.net
www.reflink.net
Managing director: Peter Downey
87.7 to 105 kHz. Rugby referees

SNCR
0115 914 6467
1278 kHz

Solar 1287 AM Campus Radio
01744 623454
solar1287am@hotail.com
Station manager: Terry Broughton
1287 kHz

The Source
01925 494602
1251 kHz

Sportslink UK
01225 835553
pd@officiallink.net
www.officiallink.net
Managing director: Peter Downey
87.7 to 105 kHz. Tennis, dressage, racing

Stoke Mandeville Hospital Radio
01296 331575
1575 kHz

Storm Radio
01206 500700
storm@colchsfc.ac.uk
Station manager: Neil Kelly
999kHz

Subcity Radio
0141 339 8855
1350 kHz

Surge
07971 421505
1287 kHz

Trust AM
01909 484476
www.trustam.com
1278 kHz
Bassetlaw District General Hospital

UCA
01292 886385
87.7 MHz

UKC Radio
01227 824201
ukcr@kent.ac.uk
www.ukcr.net
Contact: Mary Digg
1350 kHz

University Radio Falmer
01273 678287
999 kHz
University Radio York
01904 433840
1350 kHz
URB
01225 826611
1449 kHz
URF
01273 678999
1431 kHz
URN
01273 678999
1350 kHz
VRN
07940 591479
info@brn1287.com
www.brn1287.com
Managing director: Hal London
1287 kHz
WCR AM
01902 317700
training@wcr1350.co.uk
www.wcr1350.co.uk
1350 kHz
Whitechapel AM
020 7377 7000 x 2928
999 kHz
Withybush FM
01437 773562
87.7MHz
Xpression
01392 263568
stationmanager@Xpressionfm.com
www.Xpressionfm.com
Communications officer: Jonty Crane
87.7 MHz
Xtreme
01792 295989
1431 kHz

Cable radio

Angel Radio
01983 242471
angelradio@37.com
www.angelfm.co.uk
Station manager Martin Kirby
BCB 96.7FM
01274 771677
info@bcb.yorks.com
www.bcb.yorks.com/
Project director: Mary Dowson
CRMK
01908 265266
Contact: Mike Barry
Cable Radio
01273 418181
office@cableradio.co.uk
www.cableradio.co.uk
Contact: R Mustapha
Coppernob Radio
020 7588 5665
pr@coppernob.net
www.coppernob.com/

Kerrang!
0114 209 1034
natalie.johnson@emap.com
www.Emapdigitalradio.com
Contact: Natalie Johnson
Kiss
0114 209 1034
natalie.johnson@emap.com
www.Emapdigitalradio.com
Contact: Natalie Johnson
Kool AM
020 8373 1075
steve.saunders@paradisefm.co.uk
www.koolam.co.uk
Programme controller: Joe Bone
1134 kHz. Harlow
Ozone Radio
01482 300699
robbie.harrison@ozoneradio.com
Contact: Robert Harrison
Radio Forth
0131 556 9255
marketing@radioforth.com
www.forthonline.com
Managing director: Sandy Wilkie
Radio Orient
01440 50010
www.radioorient.com
Contact: Nabil Moumtaz
Radio Verulam
01442 398099
studio@radio-verulam.co.uk
www.radio-verulam.co.uk
Contact: Phil Richards
Smash! Hits
0114 209 1034
natalie.johnson@emap.com
www.Emapdigitalradio.com
Contact: Natalie Johnson
Trouble Radio
020 7299 5641
gisi_ball@flextech.co.uk
www.trouble.co.uk
Contact: Kathy McGarvey

Satellite radio

Adventist World Radio
01344 401401
whitegates@AWR.org
www.awr.org
Contact: Bert Smit
Akash Radio
020 8571 3629
akashradio@hotmail.com
Contact: Sukhwinder Singh
Al-Balagh
020 8961 4001
aljuboury@hotmail.com
Contact: Mahmood Al-Husari
All: Sports Live
0113 399 2043
cheryl.Westerman@teamtalk.com
Contact: Cheryl Westerman
Amrit Bani
020 8606 9292
info@amjritbani.com
www.amritbani.com
Operational director: Pritam Singh

Apna Radio
0121 555 5964
priya@apnaradio.net
www.apnaradio.net
Contact: Priya Singh
Asian Gold
020 8571 7200
info@asiangoldradio.co.uk
www.asiangoldradio.com
Contact: Zorawar Gakhal
BBA Radio
020 8574 7474
Contact: Harbans Singh Palda
Bengali Radio
0121 554 4555
bengaliradio@bengaliradio.co.uk
Contact: Mohammed Solim
Big Blue
01273 384260
firstname@radiofirst.com
Contact: John Aumonier
CMR/Pulse 202
020 8941 4144
Contact: Paul Gibbs
Calvary Chapel Radio
020 8466 5365/0777 950 7032
ccradio@btconnect.com
www.calvarychapelradio.co.uk
Programmer: Mark Seddi
Capital Gold
020 7766 6006
Contact: Gills Hind
Classic Gold Digital
020 8594 6662
humerah@clubasiaonline.com
www.clubasiaonline.com
Contact: Neil Barrhkell
Club Asia
020 8594 4422
info@clubasiaonline.com
www.clubasiaonline.com
The Conversation Station
01993 813767
jjclews@ukonline.co.uk
JJ Clews
Costcutter Digital Radio
01904 488811
costcutter@minsterfm.com
www.costcutter.com
Contact: John Harding
Cross Rhythms
0870 011 8008
admin@crossrhythms.co.uk
www.crossrhythms.co.uk
Contact: Jonathan Bellamy
The Dream
0191 495 2244
info@god.tv
www.GOD.tv
Contact: Rory Alex Perrins
ETBC London
020 8795 0045
atbcradio@yahoo.co.uk
www.atbclondon.com
Contact: SB Jayakumar
EWTN
00 1 205 2712 9000
gtapley@ewtn.com
www.ewtn.com
Contact: Michael Warsaw

Family Radio
00 1 510 5686200
international@familyradio.com
www.familyradio.com
Contact: David Hoff

Family Radio International
00 1 510 6326385
manager@kftl.com
Contact: Matt Tuter

Galaxy
020 7465 6100
steve.parkinson@chrysalis.com
www.galaxyfm.co.uk
Contact: Steve Parkinson

Gaydar Radio
020 8893 9550
gary@qsoft.co.uk
Contact: Gary Frisch

Heart 106.2
020 7468 1062
www.heart1062.co.uk
Contact: Steve Parkinson
106.2 FM
Greater London

Holiday FM
00 350 76651
marvina@fiduciarygroup.com
Contact: Marvina Debono

Homebase FM
020 7692 0200
Contact: Tim Saunders

International Broadcasting Corporation
020 7787 8000
radio@ibctamil.com
Contact: S Shivaranjith

jazz fm
020 7298 7209
alistair@jazzfm.com
Contact: Alistair Mackenzie

Laser Radio
01342 327842
laser@ukmail.com
www.laserradio.net
Managing director: Andrew Yeates
1557 kHz
Greater Amsterdam and Sky
Subscribers

McColls FM
0113 399 2043
cheryl.Westerman@teamtalk.com
Contact: Cheryl Westerman

Mean Country
020 8961 5490
dean@meanfiddler.com
www.meanfiddler.com
Contact: Dean James

The Mix
020 7911 7300
mail@themix.musicradio.com
www.musicradio.com
Contact: Nick Piggott

Music Choice
020 7014 8700
www.musicchoice.com
Contact: Hannah Aiken

NPR Worldwide (National Public Radio)
00 1 202 513 2240
worldwide@npr.org
www.npr.org/worldwide
Director NPR Worldwide: Jeffrey Rosenberg

Panjab Radio
020 8848 8877
info@panjabradio.co.uk
www.panjabradio.co.uk
Contact: Paramjit Kaur Nizzar

Premier Christian Radio
020 7316 1300
premier@premier.org.uk
www.premier.org.uk
Contact: Peter Kerridge

Purple Radio
020 7647 7605
peter@purpleradio.net
Contact: Peter Flynn

Radio Al Mahabba
01274 721810
rthurgoo@hcjb.org.uk
www.hcjb.org
Contact: RW Thurgood

Radio Caroline
020 8340 3831
Piratecaroline@aol.com
www.radiocaroline.co.uk
Station manager: Peter Moore

Radio France Internationale (RFI)
00 33 1 56401212
name@rfi.fr
www.rfi.fr
President: Jean Paul Cluzel

Radio London
077 7480 1945
bigl@radiofab.com
Contact: Ray Anderson

Radio Sahan
07719 315946

Radio Telefis Eireann
00 353 4238414
russelp@rte.ie

Rampage
01273 384 1260
john@radiofirst.com
Contact: John Aumonier

Real Radio
02920 315100
terry.underhill@realradiofm.com
www.realradiofm.com
Contact: Terry Underhill

The Saint
01273 384260
firstname@radiofirst.com
Contact: John Aumonier

SBN
020 7691 4777
info@channelfly.com
www.channelfly.com
Station manager: Marina Lois

Scene 889
0870 3211980
admin@raq262.uknet.com
Contact: Leslie Plock

Sky Radio 100.7 FM
00 31 356991050
carla.stone@newsint.co.uk
www.skyradio.com

Solar Radio
020 8693 2933
Contact: Carl Webster

Stichting Trans World Radio Europe
00 43 1 863 120
International Director: Werner Kromer
UK

The Storm
020 7911 7300
reception@stormradio.co.uk
www.stormradio.co.uk
Contact: Nick Piggott

Sukh Sagar Radio
020 8571 7200
info@asiangoldradio.co.uk
www.asiangoldradio.co.uk
Manager: Mani Bedi

Sunrise Radio (UK and Europe)
020 8574 6666
name@sunriseradio.com
www.sunriseradio.com
Contact: David Landau

talkGospel.com
020 7316 1300
enquiries@talkgospel.com
www.talkgospel.com
Chairman: Noble McLean

The Talking Bible
0191 495 2244
info@god.tv
www.god-digital.com
Contact: Graeme Spencer

Tamil Broadcasting Corporation
020 8868 2687
tbcradio@hotmail.com
Contact: S Ramarajaha

TBC Radio
07817 063682
info@tbcuk.com
www.tbcuk.com

TEAMtalk 252
0113 399 2030
polli.betts@teamtalk.com
www.teamtalk.com
Contact: Polli-Anne Betts

Teds FM
020 7692 0200
Contact: Dean Miles

TotalRock
020 7731 6696
bs@totalrock.com
www.totalrock.com
Contact: Tony Wilson

Trans World Radio Europe
01225 831390
web@twr,org,uk
www.twr.org.uk
Contact: Russell Farnworth

Trans World Radio
00 43 1 8631211
Contact: Werner Kroemer

UCB Bible
01782 642000
ucb@ucb.co.uk
www.ucb.co.uk
Contact: Ian Mackie

UCB Europe
01782 642000
ucb@ucb.co.uk
www.ucb.co.uk
Contact: Ian Mackie

INDEPENDENT RADIO NEWS

the big news on radio

270 stations – 29 million listeners
Source: Rajar

MediaGuardian
Edinburgh
International
Television
Festival

27-29 August 2004

THINKING INSIDE THE BOX

Find out the latest thinking from inside the industry at the annual gathering of creative and business professionals at the 29th annual TV Festival. This is *the* leading event in the TV calendar, attended by over 1,600 delegates from across the industry. With over 50 sessions addressing the most pertinent issues facing the industry today, including keynotes from the major players; Channel of the Year Awards; Controller interviews; preview screenings, parties and receptions.

Plus London evening events – interviews with key influential industry figures.

26-30 August 2004

A FREE five day event with Masterclasses, Workshops and Career Surgeries for 18 - 21 year olds aspiring to work in television.

Plus, the new placement scheme TVYP at Work, offering jobs and bursaries to 13 TVYP delegates at top broadcasters and production companies. Applications available in March 2004.

25-30 August 2004

A FREE talent initiative that offers a programme of Masterclasses and access to the TV Festival for 40 industry hot shots. Applications available in May 2004.

For further information and to sign up to our newsletters, visit www.mgeitf.co.uk

UCB Inspirational
01782 642000
ucb@ucb.co.uk
www.ucb.co.uk
Contact: Ian Mackie

UCB Talk
01782 642000
ucb@ucb.co.uk
www.ucb.co.uk
Contact: Ian Mackie

The Villain
01273 384260
firstname@radiofirst.com
Contact: John Aumonier

Voice of America
020 7896 9000
voanews@voanews.com
www.voa.gov
Contact: Sanford Unger

WRN Euromax (English, French, German services)
020 7896 9000
online@wrn.org
http://wrn.org
Contact: Tim Ayris

WorldSpace UK
020 7494 8200
ukservice@worldspace.com
www.worldspace.com
Contact: Safia Safwat

XFM
020 7766 6606
firstname.lastname@xfm.co.uk
www.xfm.co.uk
Contact: Andrew Phillips

Digital multiplex licence-holders

Capital Radio
Cardiff/Newport; south Hampshire; Sussex coast; Kent

CE Digital
Capital Radio; Emap Radio Birmingham; Greater London; Manchester

Emap Digital Radio
Emap Performance
Central Lancashire; Humberside; Leeds; Liverpool; South Yorkshire; Teesside; Tyne and Wear

MXR
Chrysalis Radio
GMG Radio Holdings
www.getdabdigitalradio.com
North-east England; north-west England; South Wales/Severn estuary; West Midlands; Yorkshire

Now Digital
www.now-digital.com
Bournemouth; Bristol/Bath; Coventry; Exeter and Torbay; Leicester; Norwich; Nottingham; Peterborough; Reading and Basingstoke; Southend and Chelmsford; Swindon/West Wiltshire; Wolverhampton

Score Digital
Scottish Radio Holdings
Ayr; Dundee and Perth; Edinburgh; Glasgow; Inverness; Northern Ireland

Switchdigital (Scotland)
The Wireless Group
Aberdeen; Central Scotland; Greater London II

The Digital Radio Group
GWR Group, The Wireless Group
Greater London III

TWG Digital
The Wireless Group
Bradford and Huddersfield

TWG Emap Digital
The Wireless Group
Stoke-on-Trent; Swansea

Radio associations

British Academy of Composers and Songwriters
British Music House
26 Berners Street, London W1T 3LR
020 7636 2929
info@britishacademy.com
www.britishacademy.com
Music writers' trade association

Broadcasting Press Guild
Tiverton, The Ridge, Woking
Surrey GU22 7EQ
01483 764895
torin.douglas@bbc.co.uk

Commercial Radio Companies Association
77 Shaftesbury Avenue
London W1D 5DU
020 7306 2603
info@crca.co.uk
www.crca.co.uk

Creators' Rights Alliance
British Music House
26 Berners Street, London W1T 3LR
020 7436 7296
info@creatorsrights.org
www.creatorsrights.org

Digital Radio Development Bureau (DRDB)
The Radiocentre
77 Shaftesbury Avenue
London W1D 5DU
020 7306 2630
info@drdb.org
www.drdb.org

Musicians Union
60–62 Clapham Road
London SW9 0JJ
020 7582 5566
webmaster@musiciansunion.org.uk
www.musiciansunion.org.uk

Office of Communications (Ofcom)
Riverside House
2A Southwark Bridge Road
London SE1 9HA
020 7981 3000
mediaoffice@ofcom.org.uk
www.ofcom.gov.uk
New super-regulator

Performing Right Society
29–33 Berners Street
London W1T 3AB
020 7580 5544
info@prs.co.uk
www.prs.co.uk
Collects and distributes royalties

Rad10
rad10@rad10.com
www.rad10.com

Radio Academy
5 Market Place, London W1W 8AE
020 7255 2010
info@radioacademy.org
www.radioacademy.org

Radio Joint Audience Research (Rajar)
Gainsborough House
81 Oxford Street, London W1D 2EU
info@rajar.co.uk
www.rajar.co.uk

Voice of the Listener and Viewer (VLV)
101 Kings Drive, Gravesend
Kent DA12 5BQ
01474 352835
vlv@btinternet.com
www.vlv.org.uk

World Radio Network
PO Box 1212, London SW8 2ZF
020 7896 9000
email@wrn.org
www.wrn.org

Writernet
Cabin V, Clarendon Buildings
25 Horsell Road, London N5 1XL
020 7609 7474
writernet@btinternet.com
www.writernet.org.uk

New media

The heady days of the dotcom boom may be long gone, but its effect on the media industry will be lasting. Some 47% of UK homes and 65% of businesses have access to the internet, according to Oftel figures for the first quarter of 2003. More than four in 10 UK homes are connected, and the average time spent online per user in March 2003 (in all locations) was just over 20 minutes every day. And there are signs that the dotcom collapse might soon be over, too: online shopping doubled in size for Christmas 2002, online advertising is once again the fastest growing advertising sector, and Lastminute.com has posted its first profit. It's enough to make you nostalgic for 1999.

Internet access and broadband

There remains a digital divide in the UK. Internet users are still far more likely to be younger and better-off – just 17% of over-65s have ever used the internet, compared to 94% of 16- to 24-year-olds, according to a national audit office survey in 2002 – and there is also a significant minority of internet "never-users" who say they are unlikely to get online any time soon. As the government plans to spend £6bn to ensure all its services are available electronically by 2006, this is a major headache for ministers.

Access to broadband – high-speed internet access – also remains low compared to other developed nations. Britain now has more than 1.4 million broadband users, said Oftel in January 2003; but according to subscriber figures in November 2002, these accounted for only 9% of connected homes. The former telecoms monopoly, BT, is widely blamed for its long delay in reducing wholesale broadband prices to other internet service providers (ISPs).

In July 2003, Oftel cleared BT over claims that it had priced its broadband products anti-competitively, following an appeal by its rival, Freeserve.

"Broadband" can differ from provider to provider. In 2003, cable company Telewest trialled a connection speed of 2Mbps (megabytes per second), four times faster than most providers' 512kbps. Rival cable firm NTL, on the other hand, raised its service to just 150kbps in May 2003, shortly after the advertising standards authority ruled that calling its 128kbps service "broadband" without qualification was "likely to mislead". It then went on to impose a 1Gb daily cap on its customers.

In June 2003, BT revamped its Openworld internet access service by merging it with Yahoo!, offering both internet access and a range of premium content and services, to be called BT Yahoo!.

3G and mobile internet

Perhaps the biggest technology event in 2003 was the launch of "3" – the UK's first 3G (third-generation) mobile service, which launched in March. Hutchison Telecoms spent almost £5bn on the 3G licence in 2001, only to see the bottom fall out of the telecoms market later that year; it hoped to start recouping its investment by attracting a million subscribers by the end of 2003. The service, when it launched, offered video calling, location mapping, high-quality news content and video clips of Premiership goals; but handsets cost up to £399 and there were glitches as users moved in and out of 3G phone coverage.

Vodafone, the UK's biggest telecoms company, launched its cheaper Vodafone Live! service – so-called "2.5G" technology, based on picture messaging– in October 2002. By April it had signed up its millionth customer, and it launched video messaging in the same month. Vodafone said it would launch its full 3G service by Christmas 2003, while O2 – which also trialled video messaging in April – delayed the launch of its 3G service to the end of 2004.

Dotcom news

The green shoots of growth were finally seen in the dotcom industry at the start of 2003. Lastminute.com said in February it would post a £14m annual profit for the 2002-03 financial year; and Wanadoo, owner of the UK's biggest internet service provider, Freeserve, announced a £20m profit (Freeserve itself lost £61m over the year). But there were still casualties: Upmystreet, the website which gives users data about where to live in the UK, went into administration in April; Workhouse, the digital media arm of Zenith Entertainment, closed in October 2002 with 12 redundancies; and there were more redundancies at QXL.

Perhaps most tellingly, the BBC's new media arm, BBCi, shed 100 jobs in 2003 – some 8% of its workforce. The move came as the culture secretary, Tessa Jowell, told the corporation to justify the £112m it spends each year on the internet and interactive television, ahead of an independent government review on the subject. In online news, FT.com announced its website had broken even after integrating its website team with its newspaper coverage. Guardian Unlimited remained the UK's most popular newspaper website, and announced in July 2003 its intention to start charging for content including crosswords, email services and a new "electronic edition" of the newspaper.

In April, Easyinternet founder Stelios Haji-Ioannou agreed to pay the British record industry £210,000 to settle the row over music illegally downloaded at internet cafes. Google remained the web's most popular search engine; in February it bought Blogger, the service which hosts a million weblogs (see glossary, page 289). In March, Ipswich MP Chris Mole brought a private member's bill to make sure electronic publications are preserved for posterity.

Online shopping

Online shopping continued its upward trend. Between 4.4 million (Continental Research) and 8.4 million (NOP) people shopped online at Christmas 2002; in the latter survey, this was a growth of 52% compared to December 2001. December's online sales were £1.5bn.

Online ad spend

Year	Spend (£m)	Market share (%)
2002	196.7	1.4
2001	165.7	1.2
2000	154.7	1.1
1999	51.0	0.4
1998	19.4	0.2

Source: Advertising Association

Top 10 website audiences, May 2003

Web domain	Unique audience (millions)
MSN	11.7
Google	10.2
Yahoo!	9.2
Microsoft	8.8
BBC	8.1
eBay	7.4
AOL Time Warner	7.2
Wanadoo	7.0
British Telecom	6.3
Amazon	5.7

Source: Nielsen/NetRatings

War on the web

Unique audience for top news sites, March 2003 (month of war in Iraq)

1	news.bbc.co.uk	4,023,977
2	guardian.co.uk	1,335,818
3	www.sky.com	1,240,136
4	cnn.com	912,603
5	telegraph.co.uk	813,735
6	uk.news.yahoo.com	609,812
7	timesonline.co.uk	580,457
8	news.google.com 4	22,418
9	ananova.com	384,211
10	ft.com	343,828
11	thesun.co.uk	308,556

Source: Nielsen/NetRatings

Online advertising

Online advertising in the UK recovered sharply in 2002, according to a report by PriceWaterhouseCoopers and the Interactive Advertising Bureau (IAB). The sector rose 18.7% to £196.7m, which means internet advertising now accounts for 1.4% of total media spend in 2002 – up from 1.2% in 2001 – and has again overtaken cinema advertising. The IAB claims the industry will now meet its target of 2% share by autumn 2004. Budgets for internet marketing were also revised up by nearly 25% of companies in the first quarter of 2003, according to the Institute of Practitioners in Advertising; only 5% reported a downward revision.

Further reading

■ Press

MediaGuardian: New Media
media.guardian.co.uk/newmedia

Guardian Online
guardian.co.uk/online

New Media Age
www.nma.co.uk

■ Books

Weaving the Web TIM BERNERS LEE, TEXERE PUBLISHING 2000
History of the world wide web

Boo Hoo: A Dotcom story ERNST MALMSTEN ET AL, RANDOM HOUSE 2002
Rise and fall of the dotcom dream

Stealing Time: Steve Case, Jerry Levin and the Collapse of AOL Time Warner ALEC KLEIN, SIMON AND SCHUSTER 2003 Marriage of old and new media turns sour

■ Web only

Online Journalism Review
www.ojr.org

The Register: irreverent tech news
www.theregister.co.uk

ZDNet: IT and tech news
www.zdnet.co.uk

■ Other resources

Association of Online Publishers
www.ukaop.org.uk

■ My top five sites

GEORGE MONBIOT

1. Znet
www.zmag.org
Possibly the world's foremost radical comment site, set up by the great social entrepreneur Michael Albert.

2. OneWorld
www.oneworld.net
The key network hub for source material on the developing world.

3. IndyMedia
www.indymedia.org/
A global news site the media barons will never get their hands on.

4. CorporateWatch UK
www.corporatewatch.org/
The stories of corporate malpractice you won't find in the papers.

5. Project for the New American Century
www.newamericancentury.org/
Some of America's most powerful men lay out their plans for world domination. It's terrifying.

HANNAH POOL

1. Sephora
www.sephora.com
A cosmetics addicts' dream, practically gives the stuff away ... well, sort of.

2. Nerve
www.nerve.com
Smart and sassy writing on sex and relationships– even the personals are classy.

3. eBay
www.ebay.com
Unrivalled vintage clothing and accessories sites, not so great for the heart rate.

4. BBC Food
www.bbc.co.uk/food
Lifesaver when you've forgotten someone is coming over for dinner or can't face another evening of pasta and pesto.

5. Hint
www.hintmag.com
Great fashion, but it's the gossip and the attitude that make it stand out.

JULIE BURCHILL

1. The Lutheran Council Of Great Britain
www.lutheran.org.uk
... because I'm trying to learn to become one.

2. Astrid Williamson
www.astridwilliamson.net
Best singer and most beautiful woman in Britain. Also a good friend and only lives across the way but we both lead very busy lives. So we communicate by visiting each other's websites – very modern and creepy!

3. Sudor Terriers
http://pw1.netcom.com/×sudor
To drool over the sort of Bedlington I'm going to get when I'm 50.

4. Bichon Frise Live Stuffed Toy
www.bichonfrise.org
To drool over the sort of Bichon I'm going to get my boyfriend when I'm 50.

5. AmIAnnoying.com
www.amiannoying.com
Speaks for itself!

CHRIS ALDEN

1. Travel Intelligence
www.travelintelligence.net
Things to do before you die.

2. Greenpeace: Iraq
weblog.greenpeace.org/iraq
Greenpeace lifts the lid on the reality of post-war Iraq.

3. Cyprus Conflict
www.cyprus–conflict.net
Anatomy of an unresolved tragedy. Packed with primary sources.

4. World News Network
www.worldnews.com
Powerful but temperamental news search engine. When it works, better than Google News.

5. Pompey Pages
www.thepompeypages.co.uk
Daily updates for Pompey exiles.

Blog on **Chris Alden**

Blog: online journal or diary, in which content is organised in reverse order of the time it was published. Contraction of "web log".

Blogger: someone who keeps a blog.

New media

You can't yet find it in a dictionary, but it has become impossible to escape the blog. More and more people are keeping a blog: from **Salam Pax**, the "Baghdad blogger" who wrote an online journal as US troops invaded the city, to the brains behind **Sarswatch**, who linked to news on the subject as the disease swept the far east, to thousands of new bloggers that go online every month. All have one goal: to make their unique voices heard on the web.

A blog, for those who have escaped the hype, is a beautiful thing: a user-friendly way of putting stuff on the net. In a blog, newly posted content goes at the top of the page, leaving yesterday's effort to slip toward the bottom. Each post is timed and dated, and every now and then older posts are archived. That's it.

Early bloggers noticed the system's potential for "filtering" quality content from the detritus on the web. Jorn Barger's **Robot Wisdom** is little more than a list of links to the fun things its author finds, from news to talkthreads to things only a geek would understand; Jim Romenesko's **Obscure Store** is a source of daft only-in-America stories from local newspapers all over the US. The Guardian's own weblog, which began posting in April 2000, looks for esoteric and penetrating news and comment around the world.

Other bloggers saw the chance to keep personal sites. Some, like Salam Pax, hid their identities but gained recognition in the mainstream media; others, like that of Kaycee Nicole, a woman apparently dying from leukaemia, hid their identities to maintain an elaborate hoax. In 2002, Guardian Unlimited built a guide to some of the best blogs around, featuring such outré characters as Welsh transvestite **Gina**

Snowdoll and one **Glitter Splashed Britney Lovin' Lesbo**. It also launched a Best British Blog competition, attracting hundreds of entries: the winner, **Scary Duck**, was praised by the judges for its personality, design and above all, the quality of its writing.

The beauty of the blog is that anyone can do it. If you use a service such as **Blogger**, you don't need experience of web hosts, FTP, HTML or anything else acronymic. As you get more confident, you can play with the design. If you're a bit more advanced – which this writer isn't – you can use rival services such as **Movable Type**, that require a bit more knowledge but put more power to your fingers.

Early bloggers, like early internet users, were quick to see the potential of what they were doing. If blogging could drive a revolution in self-publishing, they hoped, there could be a chance to challenge the power of mainstream media: give a voice to enough individuals, they predicted, and you collectively empower them. Fox hasn't gone out of business yet, but in time there will be enough bloggers out there to be a cross-section of a certain kind of public opinion. Meanwhile, eyebrows were raised in 2003 when Pyra, makers of Blogger, was bought by Google – which means the web's most popular search engine, most popular newsgroup system and now most popular self-publishing engine are all owned by the same company. Watch this space.

Chris Alden edited the Guardian weblog until March 2003

Blog URLs

- Salam Pax *dear_raed.blogspot.com*
- Guardian weblog *www.guardian.co.uk/weblog*
- Sarswatch *www.sarswatch.org*
- Robot Wisdom *www.robotwisdom.com*
- Obscure Store *www.obscurestore.com*
- Gina Snowdoll *gina-snowdoll.blogspot.com*
- Diary of a Glitter Splashed Britney Lovin' Lesbo *glitterqueer.blogspot.com*
- Scary Duck *scaryduck.blogspot.com*
- Blogger *www.blogger.com*
- Movable Type *www.movabletype.org*

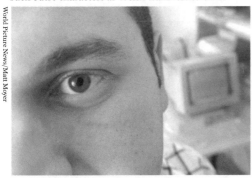

World Picture News/Matt Moyer

Salam Pax: Baghdad blogger found mainstream fame

New media Contacts

Main ISPs

AOL (UK)
80 Hammersmith Road
London W14 8UD
020 7348 8000
UKMediaOffice@aol.com
www.aol.co.uk

Breathe
Affinity Internet Holdings
Victoria House, 64 Paul Street
London EC2A 4NG
020 7670 1155
feedback@breathe.co.uk
www.breathe.co.uk

British Telecom
PO Box 163, Exeter EX1 1BX
0845 601 2949
sales@btinternet.com
www.bt.com

Claranet
Vinery Court, London EC1Y 8TX
020 7903 3034
marketing@clara.net
www.clara.net

Demon
322 Regents Park Road
Finchley, London N3 2QQ
0845 272 0666
www.demon.net

Entanet
Stafford Park 6, Telford
Shropshire TF3 3AT
0870 770 8895
marketing@entagroup.com
www.enta.net

Freeserve
PO Box 73, Leeds LS10 1WZ
020 7553 7566
www.freeserve.co.uk

nildram.net
1 Triangle Business Park
Stoke Mandeville
Buckinghamshire HP22 5BD
0800 197 1490
www.nildram.net

NTL UK
NTL House
Bartley Wood Business Park
Hook, Hampshire RG27 9UP
01256 752000
www.ntl.com

One.Tel Business
Thames Tower, 99 Burley's Way
Leicester, LE1 3XY
0800 957 0700
marketing@onetel.co.uk
www.onetel.co.uk

One.Tel Corporate
3rd Floor, Building 1, Chiswick Park
London W4 5BY
020 7181 7273
publicrelations@onetel.co.uk
www.onetel.co.uk

Pipex
Pipex House
4 Falcon Gate, Shire Park
Welwyn Garden City AL7 1TW
0845 077 8324
www.pipex.co.uk

PlusNet Technologies
Technology Building, Terry Street
Sheffield S9 2BU
0870 705 8080
www.Plus.net

Telewest
Unit 1, Genesis Business Park
Albert Way, Woking
Surrey GU21 3RW
01483 750 900
mary_o'reilly@flextech.co.uk
www.telewest.co.uk

Tiscali UK
20 Broadwick Street
London W1F 8HT
08707 450 700
www.tiscali.co.uk

Virgin.net
The Communications Buidling
48 Leicester Square
London WC2H 7LT
020 7664 6216
www.virgin.net

Yahoo! UK
10 Edbury Bridge Road
London SW1W 8PZ
020 7808 4200
www.yahoo.co.uk

Main telecoms companies

British Telecom
BT Openworld Customer Services
PO Box 163
Exeter EX1 1BX
sales@btinternet.com
www.bt.com

Cable and Wireless
124 Theobald's Road, Holborn
London WC1X 8RX
020 7315 4495
peter.eustace@cw.com
www.cableandwireless.co.uk

Colt
Beaufort House
15 St Botolph Street
London EC3A 7QN
0800 358 9945
www.colt.co.uk

Energis
185 Park Street, London SE1 9DY
0808 172 7272
www.energis.co.uk

Hutchinson 3G
27b Floral Street, Covent Garden
London WC2E 9DP
0207 010 9312
www.three.co.uk

Kingston Communications
Carr Lane
Kingston upon Hull HU1 3RE
01482 602100
info@kcom.com
www.kcltd.co.uk

MCI WorldCom
Reading International Business Park
Basingstoke Road, Reading
Berkshire RG2 6DA
0118 905 5000
customerservices@wcom.co.uk
www1.worldcom.com/uk

mmO2
Wellington Street, Slough SL1 1YP
01753 628402
www.mmo2.com

NTL UK
NTL House
Bartley Wood Business Park
Hook, Hampshire RG27 9UP
01256 752000
www.ntl.com

Orange
St James Court, Great Park Road
Almondsbury, Bristol BS32 4QJ
07973 100 150
customer.services@orange.net
www.orange.co.uk

Telewest
Unit 1, Genesis Business Park
Albert Way, Woking
Surrey GU21 3RW
01483 750 900
www.telewest.co.uk

Thus
1/2 Berkley Square
99 Berkley Street, Glasgow G3 7HR
0141 537 1234
www.thus.co.uk

T-Mobile
Elstree Tower, Borehamwood
Hertfordshire WD6 1DT
0845 412 5000
www.t-mobile.co.uk

Virgin Mobile
Willow Grove House
B.O. Box 2692, Trowbridge
West Wiltshire BA14 0TQ
020 7484 4300
www.virginmobile.com

Vodafone
Vodafone House, The Connection
Newbury, Berkshire RG14 2FN
07000 500100
www.vodafone.co.uk

UK news online

Ananova
PO Box 36, Leeds LS11 9YJ
www.ananova.com

BBCi
Bush House, The Strand
London WC2B 4PH
020 7557 1111
www.bbc.co.uk

Belfast Telegraph
Independent News and Media
(Northern Ireland)
Internet Department
124–144 Royal Avenue
Belfast BT1 1EB
028 9026 4000
www.belfasttelegraph.co.uk

FT
One Southwark Bridge
London SE1 9H2
020 7873 3000
joanna.manning-cooper@ft.com
www.ft.com

Guardian Unlimited
3–7 Ray Street, London EC1R 3DR
020 7278 2332
editor@guardianunlimited.co.uk
www.guardian.co.uk

ITN
200 Grays Inn Road
London WC1X 8X2
020 7430 4700
editor@itn.co.uk
www.itn.co.uk

Online Mirror
MGN
1 Canada Square, Canary Wharf
London E14 5AP
020 7293 3000
www.mirror.co.uk

Reuters
85 Fleet Street, London EC4P 4AJ
020 7250 1122
simon.walker@reuters.com
www.reuters.co.uk

Telegraph Group
1 Canada Square, Canary Wharf
London E14 5DT
020 7538 5000
www.telegraph.co.uk

The Independent
Independent House, 191 Marsh Wall
London E14 9RS
020 7005 2000
www.independent.co.uk

The Scotsman
Barclay House, 108 Holyrood Road
Edinburgh EH 8 8AS
0131 620820
enquiries@scotsman.com
www.scotsman.com

The Sun Online
Level 6, 1 Virginia Street
London E98 1SN
020 7782 4341
www.thesun.co.uk

The Times
1 Pennington Street, Wapping
London E98 1TA
020 782 5000
online.editor@thetimes.co.uk
www.timesonline.co.uk

Other movers and shakers

Amazon.co.uk
Patriot Court 1–9, The Grove
Slough, Berkshire SL1 1QP
020 8636 9200
www.amazon.co.uk

Apple Computer UK
2 Furzeground Way
Stockley Park East, Uxbridge
Middlesex UB11 1BB
020 8218 1000
millar.d@euro.apple.com
www.apple.com/uk/

eBay UK
Unit 6, Dukes Gate, Chiswick
London W4 5DX
020 8987 0888
ukenquiries@ebay.com
www.ebay.co.uk

Ebookers
177–178 Tottenham Court Road
London W1P 0LX
0870 010 7000
www.ebookers.com

Egg
1 Waterhouse Square
138–142 Holborn
London EC1N 2NA
020 7526 2600
www.egg.com

Google UK
18 Soho Square, London W1D 3QL
020 7025 8010
UK@google.com
www.google.co.uk

IBM UK
P. O. Box 41, North Harbour
Portsmouth, Hampshire PO6 3AU
0870 542 6426
www.ibm.com/uk

Lastminute.com
4 Buckingham Gate
London SW1E 6JP
www.lastminute.com

Lycos UK
Lycos House, 3 Sutton Lane
London EC1M 5PU
020 7250 7000
www.lycos.co.uk

Microsoft UK
Microsoft Campus
Thames Valley Park
Reading, Berkshire RG6 1WG
0870 207 7377
ukprteam@microsoft.com
www.microsoft.com/uk

Moreover
No 12 Greenhill Rents
London EC1M 6BN
020 7253 5003
publicrelations@moreover.com
www.moreover.com

New media bodies

Association of Freelance Internet Designers
admin@afid.net
www.afid.net

Association of New Media Freelancers
jon@anmf.org.uk
http://anmf.org.uk

Association of Online Publishers (AOP)
Queens House, 28 Kingsway
London WC2B 6JR
020 7400 7510
alex.daley@ukaop.org.uk
www.ukaop.org.uk

British Interactive Media Association
Briarlea House, Southend Road
South Green, Billericay CM11 2PR
01932 706810
katy.howell@immediatefuture.co.uk
www.bima.co.uk

British Internet Publishers Alliance (BIPA)
One Canada Square, Canary Wharf
London E14 5DT
020 7538 6020
your_comments@bipa.co.uk
www.bipa.co.uk

HTML Writers Guild/ International Webmasters Association
119 E. Union Street, Suite F
Pasadena CA 91103 USA
+1 626 449 3709
membership-questions@hwg.org
www.hwg.org

Interactive Advertising Bureau
PO Box 26726, London SW2 4AN
020 8683 9557
secretariat@iabuk.net
www.iabuk.net

Internet Service Providers Association
23 Palace Street
London SW1E 5HW
020 7233 7234
admin@ispa.org.uk
www.ispa.org.uk

NetMedia
info@net-media.co.uk
www.net-media.co.uk

Oftel
50 Ludgate Hill, London EC4M 7JJ
020 7634 8700
infocent@oftel.gov.uk
www.oftel.gov.uk

New media trade press

3G Mobile
Informa UK, Informa Telecoms Group
Mortimer House
37–41 Mortimer Street
London W1T 3JH
020 7017 5000
gavin.patterson@informa.com
www.telecoms.com
23pa. Editor: Gavin Patterson

Content Management Focus
Ark Publishing
86–88 Upper Richmond Road
Putney, London SW15 2UR
020 8785 2700
cmfocus@ark-group.com
www.cmfocus.com
10pa. Editor: Layisha Laypang

IT Europa
656 The Crescent
Colchester Business Park
Colchester CO4 9YQ
01206 224400
alastair.edwards@iteuropa.com
www.iteuropa.com
20pa. Editor: Alastair Edwards

Library Hi Tech News
Emerald, 60–62 Toller Lane
Bradford BD8 9BY
01274 777700
ebreen@emeraldinsight.com
www.emeraldinsight.com
10pa. Editor: Julia Gelsand/Colby Riggs

New Media Age
Centaur Communications
St Giles House, 50 Poland Street
London W1F 7AX
020 7970 4000
michael.nutley@centaur.co.uk
www.newmediazero.com
Weekly / Editor: Michael Nutley

Revolution
Haymarket Business Publications
174 Hammersmith Road
London W6 7JP
020 8267 4730
philip.smith@haynet.com
www.revolutionmagazine.com
Monthly. Editor: Philip Smith

The Online Reporter
Information Express
PO Box 2077, Verney Park
Buckingham MK18 1WQ
01280 820560
simon@g2news.com
www.g2news.com
Weekly. Editor: Maureen O'Gara

World telemedia
Network for Online Commerce
Services, Tulip House
70 Borough High Street
London SE1 1XF
0870 732 7327
paulskeldon@paulskeldon.com
www.noconline.org
Quarterly. Editor: Paul Skeldon

166

Books

On the face of it, Britain's books industry has never been healthier. There are between 6,000 and 7,000 book publishers, who together published more than 130,000 new titles in 2002 – up almost 25% on 1998. The total sales value of books in 2001 was almost £3.4bn, of which consumer books were worth more than £2bn. Adults purchased an average of eight books each in 2002, spending 4% more than in the previous years. So why isn't everyone happy?

A closer look at the figures demonstrates why. Total sales at chain stores are up 17% and supermarket sales up 32% since 1998; but sales at independents have fallen by 26%. Similarly, the number of titles published is actually falling. The main reason: discounting. Half of all adult paperbacks bought were sold at a discount in 2002, according to Nielsen Bookscan's industry figures, compared to just under a third in 1997. The chains which get the biggest discounts, chiefly Waterstone's and WH Smith, also negotiate discounts for displaying books prominently and other forms of promotional marketing; which means more sales are made by fewer publishers for fewer best-selling books. This starts to explain why, out of those 6,000 or 7,000 publishers, just six groups control 54% of the book sales in the UK; and why, in a market driven by news of seven-figure book deals to a few big names (see table), the average author earns less than £10,000 a year.

Compounding this is news from the industry's Books and the Consumer survey for 2002, which found that a third of all UK adults have not bought a single book in the past year, and 28% never read books at all; a further 27% would classify themselves as "light" book buyers.

Sales of children's books declined by 11% in 2002, perhaps because there was no Harry Potter book that year – but the fifth instalment, Harry Potter and the Order of the Phoenix, published in June 2003, was a runaway success with 1.8m copies sold in its first day. Jonathan Stroud was among the authors to capitalise on the global vogue for fantasy fiction by signing lucrative foreign rights deals (see table).

Online sales of books represented 6% of the total market in 2002. But the optimism surrounding e-books had almost evaporated.

In consolidation news, Lagardère bought reference publisher Chambers Harrap, Random House bought Everyman, and WH Smith and Random House battled to buy the book publishing division of troubled giant AOL Time Warner.

Books and the media

A traditional way of driving book sales is through the literary prize: there are more than 140 such awards in the UK, some of the winners of which are listed in the panel. The Booker in particular was in populist mood: it was ultimately won by Yann Martel's innovative The Life of Pi.

Other phenomena in 2003 were World Book Day, in March, which succeeded in raising sales in its week to £17.5m, up 13.8% on the same period in 2002; and the BBC's Big Read, in which Britons used telephone and internet voting to nominate their favourite book. Programmes on the top 10 books were broadcast in November 2003. More controversial was Granta magazine's list of the best young British novelists, most of whom had already been signed by major publishing groups.

A good way of getting media coverage for a book is to announce a seven-figure deal, usually at about the time of the London Book Fair in March: see panel for details of some of the big ones.

Further reading

■ Press

Guardian Review and Guardian Unlimited Books
guardian.co.uk/books

The Bookseller
www.thebookseller.com

Publishing News
www.publishingnews.co.uk

London Review of Books
www.lrb.co.uk

■ Books

From Pitch to Publication CAROLE BLAKE; PAN 1999
Insider's guide by one of Britain's foremost literary agents

On Writing STEPHEN KING, HODDER & STOUGHTON 2001
Part autobiography, part guide to the craft

The Art of Fiction DAVID LODGE; PENGUIN 1992
Accessible criticism for writers

■ Web only

Booksurfer
booksurfer.blogspot.com

Bloomsbury.com writers area
www.bloomsbury.com/WritersArea

Bookslut
www.bookslut.com/blog

■ Other resources

Society of Authors
www.writers.org.uk/society

Publishers Association
www.publishers.org.uk

Major rights deals, 2002–03				
July 02	Jonathan Stroud	*Bartimaeus Trilogy*, US rights	Miramax	£2m
Aug 02	Jeffrey Archer	three-book deal	Macmillan	"several million"
Sep 02	Chris Evans	autobiog, *Little Bigshot*	Harper Collins	more than £1m
Mar 03	Kate Mosse	*Labyrinth*	Orion	"seven figure sum"
Mar 03	Jane Moore	chicklit novelist	Random House	"high six-figure sum"
Mar 03	Ann-Marie Macdonald	*The Way the Crow Flies*	HarperCollins	"seven-figure deal"
Mar 03	Pamela Stephenson	three-book deal	Hodder Headline	£2m
Apr 03	John Peel	memoirs	Transworld	£1.6m

In search of young readers **Stephen Page**

Despite the lively appearance of many high street bookshops, despite the great books that win the literary prizes and (on occasion) feature on the bestseller lists, British publishing faces many challenges. Since the collapse of the net book agreement in 1995 there has been a steady remaking of the economics of the trade. Large general publishers have become vast conglomerates, leaving only a handful of independents; this has led to a market share war whose outcome is escalating investment in advance royalty payments and marketing. Yet despite the narrowing of publishers' focus on to fewer potential bestsellers, the industry continues to publish more books year on year – and this in a market that has ceased to grow.

In 2002 the percentage of the population buying books was static, but smaller than it had been five years previously: last year the value of the book market grew by just 1%, with the retail price index running at 2.5% to 3%. Publishers and retailers are pedalling ever harder to achieve, at best, the same result. Despite an 18% growth since 1998, the market appears saturated.

On top of this, there has been deflation in important markets – such as paperback fiction, where the average selling price has fallen from £5.40 to £5.02 in just one year. This deflation is driven by the supermarkets, who have moved into books in much the same way as they did music. The result has been enormous commercial pressure on key book retailers such as WH Smith and Waterstone's, both of whom have used discounting and multiple purchase offers to win market share. Independent bookselling has declined to less than 20% of the market, from 30% five years ago.

The trade has become focused on new books or front list, at the cost of the backlist. Discounting is widespread, but as a mechanism it seems little understood – what should we deduce, for example, from the fact that 45% of purchases made by the heaviest book buyers are discounted?

Publishers have struggled to afford discounting through improved efficiencies, and through mergers and painful staff cuts – particularly in editorial. This hasn't always been a good thing for most authors. But there are still some strong independent publishers who offer a different and more intimate model, and despite tougher market conditions they continue to be well supported by the trade, writers and the media.

The greater long-term worry lies in the proportion of under-35s buying books, which is in steeper decline than that for general book-buying. The trend is for a further decline in this readership – and they are our future. One has to be hopeful about Harry Potter, but looking at the children's market overall there is no suggestion that there is any uplift. We are just about managing to sell more books to less people, and those people are ageing.

Why are we losing so many of the young? In part the answer would seem cultural, but it is also about marketing and innovative publishing. Books are promoted much more vigorously and professionally than they were 10 years ago, but the economics of publishing only allows for a small percentage of revenue to be spent on marketing – around 7% – and this is thinly spread. Growth will only come if publishers and retailers can collaborate to find a way to market books to a wider audience.

Publishing fewer books than the current 120,000 titles a year will be a start, along with finding new ways to excite readers that don't depend so much on price reductions. The industry needs to attract talented young marketers, be they in publishing or bookselling roles, to break moulds and innovate.

This is a mature industry that has achieved much over the last decade – but it now needs new ideas to meet the challenges that have emerged since price maintenance was removed.

Stephen Page is chief executive of Faber and Faber

Awards

British book awards 2003
Book of the year: Stupid White Men (Michael Moore, Penguin)
Author of the year: Sarah Waters (Fingersmith, Tipping the Velvet, Affinity; all Virago)
Biography of the year: Churchill (Roy Jenkins, Pan)
Children's book of the year: Girls in Tears (Jacqueline Wilson, Random House)

Orange prize 2003
Property (Valerie Martin, Abacus)

Booker prize 2002
Life of Pi (Yann Martel, Canongate)

Guardian first book award 2002
Everything is Illuminated (Jonathan Safran Foer, Hamish Hamilton)

Guardian children's fiction prize 2002:
Thursday's Child (Sonya Hartnett, Walker)

Whitbread awards 2002
Novel award: Spies (Michael Frayn, Faber and Faber)
First novel award: The Song of Names (Norman Lebrecht, Review)
Poetry award: The Ice Age (Paul Farley, Picador)
Biography award: Samuel Pepys: The Unequalled by Self (Claire Tomalin, Viking)
Children's book award: Saffy's Angel (Hilary McKay, Hodder)

Guardian Fastsellers 2002

	Title	Genre	Author	Imprint	RRP	Total sales
1	A Painted House	novel	John Grisham	Arrow	£6.99	893,695
2	Billy Biog	Biog (B)	Pamela Stephenson	HarperCollins	£6.99	820,057
3	Atonement	Novel (B)	Ian McEwan	Vintage	£7.99	778,650
4	How To Be Good	Novel (B)	Nick Hornby	Penguin	£6.99	771,783
5	Warlock	Adventure (A)	Wilbur Smith	Pan	£6.99	615,222
6	Five Quarters of the Orange	Novel (B)	Joanne Harris	Black Swan	£6.99	569,463
7	Resurrection Men	Crime (A)	Ian Rankin	Orion	£6.99	562,924
8	One for My Baby	Novel (B)	Tony Parsons	HarperCollins	£6.99	550,710
9	A Man Named Dave	Autobiog (A)	Dave Pelzer	Orion	£6.99	537,919
10	Dead Famous	Novel (B)	Ben Elton	Black Swan	£6.99	526,315

Chart includes paperbacks published for the first time in Britain this year.
For current bestsellers and the 2003 fastsellers list, see guardian.co.uk/books.

Books Contacts

A&C Black (Publishers)
Alderman House, 37 Soho Square
London W1D 3QZ
020 7758 0200
enquiries@acblack.com
www.acblack.com
Part of Bloomsbury Publishing
Reference and non-fiction

AA Publishing
The Automobile Association
14th Floor, Fanum House
Basingstoke, Hampshire RG21 4EA
01256 491522
ian.harvey@theeaa.com
www.theaa.co.uk
Maps, atlases and guidebooks

ABC-Clio
26 Beaumont Street
Oxford OX1 2NP
01865 517222
salesuk@abc-clio.com
www.abc-clio.com
Academic and general reference works

Absolute Press
Scarborough House
29 James Street West
Bath BA1 2BT
01225 316013
info@absolutepress.co.uk
www.absolutepress.co.uk
Non-fiction

Abson Books London
5 Sidney Square, London E1 2EY
020 7790 4737
absonbooks@aol.com
Language glossaries

Acair
7 James Street, Stornoway
Isle of Lewis HS1 2QN
01851 703020
enquiries@acairbooks.com
www.acairbooks.com
Scottish history, culture and the Gaelic language

Acumen Publishing
15A Lewins Yard, East Street
Chesham
Buckinghamshire HP5 1HQ
01494 794398
steven.gerrard@
    acumenpublishing.co.uk
www.acumenpublishing.co.uk
Philosophy, history and politics

African Books Collective
The Jam Factory, 27 Park End Street
Oxford OX1 1HU
01865 726686
abc@africanbookscollective.com
www.africanbookscollective.com

Age Concern England
1268 London Road
London SW16 4ER
020 8765 7200
media@ace.org.uk
www.ageconcern.org.uk

Aidan Ellis Publishing
Whinfield, Herbert Road
Salcombe, South Devon TQ8 8HN
01548 842755
mail@aidanellispublishing.co.uk
www.aepub.demon.co.uk
General publications and non-fiction

Albatross Publishing
The Coach House, Grange Court
Grange Road, Tongham
Surrey GU10 1DW
01252 781994
sbutler@z-guides.com
www.z-guides.com
Reference & non-fiction

Allison & Busby
Suite 111, Bon Marche Centre
241 Ferndale Road
London SW9 8BJ
020 7738 7888
all@alisonandbusby.com
www.alisonandbusby.com

Amber Lane Press
Cheorl House, Church Street
Charlbury, Oxfordshire OX7 3PR
01608 810024
jamberlane@aol.com
http://members.aol.com
    /jamberlane/home.htm
Plays & theatre

Andersen Press
20 Vauxhall Bridge Road
London SW1V 2SA
020 7870 8703/8700
andersenpress@randomhouse.co.uk
www.andersenpress.co.uk
Children's books and fiction

Andrew Brodie Publications
PO Box 19, St Neots
Cambridgeshire PE19 8SF
01480 212666
sales@acblack.com
www.acblack.com
A subsidiary of A&C Black
Children's educational

Anness Publishing
Hermes House
88–89 Blackfriars Road
London SE1 8HA
020 7401 2077
sbaldwin@anness.com
General non-fiction

Anthem Press
75–76 Blackfriars Road
London SE1 8HA
020 7401 4200
inquires@wpcpress.com
www.anthempress.com
Part of Wimbledon Publishing Press
Non-fiction. Imprints and divisions
include: Lorenz Books; Aquamarine;
Hermes House; Peony Press;
Southwater

Antique Collectors' Club
Sandy Lane, Old Martlesham
Woodbridge, Suffolk IP12 4SD
01394 389950
sales@antique-acc.com
www.antique-acc.com

Anvil Press Poetry
Neptune House, 70 Royal Hill
London SE10 8RF
020 8469 3033
anvil@anvilpresspoetry.com
www.anvilpresspoetry.com

Apa Publications
58 Borough High Street
London SE1 1XF
020 7403 0284
berlitz@apaguide.co.uk
www.berlitzpublishing.co.uk
Owned by Langenscheidt Publishing
Group
Travel & languages. Imprint: Berlitz
Publishing

Appletree Press
The Old Potato Station
14 Howard Street South
Belfast BT7 1AP
028 9024 3074
reception@appletree.ie
www.appletree.ie
Cookery & Celtic interest

Arc Publications
Nanholme Mill, Shaw Wood Road
Todmorden, Lancashire OL14 6DA
01706 812338
info@arcpublications.co.uk
www.arcpublications.co.uk
Contemporary poetry

Arcadia Books
15–16 Nassau Street
London W1W 7AB
020 7436 9898
info@arcadiabooks.co.uk
www.arcadiabooks.co.uk
Literary fiction, biography, gender
studies & travel

Architectural Association Publications
36 Bedford Square
London WC1B 3ES
020 78874000
publications@aaschool.ac.uk
www.aaschool.info/publications
*Publishing arm of Architectural
Association School of Architecture*

Arcturus Publishing
26/27 Bickels Yard
151–153 Bermondsey Street
London SE1 3HA
020 7407 9400
info@arcturuspublishing.com
www.arcturuspublishing.com
Non-fiction

Ashgate Publishing
Gower House, Croft Road
Aldershot, Hampshire GU11 3HR
01252 331551
info@ashgatepub.co.uk
www.ashgate.com
and www.gowerpub.com
and www.lundhumphries.com
Business, law & art

Ashgrove Publishing
55 Richmond Avenue
London N1 0LX
020 7713 7540
gmo73@dial.pipex.com
www.ashgrovepublishing.com
*Owned by Hollydata Publishers
Non-fiction*

Ashley Drake Publishing
PO Box 733, Cardiff CF14 2YX
029 2056 0343
post@ashleydrake.com
www.ashleydrake.com
Academic, leisure & lifestyle

Ashmolean Museum Publications
Ashmolean Museum
Beaumont Street, Oxford OX1 2PH
01865 278010/ 288070
publications@ashmus.ox.ac.uk
www.ashmol.ox.ac.uk
*Owned by Oxford University
Imprints and divisions include:
Ashmolean Museum Publications;
Griffith Institute*

Atlantic Books
Ormond House
26–27 Boswell Street
London WC1N 3JZ
020 7269 1610
enquiries@groveatlantic.co.uk
www.groveatlantic.co.uk
*Literary fiction, non-fiction &
reference*

Aurum Press
25 Bedford Avenue
London WC1B 3AT
020 7637 3225
editorial@aurumpress.co.uk
www.aurumpress.co.uk
Non-fiction

Australian Consolidated Press UK
Moulton Park Business Centre
Red House Road, Moulton Park
Northampton NN3 6AQ
01604 497531
acpukltd@aol.com
Home interest

AuthorsOnline
15–17 Maidenhead Street
Hertford, Hertfordshire SG14 1DW
0870 750 0544
theeditor@authorsonline.co.uk
www.authorsonline.co.uk

Autumn Publishing
Appledram Barns
Birdham Road, Near Chichester
West Sussex PO20 7EQ
01243 531660
autumn@autumnpublishing.co.uk
www.autumnpublishing.co.uk
Early learning. Imprint: Byeway Books

Award Publications
1st Floor, 27 Longford Street
London NW1 3DZ
020 7388 7800
info@awardpublications.co.uk
*Children's fiction and reference.
Imprints and divisions include: Horus
Editions*

Axis Publishing
8C Accommodation Road
London NW11 8ED
020 8731 8080
wallace@axispublishing.co.uk
www.axispublishing.co.uk/
Health & sport

Barefoot Books
124 Walcot Street, Bath BA1 5BG
01225 322400
edit@barefootbooks.com
www.barefootbooks.com
Children's picture books

Barny Books
The Cottage, Hough on the Hill
Near Grantham
Lincolnshire NG32 2BB
01400 250246/ 01522 790009
*Children's books, adult fiction and
non-fiction*

Barrington Stoke
10 Belford Terrace
Edinburgh EH4 3DQ
0131 315 4933
info@barringtonstoke.co.uk
www.barringtonstoke.co.uk
Remedial children's reading

BBC Audio Books
St James House, The Square
Lower Bristol Road, Bath BA2 3SB
01225 878000
bbcaudiobooks@bbc.co.uk
www.bbcaudiobooks.com
*a subsidiary of BBC Worldwide
Imprints and divisions include: Black
Dagger Crime, Chivers Large Print,
Gunsmoke Westerns, Galaxy
Children's Large Print, Camden
Softcover Large Print, Paragon
Softcover Large Print, Windsor Large
Print, Chivers Audio Books, BBC Cover
to Cover Children's, BBC Word for
Word, BBC Cover to Cover Classics,
BBC Radio Collection, Harry
Potter/Cover to Cover*

BBC Books
BBC Worldwide, Woodlands
80 Wood Lane, London W12 0TT
020 8433 2000
www.bbcworldwide.com

Beaumont Publishing (London)
Grosvenor House, 1 High Street
Edgware, Middlesex HA8 7TA
020 8951 1700
info@beaumont-publishing.com
www.beaumont-publishing.co.uk
Educational material

Bentwyck Henry Publishers
36 Hart Street, Henley-On-Thames
Oxfordshire RG9 2AU
01491 413100
bentwyckhenrybks@aol.com
General non-fiction and fiction

Berg Publishers
1st Floor Angel Court
81 St Clements Street
Oxford OX4 1AW
01865 245104
enquiry@bergpublishers.com
www.bergpublishers.com
*Various academic. Imprints and
divisions include: Oswald Wolff Books*

Berghahn Books
3 Newtec Place, Magdalen Road
Oxford OX4 1RE
01865 250011
editorialuk@berghahnbooks.com
www.berghahnbooks.com
Academic books and journals

Berkswell Publishing Co
PO Box 420, Warminster
Wiltshire BA12 9XB
01985 840189
churchwardens@btinternet.com
Churches & heritage

BFI Publishing
British Film Institute
21 Stephen Street, London W1T 1LN
020 7255 1444
publishing@bfi.org.uk
www.bfi.org.uk/books
Part of the British Film Institute

BFP Books
Focus House, 497 Green Lanes
London N13 4BP
020 8882 3315
info@thebfp.com
www.thebfp.com/home.html
Publishing arm of the Bureau of
Freelance Photographers

Birlinn
West Newington House
10 Newington Road
Edinburgh EH9 1QS
0131 668 4371
info@birlinn.co.uk
www.birlinn.co.uk
Own John Donald Publishers
History & folklore

Black & White Publishing
99 Giles Street, Edinburgh EH6 6BZ
0131 625 4500
mail@blackandwhitepublishing.com
www.blackandwhitepublishing.com
General fiction and non-fiction

Black Spring Press
Burbage House, 83–85 Curtain Road
London EC2A 3BS
020 7613 3066
general@dexterhaven.demon.co.uk
Fiction and non-fiction

Blackie & Co Publishers
107–111 Fleet Street
London EC4A 2AB
020 7936 9021
editors@blackiepublishers.com
www.blackiepublishers.com
Fiction and non-fiction

Blackstaff Press
4c Heron Wharf
Sydenham Business Park
Belfast BT3 9LE
028 9045 5006
marketing@blackstaffpress.com
www.blackstaffpress.com
Fiction, non-fiction & poetry

Blackwell Publishing
108 Cowley Road, Oxford OX4 1JF
01865 791100
pamela.todd@
    oxon.blackwellpublishing.com
www.blackwellpublishing.com
Journals and textbooks

Bloodaxe Books
Highgreen, Tarset
Northumberland NE48 1RP
01434 240500
bloodaxepublicity@yahoo.co.uk
www.bloodaxebooks.com
Poetry & literature

Bloomsbury Publishing
38 Soho Square, London W1D 3HB
020 7494 2111
csm@bloomsbury.com
www.bloomsbury.com
Owns A & C Black
Adult & children's fiction & non-
fiction (incl Harry Potter)

BMJ Books
BMA House, Tavistock Square
London WC1H 9JR
020 7383 6245
customerservices@bmjbooks.com
www.bmjbooks.com
Part of the British Medical Journal
Publishing Group
Clinical medicine

Book Guild
Temple House, 25 High Street
Lewes, East Sussex BN7 2LU
01273 472534
info@bookguild.co.uk
www.bookguild.co.uk
Fiction & non-fiction

Books 4 Publishing
Lasyard House, Underhill Street
Bridgnorth, Shropshire WV16 4BB
0870 777 3339
editor@books4publishing.com
www.books4publishing.com
Online showcase for unpublished
writers

Boulevard Books & The Babel
Guides
71 Lytton Road, Oxford OX4 3NY
01865 712931
raybabel@dircon.co.uk
www.babelguides.com
Contemporary world fiction

Bowker
Farringdon House, Wood Street
East Grinstead
West Sussex RH19 1UZ
01342 310450
worldcustserv@bowker.com
www.bowker.co.uk
Part of the Cambridge Information
Group (CIG)
Reference & biography

Boydell & Brewer
PO Box 9, Woodbridge
Suffolk IP12 3DF
01394 411320
boydell@boydell.co.uk
www.boydell.co.uk
Non-fiction, principally medieval
studies

Bradt Travel Guides
19 High Street, Chalfont St Peter
Buckinghamshire SL9 9QE
01753 893444
info@bradt-travelguides.com
www.bradt-travelguides.com

Brassey's/Conway/Putnam
64 Brewery Road, London N7 9NT
020 7697 3000
www.brasseys.com
Owned by Chrysalis
Military, defence & diplomacy

Breedon Books Publishing Co
Breedon House, 3 Parker Centre
Derby DE21 4SZ
01332 384235
anton@breedonpublishing.co.uk
www.breedonbooks.co.uk
Local history and heritage

Breese Books
10 Hanover Crescent
Brighton, East Sussex BN2 9SB
01273 687555
mbreese999@aol.com
www.sherlockholmes.co.uk and
www.abracadabra.co.uk and
www.martinbreese.com
Conjuring books and Sherlock Holmes
pastiches

British Academy
10 Carlton House Terrace
London SW1Y 5AH
020 7969 5200
secretary@britac.ac.uk
www.britac.ac.uk

British Library
96 Euston Road, London NW1 2DB
020 7412 7704
blpublications@bl.uk
www.bl.uk
Publishing arm of the British Library

British Museum Press
46 Bloomsbury Street
London WC1B 3QQ
020 7323 1234
customerservices@
    bmcompany.co.uk
www.britishmuseum.co.uk
Book publishing division of the British
Museum Company

Brooklands Books
PO Box 146, Cobham
Surrey KT11 1LG
01932 865051
sales@brooklands-books.com
www.brooklands-books.com
Motoring reference & catalogues

Brown, Son & Ferguson
4–10 Darnley Street
Glasgow G41 2SD
0141 429 1234
info@skipper.co.uk
www.skipper.co.uk
Nautical textbooks & Scottish plays

Brown Watson
The Old Mill, 76 Fleckney Road
Kibworth Beauchamp
Leicestershire LE8 0HG
0116 279 6333
books@brownwatson.co.uk
General children's interest

Browntrout Publishers
Redland Office Centre
157 Redland Road, Redland
Bristol BS6 6YE
0117 973 9191
sales@browntroutuk.com
www.browntrout.com
Fine art and photography products

Bryntirion Press
Bryntirion, Bridgend
Mid-Glamorgan CF31 4DX
01656 655886
office@emw.org.uk
www.emw.org.uk
Owned by the Evangelical Movement
of Wales
Christian books in English and Welsh

BT Batsford
The Chrysalis Building
Bramley Road, London W10 6SP
020 7314 1400
info@chrysalisbooks.co.uk
www.batsford.com
Owned by Chrysalis Books Group
Non-fiction

Business Education Publishers
The Teleport, Doxford International
Sunderland, Tyne & Wear SR3 3XD
0191 525 2410
info@bepl.com
www.bepl.com

Cadogan Guides
Highlands House, 165 the Broadway
London SW19 1NE
020 8544 8051
http://info.cadogan@virgin.net
www.cadoganguides.com
Owned by US firm, Morris Publications
Travel guides

Calder Publications
51 The Cut, London SE1 8LF
020 7633 0599
info@calderpublications.com
www.calderpublications.com
Formerly John Calder (Publishers)
Biography, drama, music & poetry

Cambridge University Press
The Edinburgh Building
Shaftesbury Road
Cambridge CB2 2RU
01223 312393
information@cambridge.org
http://uk.cambridge.org/
The printing and publishing house of
the University of Cambridge

Camden Press
43 Camden Passage
London N1 8EA
020 7226 4673
Social issues. Imprints and divisions
include: Mindfield

Canongate Books
14 High Street, Edinburgh EH1 1TE
0131 557 5111
info@canongate.co.uk
www.canongate.net
Literary fiction & non-fiction, music

Capall Bann Publishing
Auton Farm, Milverton
Somerset TA4 1NE
01823 401528
enquiries@capallbann.co.uk
www.capallbann.co.uk
British traditional works and folklore

Capstone Publishing
The Atrium, Southern Gate
Chichester PO19 8SQ
01243 779777
info@wiley-capstone.co.uk
www.capstoneideas.com
Part of John Wiley & Sons
Business and personal development
books

Carcanet Press
4th Floor, Alliance House
30 Cross Street
Manchester M2 7AQ
0161 834 8730
pnr@carcanet.u-net.com
www.carcanet.co.uk
Poetry, academic works, literary
biography, fiction in translation

Cardiff Academic Press
St Fagans Road, Fairwater
Cardiff CF5 3AE
029 2056 0333
cap@drakeed.com
www.drakeed.com/cap

Carlton Publishing Group
20 Mortimer Street
London W1T 3JW
020 7612 0400
enquiries@carltonbooks.co.uk
www.carlton.com
Owned by Carlton Communications
Illustrated entertainment and leisure
titles. Imprints and divisions include:
Carlton Books, Granada Media,
Manchester United Books

Carroll & Brown Publishers
20 Lonsdale Road
London NW6 6RD
020 7372 0900
mail@carrollandbrown.co.uk
Lifestyle

Catholic Truth Society (CTS)
40–46 Harleyford Road
London SE11 5AY
020 7640 0042
editorial@cts-online.org.uk
www.cts-online.org.uk
Roman Catholic books, including
Vatican documents

Causeway Press
PO Box 13, 129 New Court Way
Ormskirk, Lancashire L39 5HP
01695 576048
causeway.press@btinternet.com
Educational textbooks

Cavendish Publishing
The Glass House, Wharton Street
London WC1X 9PX
020 7278 8000
info@cavendishpublishing.com
www.cavendishpublishing.com
Academic & practitioner law books

CBA (Publishing Department)
Bowes Morrell House
111 Walmgate, York YO1 9WA
01904 671417
info@britarch.ac.uk
www.britarch.ac.uk
Publishing arm of the Council for
British Archaeology
Archaeology, practical handbooks

CBD Research
Chancery House, 15 Wickham Road
Beckenham, Kent BR3 5JS
020 8650 7745
cbd@cbdresearch.com
www.cbdresearch.com

C Hurst & Co (Publishers)
Africa Centre, 38 King Street
Covent Garden
London WC2E 8JZ
020 7240 2666
hurst@atlas.co.uk
www.hurstpub.co.uk
Contemporary history

Chambers Harrap Publishers
7 Hopetoun Crescent
Edinburgh EH7 4AY
0131 556 5929
admin@chambersharrap.com
www.chambersharrap.com
Dictionaries and reference

Chapman Publishing
4 Broughton Place
Edinburgh EH1 3RX
0131 557 2207
chapman-pub@blueyonder.co.uk
www.chapman-pub.co.uk
Scottish writers including poetry,
drama, short stories

Chartered Institute of Personnel
and Development
CIPD House, Camp Road
London SW19 4UX
020 8263 3387
books:
　　publish@cipd.co.uk
magazine:
　　editorial@peoplemanagement.co.uk
www.cipd.co.uk
Part of CIPD Enterprises

Chicken House Publishing
2 Palmer Street, Frome
Somerset BA11 1DS
01373 454488
chickenhouse@doublecluck.com
www.doublecluck.com
Children's fiction

Children's Books Ireland
17 Lower Camden Street
Dublin 2, Ireland
00 353 1872 5854
info@childrensbooksireland.com
www.childrensbooksireland.com

Child's Play (International)
Ashworth Road
Bridgemead, Swindon
Wiltshire SN5 7YD
01793 616286
allday@childs-play.com
www.childs-play.com

Chris Andrews Publications
15 Curtis Yard, North Hinksey Lane
Oxford OX2 0NA
01865 723404
chris.andrews1@btclick.com
www.cap-ox.co.uk
Owns the Oxford Picture Library
Coffee table, calendars & diaries

Christian Focus Publications
Geanies House, Fearn
Tain, Ross-shire IV20 1TW
01862 871011
info@christianfocus.com
www.christianfocus.com

Chrysalis Children's Books
The Chrysalis Building
Bramley Road, London W10 6SP
020 7314 1400
childrens@chrysalisbooks.co.uk
www.chrysalisbooks.co.uk
A division of the Chrysalis Books Group

Cicerone Press
2 Police Square, Milnthorpe
Cumbria LA7 7PY
01539 562069
info@cicerone.demon.co.uk
www.cicerone.co.uk
Guidebooks for outdoor enthusiasts

Cico Books
1st Floor, 32 Great Sutton Street
London EC1V 0NB
020 7253 7960
mail@cicobooks.co.uk
Lifestyle and interiors

Co & Bear Productions (UK)
565 Fulham Road
London SW6 1ES
020 7385 0888
bvincenzini@cobear.co.uk
www.scriptumeditions.co.uk
*High quality illustrated books.
Imprint: Scriptum Editions*

Colin Smythe
PO Box 6, Gerrards Cross
Buckinghamshire SL9 8XA
01753 886000
sales@colinsmythe.co.uk
www.colinsmythe.co.uk
*Anglo-Irish literature, drama,
criticism and history*

Collins & Brown
The Chrysalis Building
Bramley Road, London W10 6SP
020 7314 1400
ctemple@chrysalisbooks.co.uk
www.chrysalisbooks.co.uk
*Owned by Chrysalis Group
Illustrated non-fiction, lifestyle,
photography & craft*

Colourpoint Books
Unit D5, Ards Business Centre
Jubilee Road, Newtownards
Co. Down BT23 4YH
028 9182 0505
info@colourpoint.co.uk
www.colourpoint.co.uk
*School textbooks, transport, Irish
interest*

Commonwealth Secretariat
Marlborough House, Pall Mall
London SW1Y 5HX
020 7747 6385
info@commonwealth.int
www.thecommonwealth.org
*Inter-governmental organisation
representing 54 member countries*

Compass Maps
The Coach House, Beech Court
Winford BS40 8DW
01225 445555
info@popoutmaps.com
www.mapgroup.net

Compendium Publishing
1st Floor, 43 Frith Street
London W1D 4SA
020 7287 4570
compendiumpub@aol.com

Constable & Robinson
3, The Lanchesters
162 Fulham Palace Road
London W6 9ER
020 8741 3663
enquiries@constablerobinson.com
www.constablerobinson.com
*Fiction & non-fiction, lifestyle,
reference & children's*

Continuum International Publishing Group
Tower Building, 11 York Road
London SE1 7NX
020 7922 0880
jbasic@continuumbooks.com
www.continuumbooks.com
*Academic, religious and general books.
Imprints and divisions include:
Athlone, Pinter, Sheffield Academic
Press, Geoffrey Chapman, Mowbray,
T&T Clark, Burns & Oates, Sheed &
Ward*

Countryside Books
2 Highfield Avenue
Newbury, Berkshire RG14 5DS
01635 43816
info@countrysidebooks.co.uk
www.countrysidebooks.co.uk

Cowley Robinson Publishing
8 Belmont, Lansdown Road
Bath BA1 5DZ
01225 339999
anna.sainaghi@cowleyrobinson.com
www.cowleyrobinson.com
Novelty children's books

CRC Press UK/ Parthenon Publishing
23–25 Blades Court
Deodar Road, London SW15 2NU
020 8875 4370
scrowley@crcpress.com
www.crcpress.com
*Part of the Taylor Francis Group
Books, journals, newsletters and
databases*

Crecy Publishing
Unit 1a, Ringway Trading Estate
Shadowmoss Road
Manchester M22 5LH
0161 499 0024
enquiries@crecy.co.uk
www.crecy.co.uk
Aviation and naval military history

Cressrelles Publishing Co
10 Station Road Industrial Estate
Colwall, Malvern
Worcestershire WR13 6RN
01684 540154
simonsmith@cressrelles
    4drama.fsbusiness.co.uk
*Actinic Press
Plays and theatre texts*

Crowood Press
The Stable Block, Crowood Lane
Ramsbury, Marlborough
Wiltshire SN8 2HR
01672 520320
enquiries@crowood.com
www.crowoodpress.co.uk/780
    /index.asp
Hobby and leisure pursuits

CW Daniel Company
1 Church Path, Saffron Walden
Essex CB10 1JP
01799 521909
cwdaniel@ukonline.co.uk
www.cwdaniel.com
New age

Dalesman Publishing Co
Stable Courtyard, Broughton Hall
Skipton, North Yorkshire BD23 3AZ
01756 701381
editorial@dalesman.co.uk
www.dalesman.co.uk
*Magazines and regional books
(Yorkshire, the Lake District and the
Peak District)*

Darf Publishers
277 West End Lane
London NW6 1QS
020 7431 7009
darf@freeuk.com
www.darfpublishers.co.uk
Middle East focus

Darton, Longman & Todd
1 Spencer Court
140–142 Wandsworth High Street
London SW18 4JJ
020 8875 0155
mail@darton-longman-todd.co.uk
www.darton-longman-todd.co.uk
*Spirituality, theology and the
Christian church*

David & Charles Publishers
Brunel House, Forde Close
Newton Abbot, Devon TQ12 4PU
01626 323200
mail@davidandcharles.co.uk
www.davidandcharles.co.uk
*A subsidiary of F&W (UK)
Illustrated non-fiction*

David Fulton (Publishers)
The Chiswick Centre
414 Chiswick High Road
London W4 5TF
020 8996 3610
mail@fultonpublishers.co.uk
www.fultonpublishers.co.uk
*Books and classroom resources for
teachers*

Debrett's
Brunel House
55–57 North Wharf Road
London W2 1LA
020 7915 9633
people@debretts.co.uk
www.debretts.co.uk
Specialist reference works

Dedalus
Langford Lodge, St Judith's Lane
Sawtry, Cambridgeshire PE28 5XE
01487 832382
dedaluslimited@compuserve.com
www.dedalusbooks.com
Contemporary European fiction and
classics. Imprints and divisions
include: Original Fiction in
Paperback, Contemporary European
Fiction 1992–2004, Dedalus
European Classics, Empire of the
Senses, Literary Concept Book

Dewi Lewis Publishing
8 Broomfield Road, Heaton Moor
Stockport SK4 4ND
0161 442 9450
mail@dewilewispublishing.com
www.dewilewispublishing.com
Fiction, photography and visual arts

Donhead Publishing
Lower Coombe, Donhead St Mary
Shaftesbury, Dorset SP7 9LY
01747 828422
jillpearce@donhead.com
www.donhead.com
Building, architecture and heritage

Dorling Kindersley
Penguin Group, 80 Strand
London WC2R 0RL
020 7010 3000
customerservice@dk.com
www.dk.com
Owned by Pearson
Illustrated non-fiction. Imprints and
divisions include: Ladybird, Ladybird
Audio, Funfax, Eyewitness Guides and
Eyewitness Travel Guides

Drake Educational Associates
St Fagans Road, Fairwater
Cardiff CF5 3AE
029 2056 0333
drakegroup@btinternet.com
www.drakeed.com

Dref Wen
28 Church Road, Whitchurch
Cardiff CF14 2EA
029 2061 7860
sales@drefwen.com
Welsh language

Duncan Baird Publishers
Castle House, 75–76 Wells Street
London W1T 3QH
020 7323 2229
enquiries@dbairdpub.co.uk
General non-fiction

Duncan Petersen Publishing
31 Ceylon Road, London W14 0PY
020 7371 2356
dp@macunltd.net
www.charmingsmallhotels.co.uk
Non-fiction

Eagle Publishing
6 Kestrel House, Mill Street
Trowbridge, Wiltshire BA14 8BE
01225 781111
eaglepublishing1@aol.com
Christian books & music

Edinburgh University Press
22 George Square
Edinburgh EH8 9LF
0131 650 4218
Timothy.Wright@eup.ed.ac.uk
www.eup.ed.ac.uk

Edward Elgar Publishing
Glensanda House
Montpellier Parade, Cheltenham
Gloucestershire GL50 1UA
01242 226934
info@e-elgar.co.uk
www.e-elgar.com
Economics, business & environment

Egmont Books
239 Kensington High Street
London W8 6SA
020 7761 3500
egmont@egmont.com
www.egmont.com
Children's entertainment publisher.
Imprints and divisions include:
Heinemann Young Books, Methuen
Children's Books, Hamlyn Children's
Books, Mammoth, Dean

Eland Publishing
Third Floor, 61 Exmouth Market
Clerkenwell, London EC1R 4QL
020 7833 0762
info@travelbooks.co.uk or
info@sicklemoon.co.uk
www.travelbooks.co.uk or
www.sicklemoon.co.uk
Travel poetry & literature & history of
the Islamic world

Elliot Right Way Books
Kingswood Buildings
Lower Kingswood, Tadworth
Surrey KT20 6TD
01737 832202
info@right-way.co.uk
www.right-way.co.uk
Practical guides to home improvement

Elliott & Thompson
27 John Street, London WC1N 2BX
020 7831 5013
gmo73@dial.pipex.com
Fiction, history, humour, travel, belle
lettre

Elm Consulting
Seaton House, Kings Ripton
Huntingdon
Cambridgeshire PE28 2NJ
01487 773254
sritchie@elm-training.co.uk
www.elm-training.co.uk
Educational aids

Elsevier
The Boulevard, Langford Lane
Kidlington, Oxford OX5 1GB
01865 843000
media@elsevier.com
www.elsevier.com
Parent company is Reed Elsevier
Academic & professional reference

Elsevier Publishers
32 Jamestown Road
London NW1 7BY
020 7424 4200
nlinfo-f@elsevier.com
www.elsevier.com
Owned by Elsevier
Scientific, technical and medical.
Imprints and divisions include:
Academic Press, Bailliere Tindall,
Churchill Livingstone, Mosby, W.B.
Saunders

Emissary Publishing
PO Box 33, Bicester
Oxfordshire OX26 4ZZ
01869 323447
Humorous paperbacks

Emma Treehouse
2nd Floor, The Old Brewhouse
Lower Charlton Trading Estate
Shepton Mallet, Somerset BA4 5QE
01749 330529
richard.powell4@virgin.net
Children's pre-school books

Encyclopaedia Britannica (UK)
2nd Floor, Unity Wharf
Mill Street, London SE1 2BH
020 7500 7800
enquiries@britannica.co.uk
www.britannica.co.uk

English Heritage (Publishing)
Kemble Drive, Swindon SN2 2GZ
01793 414619
robin.taylor@english-heritage.org.uk
www.english-heritage.org.uk

Enitharmon Press
26B Caversham Road
London NW5 2DU
020 7482 5967
books@enitharmon.co.uk
www.enitharmon.co.uk
Poetry, literary criticism, fiction, art
and photography

Epworth Press
Editorial
Methodist Publishing House
4 John Wesley Road
Werrington, Peterborough
Cambridgeshire PE4 6ZP
01603 612914
orders@SCM-canterburypress.co.uk
Orders to SCM-Canterbury Press
Christian books: philosophy, theology

Euromonitor
60–61 Britton Street
London EC1M 5UX
020 7251 8024
info@euromonitor.com
www.euromonitor.com
Business reference, market analysis
and information directories

Evans Publishing Group
2A Portman Mansions
Chiltern Street, London W1U 6NR
020 7487 0920
sales@evansbrothers.co.uk
www.evansbooks.co.uk
Children's and educational. Imprints
and divisions include: Cherrytree
Books, Evans Brothers, Zero to Ten

Everyman's Library
Gloucester Mansions
140a Shaftesbury Avenue
London WC2H 8HD
020 7539 7600
books@everyman.uk.com
www.everyman.uk.com
Literature, poetry, children's and travel

Exley Publications
16 Chalk Hill, Watford
Hertfordshire WD19 4BG
01923 248328
editorial@exleypublications.co.uk
www.helenexleygiftbooks.com
Giftbooks, quotation anthologies and humour

FA Thorpe (Publishing)
The Green, Bradgate Road
Anstey, Leicester LE7 7FU
0116 236 4325
sales@ulverscroft.co.uk
www.ulverscroft.co.uk
Fiction and non-fiction large print books. Imprints and divisions include: Linford Romance, Linford Mystery, Linford Western

Faber & Faber
3 Queen Square
London WC1N 3AU
020 7465 0045
info@faber.co.uk
www.faber.co.uk

Facet Publishing
7 Ridgmount Street
London WC1E 7AE
020 7255 0590/ 0505 (text phone)
info@facetpublishing.co.uk
www.facetpublishing.co.uk
Publishing arm of CILIP (The Chartered Institute of Library and Information Professionals)

Fernhurst Books
Duke's Path, High Street
Arundel, West Sussex BN18 9AJ
01903 882277
sales@fernhurstbooks.co.uk
www.fernhurstbooks.co.uk
Practical, highly illustrated handbooks on sailing and watersports

Findhorn Press
305a The Park, Findhorn
Morayshire IV36 3TE
01309 690582
books@findhorn.org
www.findhornpress.com
New Age, personal development

First & Best in Education
Unit K, Earlstrees Court
Earlstrees Road, Corby
Northamptonshire NN17 4HH
01536 399004
firstandbest@themail.co.uk
www.firstandbest.co.uk
Imprints and divisions include: School Improvement Reports

Fitzwarren Publishing
2 Orchard Drive
Aston Clinton, Aylesbury
Buckinghamshire HP22 5HR
01296 632627
pen2paper@btopenworld.com
Legal handbooks for the layman

Flicks Books
29 Bradford Road, Trowbridge
Wiltshire BA14 9AN
01225 767728
flicks.books@dial.pipex.com
Cinema and related media

Floris Books
15 Harrison Gardens
Edinburgh EH11 1SH
0131 337 2372
floris@florisbooks.co.uk
www.florisbooks.co.uk
Steiner movement books

Folens Publishers
Apex Business Centre
Boscombe Road, Dunstable
Bedfordshire LU5 4RL
0870 609 1237
folens@folens.com
www.folens.com
Educational books. Imprints and divisions include: Folens, Belair

Fountain Press
Newpro UK , Old Sawmills Road
Faringdon, Oxfordshire SN7 7DS
01367 242411
sales@newprouk.co.uk
Owned by Newpro UK
Photography and natural history

Fourth Estate
77–85 Fulham Palace Road
London W6 8JB
020 8741 4414
general@4thestate.co.uk
www.4thestate.co.uk
Owned by HarperCollins
Fiction, general interest

Frances Lincoln Publishers
4 Torriano Mews, Torriano Avenue
London NW5 2RZ
020 7284 4009
reception@frances-lincoln.com
www.franceslincoln.com
Highly illustrated non fiction

Frank Cass & Co
Crown House, 47 Chase Side
Southgate, London N14 5BP
020 8920 2100
info@frankcass.com
www.frankcass.com
Books and journals on world affairs. Imprints and divisions include: Vallentine Mitchell/ Jewish Chronicle Publications

Free Association Books
57 Warren Street, London W1T 5NR
020 7388 3182
info@fabooks.com
www.fabooks.com
Psychoanalysis and psychotherapy

Gaia Books
66 Charlotte Street
London W1T 4QE
020 7323 4010
info@gaiabooks.com
www.gaiabooks.co.uk
Lifestyle

Gairm Publications
29 Waterloo Street, Glasgow G2 6BZ
0141 221 1971
Gaelic and Gaelic-related books

Garnet Publishing
8 Southern Court, South Street
Reading, Berkshire RG1 4QS
0118 959 7847
enquiries@garnet-ithaca.demon.co.uk
www.garnet-ithaca.co.uk
Owns Ithaca Press
Mainly Middle Eastern focus, general

Geddes & Grosset
David Dale House
New Lanark ML11 9DJ
01555 665000
caroline@geddesandgrosset.co.uk
Children's and reference books

Geological Society Publishing House
Unit 7, Brassmill Enterprise Centre
Brassmill Lane, Bath BA1 3JN
01225 445046
dawn.angel@geolsoc.org.uk or
angharad.hills@geolsoc.org.uk
www.bookshop.geolsoc.org.uk
Publishing arm of the Geological Society
Undergraduate and postgraduate texts in the earth sciences

George Mann Books
PO Box 22m Maidstone
Kent ME14 1AH
01622 759591
Original non-fiction and selected reprints

Gibson Square Books
15 Gibson Square, London N1 0RD
020 7689 4790
publicity@gibsonsquare.com
www.gibsonsquare.com/
Biography & personal experience

Giles de la Mare Publishers
PO Box 25351, London NW5 1ZT
020 7485 2533
gilesdelamare@dial.pipex.com
www.gilesdelamare.co.uk
Art and architecture, biography, history, music

GMP (Gay Men's Press)
Spectrum House
32/34 Gordon House Road
London NW5 1LP
020 7424 7400
robertm@millivres.co.uk
www.millivres.co.uk
Part of the Millivres Prowler Group
Gay fiction, literary and popular

Golden Cockerel Press
Unit 304, The Chandlery
50 Westminster Bridge Road
London SE1 7QY
020 7953 8770
aup.uk@btinternet.com
Academic titles. Imprints and
divisions include: Associated
University Presses (AUP), Bucknell
University Press, University of
Delaware, Fairleigh Dickinson
University Press, Lehigh University
Press, Susquehanna University Press.

Gomer Press
Llandysul, Ceredigion SA44 4QL
01559 362371
gwasg@gomer.co.uk
www.gomer.co.uk
Adult fiction and non-fiction. Imprints
and divisions include: Pont Books

Good Web Guide
65 Bromfelde Road
London SW4 6PP
020 7720 8919
marketing@thegoodwebguide.co.uk
www.thegoodwebguide.co.uk

Graham-Cameron Publishing &
Illustration
The Studio, 23 Holt Road
Sheringham, Norfolk NR26 8NB
01263 821333
enquiry@graham
    -cameron-illustration.com
www.graham-cameron
    -illustration.com
Illustrated factual books

Granta Books
2–3 Hanover Yard, Noel Road
London N1 8BE
020 7704 9776
lcampbell@granta.com>
www.granta.com
Literary fiction and general non-fiction

Green Books
Foxhole, Dartington, Totnes
Devon TQ9 6EB
01803 863260
edit@greenbooks.co.uk
www.greenbooks.co.uk
Green issues

Greenhill Books/ Lionel Leventhal
Park House, 1 Russell Gardens
London NW11 9NN
020 8458 6314
lionelleventhal@greenhillbooks.com
www.greenhillbooks.com
Aviation, military & naval

Gresham Books
46 Victoria Road, Summertown
Oxford OX2 7QD
01865 513582
greshambks@btinternet.com
www.gresham-books.co.uk
Hymn and service books

Grub Street
The Basement, 10 Chivalry Road
London SW11 1HT
020 7924 3966/ 7738 1008
post@grubstreet.co.uk
www.grubstreet.co.uk
Lifestyle & military

Guild of Master Craftsman
Publications
166 High Street, Lewes
East Sussex BN7 1XU
01273 477374
theguild@thegmcgroup.com
www.gmcmags.com
Part of G.M.C. Services
Craft

Guinness World Records
338 Euston Road, London NW1 3BD
020 7891 4567
www.guinnessworldrecords.com
"The Guinness Book of Records" &
"British Hit Singles"

Gullane Children's Books
Winchester House
259–269 Old Marylebone Road
London NW1 5XJ
020 7616 7200
Owned by Andromeda Oxford

Gwasg Carreg Gwalch
12 Iard yr Orsaf, Llanrwst
Conwy LL26 0EH
01492 642031
books@carreg-gwalch.co.uk
www.carreg-gwalch.co.uk

Halsgrove
Halsgrove House, Lower Moor Way
Tiverton Business Park, Tiverton
Devon EX16 6SS
01884 243242
sales@halsgrove.com
www.halsgrove.com
Local history, cookery, biography and
art

Hambledon and London
102 Gloucester Avenue
London NW1 8HX
020 7586 0817
office@hambledon.co.uk
www.hambledon.co.uk
History and biography

Harcourt Education
Halley Court, Jordan Hill
Oxford OX2 8EJ
01865 311366
uk.schools@harcourteducation.co.uk
www.repp.co.uk
Member of the Reed Elsevier group
Textbooks & educational resources

Harlequin Mills & Boon
Eton House, 18–24 Paradise Road
Richmond, Surrey TW9 1SR
020 8288 2800
www.millsandboon.co.uk
Popular non-fiction

Harley Books
Martins, Great Horkesley
Colchester, Essex CO6 4AH
01206 271216
harley@keme.co.uk
www.harleybooks.com
Natural history

HarperCollins Publishers
77–85 Fulham Palace Road
London W6 8JB
020 8741 7070
human.resources@harpercollins.co.uk
www.harpercollins.co.uk
Imprints and divisions include:
Willow, Flamingo, Collins Crime,
Fourth Estate, Thorsons, Element,
Voyager, Lions, Collins Picture Books,
Collins Jet, Collins Teacher, Gems

HarperCollins Publishers (2)
Westerhill Road, Bishopbriggs
Glasgow G64 2QT
0141 772 3200
human.resources@harpercollins.co.uk
www.fireandwater.co.uk

Harvard University Press
Fitzroy House, 11 Chenies Street
London WC1E 7EY
020 7306 0603
info@HUP-MITpress.co.uk
www.hup.harvard.edu
European office of US company

Harvill Press
20 Vauxhall Bridge Road
London SW1V 2SA
020 7840 8400
enquiries@randomhouse.co.uk
www.randomhouse.co.uk
Owned by the Random House Group
Literature in translation

Haynes Publishing
Sparkford, Near Yeovil
Somerset BA22 7JJ
01963 440635
sales@haynes-manuals.co.uk
www.haynes.co.uk
Owns Sutton Publishing

Hazleton Publishing
5th Floor mermaid house,
2 Puddledock, London EC4V 3DS
0207 332 2000
info@hazletonpublishing.com
www.hazletonpublishing.com

Helicon Publishing
RM , New Mill House
183 Milton Park, Abingdon
Oxfordshire OX14 4SE
01235 826000
helicon@rm.com
www.helicon.co.uk
Reference and cartography

Helm Information
The Banks, Mountfield
Nr Robertsbridge
East Sussex TN32 5JY
01580 880561
amandahelm@
    helm-information.co.uk
www.helm-information.co.uk
Academic

Helter Skelter Publishing
4 Denmark Street
London WC2H 8LL
020 7836 1151
info@helterskelterbooks.com
www.helterskelterbooks.com
Music and film.
Imprints and divisions include:
Firefly Publishing

Hesperus Press
4 Rickett Street
London SW6 1RU
020 7610 3331
agallenzi@hesperuspress.com
www.hesperuspress.com
Classic fiction in paperback

Highbury Nexus Special Interests
Berwick House, 8/10 Knoll Rise
Orpington, Kent BR6 0EL
01689 899200
info@nexusmedia.com
www.nexusonline.com
Leisure & hobbies

Hobsons Publishing
Challenger House, 42 Adler Street
London E1 1EE
020 7958 5000
www.hobsons.com
Part of the Daily Mail & General Trust
Course and career guides

Hodder Gibson
2A Christie Street, Paisley PA1 1NB
0141 848 1609
hoddergibson@hodder.co.uk
www.hodderheadline.co.uk and
www.madaboutbooks.com
Part of the Hodder Headline Group
Textbooks & revision support

Hodder Headline
338 Euston Road, London NW1 3BH
020 7873 6000
www.hodderheadline.co.uk
Owned by WH Smith
Imprints and divisions include:
Arnold, Hodder & Stoughton, John
Murray, Wayland, Hodder &
Stoughton Educational, Hodder
Children's Books

Honeyglen Publishing
56 Durrels House, Warwick Gardens
London W14 8QB
020 7602 2876
History & fiction

Honno Welsh Women's Press
c/o Canolfan Merched Y Wawr
Vulcan Street, Aberystwyth
Ceredigion SY23 1JH
01970 623150
post@honno.co.uk
www.honno.co.uk
Fiction, poetry & short story

House of Lochar
Isle of Colonsay, Argyll PA61 7YR
01951 200232
lochar@colonsay.org.uk
www.houseoflochar.com
Mostly Scottish titles, general.
Imprints and divisions include:
Colonsay Books

House of Stratus
Thirsk Industrial Park, Thirsk
North Yorkshire YO7 3BX
01845 527700
info@houseofstratus.com
www.houseofstratus.com
fiction and non-fiction

How To Books
3 Newtec Place, Magdalen Road
Oxford OX4 1RE
01865 793806
info@howtobooks.co.uk
www.howtobooks.co.uk
Reference books

Hymns Ancient & Modern
St Mary's Works, St Mary's Plain
Norwich, Norfolk NR3 3BH
01603 612914
admin@scm-canterburypress.co.uk
www.scm-canterburypress.co.uk
Hymn books. Imprints and divisions
include: SCM Press, Canterbury Press
Norwich, Religious and Moral
Education Press (RMEP), GJ Palmer
& Sons Ltd (Church Times)

Ian Allan Publishing
Riverdene Business Park
Molesey Road, Hersham
Surrey KT12 4RG
01932 266600
info@ianallanpub.co.uk
www.ianallan.com
Transport books & magazines.
Imprints and divisions include:
Midland Publishing, OPC Railway
titles, Classic Publications

Ian Henry Publications
20 Park Drive, Romford
Essex RM1 4LH
01708 749119
iwilkes@ianhenry.fsnet.co.uk
History & Sherlock Holmes

IB Tauris & Co
6 Salem Road, London W2 4BU
020 7243 1225
enquiries@ibtauris.com
www.ibtauris.com
Culture and politics

Icon Books
Grange Road, Duxford
Cambridge CB2 4QF
01763 208008
info@iconbooks.co.uk
www.iconbooks.co.uk
History, children's fiction and non-
fiction

IMP Fiction
PO Box 14691, London SE1 2ZA
01440 788561
info@impbooks.com
www.impbooks.com
Innovative fiction

Independent Music Press
PO Box 14691, London SE1 2ZA
01440 788561
info@impbooks.com
www.impbooks.com
Music biography and youth culture

Interpet
Interpet House, Vincent Lane
Dorking, Surrey RH4 3YX
01306 873840
kevin@interpet.co.uk
Pet, aquatic and water gardening books

Inter-Varsity Press
38 De Montfort Street
Leicester LE1 7GP
0116 255 1754
ivp@uccf.org.uk
www.ivpbooks.com
Christian belief and lifestyle. Imprints
and divisions include: IVP, Apollos,
Crossway

Isis Publishing
7 Centremead, Osney Mead
Oxford OX2 0ES
01865 250333
sales@isis-publishing.co.uk
www.isis-publishing.co.uk
Part of the Ulverscroft Group
Large-print books

JA Allen & Co
Clerkenwell House
45–47 Clerkenwell Green
London EC1R 0HT
020 7251 2661
allen@halebooks.com
A specialist imprint of Robert Hale.
Publisher: Caroline Burt
Equine and equestrian non-fiction

James Clarke & Co
PO Box 60, Cambridge CB1 2NT
01223 350865
publishing@jamesclarke.co.uk
www.jamesclarke.co.uk
Parent company of the Lutterworth
Press
Theological, directory and reference

James Currey Publishers
73 Botley Road
Oxford OX2 0BS
01865 244111
editorial@jamescurrey.co.uk
www.jamescurrey.co.uk
Academic books on Africa, the
Caribbean and Third World

James Nisbet & Co
Pirton Court, Prior's Hill, Pirton
Hitchin, Hertfordshire SG5 3QA
01462 713444
alison@jamesnisbet.demon.co.uk
Business

Jane's Information Group
163 Brighton Road
Coulsdon, Surrey CR5 2YH
020 8700 3700
info@janes.co.uk
www.janes.com
Defence, aerospace and transport

Janus Publishing Company
105–107 Gloucester Place
London W1U 6BY
020 7580 7664
publisher@januspublishing.co.uk
www.januspublishing.co.uk
Fiction and non-fiction. Imprints and
divisions include: Empiricus Books

Jarrold Publishing
Whitefriars, Norwich
Norfolk NR3 1TR
01603 763300
publishing@jarrold.com
www.jarrold-publishing.co.uk
Travel and leisure. Imprints and divisions include: Pitkin, Unichrome

Jessica Kingsley Publishers
116 Pentonville Road
London N1 9JB
020 7833 2307
post@jkp.com
www.jkp.com
Social and behavioural sciences

John Blake Publishing
3 Bramber Court, 2 Bramber Road
London W14 9PB
020 7381 0666
words@blake.co.uk
www.blake.co.uk
*Owns Smith Gryphon and Metro Publishing
Mass-market non-fiction, biography*

John Brown Citrus Publishing
The New Boathouse
136–142 Bramley Road
London W10 6SR
020 7565 3000
andrew.hirsch@jbcp.co.uk
www.jbcp.co.uk
Customer magazines

John Hunt Publishing
46a West Street, New Alresford
Hampshire SO24 9AU
01962 736880
maria@johnhunt-publishing.com
www.johnhunt-publishing.com and
www.o-books.net
*Children's and world religions.
Imprints and divisions include: Hunt & Thorpe, Arthur James, O Books*

John Libbey & Co
PO Box 276, Eastleigh SO50 5YS
01342 315440
johnlibbey@aol.com
www.johnlibbey.com
Medical

John Murray (Publishers)
338 Euston Road, London NW1 3BH
020 7873 6000
enquiries@johnmurrays.co.uk
www.hodderheadline.com
*Owned by Hodder Headline
General trade books*

John Wiley Publishers
The Atrium, Southern Gate
Chichester, West Sussex PO19 8SQ
01243 779777
cs-books@wiley.co.uk
www.wileyeurope.com
Professional, scientific, technical and biomedical reference and text books

John Wiley Publishers
4th Floor, International House
7 High Street, Ealing Broadway
London W5 5DB
020 8326 3800
cs-books@wiley.co.uk
http://wileyeurope.com
*Part of the John Wiley & Sons, Inc. group
Architecture and design, science, scientific, medical*

J Whitaker & Sons
Woolmead House West, Bear Lane
Farnham, Surrey GU9 7LG
01252 742500
custserv@whitaker.co.uk
www.whitaker.co.uk
*Services for the book trade
Bibliographic reference products*

Kahn & Averill
9 Harrington Road
London SW7 3ES
020 8743 3278
kahn@averill23.freeserve.co.uk
Music and general non-fiction

Karnak House
300 Westbourne Park Road
London W11 1EH
020 7243 3620
karnakhouse@aol.com
www.karnakhouse.co.uk
African and Caribbean studies

Kenneth Mason Publications
The Book Barn, Westbourne
Emsworth, Hampshire PO10 8RS
01243 377977
info@researchdisclosure.com
www.researchdisclosure.com
*Lifestyle, nutrition and nautical.
Imprints and divisions include:
Research Disclosure*

Kenilworth Press
Addington, Buckingham
Buckinghamshire MK18 2JR
01296 715101
editorial@kenilworthpress.co.uk
www.kenilworthpress.co.uk
Equestrian interest

Kevin Mayhew Publishers
Buxhall, Stowmarket
Suffolk IP14 3BW
01449 737978
info@kevinmayhewltd.com
www.kevinmayhewltd.com
Religious titles

Kingfisher Publications
New Penderel House
283–288 High Holborn
London WC1V 7HZ
020 7903 9999
sales@kingfisherpub.com
*Formerly Larousse
Children's fiction and non-fiction*

Kluwer Academic/ Plenum Publishers
100 Borough High Street
London SE1 1LB
020 7863 3000
mail@plenum.co.uk
www.wkap.nl
*UK and European office of US company
Scientific, technical and medical teaxtbooks. Imprints and divisions include: Consultants Bureau, Plenum Press, Human Science Press*

Kluwer Law International
145 London Road
Kingston-on-Thames
Surrey KT2 6SR
020 8247 1694
sales@kluwerlaw.com
www.kulwerlaw.com
*Parent company is Wolters Kluwer Group
International law. Imprints and divisions include: Graham & Trotman, Kluwer Law and Taxation, Martinus Nyhoff*

Kogan Page
120 Pentonville Road
London N1 9JN
020 7278 0433
kpinfo@kogan-page.co.uk
www.kogan-page.co.uk or
www.earthscan.co.uk
Business and management

Kyle Cathie
122 Arlington Road
London NW1 7HP
020 7692 7215
general.enquiries@kyle-cathie.com
www.KyleCathie.com
Lifestyle

Landmark Publishing
Ashbourne Hall, Cokayne Avenue
Ashbourne, Derbyshire DE6 1EJ
01335 347349
landmark@clara.net
www.landmarkpublishing.co.uk
Travel guides, and industrial and local history

Laurence King Publishing
71 Great Russell Street
London WC1B 3BP
020 7430 8850
enquiries@laurenceking.co.uk
www.laurenceking.co.uk
Illustrated arts

Lawrence & Wishart
99A Wallis Road, London E9 5LN
020 8533 2506
lw@lwbooks.co.uk
www.lwbooks.co.uk
Current and world affairs

Lennard Associates
Windmill Cottage, Mackerye End
Harpenden, Hertfordshire AL5 5DR
01582 715866
stephenson@lennardqap.co.uk
Sporting yearbooks. Imprints and divisions include: Lennard Publishing, Queen Anne Press

Letts Educational
The Chiswick Centre
414 Chiswick High Road
Chiswick, London W4 5TF
020 8996 3333
rob.storr@lettsed.co.uk
www.letts-education.com
Part of the Granada Learning Group
Revision and study material

Lexis Nexis UK
Tolley House, 2 Addiscombe Road
Croydon, Surrey CR9 5AF
0208 662 2000
customer-services@lexisnexis.co.uk
www.butterworths.com
Part of Reed Elsevier Legal Division

Lexis Nexis UK
Halsbury House, 35 Chancery Lane
London WC2A 1EL
020 7400 2500
customer-services@lexisnexis.co.uk
www.lexisnexis.co.uk
Part of Reed Elsevier Legal Division
Legal and accountancy

Librapharm
Gemini House, 162 Craven Road
Newbury, Berkshire RG14 5NR
01635 522651
info@librapharm.com
www.librapharm.com
Partial buyout from Kluwer Academic
Publishers (UK)
Medical and scientific

Lion Publishing
Mayfield House, 256 Banbury Road
Oxford OX2 7DH
01865 302750
enquiry@lion-publishing.co.uk
www.lion-publishing.co.uk
Christian books

Little Tiger Press
Magi Publications, 1 The Coda Centre
189 Munster Road
London SW6 6AW
020 7385 6333
info@littletiger.co.uk
www.littletigerpress.com
Children's picture and novelty books

Liverpool University Press
4 Cambridge Street
Liverpool L69 7ZU
0151 794 2233
sbell@liv.ac.uk
www.liverpool-unipress.co.uk

Lonely Planet Publications
72–82 Rosebery Avenue
Clerkenwell, London EC1R 4RW
020 7841 9000
go@lonelyplanet.co.uk
www.lonelyplanet.com

Learning Institute
Honeycombe House, Bagley
Wedmore, Somerset BS28 4TD
01934 713563
courses@inst.org
www.inst.org

Lutterworth Press
PO Box 60, Cambridge CB1 2NT
01223 350865
publishing@lutterworth.com
www.lutterworth.com
Founded by the Religious Tract Society
Religious and non-fiction

Macmillan Publishers
The Macmillan Building
4 Crinan Street, London N1 9XW
020 7833 4000
www.macmillan.com

Macmillan Publishers: Macmillan Education
Macmillan Oxford
4 Between Towns Road
Oxford OX4 3PP
01865 405700
info@macmillan.com
www.macmillaneducation.com

Mainstream Publishing Co (Edinburgh)
7 Albany Street, Edinburgh EH1 3UG
0131 557 2959
editorial@mainstreampublishing.com
www.mainstreampublishing.com
General non-fiction and popular
paperbacks

Management Books 2000
Forge House, Limes Road
Kemble, Cirencester
Gloucestershire GL7 6AD
01285 771441
m.b.2000@virgin.net
www.mb2000.com

Manchester University Press
Oxford Road, Manchester M13 9NR
0161 275 2310
mup@man.ac.uk
www.manchesteruniversitypress
.co.uk

Manson Publishing
73 Corringham Road
London NW11 7DL
020 8905 5150
manson@man-pub.demon.co.uk
www.manson-publishing.co.uk
Scientific, technical, medical and
veterinary

Marion Boyars Publishers
24 Lacy Road, London SW15 1NL
020 8788 9522
marion.boyars@talk21.com
www.marionboyars.co.uk
Formerly Calder and Boyars
Fiction and non-fiction

Marshall Cavendish
119 Wardour Street
London W1F 0UW
020 7565 6000
info@marshallcavendish.co.uk
www.marshallcavendish.co.uk
Adults and children's books

Marston House
Marston House, Marston Magna
Yeovil, Somerset BA22 8DH
01935 851331
alphaimage@marstonhouse
.ndo.co.uk
Fine art, architecture, ceramics and
horticulture

Martin Dunitz
Taylor & Francis Publishing Group
4th Floor, 11 New Fetter Lane
London EC4P 4EE
020 7842 2001
daniel.tomkins@tandf.co.uk
www.dunitz.co.uk
Owned by the Taylor & Francis Group
Specialist medical texts

McGraw-Hill Education
McGraw-Hill House,
Shoppenhangers Road
Maidenhead, Berkshire SL6 2QL
01628 502500
sales@mcgraw-hill.com
www.mcgraw-hill.co.uk
Business, economics, computing and
engineering

Mercat Press
10 Coates Crescent
Edinburgh EH3 7AL
0131 225 5324
enquiries@mercatpress.com
www.mercatpress.com
Scottish fiction and non-fiction

Merlin Press
PO Box 30705, London WC2E 8QD
020 7836 3020
local rate: 0845 458 1579
info@merlinpress.co.uk
www.merlinpress.co.uk
Economics, history, philosophy, left-
wing politics. Other imprints include:
Green Print

Merrell Publishers
42 Southwark Street
London SE1 1UN
020 7403 2047
mail@merrellpublishers.com
www.merrellpublishers.com
Art, architecture, design and
photography

Methodist Publishing House
4 John Wesley Road
Werrington, Peterborough
Cambridgeshire PE4 6ZP
01733 325002
sales@mph.org.uk
www.mph.org.uk
Owned by the Methodist Church
Christian books. Imprints and
divisions include: Epworth Press,
Foundry Press

Methuen Publishing
215 Vauxhall Bridge Road
London SW1V 1EJ
020 7798 1600
sales@methuen.co.uk
www.methuen.co.uk
Fiction and non-fiction

Michael O'Mara Books
9 Lion Yard, Tremadoc Road
London SW4 7NQ
020 7720 8643
enquiries@michaelomarabooks.com
www.michaelomarabooks.com
General non-fiction

Michelin Travel Publications
Hannay House, 39 Clarendon Road
Watford, Hertfordshire WD17 1JA
01923 205240
www.viamichelin.com

Microsoft Press
Thames Valley Park, Reading
Berkshire RG6 1WG
0118 909 6009
whawkins@microsoft.com
www.microsoft.com/mspress/uk

Miles Kelly Publishing
Unit 17 & 18, Bardfield Centre
Great Bardfield, Essex CM7 4SL
01371 811309
rob@mileskelly.net
www.mileskelly.net
Children's titles

Milet Publishing
6 North End Parade
London W14 0SJ
020 7603 5477
info@milet.com
www.milet.com
Children's books

Millivres Prowler Group
Unit M, Spectrum House
32/34 Gordons House Road
London NW5 1LP
020 7424 7400
info@gaytimes.co.uk
www.millivres.co.uk
Literary and genre fiction, erotic fiction

Monarch Books
Concorde House, Grenville Place
London NW7 3SA
020 8959 3668
monarch@angushudson.com
*An imprint of Angus Hudson
Christian and social concern*

Motor Racing Publications
PO Box 1318, Croydon
Surrey CR9 5YP
020 8654 2711
mrp.books@virgin.net
www.mrpbooks.co.uk

MQ Publications
12 The Ivories
6–8 Northampton Street
London N1 2HY
020 7359 2244
kim@mqpublications.com
www.mqpublications.com
Illustrated non-fiction titles

Multi-Sensory Learning
Highgate House, Groom's Lane
Creaton, Northampton NN6 8NN
01604 505000
info@msl-online.net
www.msl-online.net

Murdoch Books UK
Erico House, 6th Floor
93–99 Upper Richmond Road
Putney, London SW15 2PG
020 8785 5995
ctilbrook@murdochbooks.co.uk

National Archives
Kew, Surrey TW9 4DU
020 8392 5289
jane.crompton@
nationalarchives.gov.uk
www.nationalarchives.gov.uk

National Trust Publications
36 Queen Anne's Gate
London SW1H 9AS
020 7222 9251
enquiries@thenationaltrust.org.uk
www.nationaltrust.org.uk/bookshop
Publishing arm of the National Trust

Nautical Data
The Book Barn, Westbourne
Emsworth, Hampshire PO10 8RS
01243 389352
info@nauticaldata.com
www.nauticaldata.com

NCVO Publications
Regent's Wharf, 8 All Saints Street
London N1 9RL
020 7713 6161
ncvo@ncvo-vol.org.uk
www.ncvo-vol.org.uk
*Publishing imprint of the National
Council for Voluntary Organisations
Directories, public policy & governance*

Neil Wilson Publishing
Suite 303, The Pentagon Centre
36 Washington Street
Glasgow G3 8AZ
0141 221 1117
info@nwp.co.uk
www.nwp.co.uk
or www.11-9.co.uk
or www.vitalspark.co.uk
or www.angelshare.co.uk
or www.theinpinn.co.uk
Scottish and Irish interest and fiction

Nelson Thornes
Delta Place, 27 Bath Road
Cheltenham
Gloucestershire GL53 7TH
01242 267100
cservices@nelsonthornes.com
www.nelsonthornes.com
*Part of the Wolters Kluwer Group
Educational*

New Beacon Books
76 Stroud Green Road
London N4 3EN
020 7272 4889
newbeaconbooks@lineone.net
*Black oriented fiction, history, politics,
poetry and language*

New Holland Publishers (UK)
Garfield House
86–88 Edgware Road
London W2 2EA
020 7724 7773
postmaster@nhpub.co.uk
www.newhollandpublishers.com
*The International Publishing Division
of Johnnic Communications
Non-fiction, lifestyle & self-
improvement*

nferNelson
The Chiswick Centre
414 Chiswick High Road
London W4 5TF
020 8996 8444
information@nfer-nelson.co.uk
www.nfer-nelson.co.uk
*Part of Granada Learning
Educational and psychological tests
and training materials*

Nicholas Brealey Publishing
3–5 Spafield Street
London EC1R 4QB
020 7239 0360
rights@nbrealey-books.com
www.nbrealey-books.com
*Includes Intercultural Press
Trade/professional books*

Nick Hern Books
The Glasshouse
49a Goldhawk Road
London W12 8QP
020 8749 4953
info@nickhernbooks.demon.co.uk
www.nickhernbooks.co.uk
Theatre and film

Nielsen BookData
Globe House, 1 Chertsey Road
Twickenham TW1 1LR
020 8843 8600
info@bookdata.co.uk
www.bookdata.co.uk and
www.whitaker.co.uk and
www.first-edition.co.uk
*Books In Print and "The Red Book"
Directory of Publishers*

NMS Enterprises – Publishing
National Museums of Scotland
Chambers Street
Edinburgh EH1 1JF
0131 247 4026
ltaylor@nms.ac.uk
www.nms.ac.uk

Nottingham University Press
Manor Farm, Church Lane
Thrumpton, Nottingham NG11 0AX
0115 983 1011
editor@nup.com
www.nup.com
*Other imprints and divisions include:
Castle Publications*

Oberon Books
521 Caledonian Road
London N7 9RH
020 7607 3637
oberon.books@btinternet.com
www.oberonbooks.com
Play texts, ballet and theatre books.
Other imprints and divisions include:
Absolute Classics

Octagon Press
PO Box 227, London N6 4EW
020 8348 9392
octagon@schredds.demon.co.uk
www.octagonpress.com
Philosophy, psychology, travel and
Eastern religion

Octopus Publishing Group
2–4 Heron Quays, London E14 4JP
020 7531 8400
info-co@conran-octopus.co.uk
info-ho@hamlyn.co.uk
info-mb@mitchell-beazley.co.uk
george.philip@philips-maps.co.uk
brimax@brimax.octopus.co.uk
bountybooksinfo-bp@
    bountybooks.co.uk
www.octopus-publishing.co.uk
www.conran-octopus.co.uk
www.hamlyn.co.uk
www.mitchell-beazley.co.uk
www.philips-maps.co.uk
Owned by French publishers, Hachette-
Livre, owns Cassell Illustrated
Lifestyle & leisure titles

Oldcastle Books
PO Box 394, Harpenden
Hertfordshire AL5 1XJ
01582 761264
info@noexit.co.uk
www.noexit.co.uk and
www.pocketessentials.com
crime/ noir fiction, gambling non-
fiction. Other imprints and divisions
include: No Exit Press, Pocketessentials,
High Stakes, Crime Time, Kamera

Oldie Publications
65 Newman Street
London W1T 3EG
020 7436 8801
theoldie@theoldie.co.uk
www.theoldie.co.uk
Book publishing arm of The Oldie
magazine

Omnibus Press
Music Sales, 8–9 Frith Street
London W1D 3JB
020 7434 0066
chris.charlesworth@musicsales.co.uk
www.omnibuspress.com
Music. Other imprints and divisions
include: Omnibus Press, Wise
Publications; UK distributors for Fire
Fly, Hal Leonard, Helter Skelter, Hollis,
Parker Mead Ltd, Rogan House and
Vision On

Oneworld Pubications
185 Banbury Road, Oxford OX2 7AR
01865 310597
info@oneworld-publications.com
www.oneworld-publications.com
Non-fiction

Onlywomen Press
40 St Lawrence Terrace
London W10 5ST
020 8354 0796
onlywomenpress@aol.com
www.onlywomenpress.com

Open University Press
Mcgraw-Hill House
Maidenhead, Berkshire SL6 2QL
01628 502179
lyndsay_scholefield@mcgraw-hill.com
www.openup.co.uk
An imprint independent of the Open
University's course materials

Orion Publishing Group
Orion House
5 Upper Saint Martin's Lane
London WC2H 9EA
020 7240 3444
info@orionbooks.co.uk
www.orionbooks.co.uk
General fiction & non-fiction. Other
imprints and divisions include:
Custom Publishing, Phoenix,
Everyman

Osprey Publishing
Elms Court, Chapel Way
Botley, Oxford OX2 9LP
01865 727022
info@ospreypublishing.com
www.ospreypublishing.com
Illustrated history, military history
and aviation

Oxford University Press
Great Clarendon Street
Oxford OX2 6DP
01865 556767
webenquiry.uk@oup.com
www.oup.com
A department of Oxford University
Imprints and divisions include:
Oxford Children's Books

Palgrave Macmillan
Brunel Road, Houndmills
Basingstoke, Hampshire RG21 6XS
01256 329242
www.palgrave.com
Higher education, business &
non-fiction

Pan Macmillan
20 New Wharf Road
London N1 9RR
020 7014 6000
www.panmacmillan.com

Paternoster Publishing
PO Box 300, Kingstown Broadway
Carlisle, Cumbria CA3 0QS
01228 554320
info@Paternoster-Publishing.com
www.paternoster-publishing.co.uk
Academic & religious

Paul Chapman Publishing
SAGE Publications, 6 Bonhill Street
London EC2A 4PU
020 7374 0645
market@sagepub.co.uk
www.paulchapmanpublishing.co.uk
Education & training

Pavilion Books
64 Brewery Road, London N7 9NT
020 7697 3000
rsamson@chrysalisbooks.co.uk
www.pavilionbooks.co.uk
Owned by Chrysalis
General illustrated books

Pearson Education
Edinburgh Gate, Harlow
Essex CM20 2JE
01279 623623
HEEnquiriesUK@
    pearsoned-ema.com
www.pearsoned-ema.com

Pegasus Elliot Mackenzie
Publishers
Sheraton House, Castle Park
Cambridge CB3 0AX
01223 370012
editors@pegasuspublishers.com
www.pegasuspublishers.com
Fiction and non-fiction, crime and
erotica. Imprints and divisions
include: Vanguard Press, Nightingale
Books, Chimera

Pen & Sword Books
47 Church Street, Barnsley
South Yorkshire S70 2AS
01226 734222
enquiries@pen-and-sword.co.uk
www.pen-and-sword.co.uk
Naval and aviation history. Other
imprints and divisions include: Leo
Cooper, Wharncliffe Publishing

Penguin Group (UK)
A Pearson Company
80 Strand, London WC2R 0RL
020 7010 3000
helena.peacock@penguin.co.uk
www.penguin.co.uk
Owned by Pearson
Other imprints and divisions include:
Viking/Penguin, Hamish Hamilton,
Michael Joseph/Penguin, Dorling
Kindersley, Ladybird

Persephone Books
59 Lamb's Conduit Street
London WC1N 3NB
020 7242 9292
sales@persephonebooks.co.uk
www.persephonebooks.co.uk
Reprint fiction and non-fiction, focus
on women

Perseus Books Group
PO Box 317, Oxford OX2 9RU
01865 865466
info@theperseuspress.com
www.perseusbooksgroup.com
UK office of US Perseus Books Group
Non-fiction. Imprints: Public Affairs,
Da Capo Press, Basic Books,
Counterpoint, Basic Civitas Books,
Westview Press

Peter Haddock
Pinfold Lane, Bridlington
Yorkshire YO16 5BT
01262 678121
enquiries@phpublishing.co.uk
www.phpublishing.co.uk
Children's books

Peter Halban Publishers
22 Golden Square
London W1F 9JW
020 7437 9300
books@halbanpublishers.com
www.halbanpublishers.com
General Non-fiction, literature &
criticism

Peter Owen
73 Kenway Road, London SW5 0RE
020 7373 5628/ 7370 6093
admin@peterowen.com
www.peterowen.com
Biography, non-fiction, literary
fiction, literary criticism, history &
the arts

Phaidon Press
Regent's Wharf, All Saints Street
London N1 9PA
020 7843 1000
esales@phaidon.com
www.phaidon.com
Arts

Pharmaceutical Press
1 Lambeth High Street
London SE1 7JN
020 7735 9141
ppodhorski@rpsgb.org.uk
The publications division of the Royal
Pharmaceutical Society of Great
Britain
Medicine

Philip Berrill International
60 Leyland Road
Southport, Merseyside PR9 9JA
01704 534725
philipberrill@hotmail.com
"Everyone's Guide To" art book series

Philip Wilson Publishers
7 Deane House
27 Greenwood Place
London NW5 1LB
020 7284 3088
pwilson@philip-wilson.co.uk
www.philip-wilson.co.uk
Art, museums and exhibition materials

Phillimore & Co
Shopwyke Manor Barn, Chichester
West Sussex PO20 2BG
01243 787636
bookshop@phillimore.co.uk
www.phillimore.co.uk
British local and family history

Piatkus Books
5 Windmill Street, London W1T 2JA
020 7631 0710
info@piatkus.co.uk
www.piatkus.co.uk
Fiction, biography, history, health &
business

Piccadilly Press
5 Castle Road, London NW1 8PR
020 7267 4492
b.gardner@piccadillypress.co.uk
www.piccadillypress.co.uk
Children's and parental books

Pluto Press
345 Archway Road, London N6 5AA
020 8348 2724
pluto@plutobooks.com
www.plutobooks.com
Academic

Policy Press
University of Bristol, Fourth Floor
Beacon House, Queen's Road
Bristol BS8 1QU
0117 331 4054
tpp-info@bristol.ac.uk
www.policypress.org.uk
Social science publisher

Politico's Publishing
215 Vauxhall Bridge Road
London SW1V 1EJ
020 7798 1600
publishing@politicos.co.uk
www.politicos.co.uk/publishing
Owned by Methuen

Polity Press
65 Bridge Street
Cambridge CB2 1UR
01223 324315
polity@dial.pipex.com
www.polity.co.uk
All books published in association
with Blackwell Publishers
General academic

Portland Press
59 Portland Place
London W1B 1QW
020 7580 5530
editorial@portlandpress.com
www.portlandpress.com
Biochemistry and medicine

Prestel Publishing
4 Bloomsbury Place
London WC1A 2QA
020 7323 5004
sales@prestel-uk.co.uk
www.prestel.com
Art, architecture, photography and
children's

Princeton Architectural Press
37 East Seventh Street
New York, NY 10003
USA
+1 212 995 9620
sales@papress.com
www.papress.com

Profile Books
58a Hatton Garden
London EC1N 8LX
020 7404 3001
info@profilebooks.co.uk
www.profilebooks.co.uk
Non-fiction. Other imprints and
divisions include: Economist Books

Proquest Information and Learning
The Quorum, Barnwell Road
Cambridge CB5 8SW
01223 215512
marketing@proquest.co.uk
www.proquest.co.uk

Publishing House
Trinity Place, Barnstaple
Devon EX32 9HJ
01271 328892
publishinghouse@
    vernoncoleman.com
www.vernoncoleman.com
Fiction, health, humour, animals and
politics

Pushkin Press
123 Biddulph Mansions
Elgin Avenue, London W9 1HU
020 7266 9136
petra@pushkinpress.com
www.pushkinpress.com
Translated classic and contemporary
European literature

Quadrille Publishing
Alhambra House
27–31 Charing Cross Road
London WC2H 0LS
020 7839 7117
enquiries@quadrille.co.uk
www.quadrille.co.uk
Lifestyle

Quartet Books
27 Goodge Street
London W1T 2LD
020 7636 3992
quartetbooks@easynet.co.uk
Contemporary literary fiction

Quarto Publishing
The Fitzpatrick Building
188–194 York Way
London N7 9QP
020 7700 6700
info@quarto.com
www.quarto.com
Highly illustrated non-fiction books

Quiller Press
Wykey House, Wykey
Shrewsbury, Shropshire SY4 1JA
01939 261616
info@quillerbooks.com
www.swanhillbooks.com
Architecture, biography, business &
lifestyle

Radcliffe Medical Press
18 Marcham Road
Abingdon, Oxfordshire OX14 1AA
01235 528820
contact.us@radcliffemed.com
www.radcliffe-oxford.com

Random House Children's Books
61–63 Uxbridge Road
Ealing, London W5 5SA
020 8231 6800
tjones2@randomhouse.co.uk
www.kidsatrandomhouse.co.uk
Part of The Random House Group
Imprints and divisions include:
Hutchinson, Jonathan Cape, The
Bodley Head, Doubleday, David
Fickling Books, Corgi, Red Fox,
Anderson Press

Random House Group
Random House
20 Vauxhall Bridge Road
London SW1V 2SA
020 7840 8400
enquiries@randomhouse.co.uk
www.randomhouse.co.uk
General fiction and non-fiction

Ransom Publishing
Rose Cottage, Howe Hill
Watlington, Oxfordshire OX49 5HB
01491 613711
jenny@ransom.co.uk
www.ransom.co.uk
Education

Reader's Digest Association
11 Westferry Circus, Canary Wharf
London E14 4HE
020 7715 8000
gbeditorial@readersdigest.co.uk
www.readersdigest.co.uk
Editorial office in the USA

Reaktion Books
79 Farringdon Road
London EC1M 3JU
020 7404 9930
info@reaktionbooks.co.uk
www.reaktionbooks.co.uk
*Architecture, Asian and cultural
studies, film and travel writing*

Reardon Publishing
56 Upper Norwood Street
Leckhampton, Cheltenham
Gloucestershire GL53 0DU
01242 231800
reardon@bigfoot.com
www.reardon.co.uk
*Member of the Outdoor Writers Guild
Cotswold area local interest*

Red Bird Publishing
Kiln Farm, East End Green
Brightlingsea, Colchester
Essex CO7 0SX
01206 303525
info@red-bird.co.uk
www.red-bird.co.uk
Special-effects books for children

Reed Business Information
Quadrant House, The Quadrant
Sutton, Surrey SM2 5AS
020 8652 3500
www.reedbusiness.co.uk

Reed Elsevier
25 Victoria Street
London SW1H 0EX
020 7222 8420
www.reedelsevier.com

Regency House Publishing
Niall House
24–26 Boulton Road, Stevenage
Hertfordshire SG1 4QX
01438 314488
regency-house@btconnect.com
Mass-market non-fiction

Richmond House Publishing Company
70–76 Bell Street, Marylebone
London NW1 6SP
020 7224 9666
sales@rhpco.co.uk
www.rhpco.co.uk
*Directories for the theatre and
entertainment industries*

Robert Hale
Clerkenwell House
45–47 Clerkenwell Green
London EC1R 0HT
020 7251 2661
enquire@halebooks.com
www.halebooks.com
Fiction and some non-fiction

Robson Books
The Chrysalis Building
Bramley Road, London W10 6SP
020 7314 1494
robson@chrysalisbooks.co.uk
www.chrysalisbooks.co.uk
*An imprint of The Chrysalis Books
Group
General non-fiction*

Rodale Books
7–10 Chandos Street
London W1G 9AD
020 7291 6000
BPKcustserv@cdsfulfillment.com
www.rodale.com
Lifestyle

RotoVision
Sheridan House
112/116A Western Road, Hove
East Sussex BN3 1DD
01273 727268
sales@rotovision.com
www.rotovision.com
Graphic arts and design

Roundhouse Publishing Group
Millstone, Limers Lane
Northam, North Devon EX39 2RG
01237 474474
roundhouse.group@ukgateway.net
Cinema and media-related titles

Routledge
11 New Fetter Lane
London EC4P 4EE
020 7583 9855
info@routledge.co.uk
www.routledge.com
*a subsidiary of Taylor & Francis
Academic and professional books*

Ryland, Peters & Small
Kirkman House
12–14 Whitfield Street
London W1T 2RP
020 7436 9090
info@rps.co.uk
www.rylandpeters.com
Highly illustrated lifestyle books

Sage Publications
6 Bonhill Street, London EC2A 4PU
020 7374 0645
market@sagepub.co.uk
www.sagepub.co.uk
Social sciences and humanities

Saint Andrew Press
Church of Scotland
121 George Street
Edinburgh EH2 4YN
0131 225 5722
standrewpress@cofscotland.org.uk
www.standrewpress.com
or www.churchofscotland.org
or www.williambarclay.org
*Owned by the Church of Scotland
Christian books*

Salamander Books
64 Brewery Road, London N7 9NT
020 7697 3000
salamander@chrysalisbooks.co.uk
www.salamanderbooks.com
*Part of Chrysalis
Colour illustrated books on lifestyle &
hobbies*

Samuel French
52 Fitzroy Street, London W1T 5JR
020 7387 9373
theatre@samuelfrench-london.co.uk
www.samuelfrench-london.co.uk
Plays

Sangam Books
57 London Fruit Exchange
Brushfield Street, London E1 6EP
020 7377 6399
sangambks@aol.com
Educational textbooks

Saqi Books
26 Westbourne Grove
London W2 5RH
020 7221 9347
publicity@saqibooks.com
www.saqibooks.com
*Fiction and non-fiction, academic and
illustrated; books on Middle East and
Arab world; Asia and European
fiction, Balkans*

SB Publications
19 Grove Road, Seaford
East Sussex BN25 1TP
01323 893498
sbpublications@tiscali.co.uk
www.sbpublications.co.uk
*Local history, travel, guides. Imprints
include Ben Gunn.*

Scholastic Children's Books
Commonwealth House
1–19 New Oxford Street
London WC1A 1NU
020 7421 9000
scbenquiries@scholastic.co.uk
www.scholastic.co.uk
*Imprints and divisions include:
Hippo, Point*

Scholastic
Villiers House, Clarendon Avenue
Leamington Spa
Warwickshire CV32 5PR
01926 887799
enquiries@scholastic.co.uk
www.scholastic.co.uk

Scitech Educational
Kent Innovation Centre
Millennium Way
Thanet Reach Business Park,
Broadstairs, Kent CT10 2QQ
01843 609300
maria.thompson@scitech-ed.com
www.scitech-ed.com
20 years in learning support

SCM Canterbury Press
9–17 St Albans Place
London N1 0NX
020 7359 8033
admin@scm-canterburypress.co.uk
www.scm-canterburypress.co.uk
Theology

Scottish Cultural Press/Scottish Children's Press
Unit 6
Newbattle Abbey Business Annexe
Newbattle Road, Dalkeith EH22 3LJ
cultural: 0131 660 6366
children's: 0131 660 4757
info@scottishbooks.com
www.scottishbooks.com

Seafarer Books
102 Redwald Road, Rendlesham
Woodbridge, Suffolk IP12 2TE
01394 420789
info@seafarerbooks.com
www.seafarerbooks.com

Search Press
Wellwood, North Farm Road
Tunbridge Wells, Kent TN2 3DR
01892 510850
searchpress@searchpress.com
www.searchpress.com
Art and craft

Seren
First Floor, 38–40 Nolton Street
Bridgend CF31 3BN
01656 663018
general@seren-books.com
www.seren-books.com
Fiction and non-fiction, with emphasis on Wales. Imprints include Border Lines Biographies

Serpent's Tail
4 Blackstock Mews, London N4 2BT
020 7354 1949
info@serpentstail.com
www.serpentstail.com
Contemporary fiction, gay fiction and non-fiction

Severn House Publishers
9–15 High Street, Sutton
Surrey SM1 1DF
020 8770 3930
info@severnhouse.com
www.severnhouse.com
Hardback fiction for library market, romance, science fiction, horror, fantasy, crime

Shepheard-Walwyn (Publishers)
Suite 604, The Chandlery
50 Westminster Bridge Road
London SE1 7QY
020 7721 7666
books@shepheard-walwyn.co.uk
www.shepheard-walwyn.co.uk
Ethical economics, philosophy, biography, gift books, books of Scottish interest

Shetland Times
Gremsta, Lerwick, Shetland ZE1 0PX
01595 693622
publishing@shetland-times.co.uk
www.shetland-books.co.uk
Shetland interest

Shire Publications
Cromwell House, Church Street
Princes Risborough
Buckinghamshire HP27 9AA
01844 344301
shire@shirebooks.co.uk
www.shirebooks.co.uk
Original non-fiction paperbacks

Short Books
15 Highbury Terrace
London N5 1UP
020 7226 1607
rebecca@shortbooks.biz
www.theshortbookco.com

Sigma Press
5 Alton Road, Wilmslow
Cheshire SK9 5DY
01625 531035
info@sigmapress.co.uk
www.sigmapress.co.uk
Outdoor, heritage, myth, sport, biography

Simon & Schuster UK
Africa House, 64–78 Kingsway
London WC2B 6AH
020 7316 1900
enquiries@simonandschuster.co.uk
web: www.simonsays.co.uk
General fiction and non-fiction; science fiction (Earthlight); trade paperback (Scribner). Imprints include Pocket Books

Skoob Russell Square
10 Brunswick Centre
off Bernard Street
London WC1N 1AE
020 7278 8760
books@skoob.com
www.skoob.com
Literary guides, cultural studies, esoterica, poetry, new writing from Orient

Society for Promoting Christian Knowledge (SPCK)
Holy Trinity Church
Marylebone Road
London NW1 4DU
020 7643 0382
publicity@spck.org.uk
www.spck.org.uk

Souvenir Press
43 Great Russell Street
London WC1B 3PD
020 7580 9307/8
and 7637 5711/2/3
souvenirpress@ukonline.co.uk
Academic. Imprints include: Condor, Human Horizons, Independent Voices, Pictorial Presentations, Pop Universal, The Story-Tellers

Spellmount
The Old Rectory, Staplehurst
Kent TN12 0AZ
01580 893730
enquiries@spellmount.com
www.spellmount.com
History

Spiro Press
17 Rochester Row
London SW1P 1LA
0870 165 8970
info@capita-ld.co.uk
www.spiropress.com
*Part of the Capita Group
Business and self-development*

Springer-Verlag London
Sweetapple House, Catteshall Road
Godalming, Surrey GU7 3DJ
01483 418800
postmaster@svl.co.uk
www.springer.co.uk
Science and medical

Stainer & Bell
PO Box 110, 23 Gruneisen Road
London N3 1DZ
020 8343 3303
post@stainer.co.uk
www.stainer.co.uk
Music and hymn

Stanley Gibbons Publications
7 Parkside, Christchurch Road
Ringwood, Hampshire BH24 3SH
01425 472363
rpurkis@stanleygibbons.co.uk
www.stanleygibbons.co.uk
Philatelic reference catalogues and handbooks

Stationery Office
St Crispins, Duke Street
Norwich, Norfolk NR3 1PD
01603 622211
customer.services@tso.co.uk
www.thestationeryoffice.com
Government and other official bodies

Straightline Publishing
29 Main Street, Bothwell
Glasgow G71 8RD
01698 853000
patrick@straightlinepublishing.com
Trade and technical, local interest

Summersdale Publishers
46 West Street, Chichester
West Sussex PO19 1RP
01243 771107
submissions@summersdale.com
www.summersdale.com
Travel literature, fiction, biography, martial arts, self-help, cookery, humour and gift books

Summertown Publishing
29 Grove Street
Summertown, Oxford OX2 7JT
01865 454130
lucy@summertown.co.uk
www.summertown.co.uk
English-language teaching

Sutton Publishing
Phoenix Mill, Thrupp, Stroud
Gloucestershire GL5 2BU
01453 731114
sales@sutton-publishing.co.uk
www.suttonpublishing.co.uk
Owned by Haynes Publishing
Academic, biography, countryside,
history, transport

Swan Hill Press
Quiller Publishing, Wykey House,
Wykey, Shrewsbury
Shropshire SY4 1JA
01939 261616
info@quillerbooks.com
www.swanhillbooks.com
Rural and cookery

Sweet & Maxwell Group
100 Avenue Road, London NW3 3PF
020 7393 7000
customer.services@
    sweetandmaxwell.co.uk
www.sweetandmaxwell.co.uk
Part of the Thomson Corporation
Legal and professional. Imprints and
divisions include W Green (Scotland),
Round Hall

T&T Clark International
The Tower Building, 11 York Road
London SE1 7NX
020 7922 0880
www.tandtclark.co.uk
Part of the Continuum International
Publishing Group
Academic theology

Taschen UK
13 Old Burlington Street
London W1X 3AJ
020 7437 4350
contact@taschen.com
www.taschen.com
Art and pop culture

Taylor & Francis
11 New Fetter Lane
London EC4P 4EE
020 7842 2001
www.taylorandfrancis.com
Academic

Telegraph Books
1 Canada Square, Canary Wharf
London E14 5DT
020 7538 6826
Morvenknowles@telegraph.co.uk
www.telegraphbooksdirect.co.uk

Templar Publishing
Pippbrook Mill, London Road
Dorking, Surrey RH4 1JE
01306 876361
info@templarco.co.uk
www.templarco.co.uk
Illustrated books for children

Terence Dalton
Water Street, Lavenham
Sudbury, Suffolk CO10 9RN
01787 249291
terence@lavenhamgroup.co.uk
www.terencedalton.com
Part of the Lavenham Group
Non-fiction

Thalamus Publishing
4 Attorney's Walk, Bull Ring
Ludlow, Shropshire SY8 1AA
01584 874977
roger@thalamus-books.com
Family reference

Thames & Hudson
181A High Holborn
London WC1V 7QX
020 7845 5000
mail@thameshudson.co.uk
www.thamesandhudson.com
Vast range of cultural non-fiction

Thomas Cook Publishing
PO Box 227
Unit 15/16 Coningsby Road,
Peterborough PE3 8SB
01733 416477
publishing-sales@thomascook.com
www.thomascookpublishing.com
Part of the Thomas Cook Group

Thompson Stanley Publishers
1/3 Leonard Street
London EC2A 4AQ
020 7553 3900
whatsnew@telecomfinance.com
www.telecomfinance.com

Thomson Learning
50–51 Bedford Row
London WC1R 4LR
020 7067 2500
communications@
    thomsonlearning.com
www.thomsonlearning.co.uk
Part of the Thomson Corporation

Time Out Group
c/o L Aldrich Publishing Consultancy
The Studio, 14 Priory Avenue
London W4 1TX
020 7813 3000
mandymartinez@timeout.com
www.timeout.com

Time Warner Books (UK)
Brettenham House, Lancaster Place
London WC2E 7EN
020 7911 8000
ukemail.timewarnerbooks.co.uk@
    timewarnerbooks.com
www.timewarnerbooks.co.uk
Part of Time-Warner Inc
Imprints and divisions include: Little,
Brown, Abacus, Time Warner, Virago

Titan Publishing
144 Southwark Street
London SE1 0UP
020 7620 0200
editorial@titanmail.com
Comic books, graphic novels, spin-offs

Top That Publishing
Marine House, Tide Mill Way
Woodbridge, Suffolk IP12 1AP
01394 386651
www.topthatpublishing.com
Children's books; adult range (Kudos)

Transworld Publishers
Random House Group
61–63 Uxbridge Road
London W5 5SA
020 8579 2652
info@transworld-publishers.co.uk
www.booksattransworld.co.uk
A subsidiary of Random House
General fiction and non-fiction.
Imprints and divisions include:
Bantam, Bantam Press, Corgi, Black
Swan, Doubleday, Eden, Expert Books

Travel Publishing
7A Apollo House, Calleva Park
Aldermaston, Berkshire RG7 8TN
0118 981 7777
info@travelpublishing.co.uk
www.travelpublishing.co.uk
Imprints and divisions include:
Hidden Places, Hidden Inns, Golfers
Guides, Country Living Rural Guides,
Off the Motorway

Trentham Books
Westview House, 734 London Road
Stoke-on-Trent
Staffordshire ST4 5NP
01782 745567/844699
tb@trentham-books.co.uk
www.trentham-books.co.uk
Education, culture and law for
professional readers

Trident Press
Empire House, 175 Piccadilly
London W1J 9TB
020 7491 8770
admin@tridentpress.com
www.tridentpress.com
TV tie-ins, history, travel, geography,
culture and fiction

Trotman & Co
2 The Green, Richmond
Surrey TW9 1PL
020 8486 1150
mail@trotman.co.uk
www.careersportal.co.uk
Careers and education

University of Exeter Press
Reed Hall, Streatham Drive
Exeter, Devon EX4 4QR
01392 263066
uep@exeter.ac.uk
www.ex.ac.uk/uep/

University of Hertfordshire Press
Learning and Information Services,
Hatfield Campus Learning
Resources Centre, College Lane
Hatfield, Hertfordshire AL10 9AB
01707 284681
w.a.forster@herts.ac.uk
www.herts.ac.uk/UHPress
Imprints and divisions include:
Interface Collection, Hertfordshire
Publications

University of Wales Press
10 Columbus Walk, Brigantine Place
Cardiff CF10 4UP
029 2049 6899
press@press.wales.ac.uk
www.wales.ac.uk/press
*Imprints and divisions include: GPC
Books, Gwasg Prifysgol Cymru*

**University Presses of California,
Columbia & Princeton**
1 Oldlands Way, Bognor Regis
West Sussex PO22 9SA
01243 842165
lois@upccp.demon.co.uk
www.ucpress.edu
or www.columbia.edu/cu/cup
or www.pup.princeton.edu

Usborne Publishing
83–85 Saffron Hill
London EC1N 8RT
020 7430 2800
mail@usborne.co.uk
www.usborne.com
*Non-fiction, fiction, computer and
family*

**Vallentine Mitchell/ Jewish
Chronicle Publications**
Crown House, 47 Chase Side
Southgate, London N14 5BP
020 8920 2100
info@vmbooks.com
www.vmbooks.com
*Imprint of Frank Cass & Co
Jewish interest*

Virago Press
Time Warner Books, Brettenham
House, Lancaster Place
London WC2E 7EN
020 7911 8000
Virago.Press@
    TimeWarnerBooks.co.uk
www.virago.co.uk
Fiction and non-fiction by women

Virgin Books
Units 5 & 6, Thames Wharf Studios
Rainville Road, London W6 9HA
020 7386 3300
info@virgin-books.co.uk
www.virginbooks.com

Vista House
Suite 676, 37 Store Street
London WC1E 7QF
020 7644 4816
edit@vistahouse.co.uk
www.vistahouse.co.uk
*Fiction and non-fiction, educational.
Divisions and imprints include:
Parragon Publishing*

Vista House
27 Greenhead Road, Huddersfield
West Yorkshire HD1 4EN
01484 427200
edit@vistahouse.co.uk
www.vistahouse.co.uk
*Divisions and imprints include:
Parragon Publishing*

W Foulsham & Co
The Publishing House
Bennetts Close, Slough
Berkshire SL1 5AP
01753 526769
info@foulsham.com
Lifestyle

Walker Books
87 Vauxhall Walk, London SE11 5HJ
020 7793 0909
enquiry@walker.co.uk
web: www.walkerbooks.co.uk
*Children's books Imprints and
divisions include: Big Books, Book
Charts, Game Books, Giggle Club.*

Wallflower Press
4th Floor, 26 Shacklewell Lane
London E8 2EZ
020 7690 0115
info@wallflowerpress.co.uk
www.wallflowerpress.co.uk
Film, media and cultural studies

Watts Publishing Group
96 Leonard Street
London EC2A 4XD
020 7739 2929
gm@wattspub.co.uk
www.wattspublishing.co.uk
*Part of Groupe Lagardere
children's non-fiction, reference, fiction,
picture and novelty. Imprints and
divisions include: Franklin Watts,
Orchard Books, Cats Whiskers*

WH Freeman
Palgrave Macmillan, Houndmills
Basingstoke, Hampshire RG21 6XS
01256 329242
j.bek@palgrave.com
www.palgrave.com
Scientific educational textbooks

Wharncliffe Publishing
47 Church Street, Barnsley
South Yorkshire S70 2AS
01226 734222
enquiries@pen-and-sword.co.uk
www.local-books.com
*An imprint of Pen & Sword Books
Local history*

Which?
2 Marylebone Road
London NW1 4DF
020 7830 6000
editor@which.net
www.which.net
*Publishing arm of the Consumers'
Association*

Whittet Books
Hill Farm, Stonham Road
Cotton, Stowmarket
Suffolk IP14 4RQ
01449 781877
annabel@whittet.dircon.co.uk
www.whittetbooks.com
Natural history, pets and rural interest

Whurr Publishers
19B Compton Terrace
London N1 2UN
020 7359 5979
info@whurr.co.uk
www.whurr.co.uk
Therapy, nursing and special education

Wild Goose Publications
Iona Community, 4th Floor
The Savoy House
140 Sauchiehall Street
Glasgow G2 3DH
0141 332 6292
admin@ionabooks.com
www.iona.books.com
*The publishing house of the Iona
Community, established in the Celtic
Christian tradition of St Columba
Religion, spiritualism and human
rights books and CDs*

William Reed Directories
Broadfield Park, Crawley
West Sussex RH11 9RT
01293 613400
directories@william-reed.co.uk
www.william-reed.co.uk
*Imprints: Yellow Jersey Press,
Vermilion, Fodor's, Rider*

Windhorse Publications
11 Park Road, Moseley
Birmingham B13 8AB
0121 449 9191
info@windhorsepublications.com
www.windhorsepublications.com
*Associated with the FWBO, a world-
wide Buddhist movement
Meditation and Buddhism*

WIT Press
Ashurst Lodge, Ashurst
Southampton
Hampshire SO40 7AA
023 8029 3223
marketing@witpress.com
www.witpress.com
Scientific and technical

Women's Press
27 Goodge Street
London W1T 2LD
020 7636 3992
sales@the-womens-press.com
www.the-womens-press.com
Part of the Namara Group

Woodhead Publishing
Abington Hall, Abington
Cambridge CB1 6AH
01223 891358
wp@woodhead-publishing.com
www.woodhead-publishing.com
*Engineering, textiles, finance and
investment, food technology and
environmental science. Imprints and
divisions include: Abington
Publishing*

Wordsworth Editions
8b East Street, Ware
Hertfordshire SG12 9HJ
01920 465167
dennis.hart@
    wordsworth-editions.com
www.wordsworth-editions.com
*Literary classics, reference books,
poetry, children's classics, military
history and folklore*

Working White
Chancery Court, Lincolns Inn
Lincoln Road
High Wycombe HP12 3RE
01494 429318
peter@workingwhite.co.uk
www.workingwhite.co.uk
Innovative children's books

WW Norton & Company
Castle House, 75–56 Wells Street
London W1T 3QT
020 7323 1579
office@wwnorton.co.uk
Non-fiction

X Press
PO Box 25694, London N17 6FP
020 8801 2100
vibes@xpress.co.uk
www.xpress.co.uk
*General fiction including black
interest. Other imprints and divisions
include: Nia, 20/20*

Y Lolfa Cyf
Talybont, Ceredigion SY24 5AP
01970 832304
ylolfa@ylolfa.com
www.ylolfa.com
*Welsh language publications and
Celtic interest. Imprints and divisions
include: Dinas*

Yale University Press (London)
47 Bedford Square
London WC1B 3DP
020 7431 4422
sales@yaleup.co.uk
www.yaleup.co.uk

Zambezi Publishing
PO Box 221, Plymouth
Devon PL2 2YJ
01752 367300
info@zampub.com
www.zampub.com
New age and self-help

Zed Books
7 Cynthia Street, London N1 9JF
020 7837 4014
hosie@zedbooks.demon.co.uk
www.zedbooks.demon.co.uk
*International and Third World affairs
and development studies*

Literary agents

Abner Stein*
10 Roland Gardens
London SW7 3PH
020 7373 0456
abner@abnerstein.co.uk
*US agents and authors, some full-
length fiction and general non-fiction*

The Agency (London)*
24 Pottery Lane, Holland Park
London W11 4LZ
020 7727 1346
info@theagency.co.uk
*Theatre, film, TV, radio and children's
writers and illustrators; also film and
TV rights in novels and non-fiction*

Alan Brodie Representation
211 Piccadilly, London W1J 9HF
020 7917 2871
info@alanbrodie.com
www.alanbrodie.com
Theatre, film and TV scripts

Alexandra Nye
Craigower, 6 Kinnoull Avenue
Dunblane, Perthshire FK15 9JG
01786 825114
*Fiction and topical non-fiction esp.
literary fiction and history*

AM Heath & Co*
79 St Martin's Lane
London WC2N 4RE
020 7836 4271
*Fiction, general non-fiction and
children's*

Andrew Lownie Literary Agency*
17 Sutherland Street
London SW1V 4JU
020 7828 1274
lownie@globalnet.co.uk
www.andrewlownie.co.uk
Non-fiction

Andrew Mann*
1 Old Compton Street
London W1D 5JA
020 7734 4751
manscript@onetel.net.uk
*Fiction; general non-fiction; film, TV,
theatre and radio scripts*

Andrew Nurnberg Associates*
Clerkenwell House
45–47 Clerkenwell Green
London EC1R 0HT
020 7417 8800
all@nurnberg.co.uk
Foreign rights

Annette Green Authors' Agency
6 Montem Street, London N4 3BE
020 7281 0009
annettekgreen@aol.com
*Literary and general fiction; non-
fiction; fiction for teenagers; upmarket
popular culture*

Antony Harwood
405 Riverbank House
1 Putney Bridge Approach
London SW6 3JD
020 7384 9209
mail@antonyharwood.com
Fiction and non-fiction

AP Watt*
20 John Street, London WC1N 2DR
020 7405 6774
apw@apwatt.co.uk
www.apwatt.co.uk
*Full-length typescripts, including
children's books, screenplays for film
and TV*

Artellus
30 Dorset House, Gloucester Place
London NW1 5AD
020 7935 6972
General fiction and non-fiction

Atlantic Syndication Partners
17–18 Hayward's Place
London EC1R 0EQ
020 7566 0360
dhowell@atlanticsyndication.com

Barbara Levy Literary Agency*
64 Greenhill, Hampstead High Street
London NW3 5TZ
020 7435 9046
*General fiction, non-fiction, TV
presenters, film and TV rights*

Bell Lomax Agency
James House, 1 Babmaes Street
London SW1Y 6HF
020 7930 4447
agency@bell-lomax.co.uk
*Fiction and non-fiction, biography,
children's, business and sport*

Bill McLean Personal Management
23B Deodar Road
London SW15 2NP
020 8789 8191
Scripts for all media

Blake Friedmann*
122 Arlington Road
London NW1 7HP
020 7284 0408
books:
    carole@blakefriedmann.co.uk
    isobel@blakefriedmann.co.uk
film and TV:
    julian@blakefriedmann.co.uk
    conrad@blakefriedmann.co.uk
www.blakefriedmann.co.uk
*Genre and literary fiction: especially
women's; specialised and general non-
fiction; scripts for TV, radio and film*

BookBlast
PO Box 20184, London W10 5AU
020 8968 3089
info@bookblast.com
www.bookblast.com
*Horror, crime, science fiction, fantasy,
poetry, short stories, academic,
children's books and lifestyle*

** member of the Association
of Authors' Agents*

Brie Burkeman*
14 Neville Court, Abbey Road
London NW8 9DD
0709 223 9113
brie.burkeman@mail.com
*Commercial and literary fiction and
non-fiction, scripts, poetry, short
stories. Independent film and
television consultant to literary agents*

Campbell Thomson & McLaughlin*
1 King's Mews, London WC1N 2JA
020 7242 0958
Fiction and general non-fiction

Capel & Land*
29 Wardour Street
London W1D 6PS
020 7734 2414
robert@capelland.co.uk
*Fiction and non-fiction; film, TV,
theatre and radio scripts and
children's books*

Caroline Davidson Literary Agency
5 Queen Anne's Gardens
London W4 1TU
020 8995 5768
*High quality fiction of originality and
non-fiction*

Caroline Sheldon Literary Agency*
Thorley Manor Farm, Thorley
Yarmouth PO41 0SJ
01983 760205
*Fiction, commercial and literary
novels, especially women's and
children's fiction*

Casarotto Ramsay and Associates
National House
60–66 Wardour Street
London W1V 4ND
020 7287 4450
agents@casarotto.uk.com
www.casarotto.uk.com
Scripts for TV, theatre, film and radio

Cat Ledger Literary Agency*
20–21 Newman Street
London W1T 1PG
020 7861 8226
cat.ledger@virgin.net
*Non-fiction: popular culture,
biography, politics, investigative
journalism and fiction (non-genre)*

Cecily Ware Literary Agents
19C John Spencer Square
London N1 2LZ
020 7359 3787
info@cecilyware.com
Scripts for TV and film in all areas

Christine Green Authors' Agent*
6 Whitehorse Mews
Westminster Bridge Road
London SE1 7QD
020 7401 8844
info@christinegreen.co.uk
www.christinegreen.co.uk
*Literary and general fiction and non-
fiction*

**The Christopher Little Literary
Agency***
10 Eel Brook Studios
125 Moore Park Road
London SW6 4PS
020 7736 4455
christopher@christopherlittle.net
*Commercial and literary full-length
fiction and non-fiction; film scripts for
established clients*

Conville & Walsh*
2 Ganton Street, Soho
London W1F 7QL
020 7287 3030
clare@convilleandwalsh.com
*literary and commercial fiction;
serious and narrative non-fiction*

Curtis Brown Group*
Haymarket House, 28/29 Haymarket
London SW1Y 4SP
020 7396 6600
cb@curtisbrown.co.uk
www.curtisbrown.co.uk
*Writers, directors, designers and
presenters.*

Curtis Brown Group*
37 Queensferry Street
Edinburgh EH2 4QS
0131 225 1286
cb@curtisbrown.co.uk
www.curtisbrown.co.uk
*Popular fiction, literary fiction, scripts
and non-fiction*

**Darley Anderson Literary, TV & Film
Agency***
Estelle House, 11 Eustace Road
London SW6 1JB
020 7385 6652
enquiries@darleyanderson.com
www.darleyanderson.com
*Fiction: young male, American, Irish,
women's, crime/mystery and humour;
non-fiction; children's fiction; selected
scripts for film and TV*

David Godwin Associates
55 Monmouth Street
London WC2H 9DG
020 7240 9992
assistant@
       davidgodwinassociates.co.uk
*Literary and general fiction, non-
fiction, biography*

David Grossman Literary Agency
118b Holland Park Avenue
London W11 4UA
020 7221 2770
dgal@aol.com
*Full-length fiction and general non-
fiction especially controversial*

David Higham Associates*
5–8 Lower John Street
Golden Square, London W1F 9HA
020 7434 5900
dha@davidhigham.co.uk
www.davidhigham.co.uk
*Fiction; general non-fiction:
biography, history, current affairs;
children's; scripts*

David O'Leary Literary Agents*
10 Lansdowne Court
Lansdowne Rise, London W11 2NR
020 7229 1623
d.oleary@virgin.net
*Fiction (popular and literary) and
non-fiction. Esp. thrillers, history,
popular science, Russia and Ireland
(history and fiction)*

Deborah Owen*
78 Narrow Street, Limehouse
London E14 8BP
020 7987 51191
do@deborahowen.co.uk
International fiction and non-fiction

Dench Arnold Agency
10 Newburgh Street
London W1F 7RN
020 7437 4551
www.dencharnold.com
Scripts for TV and film

Dinah Wiener*
12 Cornwall Grove, Chiswick
London W4 2LB
020 8994 6011
dinahweiner@enterprise.net
*Fiction and general non-fiction:
auto/biography, popular science,
cookery*

Dorian Literary Agency*
Upper Thornehill, 27 Church Road
St Marychurch, Torquay
Devon TQ1 4QY
01803 312095
*General fiction especially popular;
children's (over 10 yrs)*

Dorie Simmonds Agency
67 Upper Berkeley Street
London W1H 7QX
020 7486 9228
dhsimmonds@aol.com
*General fiction and commercial non-
fiction, children's books and associated
rights*

Duncan McAra
28 Beresford Gardens
Edinburgh EH5 3ES
0131 552 1558
duncanmcara@hotmail.com
*Literary fiction and non-fiction; also
offers editing, rewriting, copy-editing
and proof-correcting*

Ed Victor*
6 Bayley Street, Bedford Square
London WC1B 3HE
020 7304 4100
*Mostly commercial fiction and non-
fiction; children's*

Edwards Fuglewicz*
49 Great Ormond Street
London WC1N 3HZ
020 7405 6725
efla@ftech.co.uk
*Fiction: literary, some commercial;
non-fiction: biography, history,
popular culture*

Elaine Steel
110 Gloucester Avenue
London NW1 8HX
020 8348 0918
ecmsteel@aol.com
Writers and directors in film,
television and publishing

Elspeth Cochrane Personal Management
14/2 Second Floor, South Bank
Commercial Centre
140 Battersea Park Road
London SW11 4NB
020 7622 0314
ecochrane@pji.uk.com
Fiction, non-fiction, biographies,
screenplays, scripts for all media

Eric Glass
25 Ladbroke Crescent
London W11 1PS
020 7229 9500
eglassltd@aol.com
Fiction, non-fiction and scripts

Eunice McMullen Children's Literary Agent
Low Ibbotsholme Cottage
Off Bridge Lane
Troutbeck Bridge, Windermere
Cumbria LA23 1HU
01539 448551
eunicemcmullen@totalise.co.uk
Children's material

Felicity Bryan*
2A North Parade, Banbury Road
Oxford OX2 6LX
01865 513816
agency@felicitybryan.com
Fiction and non-fiction

Felix de Wolfe
Garden Offices, 51 Maida Vale
London W9 1SD
020 7289 5770
felixdewolfe@aol.com
Theatrical agency

Fox & Howard Literary Agency
4 Bramerton Street
London SW3 5JX
020 7352 8691
Non-fiction: biography, history and
popular culture, reference, business
and lifestyle

Futerman, Rose & Associates*
Heston Court Business Estate
19 Camp Road, Wimbledon
London SW19 4UW
020 8947 0188
guy@futermanrose.co.uk
www.futermanrose.co.uk
Commercial and literary fiction, non-
fiction, biography, film and television
scripts specialising in book-to-film
projects

Gillon Aitken Associates*
29 Fernshaw Road
London SW10 0TG
020 7351 7561
reception@Gillonaitken.co.uk
Fiction and non-fiction

Greene & Heaton*
37 Goldhawk Road
London W12 8QQ
020 8749 0315
info@greeneheaton.co.uk
www.greeneheaton.co.uk
Wide range of fiction and general non-
fiction; clients include Bill Bryson,
Hugh Fearnley-Whittingstall, Michael
Frayn, P.D. James and Sarah Waters

Gregory & Co*
3 Barb Mews, London W6 7PA
020 7610 4676
info@gregoryandcompany.co.uk
www.gregoryandcompany.co.uk
Fiction: literary, commercial, crime,
suspense and thrillers; general non-
fiction, poetry, screenplays and short
stories

ICM
Oxford House, 76 Oxford Street
London W1D 1BS
020 7636 6565
duncan_heath@icmlondon.co.uk
Film, TV and theatre scripts

IMG Literary UK*
McCormick House, 3 Burlington
Chiswick, London W4 2TH
020 8233 5300
www.imgworld.com
Celebrity books, commercial fiction,
non-fiction, sports-related and how-to
business books

Intercontinental Literary Agency
33 Bedford Street
London WC2E 9ED
020 7379 6611
ila@ila-agency.co.uk
Translation rights only

Jane Conway-Gordon*
1 Old Compton Street
London W1D 5JA
020 7494 0148
jconway_gordon@hotmail.com
Fiction and general non-fiction

Jane Judd Literary Agency*
18 Belitha Villas, London N1 1PD
020 7607 0273
General fiction and non-fiction:
biography, investigative journalism,
health, women's interests and travel

Jane Turnbull*
13 Wendell Road, London W12 9RS
020 8743 9580
jane.turnbull@btinternet.com
Primarily non-fiction, some fiction

Janklow & Nesbit (UK)
29 Adam & Eve Mews
London W8 6UG
020 7376 2733
queries@janklow.co.uk
Fiction and non-fiction, commercial
and literary; US and translation
rights handled by Janklow & Nesbit
Associates in New York

Jeffrey Simmons
15 Penn House, Mallory Street
London NW8 8SX
020 7224 8917
jas@london'inc.com
www.jeffreysimmons.com
Biography, cinema and theatre, quality
and commercial fiction, history, law
and crime, politics and world affairs,
parapsychology and sport

Jill Foster
9 Barb Mews, Brook Green
London W6 7PA
020 7602 1263
Scripts for TV, film and radio

JM Thurley Management
Archery House, 33 Archery Square,
Walmer, Deal CT14 7JA
01304 371721
jmthurley@aol.com
Full-length fiction, non-fiction, TV and
films

John Johnson*
Clerkenwell House
45/47 Clerkenwell Green
London EC1R 0HT
020 7251 0125
johnjohnson@btinternet.com
A division of Johnson & Alcock
General fiction and non-fiction

John Welch, Literary Consultant & Agent
Mill Cottage, Calf Lane
Chipping Camden
Gloucestershire GL55 6JQ
01386 840237
johnwelch@waitrose.com
Military, naval and aviation history,
general history, and a little biography

Jonathan Clowes*
10 Iron Bridge House
Bridge Approach
London NW1 8BD
020 7722 7674
jonathanclowes@aol.com
Fiction and non-fiction; scripts
especially situation comedy, film and
television rights; clients include Doris
Lessing, David Nobbs, Len Deighton
and the Estates of Kingsley Amis and
Conan Doyle

Josef Weinberger Plays
12–14 Mortimer Street
London W1T 3JJ
020 7580 2827
general.info@jwmail.co.uk
www.josef-weinberger.com
Scripts for the theatre; play publisher
and licensor of stage rights; publishes
plays and acts as UK agent for US
agents including the Dramatists Play
Service

Judith Chilcote Agency*
8 Wentworth Mansions
Keats Grove, London NW3 2RL
020 7794 3717
judybks@aol.com
Commercial fiction, TV tie-ins,
biography and lifestyle
* *member of the Association*
of Authors' Agents

Judy Daish Associates
2 St Charles Place
London W10 6EG
020 8964 8811
judy@judydaish.demon.co.uk
Scripts for TV, theatre, film and radio

Juri Gabriel
35 Camberwell Grove
London SE5 8JA
020 7703 6186
Quality fiction and non-fiction

Juvenilia
Avington, Near Winchester
Hampshire SO21 1DB
01962 779656
juvenilia@clara.co.uk
*Baby–teen fiction and picture books;
non-fiction and scripts for TV and radio*

Knight Features
20 Crescent Grove
London SW4 7AH
020 7622 1467
peter@knightfeatures.co.uk
*Motor sports, cartoon books, puzzles,
business, history, factual and
biographical material*

Laurence Fitch
Quadrant House
80–82 Regent street
London W1B 5AU
020 7734 9911
information@laurencefitch.com
www.laurencefitch.com
*Children's and horror books, scripts for
theatre, film, TV and radio*

Lavinia Trevor Agency*
The Glasshouse
49A Goldhawk Road
London W12 8QP
020 8749 8481
*General literary and commercial
fiction; non-fiction including popular
science*

LAW (Lucas Alexander Whitley)*
14 Vernon Street, London W14 0RJ
020 7471 7900
*Commercial and literary fiction, non-
fiction and children's books; film and
TV scripts for established clients*

Limelight Management*
33 Newman Street
London W1T 1PY
020 7637 2529
limelight.management@virgin.net
www.limelightmanagement.com
General non-fiction

Lisa Eveleigh Literary Agency*
3rd Floor, 11/12 Dover Street
London W1S 4LJ
020 7399 2803
eveleigh@dial.pipex.com
*Literary and commercial fiction and
non-fiction*

Louise Greenberg Books *
The End House, Church Crescent
London N3 1BG
020 8349 1179
louisegreenberg@msn.com
Literary fiction and non-fiction

Lutyens and Rubinstein*
231 Westbourne Park Road
London W11 1EB
020 7792 4855
susannah@lutyensrubinstein.co.uk
Adult fiction and non-fiction

Maggie Noach Literary Agency*
22 Dorville Crescent
London W6 0HJ
020 8748 2926
m-noach@dircon.co.uk
Fiction and general non-fiction

Maggie Pearlstine Associates *
31 Ashley Gardens
Ambrosden Avenue
London SW1P 1QE
020 7828 4212
post@pearlstine.co.uk
*General non-fiction and fiction,
history, current affairs, biography,
health and politics*

Manuscript ReSearch
PO Box 33, Bicester
Oxfordshire OX26 4ZZ
01869 323447
Scripts for film and TV

Margaret Hanbury Literary Agency*
27 Walcot Square
London SE11 4UB
020 7735 7680
maggie@mhanbury.demon.co.uk
*Quality fiction and non-fiction; clients
include J.G. Ballard, Simon Callow,
George Alagiah, Judith Lennox,
children's books, plays/scripts and
poetry*

Marjacq Scripts
34 Devonshire Place
London W1G 6JW
020 7935 9499
philip@marjacq.com and
luke@marjacq.com
www.marjacq.com
*All fiction and non-fiction, screenplays,
radio plays and film and tv rights*

Marsh Agency*
11/12 Dover Street
London W1S 4LJ
020 7399 2800
enquiries@marsh-agency.co.uk
www.marsh-agency.co.uk
*International rights specialists selling
English and foreign language writing*

Martinez Literary Agency
60 Oakwood Avenue
Southgate, London N14 6QL
020 8886 5829
*High quality fiction, children's books,
lifestyle, autobiography, biography,
popular music, sport and
memorabilia books*

Mary Clemmey Literary Agency*
6 Dunollie Road, London NW5 2XP
020 7267 1290
*Fiction and non-fiction – high quality
for an international market.*

MBA Literary Agents*
62 Grafton Way, London W1T 5DW
020 7387 2076
agent@mbalit.co.uk
*Writers and directors; fiction and
non-fiction, TV, film, theatre and
radio scripts*

Merric Davidson Literary Agency
12 Priors Heath, Goudhurst
Cranbrook, Kent TN17 2RE
01580 212041
authors@mdla.co.uk
www.mdla.co.uk
*Fiction especially contemporary;
authors include Francesca Clementis,
Alison Habens, Simon Scarrow*

Mic Cheetham Literary Agency
11–12 Dover Street
London W1S 4LJ
020 7495 2002
info@miccheetham.com
www.miccheetham.com
*General and literary fiction, fantasy
and science fiction, crime and some
specific non-fiction*

**Michael Alcock Management
(division of Johnson & Alcock)***
96 Farringdon Road
London EC1R 3EA
020 7837 8137
alcockmgt@aol.com
*General non-fiction, literary and
commercial mainstream fiction*

Micheline Steinberg Associates
104 Great Portland Street
London W1W 6PE
020 7631 1310
info@steinplays.com
www.steinplays.com
Plays for stage, TV, radio and film

Michelle Kass Associates*
36–38 Glasshouse Street
London W1B 5DL
020 7439 1624
Literary fiction and film

Narrow Road Company
182 Brighton Road, Coulsdon
Surrey CR5 2NF
020 8763 9895
narrowroad@freeuk.com
Scripts for TV, theatre, film and radio

Owen Robinson Literary Agents
20 Tolbury Mill, Bruton
Somerset BA10 0DY
01749 812836
jpr@owenrobinson.netlineuk.net
Fiction and non-fiction

Paterson Marsh*
11/12 Dover Street
London W1S 4LJ
020 7399 2800
steph@patersonmarsh.co.uk
www.patersonmarsh.co.uk
*World rights especially psychoanalysis
and psychotherapy*

Paul Kiernan*
PO Box 120, London SW3 4LU
*Fiction, non-fiction: biography,
lifestyle; scripts for TV, film, theatre
and radio*

Peters Fraser & Dunlop Group (PFD)*
Drury House, 34–43 Russell Street
London WC2B 5HA
020 7344 1000
postmaster@pfd.co.uk
www.pfd.co.uk
Fiction and children's, plus scripts for film, theatre, radio and TV

PVA Management
Hallow Park, Worcester WR2 6PG
01905 640663
books@pva.co.uk
Non-fiction only

Real Creatives Worldwide
14 Dean Street, London W1D 3RS
020 7437 4188
malcolm.rasala@realcreatives.com
www.realcreatives.com
Represents writers and creative media professionals

Robert Smith Literary Agency*
12 Bridge Wharf
156 Caledonian Road
London N1 9UU
020 7278 2444
robertsmith.literaryagency@virgin.net
Non-fiction; biography, health and nutrition, cookery, lifestyle, showbusiness and true crime

Robin Wade Literary Agency
1 Cormorant Lodge
Thomas More Street
London E1W 1AU
020 7488 4171
rw@rwla.com
www.rwla.com
General fiction and non-fiction

Rod Hall Agency
3 Charlotte Mews, London W1T 4DZ
020 7637 0706
office@rodhallagency.com
www.rodhallagency.com
Drama for film, TV and theatre

Roger Hancock
4 Water Lane, London NW1 8NZ
020 7267 4418
info@rogerhancock.com
Scripts for comedy, drama and light entertainment

Rogers, Coleridge & White*
20 Powis Mews, London W11 1JN
020 7221 3717
Fiction, non-fiction and children's books

Rosemary Bromley Literary Agency
Avington, Near Winchester
Hampshire SO21 1DB
01962 779656
juvenilia@clara.co.uk
Non-fiction and scripts for TV and radio

Rosemary Sandberg
6 Bayley Street, London WC1B 3HB
020 7304 4110
rosemary@sandberg.demon.co.uk
Children's picture books and novels, adult non-fiction

Rosica Colin
1 Clareville Grove Mews
London SW7 5AH
020 7370 1080
Full-length manuscripts plus theatre, film, television and sound broadcasting

Rupert Crew*
1A King's Mews, London WC1N 2JA
020 7242 8586
rupertcrew@compuserve.com
Volume and subsidiary rights in fiction and non-fiction properties

Rupert Heath Literary Agency
The Beeches, Furzedown Lane
Amport, Hampshire SP11 8BW
01264 771899
enquiries@rupertheath.com
www.rupertheath.com
Fiction, history, biography, science, the arts and popular culture

Sayle Literary Agency*
Bickerton House
25–27 Bickerton Road
London N19 5JT
020 7263 8681
Fiction, crime and general; general non-fiction

Sayle Screen
11 Jubilee Place, London SW3 3TD
020 7823 3883
info@saylescreen.com
www.saylescreen.com
Writers and directors for film, TV, theatre and radio

Sharland Organisation
The Manor House, Manor Street
Raunds, Northamptonshire NN9 6JW
01933 626600
tsoshar@aol.com
www.sharlandorganisation.co.uk
Scripts for film, TV, theatre and radio; non-fiction; specialises in national and international film, television and theatre negotiations

Sheil Land Associates*
43 Doughty Street
London WC1N 2LH
020 7405 9351
info@sheilland.co.uk
Full-length general, commercial and literary fiction and non-fiction including: theatre, film, radio and TV scripts

Sheila Ableman Literary Agency
122 Arlington Road
London NW1 7HP
020 7485 3409
sheila@ableman.freeserve.co.uk
Non-fiction including history, science and biography

Shirley Stewart Literary Agency
3rd Floor, 21 Denmark Street
London WC2H 8NA
020 7836 4440
Literary fiction and non-fiction

Sinclair-Stevenson
3 South Terrace, London SW7 2TB
020 7581 2550
Biography, current affairs, travel, history, fiction, the arts

Susijn Agency
3rd Floor, 64 Great Titchfield Street
London W1W 7QH
020 7580 6341
info@thesusijnagency.com
www.thesusijnagency.com
Sells rights worldwide in English and non-English language literature: literary fiction and non-fiction

Tamar Karet Literary Agency
56 Priory Road, Crouch End
London N8 7EX
020 8340 6460
tamar@btinternet.com
Fiction, leisure, biography, history, social affairs and politics

Tanja Howarth Literary Agency*
19 New Row, London WC2N 4LA
020 7240 5553
tanja.howarth@virgin.net
Fiction and non-fiction from British writers; represents German authors in Britain on behalf of German publishers

The Tennyson Agency
10 Cleveland Avenue
Wimbledon Chase
London SW20 9EW
020 8543 5939
agency@tenagy.co.uk
www.tenagy.co.uk
Theatre, film, radio and TV scripts

Teresa Chris Literary Agency
43 Musard Road, London W6 8NR
020 7386 0633
TeresaChris@litagency.freeserve.co.uk
Fiction: crime, general, women's, commercial and literary and non-fiction

Toby Eady Associates
9 Orme Court, London W2 4RL
020 7792 0092
toby@tobyeady.demon.co.uk
www.tobyeadyassociates.co.uk
Fiction, non-fiction especially China, Middle East and Africa

Valerie Hoskins Associates
20 Charlotte Street
London W1T 2NA
020 7637 4490
vha@vhassociates.co.uk
Scripts for film, TV and radio especially feature films, animation and TV

Vanessa Holt *
59 Crescent Road, Leigh-on-Sea
Essex SS9 2PF
01702 473787
vanessa@holtlimited.freeserve.co.uk
General fiction especially crime, commercial and literary; non-fiction; non-illustrated children's

* member of the Association of Authors' Agents

Watson, Little *
Capo Di Monte, Windmill Hill
London NW3 6RJ
020 7431 0770
sz@watsonlittle.com
www.watsonlittle.com
Commercial and literary fiction and non-fiction for adults and children

William Morris Agency (UK) *
52/53 Poland Street
London W1F 7LX
020 7534 6800
ldnmailroom@wma.com
www.wma.com
Fiction; general non-fiction; TV and film scripts

William Neill-Hall
Old Oak Cottage, Ropewalk
Mount Hawke, Truro
Cornwall TR4 8DW
01209 891427
wneill-hall@msn.com
acts in association with Alive Communications, Inc in the USA General non-fiction; clients include George Carey, Philip Yancey and Eugene Peterson

The Wylie Agency (UK)
17 Bedford Square
London WC1B 3JA
020 7908 5900
mail@wylieagency.co.uk
Fiction and non-fiction

Zebra Agency
Broadland House, 1 Broadland
Shevington, Lancashire WN6 8DH
077193 75575
admin@zebraagency.co.uk
www.zebraagency.co.uk
Non-fiction and general fiction; scripts for TV, radio, film and theatre

* member of the Association of Authors' Agents

Useful contacts

Academi (Yr Academi Gymreig)
3rd Floor, Mount Stuart House
Mount Stuart Square
Cardiff CF10 5FQ
029 2047 2266
post@academi.org
www.academi.org
Welsh national literature promotion agency

Alliance of Literary Societies
22 Belmont Grove, Havant
Hampshire PO9 3PU
023 9247 5855
rosemary@sndc.demon.co.uk
www.sndc.demon.co.uk/als.htm

Association for Scottish Literary Studies
c/o Department of Scottish History
9 University Gardens
University of Glasgow
Glasgow G12 8QH
0141 330 5309
office@asls.org.uk
www.asls.org.uk
Charity promoting language and literature of Scotland

Association of Christian Writers
All Saints Vicarage
43 All Saints Close, Edmonton
London N9 9AT
020 8884 4348
admin@christianwriters.org.uk
www.christianwriters.org.uk

Association of Freelance Editors, Proofreaders & Indexers (Ireland)
Skeagh, Skibbereen, Co. Cork
Republic of Ireland
00 353 28 38259
gloria@redbarn.ie

Association of Freelance Writers
Sevendale House, 7 Dale Street
Manchester M1 1JB
0161 228 2362

Association of Illustrators
81 Leonard Street
London EC2A 4QS
020 7613 4328
info@a-o-illustrators.demon.co.uk
www.theaoi.com

Association of Learned and Professional Society Publishers
South House, The Street, Clapham
Worthing, West Sussex BN13 3UU
01903 871457
sec-gen@alpsp.org
www.alpsp.org
For not-for-profit academic and professional publishers

Authors' Club
40 Dover Street, London W1S 4NP
020 7499 8581
circles@author.co.uk
www.author.co.uk/
Anyone involved with written word; administers Best First Novel award and Sir Banister Fletcher award

Authors' Licensing & Collecting Society (ALCS)
Marlborough Court, 14–18 Holborn
London EC1N 2LE
020 7395 0600
alcs@alcs.co.uk
www.alcs.co.uk
UK collecting society for writers and successors

Bibliographical Society
c/o The Institute of English Studies
Room 304, Senate House
Mallet Street, London WC1E 7HU
020 7862 8679
admin@bibsoc.org.uk
www.bibsoc.org.uk
Aims to encourage study of bibliography and history of publishing

Booksellers Association of the UK & Ireland
Minster House
272 Vauxhall Bridge Road
London SW1V 1BA
020 7834 5477
mail@booksellers.org.uk
www.booksellers.org.uk
Trade association. Coordinates World Book Day with Publishers Association; administers Whitbread Book Awards and Samuel Johnson prize

Booktrust
Book House, 45 East Hill
London SW18 2QZ
020 8516 2977
info@booktrust.org.uk
www.booktrust.org.uk and
www.booktrusted.com
Educational charity

British Centre for Literary Translation
University of East Anglia
Norwich, Norfolk NR4 7TJ
01603 592134/ 592785
bclt@uea.ac.uk
www.literarytranslation.com

British Copyright Council
Copyright House
29–33 Berners Street
London W1T 3AB
01986 788122
copyright@bcc2.demon.co.uk
Creators' watchdog

British Science Fiction Association
1 Long Row Close, Everdon
Daventry, Northants NN11 3BE
01327 361661
bsfa@enterprise.net
www.bsfa.co.uk

British Society of Comedy Writers
61 Parry Road, Ashmore Park
Wolverhampton
West Midlands WV11 2PS
01902 722729
info@bscw.co.uk
www.bscw.co.uk

Clé
43/44 Temple Bar
Dublin 2, Republic of Ireland
00 353 1 670 7393
info@publishingireland.com
www.publishingireland.com
Irish book publishers' association

Combrogos
10 Heol Don, Whitchurch
Cardiff CF14 2AU
029 2062 3359
meic@heoldon.fsnet.co.uk
Arts and media research and editorial services; books about Wales or by Welsh authors; contact Dr Meic Stephens

Comedy Writers' Association UK
Wisteria Cottage, Coombe Meadow
Bovey Tracey, Newton Abbot
Devon TQ13 9EZ
01626 833227
info@cwauk.co.uk
www.cwauk.co.uk

Gaelic Books Council (Comhairle nan Leabhraichean)
22 Mansfield Street
Glasgow G11 5QP
0141 337 6211
fios@gaelicbooks.net
www.gaelicbooks.net

Crime Writers' Association (CWA)
media.enquiries@thecwa.co.uk
www.thecwa.co.uk

Critics' Circle
c/o Catherine Cooper
69 Marylebone Lane
London W1U 2PH
020 7224 1410
www.criticscircle.org.uk

Directory & Database Publishers Association
PO Box 23034, London W6 0RJ
020 8846 9707
rosemarypettit@onetel.net.uk
www.directory-publisher.co.uk

Drama Association of Wales
The Old Library Building
Singleton Road, Splott
Cardiff CF24 2ET
029 2045 2200
aled.daw@virgin.net

English Association
University of Leicester
University Road
Leicester LE1 7RH
0116 252 3982
engassoc@le.ac.uk
www.le.ac.uk/engassoc

Federation of Worker Writers and Community Publishers (FWWCP)
Burslem School of Art, Queen Street
Stoke on Trent ST6 3EJ
01782 822327
thefwwcp@tiscali.co.uk
www.thefwwcp.org.uk

Fellowship of Authors and Artists
PO Box 158, Hertford SG13 8FA
0870 747 2514
fellowship@
    compassion-in-business.co.uk
www.author-fellowship.co.uk
Promotes writing and art as therapy and self-healing

Garden Writers' Guild
c/o Institute of Horticulture
14/15 Belgrave Square
London SW1X 8PS
020 7245 6943
gwg@horticulture.org.uk
www.gardenwriters.co.uk

Horror Writers Association
hwa@edclayton.com
www.horror.org/UK/

Independent Publishers Guild
PO Box 93, Royston
Hertfordshire SG8 5GH
01763 247014
info@ipg.uk.com
www.ipg.uk.com

Independent Theatre Council
12 The Leathermarket
Weston Street, London SE1 3ER
020 7403 1727
c.jones@itc-arts.org
www.itc-arts.org

Institute of Linguists
Saxon House, 48 Southwark Street
London SE1 1UN
020 7940 3100
info@iol.org.uk
www.iol.org.uk

Institute of Translation and Interpreting (ITI)
Fortuna House, South Fifth Street
Milton Keynes
Buckinghamshire MK9 2EU
01908 325250
info@iti.org.uk
www.iti.org.uk

International Booksearch Service
8 Old James Street
London SE15 3TS
020 7639 8900
scfordham@talk21.com
www.scfordham.com
Finds out-of-print books

Irish Playwrights and Screenwriters Guild
Irish Writers' Centre
19 Parnell Square, Dublin 1
Republic of Ireland
00 353 1 872 1302
moffats@indigo.ie
www.writerscentre.ie/IPSG.html

Irish Translators' and Interpreters' Association
Irish Writers' Centre
19 Parnell Square, Dublin 1
Republic of Ireland
00 353 1 872 1302
translation@eircom.net
www.translatorsassociation.ie

Irish Writers' Union
Irish Writers' Centre
19 Parnell Square, Dublin 1
Republic of Ireland
00 353 1 872 1302
words@neteireann.com
www.ireland-writers.com

ISBN Agency
Woolmead House, Bear Lane
Farnham, Surrey GU9 7LG
01252 742590
isbn@whitaker.co.uk
www.whitaker.co.uk/isbn.htm
Book numbering agency

Ludvigsen Library
Scoles Gate, Hawkedon
Bury St Edmonds IP29 4AU
01284 789246
library@ludvigsen.com
www.ludvigsen.com
Photographic archive and research facilities for writers and publishers

Medical Writers' Group
The Society of Authors
84 Drayton Gardens
London SW10 9SB
020 7373 6642
info@societyofauthors.org
www.societyofauthors.org
Specialist group within Society of Authors

National Association for Literature Development
PO Box 140, Ilkley
West Yorkshire LS29 7WP
01943 862107
steve@nald.org
www.nald.org

National Association of Writers Groups
The Arts Centre, Biddick Lane
Washington, Tyne & Wear NE38 2AB
01262 609228
nawg@tesco.net
www.nawg.co.uk

National Association of Writers in Education
PO Box 1, Sheriff Hutton
York YO60 7YU
01653 618429
paul@nawe.co.uk
www.nawe.co.uk

New Writing North
7/8 Trinity Chare, Quayside
Newcastle Upon Tyne NE1 3DF
0191 232 9991
mail@newwritingnorth.com
www.newwritingnorth.com
Literature development agency for northern arts region

Nielsen BookData
Globe House, 1 Chertsey Road
Twickenham TW1 1LR
020 8843 8600
info@bookdata.co.uk
www.bookdata.co.uk and
www.whitaker.co.uk and
www.first-edition.co.uk
Bibliographic data

Nielsen BookScan
Woolmead House West, Bear Lane
Farnham, Surrey GU9 7LG
01252 742555
info@nielsenbookscan.co.uk
www.nielsenbookscan.co.uk
International sales data monitoring

English PEN
Lancaster House
33 Islington High Street
London N1 9LH
020 7713 0023
enquiries@englishpen.org
www.englishpen.org
*Association of writers and literary
professionals. Fights for right to
freedom of expression*

Player-Playwrights
9 Hillfield Park, London N10 3QT
020 8883 0371
p-p@dial.pipex.com
www.playerplaywrights.co.uk
*Gives opportunities to writers new to
stage, radio and TV*

Public Lending Right
Richard House, Sorbonne Close
Stockton-on-Tees TS17 6DA
01642 604699
registrar@plr.uk.com
www.plr.uk.com

Publishers Association
29B Montague Street
London WC1B 5BH
020 7691 9191
mail@publishers.org.uk
www.publishers.org.uk
Trade association

Publishers Licensing Society
37–41 Gower Street
London WC1E 6HH
020 7299 7730
pls@pls.org.uk
www.pls.org.uk

Publishers Publicity Circle
65 Airedale Avenue
London W4 2NN
020 8994 1881
ppc-@lineone.net
www.publisherspublicitycircle.co.uk
*Forum for book publicists and
freelance PRs*

Romantic Novelists' Association
trisha_ashley@hotmail.com
www.rna-uk.org

Royal Society of Literature
Somerset House, Strand
London WC2R 1LA
020 7845 4676
info@rslit.org
www.rslit.org

Science Fiction Foundation
Membership:
D28, Department of Arts and Media
Buckinghamshire Chilterns University
College, High Wycombe
Buckinghamshire HP11 2JZ
ambutler@enterprise.net
www.sf-foundation.org

Scottish Book Trust
Sandeman House
Trunk's Close, 55 High Street
Edinburgh EH1 1SR
0131 524 0160
info@scottishbooktrust.com
www.scottishbooktrust.com

Scottish Print Employers Federation
48 Palmerston Place
Edinburgh EH12 5DE
0131 220 4353
info@spef.org.uk
www.spef.org.uk

Scottish Publishers Association
Scottish Book Centre
137 Dundee Street
Edinburgh EH11 1BG
0131 228 6866
info@scottishbooks.org
www.scottishbooks.org

Scottish Youth Theatre
3rd Floor Forsythe House
111 Union Street, Glasgow G1 3TA
0141 221 5127
info@scottishyouththeatre.org
www.scottishyouththeatre.org

Society for Children's Book Writers & Illustrators
scbwi_bi@hotmail.com
www.kidbookprosworld.com/

Society for Editors and Proofreaders (SfEP)
1 Riverbank House
1 Putney Bridge Approach
London SW6 3JD
020 7736 3278
admin@sfep.org.uk
www.sfep.org.uk

Society of Authors
84 Drayton Gardens
London SW10 9SB
020 7373 6642
info@societyofauthors.org
www.societyofauthors.org

Society of Authors in Scotland
Bonnyton House, Arbirlot
Angus DD11 2PY
01241 874131
info@eileenramsay.co.uk
www.writersorg.co.uk

Society of Civil and Public Service Writers
Adrian Danson, Editor
38 Cumberland Road
Bromley BR2 8PQ
editor@scpsw.co.uk
www.scpsw.co.uk/author

Society of Editors
University Centre, Granta Place
Mill Lane, Cambridge CB2 1RU
01223 304080
info@societyofeditors.org
www.societyofeditors.org

Society of Indexers
Blades Enterprise Centre
John Street, Sheffield S2 4SU
0114 292 2350
admin@indexers.org.uk
www.socind.demon.co.uk

Society of Women Writers & Journalists
Calvers Farm, Thelveton Diss
Norfolk IP21 4NG
01379 740550
zoe@zoeking.com
www.swwj.com

Society of Young Publishers
Endeavour House
189 Shaftesbury Avenue
London WC2H 8TJ
info@thesyp.org.uk
www.thesyp.org.uk

South and Mid-Wales Association of Writers (SAMWAW)
c/o I.M.C. Consulting Group
Denham House
Lambourne Crescent
Cardiff CF14 5ZW
029 2076 1170
info@imcconsultinggroup.co.uk

Spoken Word Publishing Association (SWPA)
c/o Macmillan Audio
20 New Wharf Road
London N1 9RR
020 7014 6041
z.howes@macmillan.co.uk
www.swpa.co.uk

Sports Writers' Association of Great Britain
c/o Sport England External Affairs
16 Upper Woburn Place
London WC1H 0QP
020 7273 1500
petta.naylor@sportengland.org
www.sportswriters.org.uk

Translators Association
84 Drayton Gardens
London
SW10 9SB
020 7373 6642
info@societyofauthors.org
www.societyofauthors.org

Welsh Books Council (Cyngor Llyfrau Cymru)
Castell Brychan, Aberystwyth
Ceredigion SY23 2JB
01970 624151
castellbrychan@cllc.org.uk
www.cllc.org.uk and
www.gwales.com

West Country Writers' Association
High Wootton, Wootton Lane
Limpstone, Exmouth
Devon EX8 5AY
01395 222749
judy@josser.freeserve.co.uk
www.westcountrywriters.co.uk

Women in Publishing
info@wipub.org.uk
www.cyberiacafe.net/wip

Writernet
Cabin V, Clarendon Buildings
25 Horsell Road, Highbury
London N5 1XL
020 7609 7474
writernet@btinternet.com
www.writernet.org.uk

Writers, Artists and their Copyright Holders (Watch)
The Harry Ransom Humanities
Research Center
21st and Guadalupe, PO Box 7219
Austin, Texas 78713-7219
USA
+1 512 471 8944
hrcweb@hrc.utexas.edu
www.watch-file.com

Writers' Guild of Great Britain
15 Britannia Street
London WC1X 9JN
020 7833 0777
admin@writersguild.org.uk
www.writersguild.org.uk

Books trade press

Annual Bibliography of English Language and Literature
Modern Humanities Research
Association
c/o Cambridge University Library
West Road, Cambridge CB3 9DR
01223 333058
abell@bibl.org
www.mhra.org.uk/Publication
   /Journals/abell.html
Annual

Book World Magazine
Christchurch Publishers
2 Caversham Street
London SW3 4AH
020 7351 4995
leonard.holdsworth@
   btopenworld.com
Monthly

Books
Publishing News
39 Store Street, London WC1E 7DS
020 7692 2900
lizthomson@publishingnews.co.uk
www.publishingnews.co.uk
Quarterly

Books in the Media
VNU Entertainment Media
Fifth Floor, Endeavour House
189 Shaftesbury Avenue
London WC2H 8TJ
020 7420 6178
tom.holman@bookseller.co.uk
www.thebookseller.com
Weekly

The Bookseller
VNU Entertainment Media
5th Floor Endeavour House
189 Shaftesbury Avenue
London WC2H 8TJ
020 7420 6006
joel.rickett@bookseller.co.uk
www.thebookseller.com
Weekly

Booksellers Association Directory of Members
The Booksellers Association of
the UK and Ireland
272 Vauxhall Bridge Road
London SW1V 1BA
020 7802 0802
mail@booksellers.org.uk
www.booksellers.org.uk
Annual

Digital Demand – The Journal of Printing and Publishing Technology
PIRA International
Randalls Road
Leatherhead KT22 7RU
01372 802080
publications@pira.co.uk
www.piranet.com
6pa

London Review of Books
Nicholas Spice
28 Little Russell Street
London WC1A 2HN
020 7209 1141
edit@lrb.co.uk
www.lrb.co.uk
Fortnightly

Publishing News
Publishing News
39 Store Street, London WC1E 7DS
020 7692 2900
mailbox@publishingnews.co.uk
www.publishingnews.co.uk
Weekly

Writers Forum
Writers International
PO Box 3229
Bournemouth BH8 8QS
01202 589828
editorial@writers-forum.com
www.writers-forum.com
10pa

Writers News
Warner Group Publications
PO Box 168, Wellington Street
Leeds LS1 1RF
0113 238 8333
derek.hudson@writersnews.co.uk
www.writersnews.co.uk
Monthly

Writing Magazine
Warner Group Publications
PO Box 168, Wellington Street
Leeds LS1 1RF
0113 238 8333
derek.hudson@writersnews.co.uk
www.writersnews.co.uk
6pa

Global
media

The world's media are dominated by fewer than 10 mostly US-based giants, plus around 40 very large European and American firms. Between them, these companies own most of the famous names in press, publishing and broadcasting: among them CNN, Time, CBS, Fox, Sky and Random House (see table for the biggest 11). More often than not, these conglomerates are also "vertically integrated" – that is, the same firms have expanded to gain ownership of not just many different forms of content, but also their means of distribution. Three-quarters of global advertising spend is now controlled by a mere 20 media companies.

That said, the giants have found recent years more difficult than expected. Rapid expansion into new media and telecoms left many companies overstretched when these sectors started to suffer; especially after the world advertising slump hit their traditional businesses. The result: losses equivalent to the gross national product of medium-sized countries. AOL Time Warner, the world's biggest media company, lost £60bn in 2002, the largest annual loss in US corporate history: the £94bn merger that created the company was a spectacular example of the misplaced optimism of the dotcom years. (The firm recovered to make a small £251m profit in the first quarter of 2003.) The company with the third highest revenues in 2002, Vivendi Universal, also posted the biggest loss in French corporate history, losing £15.9bn; it sold assets worth £5.3bn during the financial year and at the start of 2003 was continuing to sell. Finally, KirchMedia – Germany's second largest commercial broadcaster – went spectacularly bust in 2002 after over-spending on rights to Formula One and the World Cup.

So where are the successes? Viacom was one of the best performing media giants in 2002 (with only £710m losses), and posted net income of £283m in first quarter 2003. Rupert Murdoch is also happy: his News Corporation continued to expand, buying a £4.5bn controlling stake in DirecTV, the largest satellite television company, at the second attempt. NewsCorp becomes the largest provider of pay TV in the world; the group also reported second-quarter profits in February 2003 of some £160m.

But the global outlook is by no means rosy. According to a gloomy report by accountants PricewaterhouseCoopers in June 2003, the media industry will grow by less than 5% over the next five years.

203

World Press Freedom Index 2002 – Reporters Sans Frontières		
1=	Finland	0.5
	Iceland	0.5
	Norway	0.5
	Netherlands	0.5
5	Canada	0.75
6	Ireland	1.0
7=	Germany	1.5
	Portugal	1.5
	Sweden	1.5
10	Denmark	3.0
17	USA	4.75
21	UK	6.0
130	Iraq	79.0
131	Vietnam	81.25
132	Eritrea	83.67
133	Laos	89.00
134	Cuba	90.25
135	Bhutan	90.75
136	Turkmenistan	91.50
137	Burma	96.83
138	China	97.00
139	North Korea	97.50

* Source: Reporters Sans Frontières. Index drawn up by asking journalists, researchers and legal experts to answer 50 questions about press freedom, covering issues such as murders or arrests of journalists, censorship, pressure, state monopolies in various fields, punishment of press law offences and regulation.

Global journalism

Editorially, perhaps the biggest success story of the past year is al-Jazeera, the Qatar-based TV news channel which attracted worldwide attention for its coverage of the war in Iraq. Footage of US prisoners of war and dead British servicemen proved controversial, but the channel was a worthy antidote to the gung-ho approach of some channels. Al-Jazeera's worldwide audience rose to around 54 million.

The conflict in Iraq made it a bad year for journalists. One al-Jazeera journalist and two cameramen were killed in a US airstrike on Baghdad's Palestine Hotel, prompting accusations in the Arab media that the US was trying to repress channels that did not toe its line. In all, 22 journalists were killed worldwide in the first eight months of 2003, according to Reporters Sans Frontières, including 14 during the war in Iraq. Elsewhere, some 128 journalists were in prison as a result of their work.

In October 2002, Reporters Sans Frontières published its first index of world press freedom, based on a survey of journalists (see table). Finland, Iceland, Norway and the Netherlands came equal first in the survey; last, perhaps unsurprisingly, was North Korea. The US came 17th and the UK 21st. Meanwhile the World Press Trends survey, published by the Paris-based World Association of Newspapers, singled out Cuba and China for their record of imprisoning journalists. Worldwide newspaper circulation fell by 0.35% in 2002, it said.

In the US, the New York Times was embarrassed when it was revealed that reporter Jayson Blair had been plagiarising and fabricating articles unnoticed for years. The scandal led to the resignations of two executives and a Pulitzer-winning feature writer.

In France, President Jacques Chirac persisted with efforts to establish an international French TV channel, in the light of the "increasingly Anglophone world view" of many global news channels. Mr Chirac had threatened to veto any UN resolution authorising war in Iraq, with the result that the US-led coalition went to war without UN backing.

Further reading

■ Press
Guardian Unlimited: world news guide
guardian.co.uk/worldnewsguide

■ Books
Covering Islam EDWARD SAID; VINTAGE 1997
In-depth study of how Islam is covered by western media
The Global Media Atlas BFI PUBLISHING 2001

■ Web only
MediaChannel
www.mediachannel.org

■ Other resources
Reporters Sans Frontières
www.rsf.fr
World Association of Newspapers
www.wan-press.info
Committee to Protect Journalists
www.cpj.org
Association for International Broadcasting
www.aib.org.uk

Global voices **Chris Alden**

It's not about ad revenue. It's not about subscriber numbers. It's not about ratings, or page impressions, or ABCs. Not when the article you write has the potential to land you in jail, or worse.

As the Reporters Sans Frontières press freedom index shows, free speech is in many countries an inalienable human right; in others, it barely exists at all.

In North Korea, President Kim Jong Il has an odd idea of journalism. He gave a speech in 2001 reminding hacks that they were the "ideological standard-bearers who defend our system and our cause".

In Burma, the military junta held 18 journalists in jail as of January 2002 – making it what Reporters Sans Frontières called the "largest prison for journalists in the world".

In Eritrea, when the government in September 2001 ordered the suspension of all privately owned publications, the country became one of the few in the world without a private-sector press. That's one way to bury news.

But there is hope. The globalisation driven by the media – witness September 11, Tiananmen Square, the war in Iraq, all global media events as well as moments of great personal tragedy – has started to bring media freedom into focus.

And where there is the chance, technology has given journalists across the world the power to start building a free press from the bottom up.

Organisations such as the Institute for War and Peace Reporting (www.iwpr.net), which trains new journalists in former communist countries and beyond, publishing their work on the internet, could not have thrived a decade ago as they do now.

In Zimbabwe, one of the most repressive countries towards the media, opposition newspapers such as the Daily News (www.dailynews.co.zw) may have been banned – but dissenting voices remain on the internet for anybody in the world to read.

Add to that list the Kabul Times in Afghanistan, which – as the country's only English-language paper, though not yet on the internet – is exercising press freedom amid the desperate poverty of a ruined city.

Don't forget the bloggers, such as "Salam Pax" (http://dear_raed.blogspot.com), who (it still appears) kept an online, English-language journal in Baghdad in the months leading up to the US invasion; and "Richard", author of Peking Duck (http://pekingduck.blogspot.com), whose blog is a commentary on the crude censorship of the Beijing regime.

The Chinese government has seen the danger of the internet and banned access to organisations such as Reporters Sans Frontières, but they cannot stem the flow of free speech altogether. Not, at any rate, without jeopardising the new mantra that is international trade.

As the world becomes smaller – as the "global village" becomes our reality – the easier it may become for smaller voices to be heard.

Global media

Top 11 global media companies

(Ranked by market capitalisation at July 25, 2003)

1. **General Electric**
   £175.5bn
   Industrial behemoth producing everything from aircraft engines to cable TV. Makes the list by virtue of being owner of NBC, the US television network, and several US regional channels.

2. **Viacom**
   £49.0bn
   Owner of US television channels CBS, MTV and Nickelodeon, and publishers Simon & Schuster.

3. **AOL Time Warner**
   £42.7bn
   Product of now infamous merger between Time Warner – owners of US channels HBO and CNN, Warner Music, publishers Time and Warner Books – and internet service provider AOL, at the height of the dotcom boom.

4. **Comcast**
   £42.3bn
   US broadband cable and internet company, with stakes in networks such as E! Entertainment and the Golf Channel.

5. **Bertelsmann**
   N/A
   Privately owned German company, whose subsidiaries include Britain's Channel 5, publishers Ballantine, Bantam Dell and Random House, and global music group BMG. Thought to be ready to float within three or four years.

6. **Walt Disney**
   £26.9bn
   More than just theme parks: as well as Disney-branded channels and merchandising ventures, Walt Disney owns US network ABC, several US newspapers and magazines, plus film distributors including Miramax and Buena Vista.

7. **News Corporation**
   £25.5bn
   Rupert Murdoch's global conglomerate. NewsCorp this year gained control of DirecTV in the US, to add to BSkyB in the UK and Star TV in Asia. Also owns NewsCorp Newspapers – publishers of the Times and the Sun – and HarperCollins.

8. **Sony**
   £18.2bn
   Electronics giant: also owns Sony Music and Sony Pictures.

9. **Clear Channel**
   £15.3bn
   Owner of hundreds of US regional radio stations, now thought to be interested in extending empire into the UK.

10. **Gannett**
    £12.8bn
    Publisher: owner of Newsquest, which has aggressively acquired hundreds of British local newspapers and owns US national paper USA Today.

11. **Vivendi Universal**
    £12.2bn
    Global conglomerate: had third highest operating revenues of any media company in 2002, but suffered biggest losses in French history in same year.

Global media Contacts

Global media groups

AOL Time Warner
AOL Time Warner Building,
75 Rockefeller Plaza, New York
NY 10019, USA
00 1 212 484 8000
www.aoltimewarner.com

Bertelsmann
Carl-Bertelsmann-Strasse 270
33311 Gütersloh, Germany
00 49 5241 800
info@bertelsmann.com
www.bertelsmann.com

Clear Channel
200 East Basse Road
San Antonio, TX 78209, USA
00 1 210 822 2828
lisacdollinger@clearchannel.com
www.clearchannel.com

ComCast
1500 Market Street, Philadelphia
PA 19102-2148, USA
00 1 215 665 1700
corporate_communications@
  comcast.com
www.comcast.com

Gannett
7950 Jones Branch Drive
McLean VA 22107, USA
00 1 703 8546000
gcishare@info.gannett.com
www.gannett.com

NewsQuest Media Group
Newspaper House
34–44 London Road, Morden
Surrey SM4 5BR
020 8640 8989
www.gannett.com

General Electric
3135 Easton Turnpike
Fairfield CT 06431, USA
00 1 203 373 2039
www.ge.com/en

NewsCorp
1211 Avenue of Americas, 8th Floor,
New York NY 10036, USA
00 1 212 852 7111
www.newscorp.com

Sony
550 Madison Avenue
New York, NY 10022, USA
00 1 212 833 8000
www.sony.com

Viacom
1515 Broadway, New York
NY 10036, USA
00 1 212 258 6000
www.viacom.com

Vivendi Universal
42 avenue de Friedland
75380 Paris Cedex 08
France
00 33 17171 1000
www.vivendiuniversal.com

Walt Disney Company
500 Park Avenue, 11th Floor
New York, NY 10022, USA
00 1 212 593 8900
http://disney.go.com

Disney head office UK
3 Queen Caroline Street
London W6 9PE
020 8222 1000
http://disney.go.com

Global news outlets

Europe

El Pais
Miguel Yuste 40
Madrid 28037, Spain
00 34 91 337 82 00
redaccion@prisacom.com
www.elpais.es
Spanish

Kathimerini
D. Falireos & E. Makariou st. 2
185-47 N. Faliron
Piraeus, Greece
00 30 210 4808000
editor@ekathimerini.com
www.ekathimerini.com
English-language daily

La Repubblica
Piazza Indipendenza, 11/b
Roma 00185, Italy
00 39 6 49821
larepubblica@repubblica.it
www.repubblica.it
(In Italian.) Liberal Rome-based daily

Le Monde
21 bis, rue Claude-Bernard
75242 Paris Cedex 05, France
00 33 1 4217 3900
mail@mondepub.fr
www.lemonde.fr
France's bestselling quality daily

Moscow Times
Bldg. 4
Ulitsa Vyborgskaya 16
125212 Moscow, Russia
00 7 095 937-3399
moscowtimes@imedia.ru
www.moscowtimes.ru
Respected English-language daily

Prague Post
Stepanska 20, Prague 1
110 00, Czech Republic
00 420 02 9633 4400
info@praguepost.com
www.praguepost.com
The Czech Republic's best English-language daily

Radio France Internationale
116, avenue du President Kennedy
Paris 75016, France
00 33 1 5640 1212
english.service@rfi.fr
www.rfi.fr
A French "world service"

Süddeutsche Zeitung
Sendlinger Strasse 8
80331 Munchen, Germany
00 49 89 21830
info@sueddeutscher-verlag.de
www.sueddeutsche.de
(In German.) Major Munich-based paper. Broadly liberal

US and Canada

CBS
524 West 57th Street, New York
NY 10019, USA
00 1 212 975 4321
www.cbs.com
News network.

CNN
One CNN Center
Atlanta, GA 30348, USA
00 1 404 827 1500
cnn@cnn.com
www.cnn.com
News network

International Herald Tribune
6 bis, rue des Graviers
92521 Neuilly Cedex, France
00 33 1 4143 9322
iht@iht.com
www.iht.com
International daily, now wholly owned by the New York Times

LA Times
202 W 1st St
Los Angeles, CA 90012, USA
00 1 213 237 5000
letters@latimes.com
www.latimes.com
Biggest west-coast daily

NBC
30 Rockefeller Plaza
New York, NY 10112, USA
00 1 212 664 4444
press@nbcmv.com
www.nbc.com/
News network

New York Times
229 West 43rd Street, New York
New York 10036, USA
00 1 212 556 1234
editorial@nytimes.com
www.nytimes.com
National paper of record, rocked this
year by plagiarism scandal that cost
two senior resignations

Wall St Journal
200 Liberty Street, New York
NY 10281, USA
00 1 800 568 7625
newseditors@wsj.com
www.wsj.com
Conservative financial daily

Washington Post
1150 15th Street NW
Washington, DC 20071, USA
00 1 202 334 6000
letters@washpost.com
www.washingtonpost.com
The New York Times' main rival

Toronto Globe and Mail
444 Front Street West, Toronto
Ontario M5V 2S9, Canada
00 1 416 585 5000
newsroom@GlobeAndMail.ca
www.theglobeandmail.com
Quality daily, Canada

Middle East

Al-Jazeera
Doha, Qatar
00 974 4885 666
info@aljazeera.net.qa
http://english.aljazeera.net/ or
www.aljazeera.com
Famous Arabic-language satellite
channel, based in Qatar

Daily Star
Marine Tower 6th floor
Rue de La Ste Famille, Gemaizeh
Achrafieh, Beirut, Lebanon
00 961 1 587277
letters@dailystar.com.lb
www.dailystar.com.lb
Lebanese daily

Ha'aretz
21 Schocken St, PO Box 233
Tel Aviv 61001, Israel
00 972 3 5121204
secretary@haaretz.co.il
www.haaretzdaily.com
English edition of Israel's moderate
national daily, published in Tel Aviv

Jerusalem Post
Jerusalem Post Building
P.O. Box 81, Jerusalem 91000
Israel
00 972 2 531 5666
editors@jpost.co.il
www.jpost.com
Conservative English-language daily

Jordan Times
Jordan Press Foundation
P.O. Box 6710, Queen Rania Al
Abdullah Street, Amman, Jordan
00 962 6 5600800 ext 392
jotimes@jpf.com.jo
www.jordantimes.com
Jordan's only English-language daily

Middle East Times
Middle East Times UK Ltd
27–29 Albert Embankment, London
SE1 7TJ
020 7820 4188
editor@middleastimes.net or
egyptnews@metimes.com
www.metimes.com
Quality English-language weekly,
based in Egypt

Africa

Daily Mail and Guardian
PO Box 91667, Auckland Park
Johannesburg 2006, South Africa
00 27 011 727 7000
newsdesk@mg.co.za
www.mg.co.za
South African daily, no longer part-
owned by Guardian Media Group

Daily Nation, Kenya
PO Box 49010, Nairobi, Kenya
00 254 2 221222
comments@nationaudio.com
www.nationmedia.com
Kenya's biggest daily paper

Daily News, Zimbabwe
P O Box 1040, Trustee House
55 Samora Machel Avenue
Harare, Zimbabwe
00 263 4 753027
editorial@dailynews.co.zw
www.dailynews.co.zw
Daily independent paper

Le Matin, Algeria
18–20 Place Ahmed
Zabana 16000, Algiers, Algeria
info@lematin-dz.com
www.lematin-dz.net
(In French.) Moderate, secular paper

Monitor, Uganda
P. O. Box 12141
Plot 29–35, 8th Street
Industrial Area, Kampala, Uganda
00 256 041 232367
info@monitor.co.ug
www.monitor.co.ug
Major independent daily

Sunday Times (South Africa)
PO Box 1742
Saxonwold 2132, South Africa
00 27 11 280 3000
suntimes@sundaytimes.co.za
www.suntimes.co.za

Asia

Asahi Shimbun
5–3–2, Tsukiji, Chuo-ku
Tokyo 104-8011, Japan
00 81 3 3545 0131
www.asahi.com

Dawn – Pakistan
Haroon House
Dr Ziauddin Ahmed Road
Karachi 74200, Pakistan
00 92 21 111 444 777
webmaster@dawn.com
www.dawn.com
English-language daily

Hindustan Times
Hindustan Times House
18–20, K.G. Marg, New Delhi 1
India
00 91 11 23361234
feedback@hindustantimes.com
www.hindustantimes.com

Jakarta Post – Indonesia
Jl. Palmerah Selatan 15
Jakarta 10270, Indonesia
00 62 21 5300476
editorial@thejakartapost.com
www.thejakartapost.com

JoongAng
00 82 02 751 9215
iht@joongang.co.kr
http://joongangdaily.joins.com

South China Morning Post –
Hong Kong
16F Somerset House, Taikoo Place
979 King's Road, Quarry Bay
Hong Kong
00 852 2565 2222
info@scmp.com
www.scmp.com

Straits Times
Singapore Press Holdings Limited
News Centre, 82 Genting Lane
Singapore 349567
00 65 6319 5397
STI@sph.com.sg
http://straitstimes.asia1.com.sg
Singapore's most widely circulated
English-language paper: close ties to
the government

Taipei Times (Taiwan)
Nanking East Rd., Sec. 2, #137, 5Fl.
Taipei, ROC - 104, Taiwan
00 886 2 2518 2728
inquiries@taipeitimes.com
www.taipeitimes.com

Latin America

Jamaica Gleaner
7 North Street, PO Box 40
Kingston, Jamaica, W.I.
00 1 876 922 3400
feedback@jamaica-gleaner.com
www.jamaica-gleaner.com

La Nacion
Leandro N. Alem 728
Capital Federal, C1001AAO
Argentina
00 54 11 4893 2898
consultas@lanacion.com.ar
www.lanacion.com.ar

O Estado de Sao Paulo
Av. Celestino Bourroul, 68
1 andar, Bairro do Limao
Sao Paulo SP, Brazil
00 55 011 3856 2122
falecom@estado.com.br
www.estado.estadao.com.br

Pacific

ABS-CBN (Philippines)
Sgt EA Esguerra Ave cor
Mother Ignacia St
1103 Quezon City, Philippines
00 63 2 415 2272
feedback@abs-cbn.com
www.abs-cbnnews.com
News network

New Zealand Herald
PO Box 32, Auckland, New Zealand
00 64 09 3795050
www.nzherald.co.nz

Sydney Morning Herald
201 Sussex St, GPO Box 506
Sydney NSW 2000, Australia
00 61 2 9282 1569
readerlink@smh.com.au
www.smh.com.au
Quality daily

Global journalism bodies

Amarc (World Association of Community Radio Broadcasters)
705 Bourget Street
Suite 100, Montreal, Quebec
Canada, H4C 2M6
00 1 514 982 0351
amarc@amarc.org
www.amarc.org

Article XIX
Lancaster House
33 Islington High Street
London N1 9LH
020 7278 9292
info@article19.org
www.article19.org
Combats censorship

Association for International Broadcasting
PO Box 990, London SE3 9XL
020 8297 3993
info@aib.org.uk
www.aib.org.uk
Trade association

Committee to Protect Journalists
330 7th Avenue 12th Floor
New York NY 10001, USA
00 1 212 465 1004
info@cpj.org
www.cpj.org

Foreign Press Association in London
11 Carlton House Terrace
London SW1Y 5AJ
020 7930 0445
secretariat@foreign-press.org.uk
www.foreign-press.org.uk

Institute for War and Peace Reporting
Lancaster House
33 Islington High Street
London N1 9LH
020 7713 7130
alan@iwpr.net
www.iwpr.net
Training in conflict areas

International Centre for Journalists
1616 H Street NW, Third Floor
Washington DC 20006, USA
00 1 202 737 3700
www.icfj.org

International Federation of Journalists
IPC-Residence Palace, Bloc C
Rue de la Loi 155, B-1040 Brussels
Belgium
00 32 2 235 22 00
ifj@ifj.org
www.ifj.org

International Federation of the Periodical Press
Queens House
55–56 Lincoln's Inn Fields
London WC2A 3LJ
020 7404 4169
info@fipp.com
www.fipp.com

International Freedom of Expression
489 College Street, Ste. 403
Toronto, Ontario M6G 1A5
Canada
00 1 416 515 9622
ifex@ifex.org
www.ifex.org

International Press Institute
Spiegelgasse 2
A-1010 Vienna, Austria
00 43 1 512 90 11
ipi@freemedia.at
www.freemedia.at
Network of editors, executives and senior journalists

InterWorld Radio
editor@interworldradio.org
www.interworldradio.org

ITN International
200 Grays Inn Road
London WC1X 8XZ
itn.international@itn.co.uk
www.itn.co.uk

MediaChannel
575 8th Avenue
New York, NY I0018, USA
00 1 212 246 0202
editor@mediachannel.org
www.mediachannel.org

Panos London
9 White Lion Street
London N1 9PD
020 7278 1111
info@panoslondon.org.uk
www.panos.org.uk
Journalism in developing countries

Reporters Sans Frontieres
5, rue Geoffroy-Marie
75009 Paris, France
00 33 1 44 83 84 84
rsf@rsf.org
www.rsf.org

World Association of Newspapers
25 rue d'Astorg
75008 Paris, France
00 33 1 47 42 85 00
contact_us@wan.asso.fr
www.wan-press.info

World Press Freedom Committee
11690-C Sunrise Valley Dr.
Reston, VA 20191, USA
00 1 703 715 9811
freepress@wpfc.org
www.wpfc.org

World Press Photo
Jacob Obrechtstraat 26
1071 KM Amsterdam
The Netherlands
00 31 20 676 6096
office@worldpressphoto.nl
www.worldpressphoto.nl

World Radio Network
PO Box 1212, London SW8 2ZF
020 7896 9000
email@wrn.org
www.wrn.org

Advertising & PR

I s the media recession over? When the war ended in Iraq that was the question on every ad exec's lips. Advertising in the UK was worth almost £17bn in 2002 – back up to 2000 levels after a severe slump in 2001 – and with promising signs of recovery after October 2002. But the Iraq conflict caused many media buyers to delay campaigns, and the spring freeze it brought threatened to kill the green shoots of advertising growth: total spend rose by just 1.5% in the first quarter of 2003, a fall of 1.5% in real terms. Predictions were mixed: Initiative Media said the UK ad market would rise by 4.6% in 2003, making it one of the strongest performers in Europe; but Sir Martin Sorrell, industry guru and head of the world's largest advertising group, WPP, warned of a flat 2003 with recovery only in 2004. Zenith Optimedia, meanwhile, said the UK market would contract further.

About the industry

In theory, advertising is split into two main areas: ad agencies, who handle industry accounts and come up with creative ideas; and media agencies, who control the purchase of ad space. There are about 1,600 ad agencies in the UK and more than 300 media agencies. In practice though, many big firms are owned by one of the major, mostly US-based, advertising "supergroups", who control not only the main ad and media agencies, but many of the PR and direct marketing agencies as well.

The recession came at a bad time for the giants: at the back end of years of acquisitions and expansion, many were left looking over-stretched. **WPP**, which owns ad agencies J Walter Thompson and Ogilvy & Mather, media buyers MindShare and Mediaedge:cia, and PR firms Hill & Knowlton and Burson-Marsteller – plus a stake in leading media buyer Carat – suffered a 19% fall in profits to just over £400m. **Interpublic**, the number two group, which owns ad agencies McCann-Erickson and Lowe, plus leading PR agency Weber Shandwick, reported a 79% drop in fourth-quarter profits for 2002; this after it had to restate its financial results from 1997. **Omnicom** and **Publicis**, numbers three and four, did better: Omnicom, which owns the TBWA and Abbot Mead Vickers BBDO agencies, said earnings were up 11% in the third quarter of 2002, while Publicis, the French group which owns Saatchi & Saatchi and controls media agency Zenith Optimedia, reported a 20% increase in revenues over the year.

After a nightmare couple of years, **Cordiant** – the marketing services group formed in 1997 after demerging from Saatchi & Saatchi – was finally taken over in July 2003 by WPP. The group, which had owned Bates Worldwide and a 25% stake in Zenith Optimedia, had spent heavily during the dotcom years in a vain attempt to emulate the US giants. But in February 2003, with debts estimated at £220m, the firm

Ratecards

admitted it had to sell assets. More than 1,700 jobs were lost; in May the company won a stay of execution from lenders. After speculation that Publicis was to buy the group – a move which would have reunited Cordiant with Saatchi & Saatchi – WPP took control in a £266m deal.

Meanwhile in spring, the industry in the UK and the US was abuzz about **Cog**, the two-minute ad for the Honda Accord – in which a transmission ball bearing sets 84 other pieces of equipment, including spinning spanners and walking windscreen wipers, in motion across a floor. The ad, made by independent agency **Wieden & Kennedy**, seemed destined to win creative awards, but was beaten into third place at the Cannes international advertising festival.

"Below the line"

A relatively recent phenomenon, in the light of the overall advertising recession, has been the strong performance of "below-the-line" services such as public relations, direct marketing, market research and sales promotion, all of which have been driven by the communications revolution. Below-the-line services accounted for more than half of WPP's turnover in 2002. In Britain, direct mail expenditure reached £1.4bn, with the average British household receiving 13 adverts in the mail a month. The leading British investor in the medium, MBNA, spent more than £40m in 2002 on direct marketing alone.

Perhaps ironically, below-the-line marketing has a relatively poor reputation among consumers, as the jargon used to describe it will testify: incessant PR is just "spin"; direct mail marketing is "junk mail"; unsolicited email is "spam". This is perhaps unfair: according to estimates, 90% of spam is sent by fewer than 200 known, serial offenders. Marketers are also waking up to the potential of marketing by text message: opt-in campaigns have been shown to be successful, and the code of advertising practice has been redrawn to ensure advertisers get the permission of users. But unsolicited SMS marketing is also on the increase, damaging the reputation of the medium.

Regulation

Advertising is currently regulated in two ways. Non-broadcast media are monitored by the advertising standards authority, a self-regulatory body, which received a record 14,000 complaints in 2002; while broadcast advertising is controlled by Ofcom, which in December 2003 takes control of the ITC and the radio authority. But Ofcom in turn has the power to devolve regulation to the television and radio industry, and is widely expected to do so after Ofcom chairman, Lord Currie, said he was "quietly hopeful" of getting such a scheme off the ground.

Public health experts and campaigners celebrated in February as tobacco advertising was finally banned in the UK. The Tobacco Advertising and Promotion Act outlawed advertising in magazines, newspapers and on billboards, to add to the existing ban on broadcast ads. Direct marketing and in-pack promotion became illegal in May.

In a related move, the BMW Williams motor racing team made headlines by signing a sponsorship deal with NiQuitin, a product that helps people to give up smoking. Williams previously had close sponsorship links with the tobacco industry.

Further reading

■ Press

MediaGuardian
media.guardian.co.uk/advertising
media.guardian.co.uk/marketingandpr

Campaign
www.campaignlive.com

Marketing
www.marketing.haynet.com

Marketing Week
www.mad.co.uk/mw

Media Week
www.mediaweek.co.uk

PR Week
www.prweek.com

Promotions & Incentives
www.pandionline.com

Adbusters magazine
www.adbusters.org

■ Books

How to Get into Advertising ANDREA NEIDLE,
CONTINUUM 2002

Ogilvy on Advertising DAVID OGILVY, PRION 1995

Shared Beliefs INSTITUTE OF PRACTITIONERS IN
ADVERTISING 2001

■ Films

The Sweet Smell of Success, 1957
  Tom Curtis as a slimy press agent: unmissable

How to Get Ahead in Advertising, 2001
  Richard E Grant in post-Withnail black comedy

■ Other resources

Advertising Association
  www.adassoc.org.uk

Institute of Practitioners in Advertising
  www.ipa.co.uk

Institute of Public Relations
  www.ipr.org.uk

Advertising & PR

All advertising expenditure, by medium

	1998 £m	1999 £m	2000 £m	2001 £m	2002 £m	% change from 2001
National newspapers	1,824	1,991	2,252	2,062	1,930	−6.4
Regional newspapers	2,389	2,483	2,762	2,834	2,870	1.3
Consumer magazines	709	727	750	779	785	0.8
Business & professional magazines	1,209	1,195	1,270	1,202	1,088	−9.4
Directories	780	831	868	959	990	3.3
Press production costs	620	650	702	669	643	−3.9
Total press	**7,531**	**7,877**	**8,604**	**8,514**	**8,306**	**−2.3**
Television	4,029	4,320	4,646	4,147	4,326	4.3
Direct mail	1,666	1,876	2,049	2,228	2,378	6.7
Outdoor & transport	613	649	810	788	802	1.9
Radio	460	516	595	541	545	0.8
Cinema	97	123	128	164	180	9.8
Internet	19	51	155	166	197	18.7
Total all media	**14,415**	**15,412**	**16,988**	**16,548**	**16,374**	**1.2**

Source: Advertising Association

Out of the slow lane **Claire Cozens**

Ever since the Saatchi brothers set up their world-famous agency in 1976, the advertising industry has enjoyed a higher profile than warranted by its size. Despite employing just over 14,000 people – fewer than the biotechnology or printing industries – advertising's image has allowed it to command far more column inches than its less glamorous counterparts.

In recent years though, advertising's champagne-fuelled image has taken something of a knock, as recession-hit advertisers have cut back their spending and agencies have had to rein in their lifestyles following the excesses of the dotcom boom.

Even the bigger agencies such as Abbott Mead Vickers BBDO, which famously refused to make any redundancies during the recession of the late 80s and early 90s, have been forced to cut jobs in the worst advertising recession in three decades.

In 2002 the total amount spent on advertising in the UK rose by 1.2% to £16.7bn and although there were some signs of revival in 2003, the general consensus is that it will not be until 2004 – with the boost from the Olympics and the US presidential elections – that we will see real recovery.

Not everyone is cutting back – controversially, the amount the government spends on advertising has more than doubled since Labour came into power in 1997. Big campaigns to promote new initiatives such as the working families' tax credit helped swell the government advertising budget to £151m in 2001, making it Britain's biggest advertiser. By 2002 it had fallen back to fourth place behind Ford, Procter & Gamble and British Telecom, although it was still spending almost twice as much as the John Major government.

In spite of all the doom and gloom, the number of people working in the UK advertising industry has remained relatively static since the slowdown struck. While staff levels at the bigger agencies have dropped, there are now more people working in smaller, independent agencies than ever before, according to the latest industry figures from the Institute of Practitioners in Advertising.

Although the London advertising scene is now dominated by super groups such as WPP (owner of J Walter Thompson and Ogilvy & Mather), Omnicom (TBWA and BMP DDB) and Interpublic (Lowe and McCann-Erickson), a select few smaller independent agencies are thriving thanks to their reputation for creative thinking.

Mother, creator of the ITV Digital monkey, is the hottest new kid on the block and has won business from the likes of Unilever, Orange and the government. Others include Clemmow Hornby Inge, which stole the Tango business from its more established rival HHCL & Partners, within months of setting up in 2002; Soul – set up by a group of former executives from Levi's agency Bartle Bogle Hegarty – now creating ads for Coca-Cola; and Campbell Doyle Dye, set up by the creator of the Guinness "Surfer" ad, Walter Campbell, with a group of former colleagues from Abbott Mead Vickers.

One appeal of such smaller agencies is their ability to come up with alternatives to the traditional advertising campaign. Campbell Doyle Dye was responsible for creating a spoof movie trailer starring Benicio Del Toro to promote the launch of the new Mercedes.

While traditional TV, press and poster campaigns are on the decline, revenues from internet advertising, direct mail and so-called guerrilla marketing are booming. From urinals to students' foreheads, an entire industry is now devoted to finding new and unexpected places to put ads.

This is partly because they are cheaper alternatives for advertisers tightening their belts, but also partly because our viewing habits have changed. Gone are the days when a marketing director could buy a 30-second slot during Coronation Street, confident that 20 million people would be watching. Instead, advertisers are having to be more imaginative; the industry is changing as a result.

Claire Cozens is advertising and marketing editor for MediaGuardian.co.uk

Award winners

Cannes International Advertising Festival

- *Grand Prix:*
  "The Lamp", Crispin Porter & Bogusky/Morton Jankel Zander (Ikea)
- *Gold Lions:*
  "Sheet Metal", Goodby, Silverstein & Partners (Saturn)
  "Cog", Wieden & Kennedy (Honda Accord)

British Television Advertising Awards

- *Advertising agency of the year:*
  TBWA/London
- *ITV award for television commercial of the year:*
  Advertiser: NSPCC
  Product: NSPCC
  Title: Cartoon
  Advertising agency: Saatchi & Saatchi
  Production company: Gorgeous Enterprises
  Director: Frank Budgen
  Writer: Howard Willmott
  Art director: Duncan Marshall

Campaign magazine's top 20 UK agencies 2002

Ranked by Nielson media research billings

1	Abbott Mead Vickers BBDO	£341m
2	McCann–Erickson	£299m
3	Lowe	£275m
4	Ogilvy and Mather	£273m
5	M&C Saatchi	£251m
6	Publicis	£250m
7	J Walter Thompson	£245m
8	Saatchi & Saatchi	£234m
9	Bates UK	£183m
10	Railey Kelly Campbell Roalfe/Y&R	£177m
11	TBWA/London	£172m
12	BMP DDB	£170m
13	WCRS	£155m
14	Grey Worldwide	£151m
15	Euro RSCG Wnek Gosper	£148m
16	Bartle Bogle Hegarty	£134m
17	D'Arcy	£128m
18	Leo Burnett	£126m
19	Banks Hoggins O'Shea/FCB	£86m
20	Partners BDDH	£73m

Top 20 media brands 2002

Agencies ranked by Nielson media research billings

1	Carat	£563m
2	MediaCom	£550m
3	Zenith Media	£538m
4	MindShare	£481m
5	OMD UK	£400m
6	Starcom Motive Partnership	£372m
7	Initiative MediaLondon	£366m
8	Universal McCann London	£287m
9	PHD	£276m
10	MediaVest UK	£272m
11	Mediaedge:cia	£200m
12	Manning Gottlieb OMD	£199m
13	BBJ Communications	£186m
14	Optimedia International	£160m
15	Walker Media	£143m
16	Media Planning Group	£118m
17	Brand Connection	£81m
18	Feather Brooksbank	£76m
19	The Allmond Partnership	£74m
20	Brilliant Media	£71m

Source: Campaign Report – The Top 300 Agencies, 21 February 2003 (Data supplied by Nielsen Media Research)

Advertising & PR

Advertising & PR Contacts

Ad agencies – full service

1576 Advertising
0131 473 1576
www.1576.co.uk

23red
0870 0130023
www.23red.com

Abbott Mead Vickers BBDO
020 7616 3500
www.amvbbdo.com

Acumen Marketing Communications
01732 456444

AD 78
01670 789078
www.ad78.co.uk

Adconnection
020 8549 9751
www.adconnection.co.uk

Adpartners
0141 226 3711
www.adpartners.com

Advertising Principles
0113 226 2222
www.principlescom.com

Agency Republic
020 7942 0000
www.agencyrepublic.com

AMD Girardot
020 7349 6333
www.amdgirardot.com

APMCLR
020 7240 0727
www.apmclr.com

ARM Direct
020 7224 3040
www.arm-direct.co.uk

Arthur Wood Advertising
0161 968 6900
www.awa.uk.net

ATP Advertising & Marketing
0113 273 8555
www.atpadvertising.co.uk

Atticus Advertising & Marketing
020 7631 2021
www.atticusadvertising.com

Attinger Jack Advertising
01308 456321
www.aja.co.uk

AV Browne Advertising
028 9032 0663
www.avb.co.uk

Avian Communication Network
01382 427 000
www.avian.co.uk

Aylesworth Fleming
01202 295723
www.aylesworth-fleming.co.uk

banc
020 7437 5552
www.banc.co.uk

Banks Hoggins O'Shea FCB
020 7947 8000
www.london.fcb.com

Barker Nicholson
020 8979 3211

Barkers Communications Scotland
020 7634 1200, 0121 2369501
01224 641304
Edinburgh 0131 229 7493
Glasgow 0141 248 5030
www.barkersscotland.co.uk

Barrett Cernis
020 7663 3575
www.barrett.cernis.co.uk

Barrington Johnson Lorains & Partners
0161 831 7141
www.bjl.co.uk

Bartle Bogle Hegarty
020 7734 1677
www.bartleboglehegarty.com

Base One
020 8943 9999
www.base01.co.uk

Bates UK
020 7262 5077
www.batesuk.com

BBA Active
020 7625 7575
www.bbagenius.com

BCMB
0161 877 0521
http://bcmb.co.uk

BDH\TBWA
0161 908 8600
www.bdhtbwa.co.uk

bds beechwood
020 7439 4142
www.bds-beechwood.com

Big Communications
0116 299 1144
www.bigcommunications.co.uk

Billington Jackson Advertising
020 7351 0006
www.billingtonjackson.co.uk

Bilsland Coltman McKenna
020 7242 0039
www.bcmadvertising.co.uk

Blair Fowles Advertising
01202 558111
www.blairfowles.co.uk

BMP DDB
020 7258 3979
www.bmpddb.com

Boss UK
01202 311555
www.bossuk.net

Brahm
0113 230 4000
www.brahm.com

Brand Development Company
020 7497 9727

Bray Leino
01598 760700
www.brayleino.co.uk

Bridge
0141 552 8384
www.thebridgeuk.com

Brookes & Vernons Communications
01889 561000
01889 564931
www.brookesvernons.co.uk

Burkitt DDB
020 7893 4893
020 7320 9300
www.burkittddb.com

BWP – Barnett Williams Partnership
020 7404 2525
www.bwp.co.uk

Byron Advertising
01895 252131
www.b-different.com

Camp Chipperfield Hill Murray
020 7881 3200
www.cchm.co.uk

Campbell Doyle Dye
020 7483 9805
www.cddlondon.com

Carlson Marketing Group
020 8875 0875
01604 234300
www.carlsonmarketing.co.uk

Carrington Caunter Associates
01202 499612
www.carrington-caunter.co.uk

cdp-travissully
020 7437 4224
www.cdp-travissully.com

Ceanda Advertising & Marketing
020 8943 5580

Charterhouse Advertising & Marketing
0161 848 9050
www.charterhouse-advertising.co.uk

CHC Choir
0115 950 7800
www.choir-djl.com

Cheetham Bell JWT
0161 832 8884
www.cheethambelljwt.com

CIB
01372 371800
www.cibcommunications.co.uk

Cicero Advertising & Marketing
0161 876 5522
www.cicero-marketing.co.uk

Citigate Albert Frank
020 7282 8000
www.citigateaf.com

Citigate Smarts
0141 222 2040
Leeds 0113 297 9899
Edinburgh 0131 555 0425
Manchester 0161 829 0740
www.citigatesmarts.co.uk

Cogent
020 7434 1441
0121 627 5040
www.cogent.co.uk

Colbear Advertising
01302 368651
www.colbear.co.uk

Coltas
0141 204 5665
www.coltas.com
Communications in Business Group
020 7771 7000
www.cibgroup.co.uk
Copeland & Charrington
020 7407 0440
www.copeland-charrington.co.uk
Crammond Dickens Lerner and Partners
020 7240 8100
www.cdl-uk.com
Cravens Advertising
0113 275 3399
0191 232 6683
www.cravens.co.uk
Crazy Horse Brand Warriors
01892 516116
www.crazyhorse.co.uk
CTC
0117 311 9009
Da Costa & Co
020 7916 3791
Delaney Lund Knox Warren & Partners
020 7836 3474
www.dlkw.co.uk
Designate
01273 704040
www.designate.co.uk
Dewynters
020 7321 0488
www.dewynters.com
dfgw
020 7734 5888
www.dfgw.com
DLCF
020 7636 5552
www.dlcf.co.uk
Doner Cardwell Hawkins
020 7734 0511
www.donercardwellhawkins.co.uk
Elliott Borra Perlmutter LLP
020 7836 7722
www.ebpcreative.com
Emery McLaven Orr
01793 484828
01793 767300
www.emo.uk.com
Euro RSCG Life
020 7379 3991
www.eurorscg.com
Euro RSCG Wnek Gosper
020 7240 4111
www.eurorscg.co.uk
Fallon
020 7494 9120
www.fallon.com
Faulds Advertising
020 7908 7510
Edinburgh 0131 557 6003
www.malcolmmoore.com
Finex Communications Group
020 7361 7777
www.finexgroup.com
First City Advertising
020 7436 7020
www.firstcityadvertising.co.uk

FMG Communications
020 7731 6461
www.fmgcommunications.co.uk
Fox Kalomaski
020 7691 8090
www.foxkalomaski.co.uk
Fox Murphy
01603 621587
www.foxmurphy.co.uk
Fox Parrack Hirsch Communications
020 7436 4336
www.fphcom.com
Frank The Agency
01625 521444
www.itsfrank.com
G3 (UK)
020 7437 3235
www.G3uk.com
GCAS Advertising
028 9055 7700
www.gcasgroup.com
Geoff Chambers Associates
0113 201 8844
www.retailgains.com
Gillett & Bevan
0161 228 0023
Glasgow Advertising Agency
0141 204 1955
Glasshouse Communications
020 7291 0790
www.glasshousecommunications
.com
Golley Slater & Partners
020 8744 2630
Bristol 0117 921 1131
Cardiff 029 2038 8621
www.golleyslater.com
Golley Slater Brooker
0121 454 2323
www.golleyslater.co.uk
Grey PTK Advertising
020 7636 3399
www.ptkhealthcare.com
Grey Worldwide
020 7636 3399
www.grey.co.uk
GSB Associates
01323 722933
www.gsba.co.uk
Harris Kemp Advertising
01799 543157
www.harriskemp.co.uk
Harwood Marketing
01273 891101
HDM Total Communication
020 7321 2227
www.hdmagency.co.uk
Healthworld UK
020 7262 2141
www.brandfood.co.uk
Heresy
08701 434344
www.heresynetwork.com
HHC Advertising and Design
0117 934 9600
www.hhcfresh.co.uk
HHCL/Red Cell
020 7436 3333
www.hhclredcell.com
Holman Advertising
020 7637 3533

Hooper Galton
020 7494 6300
www.hoopergalton.com
HPS group
01494 684300
www.hpsgroup.co.uk
HR Gardens
020 7353 3223
Glasgow 0141 332 2020
Bristol 0117 925 7777
Leeds 0113 234 0251
Dublin 00 353 14174243
Cardiff 029 2038 9684,
0121 702 2244
www.hrgardens.com
HRO'C
0121 454 9707
www.hroc.co.uk
Hudson Wright Associates
020 7436 8673
www.hudsonwright.co.uk
IAS Marketing & Communication
01625 434343
www.iasbranding.co.uk
IC Group
01772 679383
www.icgonline.co.uk
Ideas Unlimited
020 7738 1900
www.ideasunlimited.co.uk
Inferno
020 7292 7070
www.inferno-group.com
Integrated Marketing & Advertising
0161 440 2770
www.i-m-a.co.uk
JJ Group
01865 343100
www.thejjgroup.com
J Walter Thompson Company
020 7656 7000
www.jwt.com
Kaleidoscope Advertising Design & Marketing
0151 707 2220
www.kadm.co.uk
Lavery Rowe Advertising
020 7378 1780
Birmingham 0121 212 2230
www.laveryrowe.com
Lawton Communications Group
023 8082 8500
www.lawton.co.uk
Leagas Delaney Group
020 7758 1758
www.leagasdelaney.com
Leith Advertising Agency
London 020 7758 1400
Edinburgh 0131 561 8600,
0131 557 5840
www.leith.co.uk
Leo Burnett
020 7591 9111
www.leoburnett.com
Link ICA
01622 683300
www.linkica.co.uk
Lovelace Advertising Associates
020 8681 5411
Lowe & Partners
020 7584 5033
www.loweworldwide.com

Lowe Broadway
020 7344 8888
01582 8855 00
www.lowebroadway.com
M&C Saatchi
020 7543 4500
www.mcsaatchi.com
M&H Communications
020 7412 2000
www.mandh.co.uk
Maher Bird Associates
020 7287 1718
MAP
0161 907 3000
www.map-plc.co.uk
Marr Associates
01828 632800
www.marr.co.uk
Marten Gibbon Associates
020 7340 1900
www.mga-advertising.co.uk
Martin Tait Redheads
0191 232 1926
www.mtra.co.uk
Martin Waxman Associates
020 7253 5500
www.waxman.co.uk
masius
020 7751 1664
www.masius.com
McCann Healthcare Manchester
01625 822599
McCann-Erickson Advertising UK
0131 558 8181
01625 822200
Birmingham 0121 713 3500
Bristol 0117 921 1764
Belfast 028 9033 1044
London 020 7837 3737,
01943 484848
www.mccann.co.uk
Mearns & Gill Advertising
01224 646311
www.mearns-gill.com
Media Junction Advertising Services
020 7460 9206
www.mediajunction.co.uk
Media Reach Advertising
020 7284 2664
www.mediareach.co.uk
MHM Grax LLP
020 7240 7767
www.mhmgrax.com
Michaelides & Bednash
020 7468 1168
www.michaelidesandbednash.com
Miles Calcraft Briginshaw Duffy
020 7073 6900
www.mcbd.co.uk
Minerva
020 7631 6900
www.amvadvance.com
Mitchell Patterson Grime Mitchell
020 7734 8087
www.mpgm.co.uk
Money Syner Communications
020 8939 2900
www.moneysyner.com
Morris Nicholson Cartwright
0161 928 9489
www.mnc-advertising.co.uk

Mostly Media
01935 478238
www.mostlymedia.co.uk
Mother
020 7689 0689
www.motherlondon.com
Mustoes
020 7379 9999
www.mustoes.co.uk
Navigator Blue
02890 246722
www.navigatorblue.com
New Media Industries
020 7436 5000
www.nmigroup.com
Nexus/H UK
01892 517777
www.nexus-h.co.uk
Oakbase
01244 391391
www.oakbase.co.uk
Oasis Communications
020 7288 7000
www.oasiscommunications.com
Ogilvy & Mather
020 7345 3000
www.ogilvy.com
Ogilvy Primary Contact
020 7468 6900
www.primary.co.uk
Paling Walters
020 7840 7444
www.palingwalters.com
Palmer Hargreaves Wallis Tomlinson
01926 452525
Birmingham 0121 233 9494
www.thisiswt.com
Partners BDDH
020 7467 9200
www.partnersbddh.co.uk
Peter Kane & Company
020 7836 4561
www.peterkane.co.uk
Phillipson Ward Longworth Camponi
0113 398 0120
www.pwlc.uk.com
Potter Dow
020 7255 0200
www.potterdow.com
Poulter
0113 285 6500
www.slipstream_studios.com
Profero
0207 700 9960
www.profero.com
Publicis
020 7935 4426
www.publicis.co.uk
Publicity Overload
020 8427 2320
www.puboverload.co.uk
Quiet Storm
020 7907 1140
www.quietstormltd.com
Radford Advertising Marketing
0161 832 8807
www.radfordnet.com
Rainey Kelly Campbell Roalfe/Y&R
020 7404 2700
www.rkcryr.com

Rapier
020 7369 8000
www.rapieruk.com
Raw Media
01305 259444
www.rawmedia.co.uk
RDW Advertising
01642 783523 /790047
www.rdw-advertising.co.uk
Reach Marketing Communications
0116 233 5565
www.reachmarketing.co.uk
Redman Jones & Partners
0161 828 2600
www.redmanjones.co.uk
RH Advertising
01392 219797
www.rhads.co.uk
rhythmm
0117 942 9786
www.rhythmm.co.uk
Richard Davies & Partners
01905 821111
www.rdp.co.uk
Richardson Birkett Communications
020 7323 6468 / 7299 0900
Richardson Carpenter Advertising
01256 353700
www.rca.co.uk
Richardson Pailin & Fallows
020 7420 7992
01274 421606
www.laddersaency.com
Ridge Advertising (Marketing)
01635 551285
01689 858565
River Communications Group
020 8876 7162
www.rivercg.co.uk
Robson Brown Communico
0191 232 2443
Manchester 0161 877 2004
www.robson-brown.co.uk
Rock Kitchen Harris
0116 233 7500
www.rkh.co.uk
Rodgers & Rodgers
01892 549444
www.rodgers.co.uk
Room 29
01604 678970
www.room29.co.uk
Roose
020 7349 6800
www.roose.co.uk
Ross Levenson Harris
020 8390 4611
Rowleys: London
0199 258 7350
www.rowleyslondon.co.uk
RPM3
020 7434 4343
www.rpm3.co.uk
Russell Associates
01767 601200
RZed
020 7436 8747
www.RZed.com
Saatchi & Saatchi
020 7636 5060
www.saatchi-saatchi.com/

Salmon Agency
020 7967 7967
www.thesalmonagency.com
Sass Panayi & Partners
01565 832832
www.puresass.com
Scholz & Friends London
020 7961 4000
www.s-f.com
Seal Group
0121 455 7788
www.sealgroup.co.uk
Senior King Communications Group
020 7734 5855
www.seniorkinggroup.co.uk
Smee's Advertising
020 7486 6644
www.smees.co.uk
SNS Group
01223 393563
01634 671167
www.snsplc.com
Sold Out Advertising
020 7704 0409
Soul
020 7292 5999
www.souladvertising.com
Spirit Advertising
020 7620 6800
www.spiritads.com
Springer & Jacoby UK
020 7863 9700
www.sjsimplicity.co.uk
SPS Advertising
01442 877711
www.spsgroup.co.uk
St Luke's Communications
020 7380 8888
www.stlukes.co.uk
Storm Media Communications
01702 719595
www.storm-media.co.uk
Strathearn Advertising
0131 553 6226
www.strathearnadvertising.co.uk
Strattons
020 7838 5000
www.strattons.com
SWK Communications
020 7637 6800
Symington Company
020 7240 0088
Target Marketing Communications
01242 633100
www.targetgroup.co.uk
Target NMI
020 7462 5800
www.targetnmi.com
TBWA\London
020 7573 6666
www.tbwa.com
Team Saatchi
020 7436 6636
www.saatchi.com
Tech Media Communications
020 7505 8439
Tenalps RMA
01329 221616
www.tenalpsrma.com

TEQUILA\ London
020 7557 6100
www.tequila-uk.com
Three's Company Communications
0121 212 2363
www.threes.co.uk
Union Advertising Agency
0113 220 6850
Edinburgh 0131 625 6000
www.union.co.uk
Unit Communications Group
0161 236 8002
www.unitcomms.co.uk
Vallance Carruthers Coleman Priest
020 7802 5803
www.vccp.com
WAA
0121 321 1411
www.waa.co.uk
Wallace Barnaby & Associates
01534 759807
01481 726052
www.wallaby.co.uk
Walsh Trott Chick Smith
0207 907 1200
www.wtcs.co.uk
Ware Anthony Rust
01223 566212
www.war.uk.com
WCRS
020 7806 5000
www.wcrs.com
WFCA Integrated
01892 511085
www.wfca.co.uk
Wieden & Kennedy
020 7299 7500
www.wklondon.com
Willoughby Stewart Associates
01425 478001
www.wsa.net.uk
Wood Burden Smith & Bergin
020 7107 2500
www.woodburden.co.uk
Woodreed Creative Consultancy
01892 515025
www.woodreed.com
Worth Communications
020 8439 8200
www.worthcommunications.com
Wyatt International
0121 454 8181
www.wyattinternational.com
Young & Rubicam EMEA HQ
020 7387 9366
www.yandr.com

Media agencies

2B on TV
020 7460 9520
www.2bontv.com
Acumen Partnership
020 7440 4300
www.acumenpartners.co.uk
All Response Media
020 7017 1450
www.allresponsemedia.com
Allmond Partnership
020 7557 5858
www.theallmondpartnership.com
AMS Media Group
020 7843 6900
www.amsgroup.co.uk
Austin West Media
020 7278 7878
Avocado Media
01892 750851
www.avocadomedia.co.uk
BBJ Communications
020 7379 9000
www.bbj.co.uk
BJK & E Media
020 7379 8080
BLM Media
020 7437 1317
www.blm-group.com
BrandConnection
020 7676 2850
www.brandconnection.com
Brilliant Independent Media Specialists
0113 394 0000
www.brilliantmedia.co.uk
BWB
01634 220498
Bygraves Bushell Valladares & Sheldon
020 7734 4445
www.bbvs.co.uk
Byrne & Company Media
0113 243 1423
Capital City Media
020 7936 9097
Carat
020 7430 6000
www.carat.com
Carat Business
020 7430 6399
www.carat.co.uk
Carat Insight
020 7430 6340
www.carat.co.uk
Carat International
020 7405 1050
www.carat-int.com
Clilverd Booth Lockett Makin
0117 934 9934
www.cblm.co.uk
Coltman Media Company
020 7930 2516
ComFederation
079 0089 8578
www.comfed.co.uk
CST Group
01273 621393
www.cst-group.com
David Coleman Media
01442 877756

David Wood & Associates
020 7833 3222
www.dwamedia.com
Design Conspiracy
020 7470 8841
www.thedesignconspiracy.com
Eldridge Ranger Advertising
01983 532636
Equinox Communications
020 7580 0186
www.zenithmedia.com
Fairfield Advertising Company
020 8680 9707
Feather Brooksbank
0131 555 2554
Manchester 0161 834 9793
Glasgow 332 3382
www.featherbrooksbank.co.uk
Fox Media Company
01487 815395
www.foxmedia.co.uk
Frontline Media
020 7436 4080
www.frontlinemedia.com
Generation Media
020 7637 1111
www.generationmedia.co.uk
Geoghegan & Company
020 8341 4369
Guy Ellis Media Associates
01932 254025
IM Media (UK)
020 7734 4445
Initiative Media London
020 7663 7000
www.initiativemedia.com
Interaction Media
020 7843 6400
www.interactionmedia.co.uk
Jackie Biggin Media Associates
01621 891200
John Ayling & Associates
020 7439 6070
Jones Britton Breckon Company
020 7557 5851
www.jbbc.co.uk
Just Media
020 7737 8000
www.justmedia.co.uk
Klondike Agency
020 7380 8939
www.klondikeagency.com
M For Media
020 8232 3033
www.matthewpoppy.com
Manning Gottlieb OMD
020 7470 5300
Matters Media
0113 209 4495
London 020 7224 6030
www.mattersmedia.com
Media Associates
01962 771997
www.mediaassociates.co.uk
Media By Design
01892 517151
www.mediabydesign.co.uk
Media Campaign Services
020 7389 0800
www.mediacampaign.co.uk

Media Connections
020 7834 0900
www.media-connections.co.uk
Media Division
0121 454 9929
Media Insight
020 7969 4141
www.mediainsight.com
Media Moguls
020 8902 5575
www.mediamoguls.com
Media Mondiale Network
01264 334419
www.media-mondiale.com
Media Options
020 7734 5855
www.media-options.co.uk
Media Planning Group
020 7393 9000
Media Shop
0141 221 0280
London 020 7766 5000
www.the-media-shop.co.uk
Media Works International
020 7566 5650
www.mediaworksinternational.com
Mediability
01625 441911
www.mediability.co.uk
MediaCom
020 7874 5500
Edinburgh 0131 555 1500
Manchester 0161 839 6600
www.mediacomuk.com
Mediaedge:cia
020 7803 2000
www.mediaedgecia.com
Mediahead Communications
020 7292 4000
www.media-head.com
MediaVest
0191 232 3282
Manchester 0161 228 3909,
International 020 7751 1800,
UK 020 7751 1661
www.musolutions.co.uk
MediaVision
01340 20318
Manchester 0161 838 4444
Mediawise Partnership
020 7419 8800
www.mediawise.co.uk
MindShare
020 7969 4040
www.mindshareworld.com
MJ Media
020 7361 0370
Naked Communications
020 7336 8084
www.nakedcomms.com/
Nutbrown Mann
020 7821 1144
www.nutbrownmann.co.uk
OMD
020 7893 4893
www.omdmedia.com
OMD Connect
020 7893 4893
020 8735 8000
www.omdmedia.com

OMD Gemini
020 7893 4893
www.omdmedia.com
OMD International
020 7908 3400
www.omd.com
OMD UK
020 7893 4893
www.omdmedia.com
Pawson Media
020 7405 9080
PHD Compass
0121 627 5009
London 020 7446 0555
Edinburgh 0113 285 6506
www.phd.co.uk
Piper Agency
020 7610 8585
www.thepiperagency.co.uk
Pure Media Group
020 7861 2525
www.puremediagroup.com
Purely Media
0161 930 9400
www.purelymedia.co.uk
R Media Services
020 7505 8439
Rathbone Media
0870 830 1850
www.rathmedia.com
RCL Media
020 7255 0330
Reactor Media
020 7388 7550
Red Media
020 7437 0633
www.redmedia.co.uk
Response Advertising Media
01423 707100
www.responsemedia.co.uk
Rocket
020 7446 0555
www.phd.co.uk
Sigma Communications
023 8081 3952
Spirit Media Scotland
0131 478 3456
Squires Robertson Gill
020 7389 0808
Starcom Motive Partnership
020 7453 4444
www.starcommedia.com
Stone Media
020 7734 4445
TCS Media North
01625 536795
www.tcsnorth.com
Thomas Media Consultants
01454 412000
www.thomasmedia.co.uk
Total Media
020 7937 3793
www.totalmedia.co.uk
Total Media North
020 7233 8000
0121 523 1144
www.totalmedia.co.uk
TPM (Media Planning & Buying)
0161 839 3527
01675 464982
www.tpmmedia.com

**UK Advertising & Marketing
Services**
01322 228899
www.ukams.co.uk
Unity Three
020 7637 7171
www.unity3.co.uk
Universal Communication
020 7837 3737
www.ucpag.com
Universal McCann EMEA
020 7833 5858
www.universalmccann.com
Universal McCann Manchester
01625 822300
www.mccannmcr.com
Universal McCann UK
020 7833 5858
www.mccann.co.uk
Upward Brown Media
020 7887 0011
www.upwardbrownmedia.com
Walker Media
020 7447 7500
www.walkermedia.com
WWAV Rapp Collins Media
020 8735 8000
www.wwavrcmedia.co.uk
Zed Media
020 7631 2777
ZenithOptimedia UK
020 7224 8500
www.zenithoptimedia.com
Zentropy Partners
020 7554 0500
www.zentropypartners.co.uk

New media agencies

Agency.com
020 7964 8200
www.i-traffic.com
AKQA
020 7494 9200
www.akqa.com
Arnold Interactive
020 7908 2700
www.arnoldinteractive.com
Citigate Online – London
020 8547 1547
www.citigatemc.com
Cocojambo
020 8822 6808
www.cocojambo.com
Digit
020 7684 6769
www.digitlondon.com
Digital Marketing Direct – London
020 7535 9909
www.incepta.co.uk
DNA Consulting
020 7357 0573
www.dna.co.uk
Dowcarter
0131 556 1172
London 020 7887 4588
www.dowcarter.com
Euro RSCG Circle
0117 311 7600
London 020 7959 7500
www.uk.circle.com

Global Beach
020 7384 1188
www.globalbeach.com
glue London
020 7739 2345
www.gluelondon.com
Grey Interactive UK
020 7453 8320
www.greyinteractive.co.uk
Hub Communications Group
020 8560 9222
www.thehub.co.uk
i-level
020 7340 2700
www.i-level.com
Incline Media
020 7239 0200
www.incline.co.uk
itraffic
020 7964 8500
www.itraffic.com
Just 2
020 7737 8000
www.just2.com
Lateral
020 7613 4449
www.lateral.net
**Media.Com – a member of the
Beyond Interactive Network**
020 7874 5500
www.mediacomuk.com
MediaVest IP
020 7751 1661
www.mediavest.co.uk
Outrider (Mediaedge:cia Digital)
013 1478 3456
Manchester 0161 930 9000
London 020 7803 2390
www.outrider.com
Oyster Partners
020 7446 7500
www.oyster.co.uk
Panlogic
020 8948 5511
www.panlogic.co.uk
PHDiQ
020 7446 0555
www.phd.co.uk
Quantum Media London
020 7287 8768
www.quantum-media.co.uk
syzygy UK
020 7460 4080
www.syzygy.net
Tangozebra
020 7535 9850
www.tangozebra.com/
The driver is
01271 323230
www.thedriveris.com
Tribal DDB
020 7262 0011
www.tribalddb.co.uk
Universal McCann Interactive
020 7833 5858
www.universalmccann.com
Wheel
020 7348 1000
www.wheel.co.uk
XM London
020 7724 7228
www.ccgxm.com

Outdoor specialists

Blade
020 7612 1300
International Poster Management
020 7388 1166
www.ipm.co.uk
Meridian Outdoor Advertising
020 7262 1328
www.meridianoutdoor.com
Outdoor Connection
020 7307 9700
www.outdoorconnection.co.uk
Outdoor MediaCom
020 7874 5500
www.mediacom.com
**Portland Outdoor Advertising
Limited**
020 7734 7434
01625 524499
www.portlandoutdoor.com
Poster Publicity
020 7592 3333
North 01423 841400
www.posterpublicity.com
Posterscope In The North
0161 848 8997
www.posterscope.co.uk
Posterscope
020 7336 6363
www.posterscope.co.uk
PSI Advertising
020 7824 1700
www.psiad.com

Direct marketing

Black Cat Agency
020 8332 0722
www.black-cat.co.uk
CBA
01179 303900
London 020 7313 8181
www.cba.co.uk
Clark McKay & Walpole
020 7487 9750
www.clarkmckayandwalpole.com
Claydon Heeley Jones Mason
020 7924 3000
www.chjm.com
Colleagues Direct Marketing
01225 447003
www.colleagues.co.uk
**Craik Jones Watson Mitchell
Voelkel**
020 7734 1650
www.craikjones.co.uk
Cramm Francis Woolf
01252 625151
www.cfw.co.uk
Datamail Direct Advertising
020 7381 0222
www.dda.uk.com
Direct MediaCom
020 7874 5500
www.mediacomuk.com
DMS
01242 584175
www.directmarketing.co.uk

EHS Brann
01285 644744
London 020 7806 7000,
01285 644744
020 7017 1000
Leeds 0113 207 0400
www.ehsbrann.com
EWA Bespoke Communications
01245 492828
www.ewagroup.com
Geoff Howe Direct Red Square
020 8941 7575
www.geoffhowe.com
Harrison Troughton Wunderman
01483 716100
London 020 7611 6333
www.htw.wunderman.com
JDA Group
0113 290 4290
www.jda.co.uk
JUMP – Joined Up Marketing Partnership
01784 704000
www.nowjump.com
LIDA
020 7544 3700
www.lidanet.com
Liquid Communications
020 7201 3555
www.liquidcommunications.co.uk
Marketing & Media Solutions
0208 861 9150
www.mms.uk.com
MBO London
020 7908 7944
01268 419343
www.mbolondon.com
Morgan Kemp & Partners
0161 236 6564
M-S-B&K London
020 7437 5268
www.msbk.co.uk
Navigator Responsive Advertising
0131 556 8002
www.navigator-ra.co.uk
OgilvyOne Worldwide
020 7566 7000
www.ogilvyone.com
Partners Andrews Aldridge
020 7462 1940
www.andrewsaldridge.com
Strata
020 7700 4540
www.stratauk.net
Target Direct Marketing
01242 258700
www.targetdirect.co.uk
TBWA\GGT
020 7439 4282
www.tbwa-ggt.com
TDA
01242 633111
www.tdaltd.com
Response Team
01761 233122
www.theresponseteam.com
Tri-Direct
01256 810656
www.tri-direct.co.uk
Tullo Marshall Warren
020 7349 4000

WWAV Rapp Collins
020 8735 8000
Leeds 0113 222 6300
Edinburgh 0131 553 9444
www.wwavrc.co.uk
Yes Direct Marketing
01889 564 931
www.yesdm.co.uk/
Young Phillips Advertising
01202 298969

Integrated services

141
020 7706 2306
www.141worldwide.com
Arc Integrated Marketing
020 7751 1662
01285 740707
Edinburgh 0131 226 5562
www.arcconnect.co.uk
Archibald Ingall Stretton
020 7467 6100
www.archibaldingallstretton.com
B'lowfish Advertising
020 7487 5588
www.blowfishnet.com
Butterfield Morris Bushell
01582 725454
www.BMB.uk.com
Chemistry Communications Group
020 7736 5355
www.chemistrygroup.co.uk
Desbrow Thompson Chaffe
020 7253 5040
www.d-t-c.co.uk
DraftWorldwide
0131 466 6300
London 020 7323 4586,
020 7589 0800, 020 7863 9773
Edinburgh 0131 662 0600,
01865 884444
www.draftworldwide.com
Exposure Promotions
020 7907 7130
www.exposureltd.com
Feel Agency
020 7359 9600
www.feelagency.com
Haygarth
020 8971 3300
www.haygarth.co.uk
Interfocus Network Limited
020 7376 9000
www.interfocus.co.uk
Joshua Agency
020 7453 7900
www.joshua-agency.co.uk
KLP Euro RSCG
0131 524 1400
London 020 7478 3478
Manchester 0161 236 2399
www.eurorscg.com
Leonardo
020 7591 9991
www.leonardocompany.com
Mercier Gray
020 7420 7900
www.merciergray.com

Open Agency
020 7740 7000
www.openagency.com
Perspectives Red Cell
020 8568 4422
www.perspectivesredcell.com
Proximity London
020 7298 1000
www.proximitylondon.com
Publicis Dialog
020 7935 7744
www.publicis-dialog.co.uk
Pulse Group
020 7288 8000
www.pulsegroup.com
Retail Marketing Partnership
020 7371 5588
www.rmp.co.uk
Sudler & Hennessey
020 7307 7800
www.yr.com
Swordfish Compelling Marketing & Promotion
020 7225 3388
www.swordfish.co.uk
TEQUILA\ Manchester
0161 908 8100
www.tequilamanchester.com
TLG Marketing
01285 650477
www.redtagdm.co.uk
Torre Lazur McCann London
020 7278 5440
TSM (UK)
020 7734 3532
www.tsm-direct.co.uk
WARL Change Behaviour
020 7400 0900
www.warl.com

Sales promotion

CBH Creative Marketing
020 7397 8100
Creative Minds Consultants
020 8418 0047
dunnhumby
020 8832 9222
www.dunnhumby.com
Dynamo Marketing
020 7386 0699
www.dynamo.net.uk
Geoff Howe Marketing Communications
020 8941 7575
www.geoffhowe.com
HH & S
020 7751 8585
www.hhs.co.uk
Odyssey Promotion & Design
01753 631165
www.odyssey-pd.com
REL Field Marketing
01344 418383
www.relfm.com
Simpson Mahoney Parrock
01892 548282
www.smp.uk.com
Teamwork Marketing
01904 486666
www.teamwork-marketing.co.uk

Marketing Store Worldwide
020 7745 2100
01675 467404
Leeds 0113 246 8266
Edinburgh 0131 226 2221
www.themarketingstore.com
Reef
020 7012 6000
www.reeflondon.com
Triangle Communications
020 7637 0322
www.trianglecommunications.co.uk

Creative consultancies

BMB Advertising
020 7240 4133
Carter Gosling
01225 465415
Clemmow Hornby Inge
020 7025 8989
www.chiadvertising.com
Clinic
020 7421 9333
www.clinic.co.uk
Cunning Stunts Communications
0207 691 0077
www.cunningstunts.net
David Pearson Advertising
020 7323 0343
Family
0131 272 2704
www.familyadvertising.co.uk
Lucid Graphics
020 7373 1663
www.lucidgraphics.co.uk
Merle
0141 242 1800
www.merleagency.com
Mortimer Whittaker O'Sullivan
020 7379 8844
www.mwo.co.uk
Orckid Design & Marketing
01784 426999
www.orckid.com
Sheppard Day
020 7821 2222
www.sheppard-day.com
Value Engineers
01494 680999
www.thevalueengineers.com
Toybox
020 7836 0002
www.toybox.biz
Village Design & Communications
01275 333777
www.villagedesign.co.uk
Volcano
020 7379 7706
www.livevolcano.co.uk

PR agencies

AD Communications
01372 464470
info@adcommunications.co.uk
www.adcommunications.co.uk
Attenborough Associates
020 7734 4455
info@attenborough.net
www.attenborough.net
August One
020 8434 5555
ukmedia&consultinggroup@
  augustone.com
www.augustone.com
Aurelia Public Relations
020 7351 2227
www.aurelia-london.com
AxiCom
020 8600 4600
lyle.closs@axicom.com
www.axicom.com
Barclay Stratton
020 8877 8600
reception@barclaystratton.co.uk
www.barclaystratton.com
Barrett Dixon Bell
0161 925 4700
info@bdb.co.uk
www.bdb.co.uk
Binns & Co Public Relations
020 7786 9600
vicki.lever@binnspr.co.uk
www.binnspr.co.uk
Bite Communications UK
020 8741 1123
elaine.omara@bitepr.com
www.bitepr.com
Bliss Lancaster Euro RSCG
020 7497 3001
www.blisslancaster.com
BMB Reputation Managers
01582 406004
susanna.orchard@thebmbgroup.com
www.thebmbgroup.com
Brodeur Worldwide
020 7298 7070
www.brodeuruk.com
Buffalo Communications
020 7292 8680
info@buffalo.co.uk
www.buffalo.co.uk
Burson-Marsteller
020 7831 6262
www.bm.com
Capital MS&L
020 7878 3181
www.capitalmsl.co.uk
Carat
020 7430 6000
mediainfo@carat.co.uk
www.carat.co.uk
Carrot Communications
020 7953 4010
richard.houghton@
  carrotcomms.co.uk
www.carrotcomms.co.uk
Chambers Cox PR
020 7631 5414
claire@ccpr.co.uk
www.ccpr.co.uk

Chameleon PR
020 7721 7875
info@chameleonmkg.com
www.chameleonmkg.com
Cherton Enterprise
028 9065 4007
staff@cherton.co.uk
www.cherton.co.uk
CIB
01372 371800
www.cibcommunications.co.uk
Citigate 1920
028 9039 5500
info@citigateni.co.uk
www.citigateni.co.uk
Citigate Communications
020 7535 9999
Birmingham 0121 456 3199
shefina.azam@citigatec.co.uk
www.citigatecommunications.co.uk
Citigate Public Affairs
020 7838 4800
Edinburgh 0131 200 6045
Cardiff 0292 050 4683
www.citigatepa.com
Citigate Smarts
0141 222 2040
info@citigatesmarts.co.uk
www.citigatesmarts.co.uk
Clareville Communications
020 7736 4022
mail@clareville.co.uk
www.clareville.co.uk
Clear
020 7432 2500
clear@clearco.co.uk
www.clearco.co.uk
Cohn & Wolfe
020 7331 5300
info@cohnwolfe.co.uk
www.cohnwolfe.co.uk
Colette Hill Associates
020 7622 8252
cha@chapr.co.uk
www.chapr.co.uk
Communication Group
020 7630 1411
enquiries@
  thecommunicationgroup.co.uk
www.TheCommunicationGroup.co.uk
Communique PR
0161 228 6677
London 020 7300 6300
info@communiquepr.co.uk
www.communiquepr.co.uk
Companycare Communications
0118 939 5900
info@companycare.com
www.companycare.com
Consolidated Communications
020 7287 2087
consol@consol.co.uk
www.consol.co.uk
Counsel Public Relations
020 7402 2272
www.counsel-huntsworth.com
Countrywide Porter Novelli
020 7853 2222
Edinburgh 0131 470 3400
Leeds 0113 381 5100
Banbury 01295 224400
www.cpn.co.uk

Cow PR
020 7360 6061
www.cowpr.com
Cubitt Consulting
020 7367 5100
USA 00 1 212 898 1021
www.cubitt.com
Dialogue Agency
020 8607 0340
enquiry@dialogueagency.com
www.dialogueagency.com
Edelman
020 7344 1200
central@edelman.com
www.edelman.com
Edson Evers LLP
01785 255146
info@edsonevers.com
www.edsonevers.com
EHPR (Elizabeth Hindmarch Public Relations)
01753 842017
London 020 7432 0545
info@ehpr.co.uk
www.ehpr.co.uk
Eulogy!
020 7927 9999
pr@eulogy.co.uk
www.eulogy.co.uk
EuroPR Group
020 8879 3033
info@europrgroup.com
www.europrgroup.com
Firefly Communications
020 7386 1400
Edinburgh 0131 553 0150
web@fireflycomms.com
www.fireflycomms.com
Flagship Group
020 7886 8440
www.flagshipgroup.co.uk
Fleishman-Hillard (UK)
020 7306 9000
www.fleishman.com
Focus PR Limited (Incorporating Silk Public Relations)
020 7432 9432
www.focuspr.co.uk
Garnett Keeler Public Relations
020 8399 1184
pr@garnett-keeler.com
www.garnett-keeler.com
GCI Healthcare
020 7072 4100
www.gciuk.com/healthcare
GMX Communications
020 7808 7976
Southampton 023 8071 3000
Manchester 0161 234 0040
info@gmxpa.com
www.gmxcommunications.com
Golin/Harris Weber
020 7067 0600
www.golinharrisweber.com
Golley Slater & Partners
020 8744 2630
londonagency@golleyslater.co.uk
www.golleyslater.com
Good Relations
020 7861 3030
info@goodrelations.co.uk
www.goodrelations.co.uk

Gough Allen Stanley
01527 579555
gough@gough.co.uk
www.gough.co.uk
Grant Butler Coomber
020 8322 1922
www.gbc.co.uk
Grayling
020 7255 1100
Warwickshire 01564 797200
Bristol 0117 922 7799
info@uk.grayling.com
www.grayling.com
Grayling Political Strategy
0131 558 8719
Cardiff 029 2050 4028
info@uk.grayling.com
www.grayling.com
Hallmark Public Relations
01962 563850
www.hallmarkpr.com
Harrison Cowley
020 7404 6777
Birmingham 0121 236 7532
Bristol 0117 929 2311
Cardiff 029 2034 4717
Edinburgh 0131 556 6600
Leeds 0113 244 2424
Manchester 0161 839 5666
Southampton 02380 337237
danielep@harrisoncowley.com
www.harrisoncowley.com
Haslimann Taylor
0121 355 3446
info@haslimanntaylor.com
www.haslimanntaylor.com
Hatch Public Affairs
020 7898 9372
Glasgow 0141 333 6440
Edinburgh 0131 220 1188
sarah.wright@hatch-group.com
www.hatch-group.com
Hatch-Group
020 7471 6867
www.hatch-group.com
Haygarth
020 8971 3300
www.haygarth.co.uk
Herald Communications
020 7340 3600
www.heraldcommunications.com
Hill & Knowlton
020 7413 3000
www.hillandknowlton.co.uk
Hotwire PR
020 7608 2500
France 00 3301 46918460,
Germany 00 49069 2566930
info@hotwirepr.com
www.hotwirepr.com
icas Public Relations
020 7240 2400
www.icas.co.uk
Impact Agency
020 7580 1770
mail@impactagency.co.uk
JBP Public Relations
0117 907 3400
pr@jbp.co.uk
www.jbp.co.uk

Kaizo (incorporating Beer Davies)
020 7580 8852
matthew.estwick@kaizo.net
www.kaizo.net
Kavanagh Communications
01932 866010
info@kavanaghcommunications.com
www.kavanaghcommunications.com
Kelso Consulting
020 7729 7595
pr@kelsopr.com
www.kelsopr.com
Ketchum
020 7611 3500
www.ketchum.com
Lansons Communications
020 7490 8828
pr@landsons.com
www.landsons.com
Leader Communications
01564 796200
mail@leader.co.uk
www.leader.co.uk
Leedex Euro RSCG
020 7497 3001
Manchester 0161 236 2277
Edinburgh 0131 524 1500
Leeds 0113 242 4999
www.leedex.com
Lexis Public Relations
020 7908 6488
intray@lexispr.com
www.lexispr.com
MacLaurin
020 7371 3333
Glasgow 0141 333 6440
Edinburgh 0131 220 5826
Birmingham 0845 072 6700
www.maclaurin.com
Manning Selvage & Lee
020 7878 3030
www.mslpr.co.uk
Mantra Public Relations
020 797 7800
www.mantra-pr.com
Mason Williams
020 7534 6080
Manchester 0161 273 5923
www.mason-williams.co.uk
McCann-Erickson Public Relations
0121 713 3500
www.mccann.com
Midnight Communications
0870 458 4182
London 0870 458 4181
enquiries@midnight.co.uk
www.midnight.co.uk
Munro & Forster Communications
020 7815 3900
contact@munroforster.com
www.munroforster.com
Nelson Bostock Communications
020 7229 4400
info@nelsonbostock.com
www.nelsonbostock.com
Nexus Communications Group Limited
020 7373 4537
info@nexuspr.com
www.nexuspr.com

Ogilvy Public Relations Worldwide
020 7309 1000
pr@uk.ogilvypr.com
www.ogilvypr.com

Partners Group
01904 610077
www.partners-group.co.uk

Penrose Financial
020 7786 4881
penrose@penrose.co.uk
www.penrose.co.uk

Phipps Public Relations
020 7759 7400
info@phippspr.co.uk
www.phippspr.com

Piranhakid
020 7413 3198
jason.gallucci@piranhakid.com
www.piranhakid.com

Portfolio Communications
020 7240 6959
www.portfoliocomms.com

PPS (Local & Regional)
020 7629 7377
Almondsbury 01454 275630
Birmingham 0121 767 1863
Manchester 0161 832 2139
Edinburgh 0131 226 1951
info@ppsgroup.co.uk
www.ppsgroup.co.uk

PR21 UK
020 7436 4060
www.pr21.com

Prospero Financial
020 7898 9380
www.prospero-financial.com

Ptarmigan Consultants
0113 242 1155
info@ptarmiganpr.co.uk
www.ptarmiganpr.co.uk

Public Relations Consultants Association
020 7233 6026
pressoffice@prca.org.uk
www.prca.org.uk

QBO Bell Pottinger
020 7861 2424
info@qbo-bellpottinger.co.uk
www.qbo-bellpottinger.co.uk

Radiator PR
020 7404 8264
steph@radiatorpr.com
www.radiatorpr.com

RED Consultancy
020 7465 7700
Nottingham 0115 852 4331
red@redconsultancy.com
www.redconsultancy.com

Regester Larkin
020 7831 3839
enquiries@regesterlarkin.com
www.regesterlarkin.com

Republic
020 7379 5000
info@republicpr.com
www.republicpr.com

Revolver Communications
020 7251 5599
enquiries@revolvercomms.com
www.revolvercomms.com

Roger Staton Associates
01628 487222
mail@rsagroup.com
www.rsagroup.com

Rowland Communications
020 7462 7766
info@rowlands.co.uk
www.rowlandcomms.co.uk

SCPR
020 7298 6530
www.huntsworth.com

Shine Communications
020 7553 3333
brilliance@shinecom.com
www.shineon-line.com

Shire Health London
020 7313 6300
info@shirehealthlondon.com
www.shirehealthlondon.com

Staniforth
020 7940 7999
Manchester 0161 274 0100
london@staniforth.co.uk
www.staniforth.co.uk

Starfish Communications
020 7323 2121
reception@star-fish.net
www.star-fish.net

Storm Communications
020 7240 2444
Bucks 01494 670444
www.stormcom.co.uk

Strategy Communications
0117 983 6400
enquiries@strategycomms.co.uk
www.strategycomms.co.uk

Target Public Relations
01242 633100
info@targetgroup.co.uk
www.targetgroup.co.uk

Text 100
020 8996 4100
sejal.parekh@text100.co.uk
www.text100.com

Twelve Consultancy
020 7631 0206
www.twelvepr.co.uk

Warman Group
0121 605 1111
enquiries@warmangroup.com
www.warmangroup.com

Weber Shandwick
020 7067 0000
Aberdeen 01224 806600
Belfast 028 9076 1007
Edinburgh 0131 556 6649
Glasgow 0141 333 0557
Manchester 0161 238 9400
wswukceo@webershandwick.com
www.webershandwick.co.uk

Westbury Communications
020 7751 9170

WhiteOaks Consultancy
01252 727313
London 020 7734 4945
Paris 00 33158 183575
comms@whiteoaks.co.uk
www.whiteoaks.co.uk

Advertising Association
020 7828 2771
aa@adassoc.org.uk
www.adassoc.org.uk
Federation of 25 trade bodies

Advertising Standards Authority (ASA)
020 7580 5555
enquiries@asa.org.uk
www.asa.org.uk
Independent, self-regulatory body

Broadcast Advertising Clearance Centre (BACC)
020 7843 8265
contact@bacc.org.uk
www.bacc.org.uk
Checks TV commercials against code of practice

Chartered Institute of Marketing
01628 427500
membership@cim.co.uk
www.cim.co.uk

European Advertising Standards Alliance
+32 2 513 7806
library@easa-alliance.org
www.easa-alliance.org

Incorporated Society of British Advertisers
020 7499 7502
info@isba.org.uk
www.isba.org.uk

Institute of Practitioners in Advertising
020 7235 7020
www.ipa.co.uk
Trade association

Institute of Public Relations
020 7253 5151 and
020 7553 3772 (press)
info@ipr.org.uk
www.ipr.org.uk

Market Research Society
020 7490 4911
info@mrs.org.uk
www.marketresearch.org.uk

Nielsen/NetRatings
01865 742742
www.nielsen-netratings.com

PRJobSeek.com
020 8894 5739
www.prjobseek.com

World Federation of Advertisers (WFA)
+32 2 502 5740
info@worldadvertisers.org
www.worldadvertisers.org

Contacts : Advertising & PR

Advertisers Annual
Hollis Publishing, Harlequin House
7 High Street, Teddington TW11 8EL
020 8943 3138
adannual@hollis-pr.co.uk
www.hollis-pr.com
Contacts listings, Annual. Editor:
Beverley Brock

Brand Strategy
Centaur Communications
St Giles House, 50 Poland Street
London W1F 7AX
020 7970 4000
elen.lewis@centaur.co.uk
www.mad.co.uk/bs
Monthly. Editor: Elen Lewis

Campaign
Haymarket Business Publications
174 Hammersmith Road
London W6 7JP
020 8943 5000
www.brandrepublic.com
Weekly. Editor: Caroline Marshall

Contact
Haymarket Marketing Business
Publications
174 Hammersmith Road
London W6 7JP
020 8267 4496
directories@haynet.com
www.contact-directory.com
Press and PR contacts. Annual

Creative Review
Centaur Communications
St Giles House, 50 Poland Street
London W1F 7AX
020 7970 4000
patrick.burgoyne@centaur.co.uk
www.creativereview.co.uk
Monthly. Editor: Patrick Burgoyne

Design Week
Centaur Communications
St Giles House, 50 Poland Street
London W1F 7AX
020 7970 6666
lyndark@centaur.co.uk
www.designweek.co.uk
Weekly. Editor: Lynda Relph-Knight

Editors Media Directories
Waymaker, Chess House
34 Germain Street
Chesham HP5 1SJ
0870 736 0010
editors@waymaker.co.uk
www.editorsmediadirectories.com
Contact listings, Annual.
Editor: Clare Redman

Financial Press Facts
Waymaker, Chess House
34 Germain Street
Chesham HP5 1SJ
0870 736 0010
fpf@waymaker.co.uk
www.financialpressfacts.co.uk
Contact listings. Quarterly.
Editor: Clare Redman

Hollis UK PR Annual
Hollis Publishing, Harlequin House
7 High Street, Teddington TW11 8EL
020 8977 7711
prannual@hollis-pr.co.uk
www.hollis-pr.co.uk
Press and PR contacts. Annual.
Editor: Sarah Hughes

Marketing
Haymarket Marketing and Media
Publications
174 Hammersmith Road
London W6 7JP
020 8267 5000
marketing@haynet.com
www.marketingmagazine.co.uk
Weekly. Editor: Craig Smith

Marketing Direct
Haymarket Business Publishing
174 Hammersmith Road
London W6 7JP
020 8267 5000
www.mxdirect.co.uk
Monthly. Editor: Holly Acland

Marketing Week
Centaur Communications
St Giles House, 50 Poland Street
London W1F 7AX
020 7970 4000
mw.editorial@centaur.co.uk
www.marketing-week.co.uk
Weekly. Editor: Stuart Smith

Media Week
Quantum Business Media
Quantum House
19 Scarbrook Road
Croydon CR9 1LX
020 8565 4326
mweeked@mediaweek.co.uk
www.mediaweek.co.uk
Weekly. Editor: Tim Burrowes
Covers media agencies, media sales
and marketers

PR Week
Haymarket Professional Publications
174 Hammersmith Road
London W6 7JP
020 8267 4429
prweek@haynet.com
www.prweek.com
Weekly. Editor: Kate Nicholas

shots
Emap Information
33–39 Bowling Green Lane
London EC1R 0DA
020 7505 8000
lyndy.stout@shots.net
www.shots.net
International advertising, 6pa.
Editor: Lyndy Stout

Agents

The more creative your role in the media, the greater the chance that there is an agent to represent you. The best authors, scriptwriters, actors, directors and presenters will always be in demand, but the wannabes far exceed the talented. So the agent's role is to be the middle man: to find the talent, sell it, and make a profit into the bargain.

There are more than 200 literary agents in the UK, of whom about 75 are members of the association of authors' agents; while the agents' association has more than 400 entertainment agencies among its members. Agencies can range from large multinational organisations such as PFD or ICM, the world-leading talent agency, which this year opened a literary agency in London, to tiny operations managed by just one overworked soul. The best agents will have an eye for a talent, a wide range of industry contacts, and above all, a hard head for a business deal.

Literary agents

It is increasingly difficult to acquire the services of a good literary agent; but then, it is harder still to sell a novel or a script without one. A good agent will not only advise an author in an editorial capacity, at least in order to make a script more saleable, they will also be able to sell writing for much more than the writer could obtain on their own. In particular, agents aim to separate out rights for different media (such as paperback, film, television, multimedia and novelisation in the case of a script), for different markets (such as potentially lucrative US rights) and even, in this post-Potter world, for merchandising. Thus they hope to earn more for the writer than if all the rights were sold at once. In return, they charge a commission, which normally ranges from 10% to 15%.

Agents complain that they are so busy trying to sell their existing authors that they have little time to find new talent. The result is that many agents, at one point or another, are either not accepting new writers or only accepting writers recommended to them by people they know and trust. Those that do receive unsolicited manuscripts are deluged: some agents receive up to 50 a day, which will usually mean the agent is looking for a reason to reject them.

The advice to an author seeking any agent, then, is to make life as easy as possible for them. Don't send work to an agent who doesn't accept unsolicited manuscripts, or who doesn't handle the genre you write in; you'll only be wasting your time and theirs. Check the agent's website to find the authors they already handle: this will help you target to agents who you know will like the kind of work you write. Spend a few moments finding out in what form the agent prefers to see a manuscript: whether complete, or in the form of a few chapters plus synopsis, and how they like the type to be set (normally use a simple font such as Times New

Roman, on decent-quality white paper, double-spaced to allow room for notes; don't forget to enclose a stamped addressed envelope). Asked when they like to see a manuscript, many agents will helpfully reply that the best time is when you've improved it as best you can – make of that what you will. Finally, if an agent offers to represent you, trust your instinct: an agent who likes you and your writing will be your best advocate. To put it another way, the better your relationship with your agent, the more likely you are to sell your work.

Finally, don't lose hope. One day it could be your script that is being sold by a top agent like Andrew Wylie or John Brockman for a seven-figure sum at the Frankfurt book fair. It won't be, but it could.

Talent agents

Talent agencies have a reputation – cemented in films such as Little Voice and Some Like It Hot – as a hard-headed, wheeler-dealing bunch. In the real world they come in a vast variety of forms: specialisms include television presenters, voice-overs for radio ads, directors of short films, actors, singers, make-up artists, cruise ship entertainers, lookalikes and of course models. Many agencies will handle some but not all of these, even though they work under the broad umbrella of "entertainment". Agents employed by artists charge about 15% commission, rising to 20% for musicians and models in particular; or they may act as talent-brokers, earning their commission as a mark-up charged to the event hirer. There are few hard and fast rules – but the Agents' Association does have a code of conduct; artists should never, for example, pay a fee to join an agency's books. Other bodies include the Personal Managers' Association, which represents actors' agents; and the Association of Voiceover Agents.

So you wanna be a star? **Lisa O'Carroll**

Media agents are not powerful and they are the first to admit it. They don't make TV programmes, publish books, or guarantee polished performances on Newsnight or Radio 4. And they certainly don't pay well. But if you are talented and you need to stand out from the crowd, engaging an agent can be one way of grabbing the attention of that producer, editor, or researcher, who could make you a modest living or even a million.

For those starting out in their careers, hiring an agent is an expensive route to fame and fortune – typically they take a 12.5% to 15% cut of your salary or fee. Unscrupulous ones will even try and take a slice of your current earnings, something that you should absolutely refuse. Trying to persuade an agent to take you on board can also be difficult, particularly if you are untried or untested. Even those with years of experience may not fit the bill – too old, too ugly, or just too high maintenance – and can be callously cast aside because they aren't worth the agent's time.

Anyone who has touted a TV or book script around the myriad of literary agents will know what a soul-destroying experience it is to get yet one Dear John letter after another. That said, media agents are a must for those with experience or expertise. Only the most successful in their trade can afford private salary and shares negotiations with the top boss; the likes of Sir Trevor McDonald or John Humphrys, for example.

But even those in the upper reaches of their careers have a use for agents – Jeremy Paxman has one, as do Desmond Lynam, Cilla Black and John Motson. At this level an agent's services are likely to be all-encompassing: everything from after-dinner bookings, handling the press (a full-time job in a crisis) to pay negotiations and the delicate subject of advice on hair, make-up and wardrobe.

But while an agent can make most of their money from the fees of their better-earning clients, they will typically have dozens of presenters on their books and should be just as keen to give a leg-up to those on the lower rungs of the ladder.

Good agents will know all the top executives in TV, radio and newspapers and will work day and night to push their clients. They will know, before the presenter, which programmes are being planned and what the controller of any channel or producer of any programme is looking for. Most will also have a good relationship with newspapers, which is valuable for PR and gaining and maintaining a high profile, thereby maximising your market window.

With the explosion of TV stations, there is also a growing demand for pundits and a parallel blossoming in the number of agents willing to deal with experts in their field, who have no media experience. Household names such as Sir Roy Strong, Robert Winston, Simon Schama and Dr David Starkey all have agents. But there is also a plethora of lesser known archaeologists, architects, gardeners and designers, who have found agents indispensable, particularly at the start of their career.

For those who suddenly find themselves thrust into the spotlight, reality TV stars are a warning not to take the first agent you find. Ask for advice from producers, directors and all those who have more experience. Listen to what the public relations people say and, although it may not seem like a good idea at the time, journalists will also have valuable observations on individuals.

There are thousands of agents operating in London – picking the right one could paralyse or kick-start your career.

Lisa O'Carroll edits MediaGuardian.co.uk

Agents

Agents Contacts

Associations

Agents Association
54 Keyes House, Dolphin Square
London SW1V 3NA
020 7834 0515
association@agents-uk.com
www.agents-uk.com

Association of Authors' Agents
c/o Curtis Brown Group , 4th Floor
Haymarket House, 28/29 Haymarket
London SW1Y 4SP
020 7396 6600
cb@curtisbrown.co.uk
www.agentsassoc.co.uk

The Personal Managers' Association
1 Summer Road, East Molesey
Surrey KT8 9LX
020 8398 9796
info@thepma.com

▶▶ LITERARY AGENTS, see p 191

Agents

Alexander Personal Management
PO Box 834, Hemel Hempstead
Hertfordshire HP3 9ZP
01442 252907
apm@apmassociates.net
www.apmassociates.net

Amanda Howard Associates
21 Berwick Street
London W1F 0PZ
020 7287 9277
mail@amanadahowardassociates
.co.uk
www.amanadahowardassociates
.co.uk

Andrew Manson
(Americans only)
288 Munster Road
London SW6 6BQ
020 7386 9158
post@andrewmanson.com
www.talentroom.com

Another Tongue Voices
10–11 D'arley, London W1F 8DS
020 7494 0300
info@anothertongue.com

Arlington Enterprises
1–3 Charlotte Street
London W1T 1RD
020 7580 0702
info@arlington-enterprises.co.uk
www.arlingtonenterprises.co.uk

Billy Marsh Associates
174–178 North Gower Street
London NW1 2NB
020 7388 6858
talent@billymarsh.co.uk

Bryan Drew
Mezzanine, Quadrant House
80–82 Regent Street
London W1B 5AU
020 7437 2293
bryan@bryandrew.com

Calypso Voices
25–26 Poland Street
London W1F 8QN
020 7734 6415
calypso@calypsovoices.com
www.calypsovoices.com

Cantor Wise Representation
At Take three Management
110 Gloucester Avenue
Primrose Hill, London NW1 8HX
020 7209 3777
melanie@take3management.com

Castaway
7 Garrick Street
London WC2E 9AR
020 7240 2345
sheila@castaway.org.uk
www.castaway.org.uk

Celebrity Management
12 Nottingham Place
London W1M 5NE
020 7224 5050
info@celebrity.co.uk
www.celebrity.co.uk

Chase Personal Management
Model Plan 4th Floor
4 Golden Square
London WA16 6PR
020 7287 8444
sue@sammon.fsnet.co.uk
www.modelplan.co.uk

Comedy Club
165 Peckham Rye
London SE15 3HZ
020 7732 3434
comedyclub@cwcom.net

Conway Van Gelder
(Kate Plumpton)
3rd Floor, 18–21 Jermyn Street
London SW1Y 6HP
020 7287 1070
kate@conwayvg.co.uk

Crawfords
16 Brook Street, London W1S 1BB
020 7629 6464
cr@wfords.com

Curtis Brown Group
Jacquie Drewe, Julian Beynon
Haymarket House, 28–29 Haymarket
London SW1Y 4SP
020 7396 6600
cb@curtisbrown.co.uk
www.curtisbrown.co.uk

David Anthony Promotions
PO Box 286, Warrington
Cheshire WA2 8GA
01925 632496
dave@davewarwick.co.uk
www.davewarwick.co.uk

Downes Presenters Agency
96 Broadway, Bexleyheath
Kent DA6 7DE
020 8304 0541
downes@presentersagency.com
www.presentersagency.co.uk

Dynamic FX
(Magical effect designers & performers)
Regent House, 291 Kirkdale
London SE26 4QD
020 8659 8130
mail@dynamicfx.co.uk
http://dynamicfx.co.uk

Eric Glass
25 Ladbroke Crescent
Notting Hill, London W11 1PS
020 7229 9500
eglass@aol.com

Evans O'Brien
115 Humber Road
London SE3 7LW
020 8293 7077
info@evansobrien.co.uk
www.evansobrien.co.uk

Excellent Talent Company
53 Goodge Street
London W1T 1TG
020 7636 1636
ruth@excellentvoice.co.uk
www.excellentvoice.co.uk

FBI Agency
PO Box 250, Leeds LS1 2AZ
07050 222747
casting@fbi-agency.ltd.uk
www.fbi-agency.ltd.uk

Foreign Versions
Bakerloo Chambers
304 Edgware Road
London W2 1DY
020 7723 5744
info@foreignversions.co.uk
www.Foreignversions.com

Fox Artist Management
Concorde House
101 Shepherds Bush Road
London W6 7LP
020 7602 8822
fox.artist@btinternet.com

Gordon & French
12–13 Poland Street
London W1F 8QB
020 7734 4818
mail@gordonandfrench.net

Hobson's Voices
62 Chiswick High Road
London W4 1SY
020 8995 3628
singers@hobson-international.com
www.hobsons-international.com

ICM Artists (London)
4–6 Soho Square, London W1D 3PZ
020 7432 0800
infoUK@icmtalent.com
www.icmtalent.com

J. Gurnett Personal Management
2 New Kings Road
London SW6 4SA
020 7736 7828
mail@jgpm.co.uk
www.jgpm.co.uk

Jacque Evans Management
Top Floor Suite, 14 Holmesley Road
London SE23 1PJ
020 8699 1202
jacque@jem.demon.co.uk
www.jaqueevans.com

James Grant Management
Syon Lodge, 201 London Road
Isleworth, Middlesex TW7 5BH
020 8232 4100
www.jamesgrant.co.uk

Jaymedia
171 Sandbach Road
Lawton Heath End
Church Lawton, Cheshire ST7 3RA
01270 884453
media@jaymedia.co.uk
www.jaymedia.co.uk

Jeremy Hicks Associates
11–12 Tottenham Mews
London W1T 4AG
020 7636 8008
hicksworld@aol.com
www.jeremyhicks.com

JLA (Jeremy Lee Associates)
4 Stratford Place, London W1C 1AT
020 7907 2800
talk@jla.co.uk
www.jla.co.uk

John Miles Organisation
Cadbury Camp Lane
Clapton-in-Gordano
Bristol BS20 7SB
01275 854675
john@johnmiles.org.uk
www.johnmiles.org.uk

John Noel Management
2nd Floor, 10A Belmont Street
London NW1 8HH
020 7428 8400
john@johnnoel.com

Julie Ivelaw-Chapman
The Chase, Chaseside Close
Cheddington, Beds LU7 0SA
01296 662441
jic@collectorsworldwide.co.uk

KBJ Management
7 Soho Street, London W1D 3DQ
020 7434 6767
candida@kbjmgt.co.uk

Knight Ayton Management
114 St Martin's Lane
London WC2N 4BE
020 7836 5333
info@knightayton.co.uk
www.knightayton.co.uk

Lip Service
60–66 Wardour Street
London W1F 0TA
020 7734 3393
bookings@lipservice.co.uk
www.lipservice.co.uk

Liz Hobbs Group
1st floor, 65 London Road
Newark, Notts NG24 1RZ
08700 702702
info@lizhobbsgroup.com
www.lizhobbsgroup.com

Mark Summer Management & Agency
9 Hansard Mews, London W14 2BJ
0870 443 5621
info@marksummers.com

Markham & Froggatt
4 Windmill Street, London W1T 2HZ
020 7636 4412
fiona@markhamfroggatt.co.uk
http://markhamfroggatt.com

McLean-Williams Management
212 Piccadilly, London W1J 9HG
020 7917 2806
alex@mclean-williams.com

MPC Entertainment
MPC House, 15–16 Maple Mews
London NW6 5UZ
020 7624 1184
mpc@mpce.com
www.mpce.com

NCI Management
51 Queen Anne Street
London W1G 9HS
020 7224 3960
nicola@nci-management.com
http://w-management.com

Noel Gay Artists
19 Denmark Street
London WC2H 8NA
020 7836 3941
mail@noelgay.com
www.noelgay.com

Off The Kerb Productions
3rd Floor, Hammer House
113–117 Wardour Street
London W1F 0UN
020 7437 0607
offthekerb@aol.com
www.offthekerb.co.uk
22 Thornhill Crescent
London N1 1BJ
info@offthekerb.co.uk
Tel: 020 7700 4477

PHA Casting
Tanzaro House
Ardwick Green North
Manchester M12 6FZ
0161 273 4444
info@pha-agency.co.uk
www.pha-agency.co.uk

Princess Talent Management
Newcombe House
45 Notting Hill Gate
London W11 3LQ
020 7243 5100
talent@princess.uk.com
www.princess.uk.com

PVA Management
Hallow Park, Hallow
Worcester WR2 6PG
01905 640663
clients@pva.co.uk

QDOS
8 King Street, Covent Garden
London WC2E 8HN
020 7240 5052
info@qdosentertainment.plc.uk
www.qdosentertainment.plc.uk

Qvoice
8 King Street, Covent Garden
London WC2E 8HN
020 7420 6825
info@qvoice.co.uk
www.qvoice.co.uk

Rabbit Vocal Management
2nd Floor, 18 Broadwick Street
London W1F 8HS
020 7287 6466
info@rabbit.uk.net
www.rabbit.uk.net

Contacts : Agents

235

Rhubarb
Bakerloo Chambers
304 Edgware Road
London W2 1DY
020 7724 1300
enquiries@rhubarb.co.uk
www.rhubarb.co.uk

Richard Stone Partnership
2 Henrietta Street
London WC2E 8PS
020 7497 0849
all@richstonepart.co.uk

RK Commercials
205 Chudleigh Road
London SE4 1EG
020 8690 6542
mail@rkcommercials.com
www.rkcommercials.com

Roseman Organisation
51 Queen Anne Street
London W1G 9HS
020 8742 0552
info@therosemanorganisation.co.uk
www.therosemanorganisation.co.uk

Roxane Vacca Voices
73 Beak Street, London W1F 9SR
020 7734 8085
mail@roxanevaccavoices.com
www.roxanevaccavoices.com

Ruby Talent
Apartment 8, Goldcrest Building
1 Lexington Street
London W1F 9TA
020 7486 4500
tara@ruby-talent.co.uk

Sally Hope Associates
108 Leonard Street
London EC2A 4XS
020 7613 5353
casting@sallyhope.biz

Sara Cameron Management
At Take three Management
110 Gloucester Avenue
Primrose Hill, London NW1 8HX
020 7209 3777
sara@take3management.com
www.take3management.com

Shining Management
82C Shirland Road
London W9 2EQ
020 7286 6092
info@shiningvoices.com
www.shiningvoices.com

Silver Fox Artists Management
8–18 Rampart Street
London E1 2LA
020 7791 2952
enquiries@silverfoxartist.co.uk
www.silverfoxartist.co.uk

Speak
140 Devonshire Road
Chiswick, London W4 2AW
020 8742 1001
info@speak..uk
www.speak..uk

Speak-Easy
1 Dairy Yard, High Street
Market Harborough
Leics LE16 7NL
0870 013 5126
enquiries@speak-easy.co.uk
www.speak-easy.co.uk

Storm Artists Management
4th Floor, 6–10 Lexington Street
London W1F 0LB
020 7437 4313
info@stormartists.co.uk

Susi Earnshaw Management
5 Brook Place, Barnet
Herts EN5 2DL
020 8441 5010
casting@susiearnshaw.co.uk
www.susiearnshaw.co.uk

Susy Wootton Voices
75 Shelly Street, Kingsley
Northampton NN2 7HZ
0870 765 9660
suzy@suzywoottonvoices
www.suzywoottonvoices.com

Take Three Management
110 Gloucester Avenue
Primrose Hill, London NW1 8HX
020 7209 3777
info@take3management.com

Talking Heads
88–90 Crawford Street
London W1H 2BS
020 7258 6161
voices@talkingheadsvoices.co.uk
www.talkingheadsvoices.co.uk

Tongue & Groove
3 Stevenson Square
Manchester M1 1DN
0161 228 2469
info@tongueandgroove.co.uk
www.tongueandgroove.co.uk

Unique Management Group
Beaumont House
Kensington Village, Avonmore Road
London W14 8TS
020 7605 1100
celebrities@uniquegroup.co.uk
www.uniquecoms.com

Venture Artistes
38 Great Queen Street
London WC2B 5AA
07000 402001
venture-artistes@msn.com

Vincent Shaw Associates
51 Byron Road, London E17 4SN
020 8509 2211
info@vincentshaw.com
www.vincentshaw.com

Vocal Point
25 Denmark Street
London WC2H 8NJ
020 7419 0700
enquiries@vocalpoint.net
www.vocalpoint.net

Voice & Script International
Aradco House, 132 Cleveland St
London W1T 6AB
020 7692 7700
info@vsi.tv
www.vsi.tv

Voice Shop
Bakerloo Chambers
304 Edgware Road
London W2 1DY
020 7402 3966
info@voice-shop.co.uk
www.voice-shop.co.uk

Voice Squad
62 Blenheim Gardens
London NW2 4NT
020 8450 4451
bookem@voicesquad.com
www.voicesquad.com

Voicebank
The Barracks, 76 Irishtown Road
Dublin 4
00 353 1 6687234
voicebank@voicebank.ie
www.voicebank.ie

Voicecall
67A Gondar Gardens
Fortune Green, London NW6 1EP
020 7209 1064
voicecall@blueyonder.co.uk
www.voicecall-online.co.uk

Whatever Artists Management
1 York Street, London W1U 6PA
020 7487 3111
wam@agents-uk.com
www.wamshow.biz

Yakety Yak
8 Bloomsbury Square
London WC1A 2NE
020 7430 2600
info@yaketyyak.co.uk
www.yaketyyak.co.uk

Media law

sk the public which professions they respect the least and you can be sure that – after politicians – lawyers and journalists will be down there somewhere. But when the two come into contact, that doesn't stop them captivating the public's imagination. High-profile cases in the past year have included Catherine Zeta-Jones' legal battle against Hello!, supermodel Naomi Campbell's action against the Daily Mirror, and DJ Chris Evans' fight against his former employers at Virgin Radio, to name but a few. The first two cases were important not only because of the reams of newsprint they inevitably occupied, but also because of their potential impact on the legal balance between privacy and freedom of expression.

"I now intend to celebrate this win with some fava beans and a nice chianti"

Daily Mirror editor Piers Morgan
after the Naomi Campbell case
(October 2002)

Privacy: Campbell, Zeta-Jones

The past year has been marked by a debate among MPs and the media over whether a "privacy law" is needed in the UK. As a look at the panel on page 244 shows, many of the highest-profile cases of the year have involved privacy, not least the cases involving Zeta-Jones, Campbell and DJ Sara Cox. Because two competing principles are at issue – the right to privacy, as enshrined in Article 8 of the European convention on human rights, and the right to freedom of expression, as enshrined in Article 10 – it has been argued that new laws are needed to cut through the mess. But in the Campbell and Zeta-Jones cases, judges felt that existing confidentiality legislation was sufficient to make a decision, leading others to suggest that a privacy law is unnecessary. A culture select committee into privacy and media intrusion, headed by Labour MP Gerald Kaufman, recommended privacy legislation to prevent a "piecemeal, ad hoc" development of the law.

The first case was the Daily Mirror's appeal victory against Campbell. The newspaper had in February 2001 printed details of the model's drug addiction, alongside a picture of her leaving a Narcotics Anonymous meeting. The original judge, Mr Justice Morland, awarded Campbell £3,500 damages in March 2002, saying the paper had exposed the model's addiction legitimately but breached her confidentiality by printing details of the treatment. But eight months later the high court upheld the newspaper's appeal, saying the facts were in the public interest. Campbell was left with £750,000 costs, although in December 2002 she applied for permission to appeal to the House of Lords.

The Zeta-Jones case was more complex. The actress had sold to OK! magazine the rights to her wedding to actor Michael Douglas, but a photographer working for rival Hello! gained entrance surreptitiously and took pictures at the event. (Zeta-Jones sought an injunction stopping Hello! from printing the snaps, but it produced a statement signed by the Marquesa de Varela saying she had sold the pictures – a claim

Media law

later shown to be false – and went to press.) Zeta-Jones and OK! sued Hello! for a total of £2.25m, winning on four out of 13 points – notably that Hello! had breached the actress' confidence by printing the pictures. The judge partly based his ruling on a broad interpretation of the press complaints commission code, saying that if long-lens photography was against the code, then so was surreptitious short-range photography. He pointed out that the ruling was not based on any breach of privacy; but nonetheless warned that if no legislation was passed to remedy any gap in the law, then further legal developments would most likely be made by judges.

The result is some uncertainty. For a start, neither case particularly affects the man in the street: both Campbell and Zeta-Jones have made a career from being in the public eye, and it is a widely held view that their right to privacy might thus somehow be compromised. In any case both judges relied on existing confidentiality law, and the only difference was that in the Campbell case there was held to be a public interest in publishing the information.

There are two interesting codas. First, Cox won a £50,000 settlement from the People after it published nude pictures of her and her husband on their honeymoon – though the case did not come to judgment, it increased pressure on the press complaints commission by demonstrating that complainants can get better results through recourse to law. Second, London's Evening Standard newspaper reported the Zeta-Jones verdict with the headline "Zeta-Jones loses privacy claim". Richard Desmond, the owner of OK! – who also plans to launch a free paper to compete with the Standard in London – responded by taking the Standard to the PCC; but was rejected on the grounds that the PCC does not adjudicate on disputes between rival publishers. It's a small world.

Contempt of court

In March 2003 the attorney general, Lord Goldsmith, warned editors to pay more attention to the potential of being in contempt of court. His comments followed widespread and sometimes sensationalist coverage of the deaths in Soham last year of two 10-year-old girls, Holly Wells and Jessica Chapman. Lord Goldsmith said: "If a trial cannot take place because of prejudicial publicity then justice is denied to victims and the public." Nevertheless, several months later the Soham trial went ahead. It was argued that the coverage in the case of the Soham murders was not prejudicial, coming as it did some months before the trial began.

Writing more generally, John Battle – a barrister and head of compliance at ITN – condemned in MediaGuardian what he called the "creeping encroachment" on what journalists can report in court. "Rarely does a day go by," he wrote, "without new court orders and new types of court order arriving on news desks. Many of these orders are unprecedented in their breadth and restrict what are bread-and-butter areas of court reporting – the names and addresses of the accused, the charges, photographs of the defendants and court sketches. It is a worrying development when a criminal court hearing can take place and no one can report that it has taken place. This has happened."

Protection of sources: the Interbrew case

The Guardian – along with Reuters, the Independent, the Financial Times and the Times – was involved in an extraordinary legal fight with Belgian brewer Interbrew, in an effort to protect the identity of a source. All five news organisations had printed a story, based on a leaked document from an unidentified source, saying Interbrew was about to launch a takeover of a South African brewer. Interbrew sued for return of the document and won, with a judge ruling that the leaker was trying to "rig the market", and that public interest in Interbrew's right to identify the leak outweighed that in the journalists' right to protect their source. After the House of Lords refused to hear an appeal, Interbrew threatened to sequester the Guardian's assets because it refused to comply with the order to hand over the document; amid the political backlash that followed, the brewer made a tactical withdrawal and referred the case to the financial services authority, the powerful financial watchdog. The news organisations announced in December 2002 their intention to take the case to the European court of human rights.

Chequebook journalism

With the establishment of Ofcom, the press complaints commission has come under pressure to make self-regulation work more effectively or lose some if its powers. Accordingly, in March 2003 – and after months of saying it would do no such thing – the commission added to its code an outright ban on payments to witnesses in criminal trials. The then lord chancellor, Lord Irvine, had raised the issue after payments to witnesses in trials involving murderer Rosemary West, acquitted schoolteacher Amy Gehring, and disgraced pop star Gary Glitter.

In a further development, Sun editor Rebekah Wade made the startling revelation to the culture select committee that News International titles had paid police officers for information. After the hearing Alison Clark, the director of corporate affairs at the company, told reporters: "It is not company practice to pay police for information."

The News of the World's investigative journalism methods also came under scrutiny when the trial of men alleged to have plotted to kidnap Victoria Beckham collapsed. The crown prosecution service said it could no longer offer evidence, because its main witness had been paid £10,000 by the News of the World. But in July 2003, the Guardian learned that the press complaints commission would clear the tabloid of breaching its code.

Internet law

The confusing areas of law on the internet continue to be clarified – slowly. A law commission report in December 2002, in particular, called on the government to protect internet service providers from libel allegations in the UK. As it stands the law pressurises ISPs to remove sites as soon as they are told that the material on them may be defamatory – but this could threaten freedom of expression, commissioners said. The commission said ISPs could be exempted from liability, as in the US, or allowed an extended version of the defence of "innocent dissemination".

In the same month, however, an Australian court allowed a Melbourne mining boss to sue Dow Jones in Australia over an article in the online version of a magazine originally published in the US – a country where free speech is better protected in law. The global implications remain uncertain.

Further reading

■ MediaGuardian.co.uk
media.guardian.co.uk/medialaw

■ Books
McNae's Essential Law for Journalists LCJ MCNAE, BUTTERWORTHS 2001

Media law

A privacy law is on its way **Peter Preston**

The conundrum grows no easier to unravel. Is there a made-in-Britain privacy law? Or is it still a figment of the imagination for media solicitors and barristers (starved of their accustomed funds by a continuing dearth of fat libel cases)? Some judges – like Mr Justice Morland in the matter of the Mirror, Ms Naomi Campbell and her drug clinic visits – think such a law exists. Others, like Lord Phillips in the court of appeal, resoundingly disagree: "Provided that publication of particular confidential information is justifiable in the public interest, the journalist must be given reasonable latitude as to the manner in which that information is conveyed to the public." The government, like the top end of the judiciary, rather thinks that Article 10 of the European convention on human rights (the public right-to-know one) trumps Article 8 (the privacy one). But nothing here is straightforward.

When Catherine Zeta-Jones and Michael Douglas sued Hello! magazine for taking unauthorised pictures of their wedding reception (the authorised version having been already sold to Richard Desmond's OK! magazine) and thus despoiling the privacy of an event in one of New York's plushest hotels, there was general hilarity and disbelief. Surely, they could not be serious? But along came good old British commercial law to rescue the litigious happy couple. Their wedding, apparently, was a valuable trade asset flourishing under the umbrella protection of commercial confidence. And if that wasn't enough, the Data Protection Act also applied. Perhaps there was no law of privacy, according to Mr Justice Lindsay; but perhaps he, in turn, was wrong about that. When the People and disc jockey Sara Cox finally locked horns over some long-lens snaps of a honeymooning Ms Cox splashing naked in a hot tub, the paper settled for £50,000 damages out of court.

Nobody quite knew why – or what paying up really meant. But the general assumption was that the case – one where the commission had already investigated and negotiated a settlement – was much influenced by that prior PCC intervention. The commission

AP/Alastair Grant

Catherine Zeta-Jones and Michael Douglas: at court over unauthorised wedding pictures in Hello! magazine

---

■ John Leslie: Trial by media

As John Leslie stood on the steps of Southwark crown court with his family on July 31 2003, it marked the end of a nightmare year for the former This Morning presenter.

Leslie had listened as sexual assault charges against him, brought after a complaint by an unidentified woman, were dropped.

But for Leslie, the real trial had happened 10 months before, when he lost his job and his reputation in the pages of the tabloid press.

It had all started with Ulrika Jonsson. In a much-hyped autobiography – serialised in the Daily Mail in October 2002 – the Swedish television presenter said she had been date-raped 15 years earlier. The assailant, she said, was "an acquaintance".

Days of speculation followed. In a TV interview with Jonsson, Jonathan Ross said the man at the centre of the allegations was a "TV presenter". Jonsson neither confirmed nor denied the statement. Within days, one name was on every journalist's lips; it did not, at that stage, appear in print.

All that changed on October 23, when Channel 5 inadvertently named Leslie. That day the Evening Standard and the Edinburgh Evening News repeated it.

What happened next was perhaps predictable. As Jonsson remained silent, tabloid newspapers – eager for every salacious detail – raked over Leslie's past. Ever more lurid allegations surfaced; tabloids enjoyed circulation rises; by the following Wednesday, Leslie had been sacked as presenter of This Morning.

The press assault was such that Simon Kelner, editor of the Independent, writing in the Spectator, accused his rivals of "bringing shame" on the journalistic profession. "His career as a television presenter is, we are told, in triumphant tones, in ruins. No defence, no cross-examination;

doesn't prevent complainants going to law subsequently; there is no legal waiver. But there is also something of a Catch 22 here. Because the government has, in effect, asked the courts to give primacy in privacy matters to the PCC and its editors' code, this means that an adverse PCC finding against a paper will weigh heavily in any later legal proceedings. Where the commission leads, the courts will follow – a rule of thumb which already operates more onerously for broadcasters, whose statutory codes effectively create a privacy law for TV and radio. They seek it here, they seek it there; they don't always find it – but it's on its way. And what will the tabloid press do then, poor things?

Probably what it seems to be doing in the other visceral controversy of the moment – newspaper payments to witnesses and potential witnesses in high-profile trials. That is, carry on more or less regardless. The last real lord chancellor, Lord Irvine, infuriated by what he saw as the tainting of justice, tried to introduce a law to ban all such payments – but the press and its PCC talked him out of it in return for a dramatic tightening of the code. Not the end of the affair. The News of the World paid £10,000 to an informant in the Posh and Becks "kidnap" case and saw the crown prosecution service pull out on the first day of the trial, crying tainted justice; a second case featuring an East 17 pop star and drugs went west, too. There seemed to be all manner of trouble brewing – trouble much exacerbated by a select committee for culture,

media and sport report which found little for anyone's comfort and called for a privacy law.

So while libel – curiously shrivelled by a judicial shrinkage in damages awards and the continuing impact of the Aitken and Archer perjuries – may be largely in abeyance, gathering dust as public interest defences for newspapers grow tentatively stronger, there is much law heading in the other direction. Whatever became of the Freedom of Information Act, still lost in the backwash of 9/11? The Criminal Justice Act and Courts Act sought to lift the mesh of restrictions on court reporting, but in fact made it rather more complex. Ofcom, the new "light touch" all-purpose regulator, gathered some heavy boots on cross-media ownership in the Lords. The attorney general, after the Soham murders, was hotter and stronger than ever on possible contempts of court. The probability that a newspaper, which unwittingly published something resulting in the abortion of a trial, could be landed with all the costs, grew. After Rebekah Wade's evidence to the select committee, the press faced the baroque demand that something already against the law – payment to police for inside tips – should also be banned by a self-regulatory code, in a unique tangle of belts and braces. The lawyers may not quite have got what they want on privacy yet. But there's no sign of them going out of business.

Peter Preston is a columnist and editorial director of Guardian Media Group

Media law

the verdict from judges Yelland, Morgan and Dacre is guilty as charged."

One woman, who had already been to the press, then went to the police. On December 5, Leslie was questioned for four hours at Belgravia police station. The following June – by which time Leslie had struck a deal to tell his story in the Daily Express – he was charged with two counts of indecent assault.

That day, Leslie stood on the steps of Forest Gate police station, east London, and protested his innocence in public. He had another six weeks to wait before it would be confirmed in court.

The Guardian/Sean Smith

John Leslie: flanked by his parents and girlfriend Abby Titmuss

October 2002
Novelist Jeffrey Archer's prison diaries are serialised in the Daily Mail, causing public controversy and an investigation by the prison service.

October 2002
Two MPs table an early day motion condemning Associated Newspapers for paying up to £100,000 for an interview with Nadia Abrahams, a South African woman who accused football manager Sir Alex Ferguson of assaulting her. Police had decided not to prosecute.

November 2002
Former Liverpool goalkeeper Bruce Grobbelaar is left owing £1m in legal costs after winning derisory £1 libel damages against the Sun. The newspaper had failed to prove that Grobbelaar had let in goals to fix matches, law lords said, but Mr Grobbelaar had acted in a way in which no decent or honest footballer would behave and that any right-thinking person would condemn.

November 2002
Daily Mirror wins high court appeal against £3,500 damages awarded to supermodel Naomi Campbell for breach of confidentiality. The court rules that information about model's Narcotics Anonymous meeting was in the public interest, leaving Ms Campbell with £750,000 costs.

November 2002
Lawyers acting for footballer David Beckham say a gossip website – believed to be Popbitch – agreed to remove rumours about him after they started circulating by email.

December 2002
War correspondents should be given a limited exemption from being compelled to testify, says the UN war crimes tribunal in the Hague.

January 2003
DJ Sara Cox wins an injunction against a French picture agency banning it from reprinting nude photographs of her and her husband on their honeymoon in the Seychelles – pictures which originally appeared in the People. Cox says she will sue for breach of privacy.

January 2003
The Sunday Telegraph is forced to print a letter by Mohamed Al Fayed on its letters page, saying it had waged a "vendetta" against the Harrods and Fulham FC boss.

March 2003
The Jersey Evening Post wins a 15-month battle to report on court proceedings involving bribes allegedly received by the Qatar foreign minister, Sheikh Hamad bin Jassim bin Jabor al Thani, from arms contractors. A police investigation against the sheikh was dropped in June 2002, and he continues to deny any wrongdoing.

April 2003: Major Charles Ingram, his wife Diana and lecturer Tecwen Whittock are given suspended jail sentences after conspiring to cheat their way to the £1m prize on the ITV quiz show, Who Wants to Be a Millionaire?

April 2003
Catherine Zeta-Jones wins a partial success against the publishers of Hello! for taking surreptitious pictures of her wedding. The judge says her confidentiality was breached, but refuses to rule on breach of privacy.

May 2003
The convicted child killer Mary Bell and her daughter win lifelong anonymity at the high court.

June 2003
Sara Cox and her husband win £50,000 settlement from the People after it published nude pictures of them on their honeymoon.

June 2003
Trial of men alleged to have plotted to kidnap Victoria Beckham collapses, after the crown prosecution service says it can no longer offer evidence because the main witness was paid £10,000 by the News of the World.

June 2003
Controversial anti-war MP George Galloway issues high court libel proceedings against the Daily Telegraph over a claim that he was in the pay of Saddam Hussein.

June 2003
Former DJ Chris Evans loses high court claim against Virgin Radio for damages and £8.6m in shares. Judge rules that Virgin is entitled to damages.

July 2003
Evans agrees to pay £7m in costs and damages to SMG, owners of Virgin Radio.

Media law Contacts

Media law firms

A&L Goodbody
Augustine House, 6a Austin Friars
London EC2N 2HA
020 7382 0800
info@algoodbody.com
www.algoodbody.ie

Aaron & Partners
5–7 Grosvenor Court
Foregate Street, Chester
Cheshire CH1 1HG
01244 405555
peteabbott@aaronandpartners.com
www.aaronandpartners.com
Full range of corporate legal services, dispute resolution and advice for business

Adlex Solicitors
22 Belsize Park Gardens
London NW3 4LH
020 7483 4455
adamt@adlexsolicitors.co.uk
www.adlexsolicitors.co.uk

Akin Gump Strauss Hauer & Feld
Citypoint, Level 32
One Ropemaker Street
London EC2Y 9AW
020 7012 9600
londoninfo@akingump.com
www.akingump.com

Allen & Overy
One New Change
London EC4M 9QQ
020 7330 3000
mcarter-jones@ts-p.co.uk
www.allenovery.com

Arnold & Porter
Tower 42, 25 Old Broad Street
London EC2N 1HQ
020 7786 6100
www.arnoldporter.com

Ashurst Morris Crisp
Broadwalk House
5 Appold Street, London EC2A 2HA
020 7638 1111
enquiries@ashursts.com
www.ashursts.com

Astburys
Bexin House, 3 St. Andrews Place
Southover Road, Lewes
East Sussex BN7 1UP
01273 897522
jastbury@astburys-law.co.uk
www.astburys-law.co.uk

Badhams Law
8 Bedford Park, Croydon
Surrey CR0 2AP
020 8688 3030
mail@badhams.net
www.badhams.net

Baily Gibson
30 High Street, High Wycombe
Buckinghamshire HP11 2AG
01494 442661
wycombe@bailygibson.co.uk
www.bailygibson.co.uk

Baker & Mckenzie
100 New Bridge Street
London EC4V 6JA
020 7919 1000
info@bakernet.com
www.bakernet.com

Beachcroft Wansbroughs
100 Fetter Lane
London EC4A 1BN
020 7242 1011
info@bwlaw.co.uk
www.bwlaw.co.uk

Beale & Company
Garrick House
27–32 King Street, Covent Garden
London WC2E 8JB
020 7240 3474
reception@beale-law.com
www.beale-law.com

Berwin Leighton Paisner
Adelaide House
London EC4R 9HA
020 7760 1000
info@blplaw.com
www.blplaw.com

Beswicks
Head Office, 50 Broad Street
Stoke-on-Trent
Staffordshire ST1 4JB
01782 205000
Stoke-on-Trent 01782 812228
nicola.quinlan@beswicks.com
www.thepotterieshasit.co.uk
      /beswicks/

Bevan Ashford
Head Office, 35–37 Colston Avenue
Bristol, Avon BS1 4TT
0117 923 0111
Birmingham 0121 634 5000
info@bevanashford.co.uk
www.bevanashford.co.uk

Bevan Ashford
Alpha Tower, Queensway
Birmingham B1 1TT
0121 634 5000
info@bevanashford.co.uk
www.bevanashford.co.uk

Bird & Bird
90 Fetter Lane, London EC4A 1JP
020 7415 6000
london@twobirds.com
www.twobirds.com

Blair & Co
Queens House
55–56 Lincoln's Inn Fields
London WC2A 3LJ
020 7400 3002
mclegal@marks-clerk.com
www.marks-clerk.com

Blake Lapthorn Linnell
Holbrook House
14 Great Queen Street
London WC2B 5DG
020 7430 1709
Oxford 01865 248607
post@blakelapthorn.co.uk
www.blakelapthorn.co.uk

BM Nyman & Co
181 Creighton Avenue
London N2 9BN
020 8365 3060
bernie.nyman@iname.com
Publishing law

Bond Pearce
Oceana House
39/49 Commercial Road
Southampton
Hampshire SO15 1GA
0870 120 0000
Bristol 0117 929 9197
Plymouth 01752 266633
srichardson@bondpearce.com
www.bondpearce.com

Boyes Turner
Abbots House, Abbey Street
Reading, Berkshire RG1 3BD
0118 959 7711
mail@boyesturner.com
www.boyesturner.co.uk

BP Collins Solicitors
Collins House, 32–38 Station Road
Gerrards Cross
Buckinghamshire SL9 8EL
01753 889995
enquiries@bpcollins.co.uk
www.bpcollins.co.uk

Bracher Rawlins
180 Fleet Street, London EC4A 2HG
020 7404 9400
info@bracherrawlins.co.uk
www.bracherrawlins.com

Briffa
Business Design Centre
Upper Street, Islington
London N1 0QH
020 7288 6003
info@briffa.com
www.briffa.com

Brightley Commercial
Lower Landrine, Mitchell
Newquay, Cornwall TR8 5BB
01872 519087
robert@brightley.com
www.brightley.com
Music business agreements and advice on music copyright

Bristows
3 Lincoln's Inn Fields
London WC2A 3AA
020 7400 8000
info@bristows.com
www.bristows.com

Brooke North
Crown House
81–89 Great George Street
Leeds, West Yorkshire LS1 3BR
0113 283 2100
contact@brookenorth.co.uk
www.brookenorth.co.uk

Browne Jacobson
44 Castle Gate, Nottingham
Nottinghamshire NG1 7BJ
0115 976 6000
info@brownejacobson.com
www.brownejacobson.com

Burges Salmon
Holbrook House
14 Great Queen Street
London WC2B 5DG
020 7405 4343
www.burges-salmon.co.uk

Cains Advocates Limited
15–19 Athol Street
Douglas, Isle Of Man IM1 1LB
01624 638300
law@cains.co.im
www.cains.co.im

Campbell Chambers
25 Hatton Garden
London EC1N 8BQ
020 7691 8777
info@campbellchambers.com
www.campbellchambers.com

Campbell Hooper
35 Old Queen Street
London SW1H 9JD
020 7222 9070
ch@campbellhooper.com
www.campbellhooper.com

Charles Lucas & Marshall
1 Wood Street, Swindon SN1 4AN
01793 511055
ask@clmsolicitors.co.uk
www.clmsolicitors.co.uk

Charles Russell
8–10 New Fetter Lane
London EC4A 1RS
020 7203 5000
Guildford 01483 252525
enquiry@cr-law.co.uk
www.charlesrussell.co.uk

Clarke Willmott
Equity House
73–75 Millbrook Road East
Southampton
Hampshire SO15 1RJ
023 8048 3200
Bristol 0117 941 6600
info@clarkewillmott.com
www.clarkewillmott.com
Sports and media law – contact:
Linda Gregory on 023 80483232.
email: lgregory@clarkewillmott.com

Class Law
1 Great Cumberland Place
London W1H 8DQ
020 7724 2526
mail@classlaw.co.uk
www.classlaw.co.uk

Clifford Chance Limited Liability
10 Upper Bank Street, Canary Wharf
London E14 5JJ
020 7006 1000
info@cliffordchance.com
www.cliffordchance.com

Clifford Miller
Burnhill Business Centre
50 Burnhill Road, Beckenham
Kent BR3 3LA
020 8663 0044
mail@millercompany.demon.co.uk
www.cliffordmiller.com

Clintons
55 Drury Lane, Covent Garden
London WC2B 5RZ
020 7379 6080
info@clintons.co.uk
www.clintons.co.uk

Cluff Hodge & Co
49 Queen Victoria Street
London EC4N 4SA
020 7489 0242
lawyers@cluffhodge.co.uk
www.cluffhodge.co.uk

Cobbetts
Ship Canal House, 98 King Street
Manchester, Lancashire M2 4WB
0161 833 3333
robert.roper@cobbetts.co.uk
www.cobbetts.co.uk

James Collins
43 Linton Street, Islington
London N1 7AN
020 7359 5852
james@collinssolicitor.demon.co.uk
www.collinssolicitor.co.uk

Collyer-Bristow
4 Bedford Row, London WC1R 4DF
020 7242 7363
cblaw@collyerbristow.com
www.collyerbristow.com

Comptons
90–92 Parkway, Regent's Park
London NW1 7AN
020 7485 0888
Advice@comptons.co.uk
www.comptons.co.uk

Constant & Constant
Sea Containers House
20 Upper Ground, London SE1 9QT
020 7261 0006
twoconstants@constantlaw.com
www.constantlaw.com

Couchman Harrington Associates
8 Bloomsbury Square
London WC1A 2LQ
020 7611 9660
enquiries@chass.co.uk
www.chass.co.uk

Coudert Brothers
60 Cannon Street
London EC4N 6JP
020 7248 3000
london@coudert.com
www.coudert.com

Courts & Co
15 Wimpole Street
London W1G 9SY
020 7637 1651
law@courtsandco.com
www.courtsandco.com

Covington & Burling – Registered Foreign Lawyers & Solicitors – London
265 Strand, London WC2R 1BH
020 7067 2000
KWimmer@cov.com
www.cov.com

Cripps Harries Hall
Wallside House
12 Mount Ephraim Road
Tunbridge Wells, Kent TN1 1EG
01892 515121
reception@crippslaw.com
www.e-cripps.co.uk

Crosse & Crosse Incorp Jonathan H Ogley & Co
14 Southernhay West
Exeter, Devon EX1 1PL
01392 258451
mail@crosse.co.uk
www.crosse.co.uk

Cuff Roberts
100 Old Hall Street, Liverpool
Merseyside L3 9TD
0151 237 7777
email@cuffroberts.co.uk
www.cuffroberts.co.uk

Cumberland Ellis Peirs (Incorporating Barth & Partners)
Columbia House
69 Aldwych, London WC2B 4RW
020 7242 0422
suzanneeva@cep-law.co.uk
www.cep-law.co.uk

Davenport Lyons
1 Old Burlington Street
London W1S 3NL
020 7468 2600
dl@davenportlyons.com
www.davenportlyons.com

David Price Solicitors and Advocates
5 Great James Street
London WC1N 3DB
020 7916 9911
enquiries@lawyers-media.com
www.lawyers-media.com

Dawsons
2 New Square, Lincoln's Inn
London WC2A 3RZ
020 7421 4800
info@dawsons-legal.com
www.dawsons-legal.com

Dean Marsh & Co
20 Bowling Green Lane
London EC1R 0BD
020 7553 4400
info@deanmarsh.com
www.deanmarsh.com

Denton Wilde Sapte
Five Chancery Lane, Clifford's Inn
London EC4A 1BU
020 7242 1212
020 7246 7000
info@dentonwildesapte.com
www.dentonwildesapte.com

Dickinson Dees
St Ann's Wharf, 112 Quayside
Newcastle Upon Tyne
Tyne And Wear NE99 1SB
0191 279 9000
marketing@dickinson-dees.com
www.dickinson-dees.com

DLA
3 Noble Street, London EC2V 7EE
08700 111111
www.dla-law.co.uk

DMA Legal
14 Coach & Horses Yard
Savile Row, London W1S 2EJ
020 7534 5850
info@dmalegal.com
www.dmalegal.com

DMH Solicitors
100 Queens Road, Brighton
East Sussex BN1 3YB
01273 329833
james.quarmby@dmh.co.uk
www.dmh.co.uk

Dorsey & Whitney
21 Wilson Street
London EC2M 2TD
020 7588 0800
london@dorsey.com
www.dorseylaw.com

DWF
5 Castle Street
Liverpool, Merseyside L2 4XE
0151 236 6226
Manchester 0161 228 3702
enquiries@dwf.co.uk
www.dwf.co.uk

Dyer Burdett & Co
64 West Street, Havant
Hampshire PO9 1PA
023 9249 2472
mail@dyerburdett.com
www.dyerburdett.com

Edwards Duthie
517–519 Barking Road
London E13 8PT
020 8514 9000
c&c_enq@edwardsduthie.com
www.edwardsduthie.com

Edwin Coe
2 Stone Buildings
London WC2A 3TH
020 7691 4000
info@edwincoe.com
www.edwincoe.com

EMW Law
Seckloe House
101 North 13th Street
Central Milton Keynes
Buckinghamshire MK9 3NX
01908 399600
paulb@emwlaw.com
www.emwlaw.co.uk

Eversheds LLP
Senator House
85 Queen Victoria Street
London EC4V 4JL
020 7919 4500
Manchester 0161 831 8888
Cardiff 02920 471147
www.eversheds.com

Farrer & Co
66 Lincoln's Inn Fields
London WC2A 3LH
020 7242 2022
enquiries@farrer.co.uk
www.farrer.co.uk

Fennemores
200 Silbury Boulevard
Central Milton Keynes
Buckinghamshire MK9 1LL
01908 678241
info@fennemores.co.uk
www.fennemores.co.uk

Ferdinand Kelly
21 Bennetts Hill, Birmingham
West Midlands B2 5QP
0121 643 5228
ferdinand-kelly@dial.pipex.com
www.ferdinandkelly.co.uk

Field Fisher Waterhouse
35 Vine Street, London EC3N 2AA
020 7861 4000
info@ffwlaw.com
www.ffwlaw.com

Fieldings Porter
Silverwell House, 32 Silverwell Street
Bolton, Lancashire BL1 1PT
01204 387742
info@fpsols.co.uk
www.fieldingsporter.co.uk

Finers Stephens Innocent
179 Great Portland Street
London W1W 5LS
020 7323 4000
mstephens@fsilaw.co.uk
www.finersstephensinnocent.co.uk

Fladgate Fielder
25 North Row, London W1K 6DJ
020 7323 4747
fladgate@fladgate.com
www.fladgate.com

Foot Anstey Sargent
Pynes Hill, Rydon Lane
Exeter, Devon EX2 5AZ
01392 685351
tony.jaffa@foot-ansteys.co.uk
www.foot-ansteys.co.uk
        /businessadvice/media
*Specialist media, commercial, and
employment advice to newspapers,
publishers and ISPs*

Forshaws
1 Palmyra Square, Warrington
Cheshire WA1 1BZ
01925 230000
info@forshaws.co.uk
www.forshaws.co.uk

Forsters
67 Grosvenor Street
London W1K 3JN
020 7863 8333
mail@forsters.co.uk
www.forsters.co.uk

Fox Williams
10 Dominion Street
London EC2M 2EE
020 7628 2000
mail@foxwilliams.com
www.foxwilliams.com

Freethcartwright
Willoughby House
20 Low Pavement, Nottingham
Nottinghamshire NG1 7EA
0115 936 9369
Leicester 0116 201 4000
postmaster@freethcartwright.co.uk
www.freethcartwright.co.uk

Freshfields Bruckhaus Deringer
65 Fleet Street, London EC4Y 1HS
020 7936 4000
www.freshfields.com

Fuglers
70 Charlotte Street
London W1T 4QG
020 7323 6450
admin@fuglers.co.uk
www.fuglers.co.uk

Gamlins
31–37 Russell Road
Rhyl, Clwyd LL18 3DB
01745 343500
www.gamlins.co.uk

Gateley Wareing
14 Regent Street, Nottingham
Nottinghamshire NG1 5BQ
0115 983 8200
gsmith@gateleywareing.com
www.gateleywareing.co.uk

George Davies
Fountain Court, 68 Fountain Street
Manchester, Lancashire M2 2FB
0161 236 8992
mail@georgedavies.co.uk
www.georgedavies.co.uk

Gersten & Nixon
National House
60–66 Wardour Street
London W1F 0TA
020 7439 3961
law@gernix.co.uk
www.gernix.co.uk
*All aspects of media and
entertainment law*

Goodman Derrick
90 Fetter Lane, London EC4A 1PT
020 7404 0606
pherbert@gdlaw.co.uk
www.gdlaw.co.uk

Gordon Dadds
80 Brook Street, Mayfair
London W1K 5DD
020 7493 6151
cormaccawley@gordondadds.com
www.gordondadds.com

Gray & Co
Habib House, 9 Stevenson Square,
3rd Floor, Piccadilly, Manchester
Lancashire M1 1DB
0161 237 3360
grayco@grayand.co.uk
www.grayand.co.uk

Greenwoods
Monkstone House, City Road
Peterborough
Cambridgeshire PE1 1JE
01733 887700
showard@greenwoods.co.uk
www.greenwoods.co.uk

Grundberg Mocatta Rakison
4th Floor Imperial House
15–19 Kingsway
London WC2B 6UN
020 7632 1600
post@gmrlaw.com
www.grundbergmocatta.com/

Gsc Solicitors
31–32 Ely Place, London EC1N 6TD
020 7822 2222
Srsheikh@gsc-solicitors.co.uk
www.gsc-solicitors.co.uk

H2O
The Media Centre
3–8 Carburton Street
London W1W 5AJ
020 7886 0740
h2o@h2o-law.com
www.h2o-law.com

Hale And Dorr
Alder Castle House
10 Noble Street, London EC2V 7QJ
020 7645 2400
webmaster@haledorr.com
www.bhd.com

Halliwell Landau
75 King William Street
30 Brown Street
London EC4N 7BE
020 7929 1900
info@halliwells.co.uk
www.halliwells.co.uk

Hamlins
Roxburghe House
273–287 Regent Street
London W1B 2AD
020 7355 6000
admin@hamlins.co.uk
www.hamlins.co.uk

Hammonds
7 Devonshire Square
Cutlers Gardens
London EC2M 4YH
0870 839 0000
enquiries@ hammonds.com
www.hammondsuddardsedge.com

Harbottle & Lewis
Hanover House, 14 Hanover Square
London W1S 1HP
020 7667 5000
rporter@harbottle.co.uk
www.harbottle.co.uk

Harrison Curtis
8 Jockey's Fields
London WC1R 4BF
020 7611 1720
mail@harrisoncurtis.co.uk
www.harrisoncurtis.co.uk

Hart Jackson Hall Smith
Watson House, Pilgrim Street
Newcastle Upon Tyne
Tyne And Wear NE1 6QE
0191 261 5181
www.hartjacksonhallsmith.com

Haynes Phillips
73 Farringdon Road
London EC1M 3JQ
020 7242 2213
hello@haynesphillips.com
www.haynesphillips.com

Herbert Mallam Gowers
126 High Street, Oxford
Oxfordshire OX1 4DG
01865 244661
enquiries@hmg.law.co.uk
www.hmg-law.co.uk

Herbert Smith
Exchange House, Primrose Street
London EC2A 2HS
020 7374 8000
contact@herbertsmith.com
www.herbertsmith.com

Hewitsons
Shakespeare House
42 Newmarket Road, Cambridge
Cambridgeshire CB5 8EP
01223 461155
Northampton 01604 233233
mail@hewitsons.com
www.hbslaw.co.uk

Hextalls
28 Leman Street, London E1 8ER
020 7488 1424
info@hextalls.com
www.hextalls.com

Hill Dickinson
Sun Court, 66–67 Cornhill
London EC3V 3RN
020 7695 1000
Liverpool 0151 236 5400
law@hilldicks.com
www.hilldickinson.com

HLW
Princess House, 122 Queen Street
Sheffield, South Yorkshire S1 2DW
0114 276 5555
info@hlwlaw.co.uk
www.hlw-solicitors.co.uk

Holme Roberts & Owen
Heathcoat House, 20 Savile Row
London W1S 3PR
020 7494 5600
information@hro.com
www.hro.com

Howard Kennedy
Harcourt House
19 Cavendish Square
London W1A 2AW
020 7636 1616
Info@hk.law.co.uk
www.howardkennedy.com

Howell-Jones Partnership
75 Surbiton Road
Kingston upon Thames
Surrey KT1 2AF
020 8549 5186
kingston@hjplaw.co.uk
www.hjplaw.co.uk

Hugh James
Arlbee House, Greyfriars Road
Cardiff
South Glamorgan CF10 3QB
029 2022 4871
cardiff@hughjames.com
www.hughjames.info

Humphreys & Co
14 King Street, Bristol
Avon BS1 4EF
0117 929 2662
lawyers@humphreys.co.uk
www.humphreys.co.uk
*Specialists in interlectual property
and commercial law*

Ingram Winter Green
Bedford House, 21A John Street
London WC1N 2BL
0207 7845 7400
backchat@iwg.co.uk
www.iwg.co.uk

James Chapman & Co
76 King Street, Manchester
Lancashire M2 4NH
0161 828 8000
mike.blood@james-chapman.co.uk
www.james-chapman.co.uk

Kemp Little LLP
Saddlers House, Gutter Lane
London EC2V 6BR
020 7600 8080
amanda.millar@kemplittle.com
www.comlegal.com

Kendall Freeman
43 Fetter Lane, London EC4A 1JU
020 7583 4055
davidkendall@kendallfreeman.com
www.kendallfreeman.co.uk
Formerly DJ Freeman

Kent Jones and Done
Churchill House, Regent Road
Stoke-On-Trent
Staffordshire ST1 3RQ
01782 202020
mail@kjd.co.uk
www.kjd.co.uk

Kidd Rapinet
14 & 15 Craven Street
London WC2N 5AD
020 7925 0303
Slough 01753 532541
info@krlondon.co.uk
www.kiddrapinet.co.uk

Kimbells LLP
Power House, Davy Avenue
Knowlhill, Milton Keynes
Buckinghamshire MK5 8RR
01908 668555
alison.foxton@kimbells.com
www.kimbells.com

King Solicitors
18–20 Kingsley Road
London NW3 6NE
020 7431 1111
www.kingsolicitors.com

Kirkland & Ellis International
Tower 42, 25 Old Broad Street
London EC2N 1HQ
020 7816 8700
info@kirkland.com
www.kirkland.com

KLegal
1–2 Dorset Rise, London EC4Y 8EN
020 7694 2500
www.klegal.com

Knight & Sons
The Brampton
Newcastle-Under-Lyme
Staffordshire ST5 0QW
01782 619225
christine.dyson@
    knightandsons.co.uk
www.knightandsons.co.uk

Kuit Steinart Levy
3 St. Marys Parsonage
Manchester, Lancashire M3 2RD
0161 832 3434
ksllaw@kuits.com
www.kuits.com

Langleys
Queens House, Micklegate
York, North Yorkshire YO1 6WG
01904 610886
info@langleys.co.uk
www.langleys.co.uk

Lanyon Bowdler
Brodie House, Town Centre
Telford, Shropshire TF3 4DR
01952 291222
telford@lblaw.co.uk
www.lblaw.co.uk

Latham & Watkins
99 Bishopsgate, Eleventh Floor
London EC2M 3XF
020 7710 1000
joe.blum@lw.com
www.lw.com

Lawdit Solicitors
Mede House, Salisbury Street
Southampton
Hampshire SO15 2TZ
023 8024 8551
info@lawdit.co.uk
www.lawdit.co.uk

Lawrence Graham
190 Strand, London WC2R 1JN
020 7379 0000
jonathan.riley@lawgram.com
www.lawgram.com

Lawrence Jones
Sea Containers House,
20 Upper Ground, Blackfriars Bridge
London SE1 9LH
020 7620 1311
contact@lawrencejones.co.uk
www.lawrencejones.co.uk

Laytons
Carmelite, 50 Victoria Embankment
Blackfriars, London EC4Y 0LS
020 7842 8000
Bristol 0117 930 9500
Guildford 01483 407000
Manchester 0161 834 2100
london@laytons.com
www.laytons.com

Leathes Prior
74 The Close, Norwich
Norfolk NR1 4DR
01603 610911
info@leathesprior.co.uk
www.leathesprior.co.uk

Lee & Thompson
Greengarden House
15–22 St. Christophers Place
London W1U 1NL
020 7935 4665
mail@leeandthompson.com
www.leeandthompson.com

Lee Crowder
39 Newhall Street, Birmingham
West Midlands B3 3DY
0121 236 4477
info@leecrowder.co.uk
www.leecrowder.co.uk

Lemon & Co
34 Regent Circus, Swindon
Wiltshire SN1 1PY
01793 527141
enquiries@lemon-co.co.uk
www.lemon-co.co.uk

Lennox Bywater
9 Limes Avenue, London NW7 3NY
020 8906 1206

Leonard Lowy & Co
500 Chiswick High Road
London W4 5RG
020 8956 2785
leonard@leonardlowy.co.uk
www.leonardlowy.co.uk
Solicitors to the music industry

Lester Aldridge
Russell House, Oxford Road
Bournemouth, Dorset BH8 8EX
01202 786161
info@LA-law.com
www.Lester-Aldridge.co.uk

Lewis Silkin
12 Gough Square
London EC4A 3DW
020 7074 8000
mark.king@lewissilkin.com
www.lewissilkin.com

Linklaters
One Silk Street, London EC2Y 8HQ
020 7456 2000
enquiries@linklaters.com
www.linklaters.com

Lovells
Atlantic House, Holborn Viaduct
London EC1A 2FG
020 7296 2000
information@lovells.com
www.lovells.com

Macfarlanes
10 Norwich Street
London EC4A 1BD
020 7831 9222
iain.mackie@macfarlanes.com
www.macfarlanes.com

Maclay Murray & Spens London
10 Foster Lane, London EC2V 6HR
020 7606 6130
magnus.swanson@mms.co.uk
www.mms.co.uk

Magrath & Co
52–54 Maddox Street
London W1S 1PA
020 7495 3003
admin@magrath.co.uk
www.magrath.co.uk

Manches
Aldwych House, 81 Aldwych
London WC2B 4RP
020 7404 4433
manches@manches.co.uk
www.manches.com

Mann & Partners Limited
New Court Chambers
23–25 Bucks Road, Douglas
Isle Of Man IM99 2EN
01624 695800
law@mannandpartners.com
www.mannandpartners.com

Marcus J O' Leary
Anvil Court, Denmark Street
Wokingham, Berkshire RG40 2BB
0118 989 7110
moleary@mjol.co.uk
www.mjol.co.uk
National IT intellectual property firm.
Clients include Microsoft and Dell

Marriott Harrison
12 Great James Street
London WC1N 3DR
020 7209 2000
astacha@marriottharrison.co.uk
www.marriottharrison.com

Marshall Ross & Prevezer
4 Frederick's Place
London EC2R 8AB
020 7367 9000
mail@mrp-law.co.uk
www.mrp-law.co.uk

Martineau Johnson
78 Cannon Street
London EC4N 6NQ
020 7618 6610
marketing@martjohn.com
www.martineau-johnson.co.uk

Masons
30 Aylesbury Street
London EC1R 0ER
020 7490 4000
info@masons.com
www.masons.com

Massers
15 Victoria Street, Nottingham
Nottinghamshire NG1 2JZ
0115 851 1666
www.masser.co.uk

Max Gold Partnership
Unit 2, Acorn Business Park
2 Livingstone Road, Hessle
North Humberside HU13 0EG
01482 642800
law@maxgold.com
www.maxgold.com

Mcclure Naismith
Pountney Hill House
6 Laurence Pountney Hill
London EC4R 0BL
london@mcclurenaismith.com
www.mcclurenaismith.com

Mccormicks
Britannia Chambers, 4 Oxford Place
Leeds, West Yorkshire LS1 3AX
0113 246 0622
p.mccormick@
    mccormicks-solicitors.com
www.mccormicks-solicitors.com

Mcgrigor Donald
Princes Exchange, 1 Earl Grey Street
Edinburgh, Scotland EH3 9AQ
0131 777 7000
enquiries@mcgrigors.com
www.mcgrigors.com

Mcneive Solicitors
2 Calverts Buildings
52 Borough High Street
London SE1 1XN
020 7357 9222
law@mcneive.com
www.mcneive.com

Memery Crystal
31 Southampton Row
London WC1B 5HT
020 7242 5905
info@memerycrystal.com
www.memerycrystal.com

Merricks LLP
10 Babmaes Street
London SW1Y 6HD
020 7959 0202
Info@MerricksLLP.com
www.merricks.co.uk

MLM
Pendragon House, Fitzalan Court
Newport Road, Cardiff
South Glamorgan CF24 0BA
0292 046 2562
enquiries@mlmsolicitors.com
www.mlmsolicitors.com

Moorcrofts
Mere House, Mere Park
Dedmere Road, Marlow
Buckinghamshire SL7 1PB
01628 470000
enquiry@moorcrofts.com
www.moorcrofts.com
*Corporate, IP and regulation. Clients
include RDF, Video Arts and Shop on
the Box*

Morgan Cole
Buxton Court, 3 West Way
Oxford, Oxfordshire OX2 0SZ
01865 262600
Cardiff 029 2038 5385
Reading 0118 955 3000
info@morgan-cole.com
www.morgan-cole.com

Morrison & Foerster Mnp
21 Garlick Hill, London EC4V 2AU
020 7815 1150
london@mofo.com
www.mofo.com

Myers Fletcher & Gordon
15 Cambridge Court
210 Shepherds Bush Road
Hammersmith, London W6 7NJ
020 7610 4433
mfg@mfglon.co.uk
www.mfg-law.com

Nabarro Nathanson
Lacon House, Theobalds Road
London WC1X 8RW
020 7524 6000
info@nabarro.com
www.nabarro.com

Neil McQueen Duncan & Egner
Floor E, Milburn House, Dean Street
Newcastle Upon Tyne
Tyne and Wear NE1 1LF
0191 232 7469
info@solicitorsupontyne.co.uk
www.solicitorsupontyne.co.uk

New Media Law LLP
102 Dean Street, London W1D 3TQ
0207 734 9777
ian.penman@newmedialaw.biz
www.newmedialaw.biz
*Copyright and contract law for music,
TV and film*

Nexus Solicitors
Carlton House, 16–18 Albert Square
Manchester, Lancashire M2 5PE
0161 819 4900
help@nexussolicitors.co.uk
www.nexussolicitors.co.uk
Contacts: Tony Brook or Nick Marshall.

Nicholson Graham & Jones
110 Cannon Street
London EC4N 6AR
020 7648 9000
marketing@ngj.co.uk
www.ngj.co.uk

Nicolaou Solicitors
The Barn Studios, Burnt Farm Ride,
Goffs Oak, Herts EN7 5JA
01707 877707
niclaw@tiscali.co.uk

Norton Rose
Kempson House, Camomile Street
London EC3A 7AN
020 7283 6000
marketing@nortonrose.com
www.nortonrose.com
*Advice on rights management,
marketing law and dispute resolution*

Olswang
90 High Holborn
London WC1V 6XX
020 7067 3000
john.enser@olswang.co.uk
www.olswang.com
*Full-service law firm with focus on
media and communications*

Orchard
6 Snow Hill, London EC1A 2AY
020 7246 6100
info@orchardlaw.com
www.orchardlaw.com

Osborne Clarke
26 Old Bailey, London EC4M 7HW
020 7809 1000
info@osborne-clarke.co.uk
www.osborneclarke.com

Palser Grossman
Discovery House
Scott Harbour, Cardiff
South Glamorgan CF10 4HA
029 2045 2770
law@palsergrossman.com
www.palsergrossman.com

Paul Davidson Taylor
City Gate Business Centre
Southampton Street, Reading
Berkshire RG1 2QW
0118 922 7220
law@pdt.co.uk
www.pdt.co.uk

Peachey & Co
95 Aldwych, London WC2B 4JF
020 7316 5200
oml@peachey.co.uk
www.PEACHEY.co.uk

Penningtons
Bucklersbury House
83 Cannon Street
London EC4N 8PE
020 7457 3000
information@penningtons.co.uk
www.penningtons.co.uk

Peter Carter-Ruck and Partners
London International Press Centre
76 Shoe Lane, London EC4A 3JB
020 7353 5005
lawyers@carter-ruck.com
www.carter-ruck.com
*Defamation, media, human rights,
IP and employment law*

Pictons
Keystone Building, 60 London Road
St. Albans, Hertfordshire AL1 1NG
01727 798000
marketing@pictons.co.uk
www.pictons.co.uk
Intellectual property in technology

Pinsents
Dashwood House
69 Old Broad Street
London EC2M 1NR
020 7418 7000
Leeds 0113 244 5000
Birmingham 0121 200 1050
susan.biddle@pinsents.com
www.pinsents.com

Pritchard Englefield
14 New Street, London EC2M 4HE
020 7972 9720
po@richardenglefield.eu.com
www.pritchardenglefield.eu.com

Putsman.Wlc.
Britannia House
50 Great Charles Street
Birmingham, West Midlands B3 2LT
0121 237 3000
info@pwlc.co.uk
www.pwlc.co.uk

Rawlison Butler
Griffin House, 135 High Street
Crawley, West Sussex RH10 1DQ
01293 527744
info@rawlinsonbutler.com
www.rawlisonbutler.com

Readman Toyn & Associates
61 Waldram Park Road
Forest Hill, London SE23 2PW
020 8699 7769
sarah@readmantoyn.co.uk
www.readmantoyn.co.uk

Reed Smith
Minerva House, 5 Montague Close
London SE1 9BB
020 7403 2900
tfoster@reedsmith.com
www.reedsmith.co.uk

Reid Minty
14 Grosvenor Street, Mayfair
London W1K 4PS
020 7318 4444
lawyers@reidminty.co.uk
www.reidminty.co.uk

Reynolds Porter Chamberlain
Chichester House
278–282 High Holborn
London WC1V 7HA
020 7242 2877
enquiries@rpc.co.uk
www.rpc.co.uk
*Advice to press, publishers, TV on
content-related issues*

Richard Howard & Co
45–51 Whitfield Street
London W1T 4HB
020 7851 4511
richard.howard@richardhoward.co.uk
www.richardhoward.tv

Richards Butler International
Beaufort House
15 St. Botolph Street
London EC3A 7EE
020 7247 6555
pma@richardsbutler.com
www.richardsbutler.com

Ricksons
6 Winckley Square, Preston
Lancashire PR1 3JJ
01772 556677
james.cowell@ricksons.co.uk
www.ricksons.co.uk

Robert Muckle
Norham House
New Bridge Street West
Newcastle Upon Tyne
Tyne And Wear NE1 8AS
0191 232 4402
enquiries@robertmuckle.co.uk
www.robertmuckle.co.uk

Roiter Zucker
Regent House
5–7 Broadhurst Gardens
Swiss Cottage, London NW6 3RZ
020 7328 9111
mail@roiterzucker.co.uk
www.roiterzucker.co.uk

Rollits
Wilberforce Court, High Street
Hull, North Humberside HU1 1YJ
01482 323239
info@rollits.com
www.rollits.com

Rooks Rider
Challoner House
19 Clerkenwell Close
London EC1R 0RR
020 7689 7000
lawyers@rooksrider.co.uk
www.rooksrider.co.uk

Rosenblatt
9–13 St. Andrew Street
London EC4A 3AF
020 7955 0880
info@rosenblatt-law.co.uk
www.rosenblatt-law.co.uk

Ross & Craig
12a Upper Berkeley Street
London W1H 7QE
020 7262 3077
reception@rosscraig.com
www.rosscraig.com

Rowberry Morris
17 Castle Street, Reading
Berkshire RG1 7SB
0118 958 5611
admin@rowberrymorris.co.uk
www.rowberrymorris.co.uk
*All aspects of media law. Specialist
unit advises new bands and writers*

RT Coopers
Office 5, Telfords Yard
6/8 The Highway, London E1W 2BS
020 7488 2985
enquiries@rtcoopers.com
www.rtcoopers.com
*Film, TV, music, intellectual property,
copyright, branding, licensing,
publishing etc*

Salans
Clements House
14–18 Gresham Street
London EC2V 7NN
020 7509 6000
rabrahams@salans.com
www.salans.com

Schillings
Royalty House, 72–74 Dean Street
London W1D 3TL
020 7453 2500
legal@schillings.co.uk
www.schillings.co.uk

Seddons
5 Portman Square
London W1H 6NT
020 7725 8000
postmaster@seddons.co.uk
www.seddons.co.uk

Shepherd And Wedderburn
Bucklersbury House
83 Cannon Street
London EC4N 8SW
020 7763 3200
london@shepwedd.co.uk
www.shepwedd.co.uk

Sheridans
14 Red Lion Square
London WC1R 4QL
020 7775 9469
staylor@sheridans.co.uk
www.sheridans.co.uk
Contact: Stephen A Taylor.
*Specialising in commercial litigation
and media work*

Simcocks Advocates
Ridgeway House, Ridgeway Street
Douglas, Isle Of Man IM99 1PY
01624 690300
mail@simcocks.com
www.simcocks.com

Simkins Partnership
45–51 Whitfield Street
London
W1T 4HB
020 7907 3000
antony.gostyn@simkins.com
www.simkins.com

Simmons & Simmons
Citypoint, 1 Ropemaker Street
London EC2Y 9SS
020 7628 2020
enquiries@simmons-simmons.com
www.simmons-simmons.com

Simons Muirhead & Burton
50 Broadwick Street, Soho
London W1F 7AG
020 7734 4499
info@smab.co.uk
www.smab.co.uk

Sinclairs
234 Cowbridge Road East
Cardiff
South Glamorgan CF5 1GY
029 2038 8398
sinclairs@sinclairslaw.co.uk
www.sinclairs.co.uk

SJ Berwin
222 Gray's Inn Road
London WC1X 8XF
020 7533 2222
info@sjberwin.com
www.sjberwin.com

Slaughter & May
One Bunhill Row
London EC1Y 8YY
020 7600 1200
mail@slaughterandmay.com
www.slaughterandmay.com

Smyth Barkham
29 Fleet Street, London EC4Y 1AA
020 7353 4777
sb@smythbarkham.co.uk
www.smythbarkham.co.uk

Spearing Waite
41 Friar Lane, Leicester
Leicestershire LE1 5RB
0116 262 4225
info@spearingwaite.co.uk
www.spearingwaite.co.uk

Spring Law
40 Craven Street
London WC2N 5NG
020 7930 4158
tim.perry@spring360.com
www.Spring360.com

Squire Sanders & Dempsey
Royex House
5 Aldermanbury Square
London EC2V 7HR
020 7776 5200
ssdinfo@ssd.com
www.ssd.com

Steele & Co
11 Guilford Street
London WC1N 1DH
020 7421 1720
finplan@steele.co.uk
www.steele.co.uk

Stephenson Harwood
1 St. Paul's Churchyard
London EC4M 8SH
020 7329 4422
info@shlegal.com
www.shlegal.com

Stringer Saul
17 Hanover Square
London W1S 1HU
020 7917 8500
info@stringersaul.co.uk
www.stringersaul.co.uk

Tarlo Lyons
Watchmaker Court
33 St. John's Lane
London EC1M 4DB
020 7405 2000
www.tarlo-lyons.com

Taylor Wessing
Carmelite
50 Victoria Embankment
London EC4Y 0DX
020 7300 7000
london@taylorwessing.com
www.taylorwessing.com
*Patents, copyright and other
intellectual property*

Teacher Stern Selby
37–41 Bedford Row
London WC1R 4JH
020 7242 3191
g.shear@tsslaw.com
www.tsslaw.com
All areas of media and entertainment

Thompsons
Congress House
23–28 Great Russell Street
London WC1B 3LW
020 7290 0000
info@thompsons.law.co.uk
www.thompsons.law.co.uk
Represents several media unions

Thomson Snell & Passmore
3 Lonsdale Gardens
Tunbridge Wells, Kent TN1 1NX
01892 510000
mcarter-jones@ts-p.co.uk
www.ts-p.co.uk

Tomorrow's Law
30 Harrington Gardens
London SW7 4LT
020 7244 9042
info@tomorrowslaw.com
www.tomorrowslaw.com

Travers Smith Braithwaite
10 Snow Hill, London EC1A 2AL
020 7295 3000
travers.smith@traverssmith.com
www.TraversSmith.com

Truman & Co Solicitors
76 Fore Street, Topsham
Exeter, Devon EX3 0HQ
01392 879414
info@truelegal.co.uk
www.truelegal.co.uk

Turner Parkinson
Hollins Chambers, 64a Bridge Street
Manchester, Lancashire M3 3BA
0161 833 1212
tp@tp.co.uk
www.tp.co.uk

Tweedie & Prideaux
5 Lincoln's Inn Fields
London WC2A 3BT
020 7405 1234
enquiry@tweedieandprideaux.co.uk
www.tweedieandprideaux.co.uk

Veale Wasbrough
Orchard Court
Orchard Lane, Bristol
South Gloucestershire BS1 5WS
0117 925 2020
atucker@vwl.co.uk
www.vwl.co.uk

Wake Smith
68 Clarkehouse Road, Sheffield
South Yorkshire S10 2LJ
0114 266 6660
legal@wake-smith.com
www.wake-smith.com

Watson Farley & Williams
15 Appold Street
London EC2A 2HB
020 7814 8000
Aturrell@wfw.com
www.wfw.com

Weightman Vizards
High Holborn House
52–54 High Holborn
London WC1V 6RL
020 7067 4506
www.weightmanvizards.com

Wiggin & Co
95 Promenade, Cheltenham
Gloucestershire GL50 1WG
01242 224114
law@wiggin.co.uk
www.wiggin.co.uk

Willoughby & Partners
The Isis Building, Thames Quay
193 Marsh Wall, London E14 9SG
020 7345 8888
Oxford 01865 791990
rouse@iprights.com
www.iprights.com

Willoughby & Partners
Pembroke House
36–37 Pembroke Street
Oxford, Oxfordshire OX1 1BP
01865 791990
rouse@iprights.com
www.iprights.com

Wilmer Cutler & Pickering
4 Carlton Gardens
London SW1Y 5AA
020 7872 1000
www.wilmer.com

Wollastons
Brierly Place, New London Road
Chelmsford, Esssex CM2 0AP
01245 211211
enquiries@wollastons.co.uk
www.wollastons.co.uk

Wragge & Co LLP
3 Waterhouse Square, 142 Holborn
London EC1N 2SW
0870 903100
mail@wragge.com
www.wragge.com

Wright Hassall
9 Clarendon Place, Leamington Spa
Warwickshire CV32 5QP
01926 886688
email@wrighthassall.co.uk
www.wrighthassall.co.uk

Wright Johnston & Mackenzie
302 St Vincent Street
Glasgow G2 5RZ
0141 248 3434
enquiries@wjm.co.uk
www.wjm.co.uk

Useful contacts

Authors' Licensing & Collecting Society (ALCS)
Marlborough Court
14–18 Holborn, London EC1N 2LE
020 7395 0600
alcs@alcs.co.uk
www.alcs.co.uk
UK collecting society for writers and their successors

British Copyright Council
Copyright House
29–33 Berners Street
London W1T 3AB
01986 788122
copyright@bcc2.demon.co.uk
Copyright watchdog

Campaign for Freedom of Information
Suite 102, 16 Baldwins Gardens
London EC1N 7RJ
020 7831 7477
admin@cfoi.demon.co.uk
www.cfoi.org.uk

Campaign for Press and Broadcasting Freedom
Second Floor, 23 Orford Road
Walthamstow
London E17 9NL
020 8521 5932
freepress@cpbf.org.uk
www.cpbf.org.uk

Copyright Licensing Agency
90 Tottenham Court Road
London W1T 4LP
020 7631 5555
cla@cla.co.uk
www.cla.co.uk
Administers copying rights

Design and Artists Copyright Society Limited (DACS)
Parchment House
13 Northburgh Street
London EC1V 0JP
020 7336 8811
info@dacs.org.uk
www.dacs.org.uk
Copyright and collecting society for visual artists

Federation Against Copyright Theft (Fact)
Unit 7, Victory Business Centre
Worton Road, Isleworth
Middlesex TW7 6DB
020 8568 6646
bc@fact-uk.org.uk
Anti-piracy

Irish Copyright Licensing Agency
Irish Writers' Centre
19 Parnell Square, Dublin 1
Republic of Ireland
00 353 1 872 9202
icla@esatlink.com
Operates scheme for providing and requesting copyright

ISBN Agency
Woolmead House, Bear Lane
Farnham, Surrey GU9 7LG
01252 742590
isbn@whitaker.co.uk
www.whitaker.co.uk/isbn.htm

Nielsen BookData
Globe House, 1 Chertsey Road
Twickenham TW1 1LR
020 8843 8600
info@bookdata.co.uk
www.bookdata.co.uk
www.whitaker.co.uk
www.first-edition.co.uk

Patent Office
London Office:
Harmsworth House
13–15 Bouverie Street
London EC4Y 8DP
0845 950 0505
enquiries@patent.gov.uk
www.patent.gov.uk

Performing Right Society
29–33 Berners Street
London W1T 3AB
020 7580 5544
see website
www.prs.co.uk
Collects and distributes music royalties

Press Complaints Commission
1 Salisbury Square
London EC4Y 8JB
020 7353 1248
complaints@pcc.org.uk
www.pcc.org.uk

Public Lending Right
Richard House, Sorbonne Close
Stockton-on-Tees TS17 6DA
01642 604699
registrar@plr.uk.com
www.plr.uk.com
Library payment scheme for authors

Publishers Licensing Society
5 Dryden Street, Covent Garden
London WC2E 9NB
020 7829 8486
pls@pls.org.uk
www.pls.org.uk
Supports the Copyright Licensing Agency

UK Copyright Bureau
110 Trafalgar Road, Portslade
East Sussex BN41 1GS
info@copyrightbureau.co.uk
www.copyrightbureau.co.uk
Copyright service for creators

Writers, Artists and their Copyright Holders (Watch)
The Harry Ransom Humanities Research Center
21st and Guadalupe, PO Box 7219
Austin, Texas 78713-7219
USA
+1 512 471 8944
hrcweb@hrc.utexas.edu
www.watch-file.com
US database about copyright holders

City

FTSE Media index

two years to July 2003
values at close on last day of month

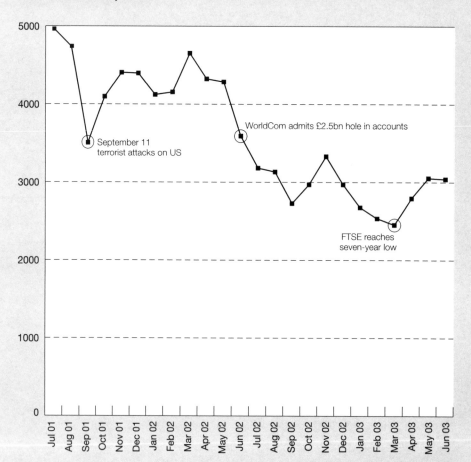

September 11
terrorist attacks on US

WorldCom admits £2.5bn hole in accounts

FTSE reaches
seven-year low

I t has been a savage few years for Britain's media business. Advertising revenues, so impressive in the two years to 2001, collapsed in the second half of that year; it was only in late 2002 that they began to show signs of recovery. Then, in late 2002 and early 2003, global stocks – some of which had recovered after the September 11 attacks on America – fell again in response to uncertainty over the war in Iraq. By March 9 2003, the FTSE-100 index had collapsed to a seven-year low: at 3436, it was less than half its December 1999 value. Media stocks did not escape the beating: October 2002, January 2003 and March 2003 were all bad months as prices took sharp plunges. Only a few companies were in any position to buck the trend.

The biggest trouble was at **Reuters**, where shares lost 90% of their value in two years plunging to a 17-year low at 95.5p by spring 2003. Beleaguered chief executive Tom Glocer closed and sold a series of investments, saying Reuters would concentrate on its "core strength as an information supplier" as it struggled to find savings of £440m by 2005. But as underlying revenues fell to £798m in the first quarter of 2003 – with subscription revenues falling 9.1% on the previous year to £624m – Glocer refused to rule out more sales.

Elsewhere it was the advertising groups which took the hardest tumbles: particularly **Cordiant**, whose shares fell from £2.50 to below 10p in the two years to spring 2003. The advertising group, once part of Saatchi & Saatchi, had tried to emulate the success of the US supergroups, but struggled to manage debts estimated at £220m. It said it would sell its 77% stake in German advertising group Scholz & Friends; PR agency Financial Dynamics; and Australian advertising group George Patterson Bates. A 25% stake in media buyer Zenith Optimedia was also expected to be sold. Amid fears that its shares could be suspended in May, the company worked out a deal with lenders by which it promised to sell assets by mid-August 2003.

UK rival **Incepta** also fared poorly in the markets, slipping from almost 70p a share to below 10p in the year to spring 2003. This left the world's biggest advertising group, **WPP**, looking relatively unscathed at having lost only half its share value in the same period, down from about £8 to around £4. WPP experienced a 3.5% fall in UK growth in the first quarter of 2003. Chief executive Sir Martin Sorrell warned in April 2003 that: "There's stabilisation, but still no oomph."

Pearson, whose fortunes often reflect the market as a whole, was another weak performer: shares in the publisher, which owns the Financial Times and Penguin books, slipped from £14 in spring 2001 to below £6 in spring 2003. Despite the end of war in Iraq, the group warned in April that advertising revenues had fallen by 18% during

City

FTSE media and photography, content and advertisers, capitalisation greater than £20m

BSkyB	£13.6bn	broadcasting
Vivendi	£12.2bn	conglomerate
Reed Elsevier	£6.3bn	publishing
WPP	£6.0bn	advertising & PR
Pearson	£4.56bn	publishing
Reuters	£3.3bn	news and market information
Granada	£2.65bn	broadcasting
Emap	£2.3bn	broadcasting and publishing
Trinity Mirror	£1.4bn	publishing
Johnston Press	£1.2bn	publishing
United Business Media	£1.1bn	publishing
Carlton	£1.06bn	broadcasting
Aegis	£973.1m	advertising & PR
TaylorNelson Sofres	£721.9m	market information
Independent News and Media	£684.9m	publishing
Capital Radio	£424.0m	broadcasting
Taylor & Francis	£423.5m	publishing
Chrysalis	£352.0m	broadcasting
Informa	£332.2m	publishing
GWR	£279.3m	broadcasting
Scottish Radio	£257.5m	broadcasting
SMG	£255.8m	broadcasting
Euromoney	£239.2m	market information/publishing
Daily Mail & General Trust	£237.2m	publishing and broadcasting
Future Network	£206.3m	publishing
Ulster TV	£166.8m	broadcasting
Incepta	£125.3m	advertising & PR
Maiden	£111.1m	advertising & PR
Itouch	£99.0m	new media
Wilmington	£85.3m	market information
Incisive Media	£71.5m	publishing
Highbury House	£64.9m	publishing
Datamonitor	£51.7m	market information
Chime	£48.4m	advertising & PR
Wireless Group	£45.9m	broadcasting
Bloomsbury	£41.1m	publishing
TVCorp	£26.8m	broadcasting
Quarto	£23.8m	publishing
Haynes	£21.0m	publishing

Capitalisation as at July 2003

the previous year, and that outlook remained "uncertain". It spent more than £3m on revamping the FT in April in an attempt to reach a wider audience.

Most other badly performing stocks were advertising-dependent publishers and broadcasters. Merger hopefuls **Carlton** and **Granada** both lost share value in the year to spring 2003; Carlton slipped from around £2.50 to about £1, and Granada from about £1.80 to 60p. Publisher and broadcaster **SMG** also slumped, standing at £2.20 in 2001 but only 60p in March 2003; and **United Business Media** fell from £6 in April 2002 to below £2 in March 2003.

Companies less dependent on advertising did better. **Reed Elsevier**, which publishes relatively recession-proof science titles alongside its badly hit business magazines, only slipped to £5 in April 2003 from a £6.90 peak in April 2002; **Daily Mail & General Trust**, which owns Associated Newspapers and regional publisher Northcliffe, slipped from £8 to £5.50 over the same period. **Trinity Mirror** slipped just 60p to £4.20 in the same time, buoyed by the arrival at the end of 2002 of former IPC chief Sly Bailey as chief executive. Last year's star performer, regional publisher **Johnston Press**, maintained its price after July 2002, keeping shares steady between £2 and £3.

Emap recovered twice from major slumps in late 2001 and late 2002, finishing at a solid £8, roughly the same as its pre-September 11 price, while Rupert Murdoch's **BSkyB**, which derives most of its revenue from its satellite TV subscriptions, recovered from a £4 low in October 2002 to reach £6.50 in April 2003.

City

259

Diversity

It was three years ago – January 2001 – that the BBC's director-general, Greg Dyke, used the phrase which would ignite the issue of cultural diversity in the media. The BBC, he said, was "hideously white"; not institutionally racist as others would allege, but disproportionately staffed by white people, and especially so in management ranks. "I had a management Christmas lunch and as I looked around I thought, 'We've got a real problem here'. There were 80-odd people there and only one person who wasn't white."

That was then. The Macpherson report into race relations had just come out; with a general election looming, cultural diversity was at the top of the agenda. Since then, according to Lord Ouseley, the former chairman of the commission for racial equality, momentum on race relations in the UK has been lost. Sections of the press have mounted sustained and often blunt campaigns against "invasions" of illegal immigrants, with little regard for their effect on minorities; the new editor of the Sun, in her first week in the job, published a "Mr Men" spoof with characters such as Mr Asylum Seeker, a roving migrant seeking a country where everything is free, and Mr Albanian Gangster, who carries a knife and invites men to come and visit his "friends' sisters". Taki, the outspoken rightwing columnist in the Spectator, wrote a column so full of racist bile that Scotland Yard sent a file to the CPS to rule on whether it constituted incitement to racial hatred.

There are no current studies into the number of non-white journalists working in British national papers, but the number is still thought to be no more than a few dozen out of 3,000. In a column in the Guardian in December 2002, columnist Gary Younge was moved to conclude that racism still "impedes your advancement" in the media.

But there is slow progress. It can only help that Trevor Phillips – the new chairman of the commission for racial equality, which runs the annual Race in the Media awards – is an ex-journalist. He presented the London Programme, which focused on important issues such as stop-and-search and the murder of Stephen Lawrence. The broadcasting industry in particular has begun to implement change. Projects include the cultural diversity network (www.channel4.com/diversity), an online directory of black, Asian and other ethnic minority TV freelancers and staff. The Skillset survey of TV and radio showed that, in the two years to 2002, representation of ethnic minorities rose from 5.4% to 8.6% among staff. Meanwhile at the BBC, where 8.7% of the workforce came from ethnic minority backgrounds in 2002, the target was to increase the figure to 10%, although this was still criticised as too low. Research published by both the BBC and broadcasting regulators in November 2002 concluded there had been "significant progress" in the representation of minorities on screen and behind the scenes; Goodness Gracious

Diversity

Commission for racial equality: race in the media awards

Media Personality of the Year
Ms Dynamite

Broadcaster of the Year
GMTV

National newspaper
Anne Karpf, Guardian Weekend:
"We've been here before"

Regional newspaper
Paul Barry, Coventry Evening
Telegraph: asylum seekers in
Coventry

Specialist magazine
Personnel Today: refugees in
employment campaign

Consumer Magazine
Time Out: Body of Work

Television News
Kurt Barling, BBC London
News/Channel 4 News: Body of Work

Television Factual
Fatima Salaria: Blood and Fire

Television Entertainment
Hat Trick: The Kumars At No 42
(episode with Stephen Fry)

Television Drama
Granada Television: The Jury

Serial Drama
Shobna Gulati: Coronation Street

Website
Patrick Vernon/Pamela Adjei:
www.everygeneration.co.uk

Me and Ali G were singled out for praise, while Choice FM and Kiss FM were commended for their commitment to minority interests.

Nonetheless, said the report, broadcasters were guilty of stereotyping ethnic minorities, with the result that people from ethnic groups often turned to multichannel and specialist media instead. The BBC's Asian Network, a Five-Live style station with Asian music, went national on digital radio in October 2002. Despite this, said the BBC annual report in July 2003, there was "little evidence" of success in recruiting more ethnic minority viewers and listeners to the BBC. A survey of south Asian consumers, commissioned by Sky, said the lack of Asian-oriented programming on terrestrial was a driver for digital TV, with six out of 10 receiving multichannel compared to a national average of just over four in 10.

The fledgling "access radio" was a success, but several commercial ethnic minority radio stations voiced fears that Rajar figures discriminated against them by not representing their communities; without Rajar, they were able to attract less money in advertising. In the press, there are about 200 black and Asian journals – although the death of Val McCalla, the owner of Britain's best-known black newspaper the Voice, was a blow. The Ethnic Multicultural Media Awards (Emmas) exist to highlight the best of ethnic minority media.

A race row blew up at Channel 4 – the commercial channel with the greatest commitment to multicultural programming – in November 2002. A group of about 20 black and Asian television producers said they were considering taking legal action against the channel, claiming it had "wiped out a generation" of film makers from ethnic minorities by not sending out tender documents to black-owned companies. Managing editor Janey Walker said she "absolutely refuted that Channel 4 is racist in how it makes its commissioning decisions". Nonetheless, Channel 4 closed its multicultural programming department as part of its restructuring: writing in the Guardian, the station's former commissioning editor from 1984 to 1987, Farrukh Dhondy, said that even before this "Channel 4, ratings-led and culturally bled, ceased taking its multicultural programme remit with any seriousness."

Advertisers are beginning to realise that ethnic minorities are financially valuable – a £12bn market, according to most estimates, and better educated than the population as a whole. But a survey of people from minority backgrounds, conducted by media buyer Mediaedge:cia, showed that "ethnic marketing can be a double-edged sword". Some saw representations of people from minorities as positive, while others thought it tokenistic or stereotypical. Meanwhile a separate survey, carried out by the Institute of Practitioners in Advertising, showed that more than 95% of advertising employees are from a white, British background while just 1.4% are black and 1.3% are Asian. In London – where the advertising industry is predominantly based – about 30% of the population are from an ethnic minority, according to the commission for racial equality.

Women

The institutionalised sexism of the media industry of the 1970s is now largely a thing of the past, but problems remain. In particular, women find it difficult to break into the higher echelons of management: just 19 of the 2003 MediaGuardian 100 are women, though this was more than ever before.

In broadcasting, the Skillset 2002 survey showed that women make up 44% of the workforce: but they were only a significant majority in certain roles, such as make-up and hairdressing (93%), wardrobe (82%) and cinema cleaners (77%). Some 54% of workers in distribution and TV broadcasting were women, plus 52% of runners and 50% of staff in library and archives.

The conservative press continues to display an instinctive opposition to feminism. The Daily Mail, though bought mostly by women, still maintains the broad view that a woman's place is in the home. Meanwhile, any hopes for an end to topless models in the Sun were quashed when Rebekah Wade, the paper's first female editor, turned up for work on a first day with a "Page 3" badge on her lapel.

Age

Ageism is still the media's dirty little secret. Many media companies – in common with the rest of industry – still recruit younger, relatively inexperienced (and cheaper) staff in preference to someone over 40. A (self-selecting) survey for MediaWeek in April 2003 found that 94% of respondents were under 44, while research by the Institute of Practitioners in Advertising found that 51% of ad agency staff were between 25 and 34.

The issue was taken up by Peter Sissons, the 60-year-old TV news presenter, on his retirement from BBC news in September 2002. He told the Observer: "The BBC does have one or two blind spots and its biggest blind spot is its tendency to ageism. I've been to too many leaving parties for people who've turned 50 and they're at the height of their powers and they're out." Sissons' comments followed the delicious remark the previous year from experienced news correspondent Kate Adie, who criticised television executives for valuing "women with cute faces, cute bottoms and nothing else in between".

Disability

Disability also remains a problem. Just 2% of people employed in broadcasting or the creative industries are disabled, prompting culture secretary Tessa Jowell in June to call on broadcasters to recruit a representative number. On the same day, research commissioned by the independent television commission, broadcasting standards commission and the BBC, showed that viewers want to see more disabled people on TV in a variety of roles, including presenters and news readers.

Diversity

Further reading

■ Press

MediaGuardian
media.guardian.co.uk/race

■ Books

Black Journalists, White Media BEULAH AINLEY

■ Other resources

Commission for racial equality
www.cre.gov.uk

Cultural diversity network
www.channel4.com/diversity

Age Positive
www.agepositive.gov.uk

Race matters **Randeep Ramesh**

One of the reasons I got to be a journalist was my colour. Shocking maybe, but true. Every year the Guardian offers grants for journalism school — and reserves a number for ethnic minority candidates. More than a decade ago, I secured one of these despite my experience of newspapers being limited to reading them. The first thing I noticed about Fleet Street was that there were more black and Asian people in the canteen than in the newsroom. In the early 90s, non-white reporters were notable for their absence. Journalism then resembled a gentleman's club — membership to which relied upon having good connections and the wealth to support yourself in London for a year or so freelancing.

Fleet Street has changed, but not as quickly as the rest of society. This is partly because British newspapers have yet to understand that minority does not mean marginal. From Denise Lewis to Panjabi MC, black and brown Britons are now mainstream. So much so that we can imagine a non-white prime minister. But not, alas, a black newspaper editor or an Asian director general of the BBC.

Britain should take its cue from America, where the candour of editors and reporters about race is refreshing. Across the Atlantic, there are race relations correspondents and staff diversity committees on many big newspapers. But in the US, there is an ongoing conversation about the nature of national identity and ethnicity. Here we make do with the odd chat about it.

This perception will have to alter in the years to come. The reason is that race matters in modern-day Britain. Having a diverse work force is not about tokenism, but talent. If ethnic minorities can succeed in sport, business and the arts then why is news reporting any different? Having a workforce that appears to exclude sections of society also signals to readers that you are not prepared to reflect the breadth and depth of the British experience. In the chase for audiences, the advantages of being hip and inclusive are too great an incentive to resist.

None of this means there will be an overnight change in the fortunes of aspiring journalists from Britain's ethnic minorities. There are still far too many people hired because their father knew the editor or they impressed somebody at a dinner party. The number of these openings should dwindle in the future as I hope will the need for positive discrimination.

Randeep Ramesh is the Guardian's Delhi correspondent and a former leader writer

Diversity Contacts

Media diversity associations

Age Concern
Astral House, 1268 London Road
London SW16 4ER
020 8765 7200
www.ageconcern.co.uk

Age Positive
Department for Work and Pensions
Room W8d, Moorfoot
Sheffield S1 4PQ
agepositive@dwp.gsi.gov.uk
www.agepositive.gov.uk/
Age diversity in employment

Broadcaster and Creative Industries Disability Network (BCIDN)
Employers' Forum on Disability
Nutmeg House, 60 Gainsford Street
London SE1 2NY
jenny.stevens@
    employers-forum.co.uk
www.employers-forum.co.uk

Creative Collective
020 8683 0147
collectively@thecreativecollective.com
www.thecreativecollective.com
Aims to develop social policy on diversity and to empower community groups to harness the media

Cultural Diversity Network (CDN)
c/o Channel 4, 124 Horseferry Road
London SW1P 2TX
diversitydatabase@channel4.co.uk
www.cdndiversitydatabase.tv

Digital Media Access Group
Applied Computing
University of Dundee
Dundee DD1 4HN
01382 345050
info@dmag.org.uk
www.dmag.org.uk/aboutus
    /default.asp
Promotes new media accessibility

Disability Rights Commission
Freepost MID02164
Stratford upon Avon CV37 9BR
08457 622633
enquiry@drc-gb.org
www.drc-gb.org

Diversity Database
BBC Television Centre
London W12 7RJ
020 8743 8000
www.bbc.co.uk/info
    /policies/diversity.shtml

Emma Awards
67–69 Whitfield Street
London W1P 5RL
020 7636 1233
mail@emma.tv
www.emma.tv
Multicultural media awards

Spoken Word Publishing Association (SWPA)
c/o Macmillan Audio
120 New Wharf Road
London N1 9RR
020 7014 6000
audio@penguin.co.uk
www.swpa.co.uk

Gay.com UK
22–23 Carnaby Street
London W1F 7DB
020 7734 3700
info@uk.gay.com
http://uk.gay.com

Equal Opportunities Commission
Arndale House, Arndale Centre
Manchester M4 3EQ
0845 601 5901
info@eoc.org.uk
www.eoc.org.uk

International Association of Women in Radio and Television
Radio Norway International,
Norwegian Broadcasting NRK
0340, Oslo Norway
+47 230 48441
nik@netactive.co.za
www.iawrt.org

International Women's Media Foundation
1726 M Street NW, Suite 1002
Washington, DC 20036, USA
+1 202 496 1992
info@iwmf.org
www.iwmf.org

PressWise Trust
38 Easton Business Centre
Felix Road, Bristol BS5 0HE
0117 941 5889
pw@presswise.org.uk
www.presswise.org.uk
Independent media ethics charity

Society of Women Writers & Journalists
4 Larch Way, Haywards Heath
West Sussex RH16 3TY
01444 412087
swwriters@aol.com

Women and Equality Unit
35 Great Smith Street
London SW1P 3BQ
0845 001 0029
info-womenandequalityunit@
    dti.gsi.gov.uk
www.womenandequalityunit.gov.uk

Women in Film and Television
6 Langley Street
London WC2H 9JA
020 7240 4875
emily@wftv.org.uk
www.wftv.org.uk

Women in Journalism
wijUK@aol.com
www.womeninjournalism.co.uk

Women in Publishing
wipub@hotmail.com
www.wipub.org.uk

Women's Radio Group
27 Bath Road, London W4 1LJ
wrg@zelo.demon.co.uk
www.womeninradio.org.uk

Minority press

Disability

Big Print
2 Palmyra Square North
Warrington WA1 1JQ
01925 242222
sales@big-print.co.uk
www.big-print.co.uk
Weekly. Editor: Trevor Buckley

Break Times
Winged Fellowship Trust
20–32 Pentonville Road
London N1 9XD
020 7833 2594
admin@wft.org.uk
www.wft.org.uk
2pa, Physical disabilities and carers

Breathe Easy
The British Lung Foundation
78 Hatton Garden
London EC1N 8LD
020 7831 5831
info@britishlungfoundation.com
www.lunguk.org/
Quarterly, Lung disease.
Editor: Darren Sanders

Communication
The National Autistic Society
393 City Road, London EC1V 1NG
020 7833 2299
publications@nas.org.uk
www.nas.org.uk
3pa, Autism. Editor: Anne Cooper

Devon Link
Devon County Council and Torbay
Council, Room A123
Social Services Directorate
County Hall, Topsham Road
Exeter EX2 4QR
01392 382332
jlwhite@devon.gov.uk
Quarterly. Editor: Joanne White

Disability Now
Scope, 6 Market Road
London N7 9PW
020 7619 7323
editor@disabilitynow.org.uk
www.disabilitynow.org.uk
Monthly. Editor: Mary Wilkinson

Disability Times
Disability Times, 58 Uxbridge Road
London W5 2TL
020 8566 1202
dtnews@btclick.com
www.disabilitytimes.co.uk
9pa. Editor: Teresa Moore

Disabled and Supportive Carer
Euromedia Associates
Unit 8, Chorley West Business Park
Ackhurst Road, Chorley PL7 1NL
0870 444 8955
editorial@euromedia-al.com
6pa. Editor: Richard Cheeseborough

Disabled Motorist
Cottingham Way
Thrapston NN14 4PL
01832 734724
Lesley E Browne@aol.com
www.ddmc@ukonline.co.uk
Monthly. Editor: Lesley Browne

DISH Update
DISH, 45 Grosvenor Road
St Albans AL1 3AW
01727 813815
info@dish4info.co.uk
www.dish4info.co.uk
Quarterly, Hertfordshire.
Editor: Jane Fookes

Epilepsy Today
Epilepsy Action, New Anstey House
Gate Way Drive, Yeadon
Leeds LS19 7XY
0113 210 8800
smitchell@epilepsy.org.uk
www.epilepsy.org.uk
Quarterly. Editor: Sue Mitchell

FreeHand
Abucon, 13 Vincent Square
London SW1P 2LX
020 7834 1066
info@abucon.co.uk
6pa. Editor: Liza Jones

I Can Do That
Liverpool Daily Post and Echo
PO Box 48, Old Hall Street
Liverpool L69 3EB
0151 227 2000
editor@i-can-do-that.co.uk
www.icliverpool.co.uk/icandothat
6pa. Editor: Tom Dowling

Jigsaw
DISH, 45 Grosvenor Road
St Albans AL1 3AW
01727 813815
info@dish4info.co.uk
www.dish4info.co.uk
Quarterly, Young people.
Editor: Jane Fookes

London Disability News
Greater London Action on Disability
336 Brixton Road
London SW9 7AA
020 7346 5800
b.humphreys@glad.org.uk
www.glad.org.uk
10pa. Editor: Michael Turner

Magic Carpet
Warners Group Publishing.
The Maltings, West Street
Bourne PE10 9PH
01778 391000
clivef@warnersgroup.co.uk
www.dda.org.uk
Quarterly, Members of Disabled
Drivers Association. Editor: Clive
Frusher

Motability Lifestyle
CBC Media
Unit 4–5 Greenwich Quay
Clarence Road, London SE8 3EY
020 8469 9700
mike.trounce@cbcmedia.co.uk
www.lifestylemag.co.uk
Quarterly, Motability vehicles.
Editor: Mike Trounce

MS Matters
MS Society, 372 Edgware Road
London NW2 6ND
020 8438 0700
info@mssociety.org.uk
www.mssociety.org.uk
6pa. Editor: Debbie Reeves

New Beacon
Royal National Institute of the Blind
Falcon Park, Neasden Lane
London NW10 1RN
beacon@rnib.org.uk
11pa. Editor: Ann Lee

New Pathways
The MS Resource Centre
Unit 7, Peartree Business Centre
Peartree Road, Stanway
Colchester CO3 0JN
01206 505444
info@msrc.co.uk
www.msrc.co.uk
6pa. Editor: Judy Graham

One in Seven Magazine
The Royal National Institute
for Deaf People
19–23 Featherstone Street
London EC1Y 8SL
020 7296 8000
oneinseven@rnid.org.uk
www.rnid.org.uk
6pa. Editor: Dawn Egan

Pinpoint
Disability West Midlands
Prospect Hall, College Walk
Selly Oak, Birmingham B29 6LE
0121 414 1616
pinpoint@dwm.org.uk
www.dwm.org.uk
6pa. Editor: Pete Millington

Positive Nation
The UK Coalition of People Living
with HIV and Aids (UKC)
250 Kennington Lane
London SE11 5RD
020 7564 2121
editor@positivenation.co.uk
www.positivenation.co.uk
10pa. Editor: Gus Cairns

Pure
The National Kidney Research Fund
Kings Chambers, Priestgate
Peterborough PE1 1FG
01733 704650
louisecox@nkrf.org.uk
www.nkrf.org.uk
Quarterly. Editor: Louise Cox

RADAR Bulletin
Royal Association for Disability
and Rehabilitation
12 City Forum, 250 City Road
London EC1V 8AF
020 7250 3222
radar@radar.org.uk
www.radar.org.uk
11pa. Editor: John Stanford

Soundaround
Soundaround Associations
74 Glentham Road, Barnes
London SW13 9JJ
020 8741 3332
nigel@soundaround.org
www.soundaround.org.
Monthly, Visually impaired,
worldwide. Editor: Nigel Vee

Stroke News
The Stroke Association
Stroke House, 240 City Road
London EC1V 2PR
020 7566 0300
www.stroke.org.uk
Quarterly. Editor: Ricki Ostrov

Talk
The National Deaf Children's Society
15 Dufferin Street
London EC1Y 8UR
020 7490 8656
emma@ndcs.org.uk
www.ndcs.org.uk
6pa. Editor: Emma Knight

Talking Sense
Sense, National Deafblind
and Rubella Association
11–13 Clifton Terrace
Finsbury Park, London N4 3SR
020 7272 7774
enquiries@sense.org.uk
www.sense.org.uk
3pa, Deafblind. Editor: Colin Anderson

The Parkinson Magazine
Parkinson's Disease Society
of the UK
215 Vauxhall Bridge Road
London SW1V 1EJ
020 7931 8080
bcormie@parkinsons.org.uk
www.parkinsons.org.uk
Quarterly. Editor: Barbara Cormie

Typetalk Update
Paver Downes Associates
2 Queens Square
Liverpool L1 1RH
0151 293 0505
hogan@paverdownes.co.uk
www.typetalk.org
6pa. Editor: Rachel Brough

Viewpoint
Mencap, 123 Golden Lane
London EC1Y 0RT
020 7696 5599
viewpoint@mencap.org.uk
www.mencap.org.uk/viewpoint
6pa, Learning disabilities.
Editor: Faiza Fareed

Yes! Magazine
Yes! Promotions
36–38 Avenue Road
Hartlepool TS24 8AT
01429 282009
www.yesmagazine.co.uk
6pa. Editor: Stephen Wharton

Gay and lesbian

3sixty
Newsquest (Sussex)
Argus House, Crowhurst Road
Hollingbury, Brighton BN1 8AR
01273 561618
info@3sixtymag.co.uk
Monthly. Editor: Judith Manson

Attitude
Northern and Shell
Northern and Shell Tower
4 Selsdon Way, London E14 9GL
020 7308 5090
attitude@nasnet.co.uk
Monthly. Editor: Adam Mattera

AXM
Hallmark Communications
2nd Floor, Summit House
48 Great Eastern Street
London EC2A 3EP
020 7613 1116
mike@axm-mag.com
www.axm-mag.com
Monthly. Editor: Mike Dent

Boyz
PP and B
63–69 New Oxford Street
London WC1A 1DG
020 7845 4300
hudson@boyz.co.uk
www.boyz.co.uk
Weekly. Editor: David Hudson

Diva
Millivres-Prowler
Unit M, Spectrum House
32–34 Gordon House Road
London NW5 1LP
020 7424 7400
edit@divamag.co.uk
www.divamag.co.uk
Monthly. Editor: Gillian Rodgerson

G3
G3 Magazine, Oxford House
49a Oxford Road, London N4 3EY
020 7272 0093
info@g3magazine.co.uk
www.g3magazine.co.uk
Monthly. Editor: Sarah Garrett

Gay Times inc. Gay News
Millivres-Prowler
Unit M, Spectrum House
32–34 Gordon House Road
London NW5 1LP
020 7424 7400
edit@gaytimes.co.uk
www.gaytimes.co.uk
Monthly. Editor: Vicky Powell

Man Magazine
Man Media UK, 2 Wakefield Street
Manchester M1 5NE
0161 228 3512
mail@manmagazine.org
www.manmagazine.org
Monthly. Editor: Aeron Haworth

Midlands Zone
What's On Magazine Group
5–6 Shoplatch
Shrewsbury SY1 1HF
01743 281777
info@zonemag.com
Monthly. Editor: Martin Monahan

Now UK
All Points North Publications
Walk 34, Middleton Road
Leeds LS27 8BB
0870 125 5555
editor@nowuk.net
www.nowuk.net
11pa. Editor: Christopher Amos

Pink Paper
PP and B
63–69 New Oxford Street
London WC1A 1DG
020 7845 4300
editorial@pinkpaper.co.uk
www.pinkpaper.com
Weekly. Editor: Tris Reid-Smith

Refresh
CBC Media
Unit 4–5 Greenwich Quay
Clarence Road, London SE8 3EY
020 8469 9700
refresh@cbcmedia.co.uk
www.refreshmag.co.uk
Monthly. Editor: David Tickner

ScotsGay
Pageprint, PO Box 666
Edinburgh EH7 5YW
0131 539 0666
editorial@scotsgay.co.uk
www.scotsgay.co.uk
Monthly. Editor: John Hein

Stonewall Newsletter
Stonewall, 46 Grosvenor Gardens
London SW1W OEB
020 7881 9440
info@stonewall.org.uk
www.stonewall.org.uk
Quarterly. Editor: Jodie West

Cultural and ethnic minorities

African Times
Ethnic Media Group, Unit 2
Whitechapel Technology Centre
65 Whitechapel Road
London E1 1DU
020 7650 2000
africantimes@ethnicmedia.co.uk
www.ethnicmedia.co.uk
Weekly. Editor: Eminike Pio

Al Arab
Al Arab Publishing House
159 Acre Lane, London SW2 5UA
020 7274 9381
editor@alarab.co.uk
www.alarab.co.uk
Daily. Editor: As Elhouni

Al-Jamila
Saudi Research and Marketing UK
Arab Press House
184 High Holborn
London WC1V 7AP
020 7831 8181
aljamila@hhsaudi.com
www.alkhaleejiahadv.com.sa/sprc
/jamila
Monthly, Upper and middle-income
Arab women
Editor: Sanaa Al-Hadethee

Al-Majalla
Saudi Research and Marketing UK
Arab Press House
184 High Holborn
London WC1V 7AP
020 7831 8181
al-majalla@hhsaudi.com
www.al-majalla.com
Weekly. Editor: Fahed Al-Tayash

Anglo-Hellenic Review
Anglo-Hellenic League
23 Jeffreys Street
London NW1 9PS
020 7267 3877
paul.watkins@virgin.net
www.hellenicbookservice.com
/ahr.htm
2pa. Editor: Paul Watkins

Asharq Al-Awsat
Saudi Research and Marketing UK
Arab Press House
184 High Holborn
London WC1V 7AP
020 7831 8181
editorial@asharqalawsat.com
www.aawsat.com
Daily
Editor: Abdul Rahman Al-Rashid

Asian Express
Smart Asian Media, 3rd Floor
Bow House Business Community
153–159 Bow Road
London E3 2SE
020 8981 6333
newsdesk@asianxpress.co.uk
www.asianxpress.co.uk
Weekly. Editor: Shihab Salim

Asian Times
Ethnic Media Group, Unit 2
Whitechapel Technology Centre
65 Whitechapel Road
London E1 1DU
020 7650 2000
asiantimes@ethnicmedia.co.uk
www.ethnicmedia.co.uk
Weekly. Editor: Isaarc Hamza

Asians in Media
243 North Hyde Lane
Southall, Middlesex UB2 5TE
020 7737 0749
sunny.hundal@asiansinmedia.org
www.asiansinmedia.org
*Guide to the British Asian media
industry*

Blacknet
0870 746 5000
infomation@blacknet.co.uk
www.blacknet.co.uk
*Community website for black people in
Britain*

Canada Post
RosEmaple Media, Top Floor
6 Pembridge Road, Notting Hill Gate
London W11 3HL
020 7243 4243
info@canadapost.co.uk
www.canadapost.co.uk
Monthly. Editor: Paula Adamick

Caribbean Times
Ethnic Media Group, Unit 2
Whitechapel Technology Centre
65 Whitechapel Road
London E1 1DU
020 7650 2000
caribbeantimes@ethnicmedia.co.uk
www.ethnicmedia.co.uk
Weekly. Editor: Ron Shillingford

Chinatown
CTM Publishing, PO Box 342
Stockport SK4 1XY
0161 476 1574
chinatownthemag@hotmail.com
*Bi-monthly. English language for
Chinese*

Daily Jang London
Jang Publications
1 Sanctuary Street
London SE1 1ED
020 7403 5833
editor@jang.globalnet.co.uk
www.jang.com.pk
Daily. Asian

Des Pardes
8 The Crescent, Southall UB1 1BE
020 8571 1127
despadesuk@btconnect.com
*Weekly, Indian expatriates.
Editor: Gs Virk*

Dziennik Polski
The Polish Daily (Publishers)
63 Jeddo Road, London W12 9ED
020 8740 1991
editor@dziennikpolski.co.uk
*Daily, Polish community in UK
Editor: Jaroslaw Kovninski*

Eastern Eye
65 Whitechapel Road
London E1 1DU
020 7650 2000
aeditor@easterneyeuk.co.uk
www.ethnicmedia.co.uk
*Weekly, Second- and third-generation
UK Asians. Editor: Aram Singh*

Eikoku News Digest
News Digest International
8–10 Long Street, London E2 8HQ
020 7749 8000
info@newsdigest.co.uk
www.newsdigest.co.uk
*Weekly, Japanese.
Editor: Mikiko Toshima*

Filipino Observer
Filipino Observer
PO Box 20376, London NW11 8FE
020 8731 7195
editor@filipino.co.uk
Monthly. Editor: Bong Forrouzan

Garavi Gujarat
Garavi Gujarat Publications
Garavi Gujarat House
1 Silex Street, London SE1 0DW
020 7928 1234
garav@gujarat.co.uk
www.gg2.net
Weekly. Editor: Ramniknal Solanki

Gujarat Samachar
Asian Business Publications
8–12 Hoxton Market,
Off Coronet Street, London N1 6HG
020 7749 4080
support@abplgroup.com
www.gujarat-samachar.com/
Weekly. Editor: C Patel

Hia
Saudi Research and Marketing UK
Arab Press House
184 High Holborn
London WC1V 7AP
020 7831 8181
hia@hhsaudi.com
*Monthly, Arab women
Editor: Mai Badr*

India weekly
Ethnic Media Group
White Chapel Technology Centre
65 Whitechapel Road
London E1 1DU
020 7650 2000
newsdesk@indiaweekly.co.uk
Weekly. Editor: Dr Premenaddy

Irish Post
Cambridge House
Cambridge Grove, Hammersmith
London W6 OLE
020 8741 0649
irishpost@irishpost.co.uk
www.irishpost.co.uk
Weekly. Editor: Frank Murphy

Irish World
934 North Circular Road
London NW2 7JR
020 8453 7800
sales@theirishworld.com
www.theirishworld.com
Weekly. Editor: Donal Mooney

Janomot Bengali Newsweekly
Creative Media Publications
Unit 2 20B Spelman Street
London E1 5LQ
020 7377 6032
janomot@easynet.co.uk
*Weekly, Older Bangladeshi
immigrants. Editor: Nabob Udden*

Jewish Telegraph
Maccabi Complex, May Terrace
Glasgow G46 6LD
0141 621 4422
mail@jewishtelegraph.com
www.jewishtelegraph.com
Weekly. Editor: Paul Harris

La Voce degli Italiani
Scalabrine Fathers, 20 Brixton Road
London SW9 6BU
020 7735 5164
ziliotto@dircon.co.uk
*55pa, Italians in Europe.
Editor: Umberto Marin*

London Welsh Magazine
London Welsh Association
157–163 Gray's Inn Road
London WC1X 8UE
020 7837 3722
gethinest@aol.com
Quarterly. Editor: Gethin Williams

Maghreb Review
45 Burton Street
London WC1H 9AL
020 7388 1840
maghrab@maghrabreview.com
*Quarterly. Editor: Mohammed
Ban-madani*

Matchmaker Magazine
Matchmaker International
PO Box 430, Pinner HA5 2TW
020 8868 1879
matchintro@aol.com
www.perfect-partner.com
*Quarterly, Asians seeking partners.
Editor: Mr Bharat Raipthatha*

Mauritian Abroad
Sankris Publishing
32 Ethelbert Road
Faversham ME13 8SQ
01795 539499
eveer77807@aol.com
Quarterly. Editor: Krish Veeramah

Mauritius News
Mauritius Publishers Co. Ltd
583 Wandsworth Road
London SW8 3JD
020 7498 3066
editor@mauritiusnews.co.uk
www.mauritiusnews.co.uk
Monthly. Editor: Mr Chellen

Milap Weekly
Masbro Centre, 87 Masbro Road
London W14 0LR
020 7385 8966
Weekly, Urdu-speaking community.
Editor: Ramesh Soni

Muslim News
Visitcrest, PO Box 380
Harrow HA2 6LL
020 8863 8586
editor@muslimnews.co.uk
www.muslimnews.co.uk
Monthly

Navin Weekly
Navin Weekly, Masbro Centre
87 Masbro Road, London W14 0LR
020 7385 8966
Weekly, South Asian community.
Editor: Ramesh Soni

New Nation
Ethnic Media Group, Unit 2
Whitechapel Technology Centre
65 Whitechapel Road
London E1 1DU
020 7650 2000
newsdesk@newnation.co.uk
www.ethnicmedia.co.uk
Weekly, Black news.
Editor: Michael Eboda

New Zealand News UK
Southern Link Media
2nd Floor, Quadrant House
250 Kennington Lane
London SE11 5RD
020 7820 0885
editor@southernlink.co.uk
www.nznewsuk.co.uk
Weekly. Editor: Clare Watts

Noticias Latin America
St Martins House
59 St Martin's Lane
London WC2N 4JS
020 7686 1633
informacion@noticias.co.uk
www.noticias.co.uk
Monthly. Editor: Albrairto Rojas

Notiun Din Bengali Newsweekly
Din Publishers, 46g Greatorex Street
London E1 5NP
020 7247 6280
notun@din.demon.co.uk
Weekly. Editor: Mohib Choudhury

Occasions Magazine
Ethnic Media Group, Unit 2
65 White Chapel Road
Edgware, London E1 1DU
020 7650 2000
reva@dircon.co.uk
Quarterly, Asians worldwide.
Editor: Terry Tan

Parikiaki
Parikiaki, 534a Holloway Road
London N7 6JP
020 7272 6777
parikiakinews@yahoo.co.uk
Weekly, Cypriots in UK.
Editor: Bambos Charalambous

Perdesan Monthly
PTI Media, 24 Cotton Brook Road
Sir Francis Ley Industrial Estate
Derby DE23 8YJ
01332 372851
punjabtimes@aol.com
Monthly, Asian community.
Editor: Mr Purewal

Punjab Times International
PTI Derby Media
24 Cotton Brook Road
Sir Francis Ley Industrial Estate
Derby DE23 8YJ
01332 372851
punjabtimes@aol.com
Weekly, Punjabi community in UK.
Editor: A Purewal

Red Hot Curry
Unit 9, Fulton Close, Argyle Way
Stevenage, Herts SG1 2AF
01438 365582
www.redhotcurry.com
Asian community website

Sayidaty
Saudi Research and Marketing UK
Arab Press House
184 High Holborn
London WC1V 7AP
020 7831 8181
sayidaty@hhsaudi.com
www.sayidaty.net
Weekly. Editor: Adnam Al-Kateb

Sikh Courier International
The World Sikh Foundation
33 Wargrave Road
Harrow HA2 8LL
020 8864 9228
2pa, Sikhs. Editor: Dr SS Kapoor

Snoop
Britasian Media, 5a High Street
Southall UB1 3HA
020 8571 7700
raj@snooplife.co.uk
www.snooplife.com
Monthly, Second- and third-generation
UK Asians. Editor: Raj Kaushal

Spice Introductions
Spice Introductions
Amex 405 Bond Way Commercial
Centre, 71 Bond Way
London SW8 1SQ
0870 011 0020
editor@vismediaint.com
www.vismediaint.com
Quarterly, Asians in UK.
Editor: Satish Vivavadia

The American
British American Newspapers
28 Ely Gardens, The Ridgeway
Tonbridge TN10 4NZ
01732 363624
bulldog@netway.co.uk
Monthly. Editor: Cheryl Powell

The Weekly Gleaner
Unit 220–223
Elephant and Castle Shopping
Centre, London SE1 6TE
020 7277 1714
editorial@gleaner1.demon.co.uk
http://jamaica-gleaner.com
Weekly, Caribbean and Jamaican.
Editor: Michael Oban

TNT Magazine
Trader Media Group
14–15 Child's Place, Earls Court
London SW5 9RX
020 7373 3377
ian.wakeling@tntmag.co.uk
www.tntmagazine.com
Weekly, International travellers.
Editor: Ian Wakeling

Ukrainian Thought
Association of Ukrainians in GB
49 Linden Gardens
London W2 4HG
020 7229 8392
Weekly, Ukrainian.
Editor: Dr Swiatomyr Forston

Ultra Journey
Japan Journals, 93 Newman Street
London W1T 3EZ
020 7255 3838
info@japanjournals.com
www.japanjournals.com
Monthly, Japanese. Editor: Ko Tejima

Weekly Journey
Japan Journals, 93 Newman Street
London W1T 3EZ
020 7255 3838
lina@japanjournals.com
www.japanjournals.com
Weekly, Japanese in Britain.
Editor: K Tejima

Zoneast
Elm Media Communications
4th Floor, 44 Gerrard Street
London W1D 5QG
020 7439 2288
zoneast@hotmail.com
Monthly, Chinese in Europe.
Editor: Mrs Lei Wang

Religion

All The World
The Salvation Army
101 Queen Victoria Street
London EC4P 4EP
020 7332 0101
kevin-sims@salvationarmy.org
www.salvationarmy.org
Quarterly. Editor: Kevin Sims

Amar Deep Hindi Weekly
2 Chepstow Road
London W7 2BG
020 8840 3534
alphabet@globalnet.co.uk
Weekly, India and diaspora.
Editor: M Kaushal

Baptist Times
PO Box 54, 129 Broadway
Didcot OX11 8XB
01235 517670
btadmin@bluecom.net
Weekly, Church leaders.
Editor: Hazel Southam

Catholic Herald
Herald House, 15 Lambs Passage
London EC1Y 8TQ
020 7588 3101
editorial@catholicherald.co.uk
www.catholicherald.co.uk
Weekly. Editor: Dr William Oddie

Catholic Times
Gabriel Communications
1st Floor, St James' Buildings
Oxford Street, Manchester M1 6FP
0161 236 8856
kevin.flaherty@the-universe.net
Weekly. Editor: Kevin Flaherty

Challenge
Authentic Media, PO Box 300
Carlisle CA3 0QS
01228 554320
steven.burn@whsmithnet.co.uk
www.paternoster-publishing.com
Monthly, Christian.
Editor: Debbie Bunn

Christian Aid News
Christian Aid, PO Box 100
London SE1 7RT
020 7620 4444
press@christian-aid.org
www.christian-aid.org.uk
Quarterly. Editor: Susan Roberts

Christian Herald
Christian Media Centre
Garcia Estate, Canterbury Road
Worthing, West Sussex BN13 1EH
01903 821082
editor@christianherald.org.uk
www.christianmedia.org.uk
Weekly, Evangelical Christian
community. Editor: Russ Bravo

Christianity and Renewal
Premier Media Group (PMG)
PO Box 17911, London SW1P 4YX
020 7316 1450
john.buckeridge@premier.org.uk
www.christianityandrenewal.com
Monthly. Editor: John Buckeridge

Daily Bread
Scripture Union Publishing
207–209 Queensway, Bletchley
Milton Keynes MK2 2EB
01908 856000
jamesd@scriptureunion.org.uk
www.dailybread.org.uk
Quarterly, Adult Bible readers.
Editor: James Davies

Home and Family
The Mothers' Union
Mary Sumner House
24 Tufton Street, London SW1P 3RB
020 7222 5533
homeandfamily@
    themothersunion.org
www.themothersunion.org
Quarterly. Editor: Jill Worth

Jewish Telegraph
Maccabi Complex, May Terrace
Glasgow G46 6LD
0141 621 4422
mail@jewishtelegraph.com
www.jewishtelegraph.com
Weekly. Editor: Paul Harris

The Life
Scripture Union Publishing
207–209 Queensway, Bletchley
Milton Keynes MK2 2EB
01908 856000
media@scriptureunion.org.uk
www.scriptureunion.org.uk/thelife
Quarterly. Editor: Alister Metcalfe

LifeandWork
Board of Communications
121 George Street
Edinburgh EH2 4YN
0131 225 5722
magazine@lifeandwork.org
www.lifeandwork.org
Monthly, Church of Scotland.
Editor: Lynne Robertson

The Muslim News
Visitcrest, PO Box 380
Harrow HA2 6LL
020 8863 8586
editor@muslimnews.co.uk
www.muslimnews.co.uk
Monthly

New Day
The Leprosy Mission, Goldhay Way
Orton, Goldhay
Peterborough PE2 5GZ
01733 370505
post@tilew.org.uk
www.leprosymission.org
2pa. Editor: Mr Simon Watkinson

Presbyterian Herald
Church House, Fisherwick Place
Belfast BT1 6DW
028 9032 2284
herald@presbyterianireland.org
www.presbyterianireland.org
Monthly, Presbyterian. Editor: Rev
Arthur Clarke

Scottish Catholic Observer
19 Waterloo Street
Glasgow G2 6BT
0141 2214956
info@scottishcatholicobserver.com
www.scottishcatholicobserver.com
Weekly. Editor: Harry Conroy

Share
Allen Gardiner House, 12 Fox Hill
Birmingham B29 4AG
0121 472 2616
med@sandsgb.org
www.sandsgb.org
Quarterly, Missionaries in South
America and Iberia. Editor: Robert Lunt

The Sikh Courier International
The World Sikh Foundation
33 Wargrave Road
Harrow HA2 8LL
020 8864 9228
2pa, Sikhs. Editor: Dr SS Kapoor

The Universe
Gabriel Communications
1st Floor, St James' Building
Oxford Street, Manchester M1 6FP
0161 236 8856
newsdesk@the-universe.net
www.totalcatholic.com
Weekly. Roman Catholics and Ireland.
Editor: Joe Kelly

War Cry
101 Newington Causeway
Elephant and Castle
London SE1 6BN
020 7367 4900
warcry@salvationarmy.org.uk
www.thesalvationarmy.org.uk
Monthly, Christian Current Affairs.
Editor: Major Nigel Bovey

Careers & training

Ask any student if they would like a career in "the media" and they would probably say yes. Ask anyone in the media industry if they would rather still be a student, and they would most likely give the same answer. While a "creative" career might sound glamorous, everyone else thinks so too. Many employers, recognising this, get away with paying low or mediocre salaries for long hours and even then offer little formal training to help employees develop. To get their foot in the door, most people will probably at some stage have to work for free; to develop professionally, many end up having to train at their own expense. Some give it up and go off to become an accountant instead.

That said, if accountancy is not for you, there are many different kinds of media roles to choose from. In press and publishing, to name but a few, you could be a news reporter, a writer of features or specialist articles, a subeditor, a production editor, a commissioning editor, or a writer for the web. In broadcasting, you could be a journalist, a presenter, a researcher, a camera operator, a director or producer. You could be a creative in advertising, a PR agent, or a media buyer whose job it is to know the industry inside out (tip: read this book). And most, if not all these areas, need their designers, graphic artists, production gurus, marketers, sales managers, distributors and managers who – in theory at least – make the whole enterprise tick. Which is better than spending all day sitting in front of a spreadsheet.

Entry-level: courses and work experience

There are two ways of getting into any media career: first, go off and train yourself to do the job; second, do the job. You don't always have to do the first. You always have to do the second.

More and more entrants into the media are well qualified, with good degrees in media studies or other subjects; having such a degree will not necessarily make you stand out from the crowd. Indeed, rightly or wrongly (and partly as a result of articles written by wizened old hacks who worked the way up through the regional press) "media studies" still has a poor reputation among employers as a soft option. What can make the difference is a practical qualification which suggests you have the commitment and ability to do the job.

The National Council for the Training of Journalists (NCTJ) is the accrediting body for journalism courses. These are run either through a training contract at a regional or local paper – the traditional route, with much to recommend it – or, popularly but competitively, at a university. Courses try to be practical as possible: those in newspaper journalism, for example, will include all the knowledge you need plus 100wpm of shorthand, while journalism students at Preston were this year issued with a stylebook as if working in a newsroom. Courses will also include

From top to bottom

Broadcasting

Greg Dyke, director-general of the BBC: £368,000 in 2002-03 (plus £96,000 benefits and bonuses)

Technical trainee, BBC Resources, London: under £15,000 (source: Bectu)

Advertising

Sir Martin Sorrell, chief executive of WPP: £873,000 in 2002 (plus options)

Trainee account executive: typically £17,000

Newspapers

Paul Dacre, editor in chief of the Daily Mail: £830,000 in 2002

Lowest-paid trainee reporters on local papers in London: £10,000 to £12,000 (source: NUJ)

Magazines

Robin Miller, chief executive, Emap: £155,000 in 2002

Minimum salary, Emap Healthcare: £21,000

---

work experience, although students usually need some work experience to get on the course in the first place.

In broadcasting, journalism courses are accredited by the Broadcast Journalism Training Council (BJTC); there are also a few highly competitive broadcast training schemes, often funded by Skillset – the skills council for the broadcast industry in general. But many people start as a "runner" or in a similar junior training position and gain qualifications as they progress.

The real key to getting any job in the media, though, is work experience. The best way to get work experience is to target an individual in the organisation closest to where you want to work; send them your CV and follow it up a day or two later with a phone call. Be persistent but polite; if they are busy (and they will always say they are) ask when would be the best time to call, or – as a last resort – if there is someone else they think might be able to help you. When doing work experience, dress fairly smartly, put on your most personable manner, and try to be as helpful as you can. If in doubt, make tea.

The job market

Jobs in the media are advertised in the Guardian on a Monday, on Guardian Unlimited Jobs (jobs.guardian.co.uk) and in other newspapers and the trade press. Most jobs that are advertised nationally attract large numbers of applications, so spend time targeting your CV and covering letter by thinking hard about how your skills and experience best relate to the job description. Keep the CV down to one page (two at most), use a simple font such as Times New Roman (Arial if you love sans serif) and get someone who knows how to spell to read it through – not just Bill Gates.

Remember, most jobs aren't advertised: with the happy exception of the inclusive BBC, many media organisations simply recruit internally or give a job to a freelancer who's been around a while. So if you're looking for a job, the best place to be is working: carry on working for free, or if you are experienced enough, charge freelance rates. So don't apply for jobs simply because they're advertised in the Guardian; better to target the right job for you, or you'll end up back where you started in a few months.

One other problem to bear in mind when looking for a job: perhaps up to 80% of media positions are based in London and the south-east. National newspapers, TV production and advertising are based almost exclusively in London; most magazines are also in the capital, with small concentrations elsewhere. Only radio, some TV, and (of course) the regional press are truly nationwide.

Freelancing

Many people who work in the media are freelancers. That is, self-employed workers who are paid by the day or by the job. Many experienced journalists and producers choose to become freelancers for the relative freedom it offers; others freelance by necessity while they look for a job. In broadcasting, according to the Skillset survey 2002, a quarter of the workforce was freelance: independent television production, with its unpredictable workload, is particularly dependent on freelancers. Many newspaper and magazine journalists also work on a freelance basis, either writing from home or coming into the office to do reporting or subediting shifts.

There are several major advantages to freelancing: you get to be your own boss, no one tells you what time you have to get up in the morning and you have the freedom to move your career in whichever direction you choose. That's about the size of it. On the other hand, there are many serious disadvantages: you never know where the next pay cheque is coming from; you have little power against companies who pay too little, too late, or attempt to appropriate the rights for your work; and you have to fill in a tax return. Remember, you should be entitled to statutory holiday pay in addition to the pay you receive, but many companies will not pay up unless you ask for it.

In broadcasting, you will work a lot of short-term contracts; so ask to see a contract up front, check their rates of pay with broadcasters' union Bectu and watch out for terms covering intellectual copyright and statutory holiday pay (companies often try to include holiday pay in the headline figure). In journalism, the biggest issue is rates of pay: publishers are paying reporters and sub-editors less and less in real terms each year for a shift, usually by setting arbitrarily low "ceilings" for a day rate. It is up to freelancers and the NUJ to work together to get the pay they deserve.

Further training

Training and professional development, or the lack of it, is a serious problem for media employees. A 2003 survey for **Media Week** magazine showed that four out of 10 employees wanted to quit their jobs, while nearly 60% felt that it was a lack of training that had affected their ability to progress their careers.

In the broadcast industry, Skillset subsidises 60% of the cost of a range of short courses for freelancers, who often have to pay the rest themselves. The BBC also subsidises training and the industry body Pact can organise training for its members, though regular freelancers will often have less formal training than if they worked for a big in-house team such as the BBC.

Further reading

■ Press

Guardian Unlimited Jobs
jobs.guardian.co.uk/media

■ Books

McNae's Essential Law for Journalists
LCJ MCNAE, BUTTERWORTHS 2001

Broadcast Journalism
ANDREW BOYD; FOCAL PRESS 2000

Writing Feature Articles
BRENDAN HENNESSY; FOCAL PRESS 1996

How to Get into Advertising
ANDREA NEIDLE, CONTINUUM 2002

■ Other resources

Skillset
www.skillset.org

Skillsformedia
www.skillsformedia.com

NCTJ
www.nctj.com

Broadcast Journalism Training Council
www.bjtc.org.uk

Pact
www.pact.co.uk

Careers & training

A Mickey Mouse degree? **Steven Barnett**

I still remember my grandfather's reaction when I told him what I was going to study at university back in 1971. "Classics? What's the point of that? Who on earth's going to offer you a job after three years learning Latin and Greek? Go and do something useful." Like media studies, perhaps, which in the early 70s was about to be inaugurated as a degree course at Regent Street Poly – the first of its kind in the country.

That poly is now the University of Westminster, and media studies courses have proliferated at about the rate that classics is being abandoned. Some media studies courses are better than others – although they are traditionally lumped together by smug, ill-informed politicians trying to make a cheap point about the state of higher education. At some point, this bigotry usually extends to jibes about Mickey Mouse degrees, and ends with a weary lament about the decline of "proper" university subjects – like classics.

Any aspiring, or even existing, media studies undergraduate should have their defences prepared for the inevitable sneer – which follows a long and honourable tradition from the dismissal of English literature at the turn of the century to contempt for sociology in the 1960s. So here are three arguments to help you turn the tables on your accusers.

First, good media studies courses do not consist of sitting around watching EastEnders. In most cases, you can expect to learn about and understand the basics of a number of intellectual disciplines – including economics, philosophy, sociology, history and literature.

Debates about the nature and role of the press complaints commission, for example, can be placed in the wider context of the right to free expression, going back to Aristotle and Milton. The Human Rights Act is based on a philosophical contradiction which policymakers are still trying to unravel: free speech versus the right to privacy. Most debate about the new Communications Act presupposes an understanding of the economics of the media –

conspicuously lacking in many commentators. And that's before we get into the theory and practice of journalism.

This leads to the second point, which is that no media studies degree is a passport to a job in journalism or anywhere else. Most national newspaper editors – tabloid and broadsheet – still fall into the sneer category, preferring ability and experience on the Skegness Sentinel to any kind of media degree. Don't walk into an editor's office waving your hard-earned upper second in media studies and expect to impress.

But it won't do any harm either. In areas like broadcasting, web design, PR or advertising, having some kind of specialist or technical knowledge on which to build can give you an edge over non-specialist graduates – as long as it's combined with all the other individual qualities of flair, drive, common sense and intelligence that good employers look for. Michael Jackson did not become chief executive of Channel 4 because he started with a media studies degree from Westminster, but it was a start.

Finally, all good university courses serve the same purpose, almost regardless of content: to produce self-motivated, critical, thinking adults for whom the ability to pursue independent inquiry is more important than the acquisition of knowledge for its own sake. Once you have the tools for self-improvement, you can teach yourself history, Serbo-Croat, advanced needlework or even classics. When someone asks what's the point of doing media studies, the answer is simple: what's the point of doing English, history or classics?

It will still be a while before the sneerers stop looking down their noses, but I'm hoping that one day we may see their final humiliation: when the first media studies graduate is appointed a professor of classics. My grandfather would have approved.

Steven Barnett (classics at Pembroke College, Cambridge, 1971-74) is professor of communications at the University of Westminster.

Media Studies courses

Courses in communication studies, journalism, media studies, publishing and librarianship, ranked by Guardian teaching score: based on staff/student ratio, job prospects, money spent per student, government inspections and academic performance.

Institution	Guardian teaching score /100	Institution	Guardian teaching score /100
Westminster	89.2	Cardiff	68.3
Birmingham	86.9	Trinity & All Saints College	67.9
Luton	83.5	London South Bank	67.5
Leeds Met	83.5	Queen Margaret UC	67.2
Chichester UC	82.7	Sheffield Hallam	67.0
Royal Holloway	81.8	Gloucestershire	67.0
City	81.2	Wolverhampton	67.0
Central England	80.5	Robert Gordon	66.7
Leicester	79.0	Canterbury Christ Church	65.8
Nottingham T	78.5	Middlesex	65.6
Glamorgan	77.8	Brunel	64.5
Bournemouth	77.2	Glasgow Caledonian	64.4
Loughborough	76.7	De Montfort	64.0
Sunderland	76.3	Uni Coll Worcester	63.7
Leeds	76.3	Falmouth College of Arts	63.5
Sussex	76.0	Southampton Institute	62.8
East London	75.8	Surrey Inst of Art & Design	62.0
Sheffield	75.8	Teesside	61.4
Staffordshire	75.7	Coll of St Mark & St John	61.3
Central Lancashire	75.3	King Alfred's Winchester	60.5
Ulster	75.0	Wales, Bangor	60.0
West of England	74.8	Napier	59.7
Oxford Brookes	73.5	Paisley	59.2
London Institute	73.2	Huddersfield	59.0
Liverpool John Moores	72.2	Edge Hill College	56.7
Greenwich	72.0	London Met	56.5
York St John College	70.8	Thames Valley	56.3
Stirling	70.7	Lincoln	55.7
Coventry	70.2	St Mary's College	53.9
Brighton	69.3	Buckinghamshire Chilterns	52.2
Uni Coll Northampton	69.2	Salford	45.2

Source: Guardian University Guide 2004. For interactive tables, visit www.educationguardian.co.uk

Careers & training Contacts

Unions and associations

Bectu
Broadcasting Entertainment
Cinematographic and Theatre Union
373–377 Clapham Road
London SW9 9BT
020 7346 0900
info@bectu.org.uk
www.bectu.org.uk
Entertainment and media union

National Union of Journalists
Headland House
308–312 Gray's Inn Road
London WC1X 8DP
020 7278 7916
training@nuj.org.uk
www.nujtraining.org.uk

Producers Alliance for Cinema and Television
45 Mortimer Street
London W1W 8HJ
020 7331 6000
enquiries@pact.co.uk
www.pact.co.uk
Independent TV and film production

Training bodies

BBC Training and development: Broadcast Training
BBC Training & Development
35 Marylebone High Street
London W1U 4PX
0870 122 0216
training@bbc.co.uk
www.bbctraining.co.uk
Broadcast production training courses

British Kinematograph Sound and TV Society
The Moving Image Society
Pinewood Studios, Iver Heath
Bucks SL0 0NH
01753 656656
training@bksts.com
www.bksts.com
Film foundation, TV tech, foundation sound for film and video, broadcasting engineering

Broadcast Journalism Training Council
The Secretary, BJTC
18 Miller's Close, Rippingale
Lincolnshire PE10 0TH
01778 440025
Secretary@bjtc.org.uk
www.bjtc.org.uk
Accredits courses

City & Guilds
1 Giltspur Street, London EC1A 9DD
020 7294 2800
enquiry@city-and-guilds.co.uk
www.city-and-guilds.co.uk
Vocational qualifications

Film and Television Freelance Training
Fouth Floor, Warwick House
9 Warwick Street, London W1R 5RA
020 7734 5141
info@ft2.org.uk
www.ft2.org.uk
Training for new broadcast freelancers

Film Education
21–22 Poland Street
London W1F 8QQ
020 7851 9450
postbox@filmeducation.org
www.filmeducation.org

Film First Foundation
9 Bourlet Close, London W1W 7BP
020 7580 2111
info@firstfilm.co.uk
www.firstfilm.co.uk
Training for new film writers, producers and directors

Learning on Screen
The Society for Screen Based Learning
9 Bridge Street, Tadcaster
North Yorkshire LS24 9AW
01937 530520
Josie.Key@
    Learningonscreen.u-net.com
www.learningonscreen.org.uk
Screen-based learning support

National Association for Higher Education in the Moving Image
Sir John Cass Department of Art, Media and Design, Central House
London Metropolitan University
59-63 Whitechapel High Street
London E1 7PF
020 7320 1000 x1956
engs@lgu.ac.uk
www.lgu.ac.uk

National Council for the Training of Journalists
Latton Bush Centre, Southern Way
Harlow, Essex CM18 7BL
01279 430009
info@NCTJ.com
www.nctj.com
Runs schemes for print journalists. Accredits courses

Periodicals Training Council
Queens House, 28 Kingsway
London WC2B 6JR
020 7400 7533
ella.munns@ppa.co.uk
www.ppa.co.uk/ptc
Training arm of PPA

PMA Training
PMA House, Free Church Passage
St Ives, Cambridgeshire PE27 5AY
020 7490 7280
admin@pma-group.com
www.pma-group.com
Runs workshops and postgrad training

Publishing National Training Organisation
Queens House
55-56 Lincoln's Inn Fields
London WC2A 3LJ
020 7405 0836
info@publishingnto.co.uk
www.publishingnto.co.uk
Good source of information about training providers

Skillset
Skillset: The Sector Skills Council for the Audio Visual Industries
Prospect House
80–110 New Oxford Street
London WC1A 1HB
020 7520 5757
info@skillset.org
www.skillset.org
Owned by broadcast industry; accredits courses, publishes handbooks and runs Skillsformedia service (www.skillsformedia.com)

yourcreativefuture.org
education@designcouncil.org.uk
www.yourcreativefuture.org/
Guide to a creative career; sponsored by government, Design Council and Arts Council

Press training courses

In-house

Archant
Prospect House, Rouen Road
Norwich, Norfolk NR1 1RE
01603 772803 / 628311
jo.chambers@archant.co.uk
www.archant.co.uk

Bristol United Press
Bristol United Press, Temple Way
Bristol BS99 7HD
0117 934 3000
www.thisisbristol.com
Owned by Northcliffe since 2000

Johnston Training Centre
Johnston Training Centre
Upper Mounts
Northampton NN1 3HR
01604 431528
www.johnstonpress.co.uk

Midland News Association
MNA Training Centre, Rock House
Old Hill, Tettenhall
Wolverhampton WV6 8QB
01902 742126
c.clark@expressandstar.co.uk
www.expressandstar.com
Mostly in-house but takes a few
non-company trainees

Newsquest Media Group
Newspaper House
34/44 London Road
Morden, Surrey SM4 5BX
020 8640 8989
ebudair@newsquest.co.uk
www.newsquest.co.uk

Press Association
The Press Association
292 Vauxhall Bridge Road
London SW1V 1AE
020 7963 7000
information@pa.press.net
www.pa.press.net

Trinity Mirror Training Centre
Trinity Mirror Editorial Training
Thomson House, Groat Market
Newcastle-upon-Tyne NE1 1ED
0191 201 6043
tony.johnston@ncj.co.uk

Universities

Bell College of Technology
Almada Street, Hamilton
Lanarkshire ML3 0JB
01698 283100
enquiries@bell.ac.uk
www.bell.ac.uk
NCTJ: 2yr HND. BJTC: PgDip
broadcast journalism

Bournemouth University
Bournemouth Media School
Fern Barrow, Poole
Dorset BH12 5BB
01202 595360
bms@bournemouth.ac.uk
http://media.bournemouth.ac.uk
MAs multimedia journalism (BJTC),
radio production, TV production,
interactive media, broadcast and film
management

Brighton College of Technology
City College Brighton and Hove
Pelham Street, Brighton
East Sussex BN1 4FA
01273 667788
info@ccb.ac.uk
www.ccb.ac.uk
NCTJ: pre-entry for academic yr;
magazine journalism

Cardiff University
JOMEC, Bute Building
King Edward VII Avenue
Cardiff CF10 3NB
029 2087 4041
jomec@cardiff.ac.uk
www.journalism.cf.ac.uk
Nine-month dip journalism. PgDip
bi-media journalism (BJTC).
Academic journalism

Cardonald College
690 Moss Park Drive
Glasgow G52 3AY
0141 272 3333
enquiries@cardonald.ac.uk
www.cardonald.ac.uk
18-week day-release NCTJs:
newswriting, shorthand, public affairs
and Scots law. comms and media,
journalism and TV production. HND
practical journalism (NCTJ)

City College of Brighton & Hove
The Brighton Centre for Journalism
11–14 Kensington Street
Brighton BN1 4AJ
01273 667788 x413
journalism@ccb.ac.uk
www.ccb.ac.uk
NCTJ pre-entry for academic yr (ft)

City Literary Institute
Stukeley Street, London WC2B 5LJ
020 7430 0542
www.citylit.ac.uk
j.baynes@citylit.ac.uk
One-day: travel journalism ,
broadcast journalism, freelance
journalism, a taste of journalism,
interviewing for journalism

City Of Wolverhampton College
Wulfrun Campus, Paget Road
Wolverhampton WV6 0DU
01902 836000
mail@wolverhamptoncollege.ac.uk
www.wolverhamptoncollege.ac.uk
NCTJ for employed journalists.
BA journalism and editorial design
(day release); national dip media
production

Coleg Gwent
Headquaters, The Rhadyr
Usk NP15 1XJ
01495 333333
info@colggwent.ac.uk
www.coleggwent.ac.uk
NCTJ pre-entry, newspaper
journalism. media-oriented GNVQs,
AVCE, HND and HNCs

Cornwall (Camborne, Pool and Redruth) College
Course enquiries
Trevenson Campus, Pool
Redruth, Cornwall TR15 3RD
01209 611611
enquiries@cornwall.ac.uk
www.cornwall.ac.uk
NCTJ PgDip. foundations newspaper
and magazine journalism, graphic
comm and design, multimedia

Crawley College
College Road, Crawley
West Sussex RH10 1NR
01293 442200
information@crawley-college.ac.uk
www.crawley-college.ac.uk
NCTJ pre-entry yr

Darlington College Of Technology
Cleveland Avenue, Darlington
County Durham DL3 7BB
01325 503050
enquire@darlington.ac.uk
www.darlington.ac.uk
NCTJs: block release pre-entry
journalism , magazine journalism
level 4. Cert digital photojournalism,
pre-entry cert newspaper journalism.
NCTJ-accredited HND

De Montfort University
The Gateway, Leicester LE1 9BH
0116 255 1551
enquiry@dmu.ac.uk
www.dmu.ac.uk
BSc: broadcast tech, joint information
and comm tech (subject to validation),
media production, media , media tech.
multimedia BA/BSc

East Surrey College
Gatton Point, Claremont Road
Redhill, Surrey RH1 2JX
01737 772611
studentservices@esc.ac.uk
www.esc.org.uk
NCTJ pre-entry yr. NCTJ postgrad
fast-track

Editorial Centre
Hanover House, Marine Court
St Leonards-on-sea
East Sussex TN38 0DX
01424 435991
pam@editorial-centre.co.uk
www.editorial-centre.co.uk

Fife College of Further Education
St Brycedale Avenue
Kirkaldy, Fife KY1 1EX
01592 268591
c-mclean-campbell@mail.fife.ac.uk
www.fife.ac.uk
HND practical journalism

Glasgow College of Building and Printing
60 North Hanover Street
Glasgow G1 2BP
0141 332 9969
joyce.wallace@gcbp.ac.uk
www.gcbp.ac.uk
HND journalism

Hackney Community College
Shoreditch Campus
Falkirk Street, London N1 6HQ
020 7613 9123
enquiries@comm-coll-hackney.ac.uk
www.comm-coll-hackney.ac.uk

Harlow College
Velizy Avenue, Town Centre
Harlow, Essex CM20 3LH
01279 868000
full-time@harlow-college.ac.uk or
trainingscheme@
    harlow-college.ac.uk
www.harlow-college.ac.uk
NCTJ: 20-week postgrad and
post-A-level pre-entry; evenings
magazine or magazine journalism;
postgrad journalism: magazines

Harrow College
Lowlands Road, Harrow
Middlesex HA1 3AQ
020 8909 6000
enquires@harrow.ac.uk
www.harrow.ac.uk
NCTJ: 18-week intensive; AVCE or GNVQ intermediate: media comm and production

Highbury College, Portsmouth
Dept. of Media and Journalism
Dovercourt Road, Portsmouth
Hampshire PO6 2SA
023 9238 3131
info@highbury.ac.uk
www.highbury.ac.uk
NCTJ: 20-week fast-track newspaper journalism. BJTC: PgDip broadcast journalism; access. PTC: magazine journalism NVQ Level Four.
HND: 2yr media journalism

Hulme Adult Educational Centre
Stretford Road
Manchester M15 5FQ
0161 226 8411
george.h@wyth.org.uk
Short courses: digital photo, scriptwriting, video production, freelance journalism. C&G Level 3 dip: TV and video media techniques

Journalism Training Centre
Unit G, Mill Green Business Park
Mill Green Road, Mitcham
Surrey CR4 4HT
020 8640 3696
info@jtctraining.com
www.jtctraining.com
PTC, NUJ-approved: foundation skills cert journalism, 3pa pre-entry

Kensington and Chelsea College
Hortensia Road
London SW10 0QS
020 7573 5346
l.gibbons@kcc.ac.uk
www.kcc.ac.uk
Cert and dip media practice: intro to journalism. 24-week ft

Lambeth College
Belmore Street, Wandsworth Road
London SW8 2JY
020 7501 5010
courses@lambethcollege.ac.uk
www.lambethcollege.ac.uk
Journalism foundation .
NCTJ: pre-entry academic yr, newspaper journalism. Teeline

Liverpool Community College
Journalism School, The Arts Centre
9 Myrtle Street, Liverpool L7 7JA
0151 252 1515
sandy.felton@liv-coll.ac.uk or
angela.birchall@liv-coll.ac.uk
www.liv-coll.ac.uk
NCTJ: day-release for working journalists; one-yr pre-entry cert; 18-week postgrad fast-track (print journalism); 20-week postgrad fast-track (periodical journ); BTEC, HNC: professional media. HND: media production

London College of Fashion
20 John Prince's Street
London W1G 0BJ
020 7514 7344
enquiries@lcf.linst.ac.uk
www.lcf.linst.ac.uk
Fashion promotion – pathways journalism, broadcast and PR. foundation fashion styling and photo. foundation specialist make-up design: film and TV

London College of Printing
10 Back Hill, Clerkenwell
London EC1R 5EN
020 7514 6853
info@lcp.linst.ac.uk
www.lcp.linst.ac.uk
NCTJ: BA and MA journalism and cert periodical journalism. BJTC: PgDip broadcast journalism. MAs: feature film, documentary research. MA/PgDip: interactive multimedia. PgDip: photojournalism, sonic arts, documentary research

Napier University
School of Communication Arts
Napier University
Craighouse Campus
Craighouse Road
Edinburgh EH10 5LG
0131 455 6150
m.tait@napier.ac.uk
www.napier.ac.uk
MSc/PgDip International English language journalism (subject to validation); BA/MSc/PgDip journalism

Norwich School of Art and Design
St George Street, Norwich
Norfolk NR3 1BB
01603 610561
info@nsad.ac.uk
www.nsad.ac.uk
Graphic design (publishing)

No Sweat Journalism Training
25b Lloyd Baker Street
London WC1X 9AT
020 7713 1000
info@nosweatjt.co.uk
www.nosweatjt.co.uk
Full or ft NCTJ. Short courses: freelance journalism, sub-editing, feature writing, web design, travel writing, sports reporting. Eve and w/e

Scottish Centre for Journalism Studies
Jordanhill Campus
University of Strathclyde
76 Southbrae Drive
Glasgow G13 1PP
0141 950 3281
gordon.j.smith@strath.ac.uk
www.strath.ac.uk/departments/scjs
NCTJ: PgDip and MLitt journalism

Sheffield College
The Norton Centre
Dyche Lane, Sheffield S8 8BR
0114 260 3603
mail@sheffcol.ac.uk
www.sheffcol.ac.uk
NCTJ: pre-entry full-yr photojournalism and press photo; reporting and journalism fast-track.
HND: media production

Surrey Institute of Art and Design
Falkner Road, Farnham
Surrey GU9 7DS
01252 722441
registry@surrart.ac.uk
www.surrart.ac.uk
BA: journalism (BJTC). PgDip/MA: animation, European film production, film and video, photo, graphic design and new media

Sutton Coldfield College
34 Lichfield Road, Sutton Coldfield
West Midlands B74 2NW
0121 362 1166
infoc@sutcol.ac.uk
www.sutcol.ac.uk
C&G media techniques; NCTJ pre-entry cert newspaper journalism

Training Direct International
Matlock, Derbyshire DE4 5AW
01629 534826
bissel@trainingdirect.demon.co.uk
www.trainingdirect.demon.co.uk
Not-for-profit NGO

Trinity All Saints College
Centre for Journalism
Brownberrie Lane, Horsforth
Leeds LS18 5HD
0113 283 7100 x398
m_Hampton@tasc.ac.uk
www.tasc.ac.uk
NCTJ PgDips: print, radio & bi-media journalism. MA/PgDip: broadcast journalism (BJTC), radio journalism (BJTC). MA print journalism

University of Central Lancashire
Department of Journalism
Preston, Lancashire PR1 2HE
01772 894730
alwalker@uclan.ac.uk
www.ukjournalism.org
NCTJ and BJTC: MA/PgDip broadcast journalism (BJTC), newspaper journalism, online journalism (BJTC), BA journalism. Provides 2yr ft visual comm. HND: music and AV production. New media (BJTC sought)

University of Sheffield
The Admissions Secretary
Department of Journalism Studies
171 Northumberland Road
Sheffield S10 1DF
01442 222 2500
Journalism@sheffield.ac.uk
www.shef.ac.uk/journalism
BA journalism (NCTJ), MA/PgDip print journalism (NCTJ), MA/PgDip broadcast journalism (BJTC); MA web journalism

UNIVERSITY OF WESTMINSTER

School of Media, Arts and Design

Westminster's Media, Arts and Design graduates are respected across the country. They come up with the goods - and they could write you an impassioned 1,500 words on why those 'goods' fit into 21st Century culture.

Understanding of key issues
Our journalism graduates don't just write a good lead, they understand the issues behind it. The same is true of graduates from all the School's disciplines, whether they be fashion designers, website producers or ceramicists.

Seeing beyond the obvious
Westminster students are encouraged - no expected - to look beyond the obvious, work across boundaries, bring together skills and ideas in a new and exciting way. They find their time at our £30 million purpose-built Harrow Campus challenging.

Commitment and enthusiasm
Our students must bring commitment and enthusiasm; paper qualifications aren't enough. In return they get the facilities, the ideas and the encouragement they need to go further than many thought possible.

Research expertise
The Communication and Media Research Institute (CAMRI) has been awarded an RAE Score of 5 in the last two Research Assessment Exercises.

For more information please contact
University of Westminster, Admissions and Marketing Office, Harrow Campus
Northwick Park, Harrow HA1 3TP
Tel: **020 7911 5903**
Fax: **020 7911 5955**
Email: **harrow-admissions@wmin.ac.uk**
Web: **www.wmin.ac.uk/mad or www.wmin.ac.uk/harrow**

Educating for professional life

skills*for*media

A partnership between **skill**set

BECTU

Interested in working in the media?

How do you get work experience?

Is it 'what you know' or 'who you know'?

Is it as glamorous as it sounds?

Do you need a degree?

Will you have to work for free at first?

In England call **08080 300 900**
or in Scotland call **0808 100 8094**

Speak to a learndirect advisor
with specialist media knowledge
who can answer these questions
and more...

**Email us via the
'contact us' page at
www.skillsformedia.com**

A skillsformedia freelance

advisor working in the

media will tell it like it is...

We tell it like it is
skillsformedia is the industry owned media careers service helping people get into the
media and move on once they're in it.

skillsformedia is funded by DfES and ESF in England and Scottish Enterprise and Scottish Screen in Scotland.

THE SURREY INSTITUTE OF ART & DESIGN
UNIVERSITY COLLEGE

Find Your Focus...

Animation
Digital Games Design
European Film
Production
Film & Video
Photography

Postgraduate programmes in media and communication

The Surrey Institute of Art & Design University College offers advanced study in a range of disciplines, giving you the opportunity to develop specialist skills and knowledge in media and communication. As a research student at the Institute you will have access to our wide range of resources and facilities, and to the practice-based and theoretical expertise of our staff. We invite you to apply for full or part-time project-based study to **PgDip/MA** level in:

Animation, Digital Games Design, European Film Production, Film & Video, and Photography

As one of Europe's largest specialist colleges of art, design, media and communication, we have over 3,000 students studying on undergraduate, postgraduate and research programmes in subjects that include Journalism, Graphic Communication and Fashion Promotion & Illustration.

We are home to the Animation Research Centre, which fosters the interdisciplinary study of animation, visual and film theories, architecture and the fine arts. The Centre's Archive houses the Halas & Batchelor Collection, the Bob Godfrey Studio Collection and the Channel 4 Animation productions.

For further information
call our Registry on

01252 722441

or email us at
registry@surrart.ac.uk

or visit
www.surrart.ac.uk

Postgraduate study in Art and Design and Electronic Arts at Middlesex University

Middlesex University

...stgraduate study or research at Middlesex University opens
...e door to an outstanding range of academic expertise in the
...lds of electronic arts, fine art, history and theory of visual
...lture, product and architectural design, textiles, fashion
...d the decorative arts, and visual communication design.

...ost taught MA programmes are available one year
...ll-time or two years part-time.

Overcome by the spirit, he danced on his

knees, moving backward and forward in a

hand of holy-away while he also cleaned
the candle and the glass with flowers...

A Film and Visual Cultures
...programme that combines the study of film and new
...edia with the broader field of visual culture and which
...allenges the traditional orthodoxies of film studies
...d art history.

A Video and MA Video Documentary
...programme for those who already have initial
...perience in video production. One year full-time only.

A/MSc Design for Interactive Media
...e programme takes a radical questioning approach to
...teraction design. Students work in small teams and
...ing their experience to bear on projects dealing with
...al issues in communication. One year full-time only.

A Sonic Arts
...research-based programme that may include
...ectroacoustic composition, installation art, acoustic
...ology and radiophonic art.

A Electronic Arts
...research-based programme particularly suited to those
...employment who wish to use their work in the areas
...interaction design, visual design, information design,
...chnological innovation, writing for new media, sound
...sign, digital architecture or other areas.

A Architectural and Spatial Culture
...hy have the physical spaces of the modern world
...veloped in the ways that they have and how do they
...fect and affect everyday lives? Spatial Culture
...amines the relationships between cultural life and the
...cial production of space.

MA Design
A structured multidisciplinary programme of
postgraduate studies in architectural and interior design,
fashion and textile design, graphic design, illustration,
jewellery design, printmaking, or product design.

MA/MFA Fine Art
A range of differently weighted options combining Fine
Art practice with theory drawn from related academic
fields: Cultural Studies, Philosophical Aesthetics and
Art Theory.

MA Fine Art Practice and Theory
A mainly studio based programme for graduates who are
intending to become professional practitioners in the
broad field of Fine Art.

MA Professional Practice
Turn your past work experience into a solid and
accredited platform for career development, a change of
direction or personal growth.

Start January 2004: Places may be available on
MA Film and Visual Culture, MA Electronic Arts and
MA Design for those wishing to start in January

Contact us today for a copy of our Postgraduate Prospectus: 020 8411 4700

Admissions Enquiries: Middlesex University,
Trent Park, Bramley Road, London N14 4YZ

Email: admissions@mdx.ac.uk
Web: www.mdx.ac.uk

University of Ulster at Coleraine
Cromore Road
Co. Londonderry BT52 1SA
08 700 400 700
online@ulster.ac.uk
www.ulster.ac.uk
NCTJ PgDip newspaper journalism.
PgDip/MA journalism

Warrington Collegiate Institute
Learner Services
Winwick Road Campus
Winwick Road
Warrington WA2 8QA
01925 494494
learner.services@warr.ac.uk
www.warr.ac.uk
NCFE multimedia

Warwickshire College
Leamington Centre
Warwick New Road
Leamington Spa
Warwickshire CV32 5JE
01926 318000
enquiries@warkscol.ac.uk
www.warkscol.ac.uk
NCTJ pre-entry academic yr

West Kent College
Brook Street, Tonbridge
Kent TW9 2PW
01732 358101
marketing@wkc.ac.uk
www.wkc.ac.uk
NCTJ pre-entry academic yr

Wolverhampton College
Wulfrun Campus, Paget Road
Wolverhampton WV6 0DU
01902 317700
mail@wolverhamptoncollege.ac.uk
www.wolverhamptoncollege.ac.uk
NCTJ pre-entry academic yr

TV & radio training courses

Anglia Polytechnic University
Bishop Hall Lane, Chelmsford
Essex CM1 1SQ
0845 271 3333
answers@apu.ac.uk
www.apu.ac.uk
*HND: multimedia, audio music
and tech.*

The Arts Institute at Bournemouth
Wallisdown, Poole
Dorset BH12 5HH
01202 533011
general@aib.ac.uk
www.aib.ac.uk
*Dips: art and design, multimedia,
photo. C&G photo*

**BBME Training, The Radio and
Television School**
7–9 The Broadway, Newbury
Berkshire RG14 1AS
01635 572819
info@bbme.co.uk
www.radiotvschool.co.uk
Short radio and TV

Bell College
Almada Street, Hamilton
Lanarkshire ML3 0JB
01698 283100
enquiries@bell.ac.uk or
r.bergman@bell.ac.uk
http://floti.bell.ac.uk/postgradradio/
BJTC PgDip broadcast journalism

Bolton Institute of Higher Education
Deane Road, Bolton BL3 5AB
01204 900600
enquiries@bolton.ac.uk
www.bolton.ac.uk
*Writing for stage screen and radio;
fashion media*

Bournemouth University
Bournemouth University
Fern Barrow, Poole
Dorset BH12 5BB
01202 595360
bms@bournemouth.ac.uk
http://media.bournemouth.ac.uk
*Courses inc multimedia journalism
(NCTJ)*

**Canterbury Christ Church
University College**
Department of Media
Canterbury Christ Church University
College, North Holmes Road
Canterbury, Kent CT1 1QU
01227 782349
Admissions@cant.ac.uk
www.cant.ac.uk
*Range of undergrad and postgrad.
MA journalism forthcoming*

Cardiff University of Wales
School of Journalism
Media and Cultural Studies
Bute Building
Kind Edward VII Avenue
Cardiff CF10 3NB
029 2087 4041
prospectus@cardif.ac.uk
www.cardiff.ac.uk/jomec
BA journalism, film and broadcasting

**Chester College (A College of the
University of Liverpool)**
Parkgate Road, Chester CH1 4BJ
01244 375444
enquiries@chester.ac.uk
www.chester.ac.uk

Chichester College
Westgate Fields, Chichester
West Sussex PO19 1SB
01243 536196
principle@chichester.ac.uk
www.chichester.ac.uk
HND media

City University
Northampton Square
London EC1V 0HB
020 7040 8028 ext 8716
ugadmissions@city.ac.uk
www.city.ac.uk
*PgDip broadcast journalism by BJTC.
Other BA and BEng*

Cleveland College of Art and Design
Green Lane, Linthorpe
Middlesbrough TS5 7RJ
01642 288888
admissions@ccad.ac.uk
www.ccad.ac.uk
foundation TV and film production

College of Ripon and York
Lord Mayors Walk, York YO31 7EX
01904 716598
admissions@yorksj.ac.uk
www.yorksj.org.uk

Derby University
Kedleston Road, Derby DE22 1GB
08701 202330
admissions@derby.ac.uk
www.derby.ac.uk

Falmouth College of Arts
Woodlane Campus
Falmouth, Cornwall TR11 4RH
01326 370400
admissions@falmouth.ac.uk
www.falmouth.ac.uk
*BJTC PgDip broadcast journalism.
PgDips broadcast TV and professional
writing*

Farnborough College of Technology
Boundary Road, Farnborough
Hampshire GU14 6SB
0125 240 7040
info@farn-ct.ac.uk
www.farn-ct.ac.uk
*Media foundation. 2yr ft HND design
tech (multimedia). Directory under
review*

Gloucestershire University
The Park, Cheltenham GL50 2QF
01242 532845
gthatcher@glos.ac.uk
www.glos.ac.uk

Goldsmiths College
Department of Media and
Communications
University of London, New Cross
London SE14 6NW
Undergrad; 020 7919 7766
Postgrad; 020 7919 7060
media-comms@gold.ac.uk or
admissions@gold.ac.uk
www.goldsmiths.ac.uk
*Postgrad media and comms.
MAs scriptwriting, radio (BJTC),
journalism. Postgrad research media
and comms*

Highbury College, Portsmouth
Highbury College, Dovercourt Road
Portsmouth, Hampshire PO6 2SA
023 9238 3131
info@highbury.ac.uk
www.highbury.ac.uk
*PgDip broadcast journalism (BJTC);
access; magazine journalism NVQ
Level 4 (PTC); 2yr HND*

The London Film School
24 Shelton Street
London WC2H 9UB
020 7836 9642
info@lfs.org.uk
www.lfs.org.uk
2yr MA film-making

National Film and Television School
The Registry
National Film and Television School
Beaconsfield Studios, Station Road
Beaconsfield, Bucks HP9 1LG
01494 731425 / 731413
admin@nfts-tv.ac.uk
www.nftsfilm-tv.ac.uk
2yr MA film and TV. MA sound post-production. Short professional courses

Neath Port Talbot College
Neath Campus, Dwr-y-Felin Road
Neath SA10 7RF
01693 648000
admissions@nptc.ac.uk
www.nptc.ac.uk
2yr ft HND broadcast media (franchised from University of Wales, Cardiff)

NE Wales Institute of Higher Education
Plas Coch, Mold Road
Wrexham LL11 2AW
01978 293045
enquiries@newi.ac.uk
www.newi.ac.uk
HND/foundation/BEng sound broadcast engineering. Uni of Wales and masters media, film, theatre & performance

Newham College of Further Education
East Ham Campus
High Street South, London E6 6ER
020 8257 4000
admissions@newham.ac.uk
www.newham.ac.uk
2yr ft foundation audio production for broadcast media. Visual comm design

Northbrook College Sussex
Little Hampton Road
Goring-by-Sea, Worthing
West Sussex BN12 6NU
01903 606060
admissions@nbcol.ac.uk
www.nbcol.ac.uk
2yr ft HND music production: comp for film and broadcasting media

Nottingham Trent University
Burton Street, Nottingham NG1 4BU
0115 941 5806
cbj@ntu.ac.uk
www.ntu.ac.uk
BA broadcast journalism (BJTC); media and comm; media and culture. Postgrad inc MA/PgDip TV, online, newspaper and radio journalism. MA/PgDip TV journalism – BJTC

Plymouth College of Art and Design
Tavistock Place
Plymouth PL4 8AT
01752 203434
enquiries@pcad.ac.uk
www.pcad.ac.uk
National dips media production; photo. C&G creative mixed media; NCFE multimedia

Ravensbourne College of Design and Communication
Walden Road, Chislehurst
Kent BR7 5SN
020 8289 4900
info@rave.ac.uk
www.ravensbourne.ac.uk
HNC: broadcast post-production. BA/BSc broadcast production 1yr top-up

University of Reading
PO Box 217, Reading RG6 6AH
0118 987 5123
ug-prospectus@reading.ac.uk
www.rdg.ac.uk
BA English and TV; film, theatre and TV

Salisbury College
Southampton Road
Salisbury, Wiltshire SP1 2LW
01722 344344
enquiries@salisbury.ac.uk
www.salisbury.ac.uk
HND photo or film and TV; foundation creative digital arts

Sheffield University
14 Favell Road, Sheffield S3 7QX
0114 222 2500
Journalism@sheffield.ac.uk
www.sheffield.ac.uk
MA broadcast journalism (BJTC). BA journalism: broadcast pathways (BJTC). MA print, broadcast, web journalism; political comm

Sheffield Hallam University
School of Cultural Studies
Sheffield Hallam University
Psalter Lane Campus
Salter Lane, Sheffield S11 8UZ
0114 225 5555
admissions@shu.ac.uk
www.shu.ac.uk
MA/PgCert/PgDip: broadcast journalism (MA BJTC); film; international broadcast journalism; media; screen arts; writing; e-learning, multimedia and consultancy. BAs

South East Essex College
Carnarvon Road
Southend-on-Sea, Essex SS6LS
01702 200400
Marketing@southend.ac.uk
www.southend.ac.uk

Southampton Institute
East Park Terrace, Southampton
Hampshire SO14 0RB
023 8031 9000
fmas@solent.ac.uk
www.solent.ac.uk
BA broadcast journalism (seeking BJTC). PgDip/MA film; MA media

Staffordshire University
College Road, Stoke-on-Trent
Staffordshire ST4 2DE
01782 294869
a.dinnivan@staffs.ac.uk
www.staffs.ac.uk
MA broadcast journalism (BJTC). BA journalism (NCTJ). Other BAs, BScs. MA media and cultural futures

The Surrey Institute of Art and Design
Falkner Road, Farnham
Surrey GU9 7DS
01252 722441
registry@surrart.ac.uk
www.surrart.ac.uk
Journalism (BJTC). PgDip/MA: animation, European film production, film and video, photo, graphic design, new media

Trinity All Saints College
Centre for Journalism
Trinity and All Saints College
Brownberrie Lane, Horsforth
Leeds LS18 5HD
0113 283 7100 x398
m_Hampton@tasc.ac.uk
www.tasc.ac.uk
BJTC MA/PgDip bi-media (radio and TV), radio or print journalism

University of Wales Institute, Cardiff
PO Box 377, Llandaff Campus
Western Avenue, Cardiff
Wales CF5 2SG
029 2041 6070
uwicinfo@uwic.ac.uk
www.uwic.ac.uk
3yr ft broadcast media and pop culture. HND (or 1yr BA/BSc top-up) design for interactive media

University of Bradford
Paula Dale, Recruitment Manager
School of Informatics
University of Bradford
Richmond Road
Bradford BD7 1DP
01274 233081
p.e.dale@Bradford.ac.uk
www.eimc.brad.ac.uk

University of Bristol
Senate House, Tyndall Avenue
Bristol BS8 1TH
0117 928 9000
admissions@bristol.ac.uk
www.bristol.ac.uk
MA film and TV production; cinema; TV; cultural performance; archaeology and media. MEng comms and multimedia engineering

University of Central England in Birmingham
Birmingham Institute of
Art and Design, Corporation Street
Birmingham B4 7DX
0121 331 5719
media@uce.ac.uk
www.uce.ac.uk
BA journalism (BJTC, NCTJ). Other BAs. PGCert/PgDip/MA broadcast journalism (PgDip BJTC). PgDip/MA: international broadcast journalism, media and comm; MA media production

University of Central Lancashire
Department of Journalism
Preston, Lancashire PR1 2HE
01772 894730
ljwilliams1@uclan.ac.uk
www.ukjournalism.org
Undergrad inc BA journalism. New media seeking BJTC. Postgrad include MA online journalism (BJTC); PgDip broadcast journalism; newspaper journalism, AV media

University of Exeter
Northcote House, The Queens Drive
Exeter EX4 4QJ
01392 661000
admissions@exeter.ac.uk
www.ex.ac.uk

University of Leeds
Institute of Communications Studies
Roger Stevens Building
Leeds, West Yorkshire LS2 9JT
Undergrad 0113 343 2336, postgrad 0113 343 4006
admissions@leeds.ac.uk
www.leeds.ac.uk
Postgrad include MA International comms and MA or MSc comms

University of Salford
Salford M5 4WT
0161 295 5000
ugadmissions-exrel@salford.ac.uk
www.salford.ac.uk
HND media production. BSc audio, video and broadcast tech; BA journalism and broadcast; BA TV and radio; BSc professional broadcast techniques (1yr top-up). NCTJ

Sandwell College
Oldbury Business Centre
Pound Road, Oldbury
West Midlands B68 8NA
0121 556 6000
enquiries@sandwell.ac.uk
www.sandwell.ac.uk
HND media production (moving image)

Solihull College
Blossomfield Road, Solihull
West Midlands B91 1SB
0121 678 7001/2
enquiries@solihull.ac.uk
www.solihull.ac.uk
HND media production (moving image)

University of Surrey, Roehampton
Roehampton Lane
London SW15 5PU
020 8392 3000
enquiries@roehampton.ac.uk
www.Roehampton.ac.uk
MEng digital broadcasting. Range of BA and BSc. MPhil/PhD: cultural studies; drama, theatre and performance; film and TV. MA/MRes/PgDip performance. MA/PgDip media and cultural. MA music and culture. Research

University of Warwick
Coventry CV4 7AL
024 7652 3723
ugadmissions@warwick.ac.uk
www.warwick.ac.uk

University of Westminster
Watford Road, Harrow HA1 3TP
020 7911 5000
Harrow-admissions@
  westminster.ac.uk
www.wmin.ac.uk
MA art and media practice; audio production; communications policy; comms; hypermedia; int journalism; journalism; photo; digital and photo imaging, visual culture; marketing comms. PGCert regulation of telecomms. PgDip: periodical, broadcast journalism (BJTC). MSc animation

University of York
Admissions Office, Heslington
York YO10 5DD
01904 433533
admissions@york.ac.uk
www.york.ac.uk
Radio frequency engineering

Media studies courses

University of Aberdeen
01224 273504
sras@abdn.ac.uk
www.abdn.ac.uk/sras

University of Abertay, Dundee
01382 308080
sro@abertay.ac.uk
www.abertay.ac.uk

Anglia Polytechnic University
0845 271333
answers@apu.ac.uk
www.apu.ac.uk/comms

Barnsley College
01226 216569/216287
programme.enquiries@barnsley.ac.uk
www.barnsley.ac.uk

Basingstoke College of Technology
01256 254141
info@bcot.ac.uk
www.bcot.ac.uk

University of Bath
01225 383019
admissions@bath.ac.uk
www.bath.ac.uk

Bath Spa University College
01225 875875
enquiries@bathspa.ac.uk
www.bathspa.ac.uk

Birmingham University
Single honours 0121 414 6645
joint honours 0121 414 5495
Single honours:
  Y.L.Jacobs@bham.ac.uk
joint honours BA:
  jointhonours@bham.ac.uk
www.bham.ac.uk/socsci

Blackburn College
01254 551440
studentservices@blackburn.ac.uk
www.blackburn.ac.uk

Blackpool and The Fylde College
01253 504346
admissions@blackpool.ac.uk
www.blackpool.ac.uk
Associated college of Lancaster University

Bolton Institute of Higher Education
01204 900600
enquiries@bolton.ac.uk
www.bolton.ac.uk

Bournemouth Media School
01202 595360
bms@bournemouth.ac.uk
http://media.bournemouth.ac.uk

University of Bradford
01274 233081
p.e.dale@Bradford.ac.uk
www.eimc.brad.ac.uk

Bradford College
01274 433333
admissions@bilk.ac.uk
www.bradfordcollege.ac.uk
Associate of University of Bradford

Brighton University
01273 600900
admissions@brighton.ac.uk
www.brighton.ac.uk

Brunel University
01985 274000
admissions@brunel.ac.uk
www.brunel.ac.uk

Bucks Chilterns University College
01494 603050
marketing@bcuc.ac.uk
www.bcuc.ac.uk

Buckingham University
01208 814080
admissions@buckingham.ac.uk
www.buckingham.ac.uk

Canterbury Christ Church University College
01227 782349
Admissions@cant.ac.uk
www.cant.ac.uk

Cardiff University
029 2087 4041
jomec@cardiff.ac.uk
www.journalism.cf.ac.uk

Carmarthenshire College
01554 748000
admissions@colegsirgar.ac.uk
www.colegsirgar.ac.uk

University of Central Lancashire
01772 894730
ljwilliams1@uclan.ac.uk
www.uclan.ac.uk/facs/lbs/depts
  /journ/index.htm

Cheltenham and Gloucester College of Higher Education
01242 532700
marketing@glos.ac.uk
www.glos.ac.uk

Chester College
01244 375444
enquiries@chester.ac.uk
www.chester.ac.uk
College of the University of Liverpool

City College Manchester
0161 957 1790
admissions@ccm.ac.uk
www.ccm.ac.uk

City University
020 7040 8028 ext 8716
ugadmissions@city.ac.uk
www.city.ac.uk

Colchester Institute
01206 518777
info@colch-inst.ac.uk
www.colchester.ac.uk

Coleg Llandrillo Cymru
01492 543338/339
admissions@llandrillo.ac.uk
www.llandrillo.ac.uk

Coleg Menai
01248 370125
student.services@menai.ac.uk
www.menai.ac.uk

Coventry University
024 7688 7439
afuture.ad@coventry.ac.uk
www.coventry.ac.uk/csad/

Croydon College
020 8760 5948
info@croydon.ac.uk
www.croydon.ac.uk

Cumbria Institute of the Arts
01228 400300
info@cumbria.ac.uk
www.cumbria.ac.uk
*Formerly Cumbria College of
Art and Design*

De Montfort University
0116 255 1551
enquiry@dmu.ac.uk
www.dmu.ac.uk

Doncaster College
0800 358 7575
infocentre@don.ac.uk
www.don.ac.uk

University of Dundee
01382 344160
srs@dundee.ac.uk
www.dundee.ac.uk

**Ealing, Hammersmith and West
London College**
020 7565 1234
cic@hwlc.ac.uk
www.westlondoncollege.ac.uk

University of East Anglia
01603 592280
eas.admiss@uea.ac.uk
www.uea.ac.uk

East London University
020 8223 3000
admiss@uel.ac.uk
www.uel.ac.uk

**Edge Hill College of Higher
Education**
01695 584274
enquiries@edgehill.ac.uk
www.edgehill.ac.uk

Edinburgh College of Art
0131 221 6027
registry@eca.ac.uk
www.eca.ac.uk

Essex University
01206 873666
admit@essex.ac.uk
www.essex.ac.uk

Falmouth College of Arts
01326 370400
admissions@falmouth.ac.uk
www.falmouth.ac.uk

Farnborough College of Technology
0125 240 7040
info@farn-ct.ac.uk
www.farn-ct.ac.uk

Glamorgan University
0800 716925
enquiries@glam.ac.uk
www.glam.ac.uk

Glasgow Caledonian University
0141 331 3181
emg2@gcal.ac.uk
(for postgrad admissions only)
www.gcal.ac.uk

University of Glasgow
0141 330 4575
admissions@gla.ac.uk
www.gla.ac.uk

Goldsmiths College
undergrad 020 7919 7766
postgrad 020 7919 7060
media-comms@gold.ac.uk or
admissions@gold.ac.uk
www.goldsmiths.ac.uk

Greenwich University
020 8331 8000
courseinfo@greenwich.ac.uk
www.gre.ac.uk

Grimsby College
01472 315536
draperih@grimsby.ac.uk
www.grimsby.ac.uk

**Guildford College of Further and
Higher Education**
01483 448500
hnd@guildford.ac.uk
www.guildford.ac.uk

Henley College Coventry
024 76 626300
info@henley-cov.ac.uk
www.henley-cov.ac.uk

Hertfordshire University
01707 284800
admissions@herts.ac.uk
www.herts.ac.uk

Hopwood Hall College
01706 345346
enquiries@hopwood.ac.uk
www.hopwood.ac.uk

Huddersfield University
01484 478414
admissions@hud.ac.uk
www.hud.ac.uk/mh/media
/welcome.htm

Hull College
01482 598976
tbarber@hull-college.ac.uk
www.hull-college.ac.uk

**Institute of Communications
Studies**
undergrad 0113 343 2336
postgrad 0113 343 4006
admissions@leeds.ac.uk
www.leeds.ac.uk/ics

Kent Institute of Art and Design
01634 830022
clynsdale@kiad.ac.uk
www.kiad.ac.uk

University of Kent
01227 827272
recruitment@kent.ac.uk
www.kent.ac.uk

**King Alfreds College of Higher
Education**
01962 841515
admissions@wtrac.ac.uk
www.kingalfreds.ac.uk

Kingston University
020 8547 7053
admissions-info@kingston.ac.uk
www.kingston.ac.uk

Lancaster University
01524 594193
ugadmissions@lancaster.ac.uk or
pgadmissions@lancaster.ac.uk
www.lancs.ac.uk

Leeds College of Art and Design
0113 202 8000
info@leeds-art.ac.uk
www.leeds-art.ac.uk

Leeds Metropolitan University
0113 283 3113
course-enquiries@lmu.ac.uk
www.lmu.ac.uk

**Leeds Trinity and All Saints Centre
For Journalism**
0113 283 7100 ext. 398
m_Hampton@tasc.ac.uk
www.tasc.ac.uk

Leeds University
undergrad 0113 343 2336
postgrad 0113 343 4006
admissions@leeds.ac.uk
www.leeds.ac.uk

University of Leicester
0116 252 2415
admissions@le.ac.uk
www.le.ac.uk

University of Lincoln
01522 882000
enquiries@lincoln.ac.uk
www.lincoln.ac.uk

UHI Millennium Institute
01463 279000
uhi.prospectus@hbnet.com
www.uhi.ac.uk

Liverpool John Moores University
0151 231 5090
recruitment@livjm.ac.uk
www.livjm.ac.uk

Liverpool University
0151 794 5928
uksro@liv.ac.uk
www.liv.ac.uk

London Institute
020 7514 6853
info@lcp.linst.ac.uk
www.lcp.linst.ac.uk

London Metropolitan University
020 7320 1616
enquiries.city@londonmet.ac.uk
www.londonmet.ac.uk

Loughborough University
01509 263171
admissions@lboro.ac.uk
www.lboro.ac.uk

Luton University
01582 489286
enquiries@luton.ac.uk
www.luton.ac.uk

Manchester Metropolitan University
0161 247 1307
prospectus@mmu.ac.uk
www.mmu.ac.uk

Mid-Cheshire College
01606 720543
mlockett@midchesh.ac.uk
www.midchesh.ac.uk

Middlesex University
020 8411 5000
admissions@mdx.ac.uk
www.mdx.ac.uk

Napier University
0131 455 5203
dama@napier.ac.uk
www.napier.ac.uk

Nescot
020 8394 3038
www.nescot.ac.uk

Newcastle College
0191 200 4000
enquiries@ncl-coll.ac.uk
www.ncl.ac.uk

New College Nottingham
0115 910 0100
enquiries@ncn.ac.uk
www.ncn.ac.uk

North East Wales Institute of Higher Education
01978 293045
enquiries@newi.ac.uk
www.newi.ac.uk

North East Worcestershire College
01527 570020
info@ne-worcs.ac.uk
www.ne-worcs.ac.uk

North Tyneside College
0191 229 5000
infocent@ntyneside.ac.uk
www.ntyneside.ac.uk

North West Kent College
0800 074 1447
enquiries@nwkcollege.ac.uk
www.nwkcollege.ac.uk

Newcastle Upon Tyne University
0191 222 5594
admissions-enquiries@ncl.ac.uk
www.ncl.ac.uk

Northbrook College Sussex
01903 606060
admissions@nbcol.ac.uk
www.nbcol.ac.uk

North London University
020 7753 3355
admissions@unl.ac.uk
www.unl.ac.uk

North Oxfordshire School of Art and Design
01295 252221
enquiries@northox.ac.uk
www.northox.ac.uk
A division of North Oxfordshire College

Norwich City College of Further and Higher Education
01603 773136
clearing@ccn.ac.uk
www.ccn.ac.uk
Regional college of Anglia Polytechnic University

Northumbria University
0191 227 4064
ca.marketing@northumbria.ac.uk
www.northumbria.ac.uk

Nottingham Trent University
0115 941 5806
cbj@ntu.ac.uk
www.ntu.ac.uk

Oxford Brookes University
01865 483040
admissions@brookes.ac.uk
www.brookes.ac.uk

Paisley University
0800 027 1000
uni-direct@paisley.ac.uk
www.paisley.ac.uk

Peterborough Regional College
01733 767366
info@peterborough.ac.uk
www.peterborough.ac.uk

Plymouth University
01752 232232
Prospectus@plymouth.ac.uk
www.plymouth.ac.uk

University of Portsmouth
023 9284 8484
info.centre@port.ac.uk
www.port.ac.uk

Queen Margaret University College
0131 317 3000
Marketing@qmuc.ac.uk
www.qmuc.ac.uk

Robert Gordon University
01224 263900
i.centre@rgu.ac.uk
www.rgu.ac.uk

Royal Holloway, University of London
01784 434455
undergrad-office@rhul.ac.uk
www.rhul.ac.uk

St Helens College
01744 733766
enquire@sthelens.ac.uk
www.sthelens.ac.uk
Associate college of Liverpool John Moores University

St Martins College
01524 384384
admissions@ucsm.ac.uk
www.ucsm.ac.uk

St Marys College
020 8240 4000
cherryb@smuc.ac.uk
www.smuc.ac.uk

Sheffield Hallam University
0114 225 5555
admissions@shu.ac.uk
www.shu.ac.uk

Sheffield University
0114 222 2500
Journalism@sheffield.ac.uk
www.sheffield.ac.uk

South Bank University
020 7815 7815
www.sbu.ac.uk

South Birmingham College
0121 694 6338
stacey.davies@sbc.ac.uk
www.sbc.ac.uk

South Devon College
01803 406406
dswann@southdevon.ac.uk
www.southdevon.ac.uk

South Nottingham College
0115 914 6400
enquiries@south-nottingham.ac.uk
www.south-nottingham.ac.uk

South Thames College
020 891 8777
studentservices@
    south-thames.ac.uk
www.south-thames.ac.uk

Southampton Institute
023 8031 9000
fmas@solent.ac.uk
www.solent.ac.uk

Southport College
01704 392627
webmasterj@
    southport-college.ac.uk
www.southport.mernet.ac.uk

University of Southampton
023 8059 6781
artsrec@soton.ac.uk
www.arts.soton.ac.uk/

Staffordshire University
01782 294869
a.dinnivan@staffs.ac.uk
www.staffs.ac.uk

Stirling University
01786 467044
stirling.media@stir.ac.uk
www.external.stir.ac.uk

Stockport College of Further and Higher Education
0161 958 3417
admissions@stockport.ac.uk
www.stockport.ac.uk

Stratford-upon-Avon College
01789 266245 x3137
college@strat-avon.ac.uk
www.strat-avon.ac.uk

Suffolk College
01473 255885
info@suffolk.ac.uk
www.suffolk.ac.uk

Sunderland University
0191 515 3000
student-helpline@sunderland.ac.uk
www.sunderland.ac.uk

Surrey Institute of Art and Design
01252 722441
registry@surrart.ac.uk
www.surrart.ac.uk

Sussex University
01273 678416
ug.admissions@sussex.ac.uk
www.sussex.ac.uk

Swansea Institute of Higher Education
01792 481094
enquiry@sihe.ac.uk
www.sihe.ac.uk

Teesside University
01642 384229
reg@tees.ac.uk
www.tees.ac.uk

Tameside College
0161 908 6789
Via Website
www.tameside.ac.uk

Thames Valley University
0800 036 888
learning.advice@tvu.ac.uk
www.tvu.ac.uk

Trinity College Carmarthen
01267 676767
registry@trinity-cm.ac.uk
www.trinity-cm.ac.uk
University College Chichester
01243 816002
admissions@ucc.ac.uk
www.ucc.ac.uk
University College Northampton
01243 735500
julie.bedster@northampton.ac.uk
www.northampton.ac.uk
University College, Worcester
01905 855000
admissions@worc.ac.uk
www.worc.ac.uk
**University of Central England in
Birmingham**
0121 331 6650
media@uce.ac.uk
www.uce.ac.uk
University of Surrey, Roehampton
020 8392 3000
enquiries@roehampton.ac.uk
www.roehampton.ac.uk
University of Ulster at Coleraine
08 700 400 700
online@ulster.ac.uk
www.ulster.ac.uk
University of Wales, Aberystwyth
01907 622021
ug-admissions@aber.ac.uk
www.aber.ac.uk
University of Wales, Bangor
01248 383216
mediastudies@bangor.ac.uk
www.bangor.ac.uk
University of Wales, Swansea
01792 295111
admissions@swan.ac.uk
www.swan.ac.uk
University of Wales, Lampeter
01570 422351
admissions@lamp.ac.uk
www.lamp.ac.uk
Wakefield College
01924 789111
courseinfo@wakcoll.ac.uk
www.wakcoll.ac.uk
**Warwickshire College, Royal
Leamington Spa, Rugby and
Moreton Morrell**
01926 318000
enquiries@warkscol.ac.uk
www.warkscol.ac.uk
University of the West of England
0117 344 3333
admissions@uwe.ac.uk
www.uwe.ac.uk
West Herts College
01923 812525
admissions@westherts.ac.uk
www.westherts.ac.uk
University of Westminster
020 7911 5000
Harrow-admissions@
    westminster.ac.uk
www.wmin.ac.uk

Wirral Metropolitan College
0151 551 7777
enquiries@wmcmail.wmc.ac.uk
www.wmc.ac.uk
University of Wolverhampton
01902 322222
admissions@wlv.ac.uk
www.wlv.ac.uk
**Yorkshire Coast College of Further
Education**
01723 372105
admissions@coastco.ac.uk
www.ycoastco.ac.uk

Glossary

Press

ABC: The Audit Bureau of Circulations, the company that monitors and verifies magazines and newspaper sales. "ABCs" is the popular term for the circulation figures it publishes: see explainer (page 21).

average issue readership: The number of people who, when surveyed, say they have read a newspaper or magazine within the lifespan of the issue. Also known as AIR.

Brad: British Rate and Data, a company that records every periodical that carries advertising in the UK

broadsheet: Larger size of paper, used by the news sections of most quality UK newspapers; usually 580mm × 380mm.

bulks: Copies of newspapers distributed free to targeted places such as hotels and airlines. See explainer on *ABCs*.

byline: A journalist's name next to an article. Reporters live for bylines like salesmen live for bonuses.

circulation: The number of copies a newspaper or magazines sells or distributes in a defined period (one month or six months). Not the same as *average issue readership*.

copy: Words submitted for publication.

DPS: Double-page spread.

freesheet: A newspaper or magazine distributed free of charge and usually paid for by advertising.

journalist: Someone who works on the editorial side of a newspaper or magazine.

leader: Editorial opinion column expressing the views of the newspaper (or its owner).

masthead: The bit with the title at the top of the front page.

news agency: Company that sells news stories to a newspaper or magazine, usually delivered electronically to each journalist's desktop over the *wires*. The biggest are Reuters, the UK-based Press Association (PA) and the US-based Associated Press (AP).

Newspaper Society: Body representing the UK's regional press.

Page 3: Famous topless model feature in the Sun. Not always on page three.

PPA: The Periodical Publishers Association. Represents magazine publishers in the UK.

reporter: Someone who writes news stories. One of many kinds of journalist.

scoop: The act of printing a news story (or, these days, a celebrity interview) before a rival. The "scoop culture" of the UK press has been criticised for getting in the way of balanced news reporting.

standfirst: The short paragraph at the top of a feature article, below the headline, that summarises it for the reader. Usually written by a subeditor.

subeditor: Journalist who lays out and edits copy in a newspaper or magazine. Will also write the headline, standfirst and other page furniture such as picture captions.

tabloid: Smaller size of paper, used by more downmarket titles and (recently) the features sections of some quality papers; usually half the size of broadsheet.

wires: Electronic delivery of news and pictures, sent by agencies to a journalist's desktop.

TV

analogue television: Television transmitted in "radio waves"; in other words, not digitally. Most terrestrial TV in the UK is still transmitted in analogue.

Barb: The Broadcasters Audience Research Board, which measures television audiences.

BBC: The British Broadcasting Corporation. The UK's public service broadcaster.

BSkyB: Britain's only satellite broadcaster, owned by Rupert Murdoch's News Corporation.

Broadcasting standards commission: Outgoing regulator of standards in fairness in broadcasting. Replaced by Ofcom from December 2003.

cable television: Television delivered into the home through an underground cable. Largely concentrated in urban areas. Can be digital or analogue.

digital television: Television transmitted in binary format; can be delivered by cable, by satellite or terrestrially. Allows greater choice of channels, better quality and interactive services.

encryption: The encoding of television signals for security purposes, usually so they can only be watched by paying subscribers.

free-to-air: A television service that can be received without decoding or paying a fee.

freeview: A commercial free-to-air digital terrestrial service; a partnership between the BBC, BSkyB and transmission firm Crown Castle.

Independent television commission (ITC): Outgoing regulator of independent television. Subsumed into Ofcom in December 2003.

ITV: Channel 3. Once the only independent television channel.

licence fee: How the BBC generates most of its revenue. A colour TV licence cost £116 in 2003.

multichannel television: TV that includes more than just the five analogue terrestrial channels. If you receive cable, satellite or digital terrestrial, you are in a "multichannel home".

multiplex: A single digital terrestrial transmission comprising several channels. There are six television multiplexes.

Pact: Producers' alliance for cinema and television. Represents independent television production companies.

pay-per-view: An individual programme, which the viewer has to pay to see.

pay-TV: A general term for subscription services the viewer has to pay to watch.

radio spectrum: The total capacity of radio frequencies that can be received. A small part of the electromagnetic spectrum, which is made up of a range of phenomena including gamma rays, X-rays, ultraviolet radiation and visible light.

terrestrial television: Television beamed from a ground transmitter directly to the home; can be analogue or digital.

satellite television: Television received through a satellite dish, controlled in Britain by BSkyB. BSkyB has switched all its television services to digital.

watershed: Before 9pm, nothing may be shown on television that is considered unsuitable for children; after 9pm, nothing may be shown that is considered unsuitable for adults. 9pm is therefore the "watershed".

Radio

access radio: Not-for-profit, community-based radio.

analogue radio: Radio transmitted in waves; in other words, not digitally. Most terrestrial radio in the UK is still transmitted in analogue.

audience share: In Rajar figures, the percentage of all radio listening hours that a station accounts for within its transmission area.

BBC: The British Broadcasting Corporation. Britain's public service broadcaster.

Broadcasting standards commission: Outgoing regulator of standards in fairness in broadcasting. Replaced by Ofcom from December 2003.

digital radio: Radio transmitted in binary format. Allows greater choice of channels, better quality and interactive services.

multiplex: A single digital terrestrial transmission, comprising several channels. There are two national and almost 50 local multiplexes.

Rajar: Radio Joint Audience Research, the company that calculates radio audience figures.

Radio authority: Outgoing regulator, whose job was to license and regulate commercial radio. Replaced by Ofcom from December 2003.

radio spectrum: The total capacity of radio frequencies that can be received. A small part of the electromagnetic spectrum, which is made up of a range of phenomena including gamma rays, X-rays, ultraviolet radiation and visible light.

Radiocommunications agency: Outgoing agency, responsible for the non-military management of the radio spectrum. Replaced by Ofcom from December 2003.

reach: In Rajar figures, the number of people aged 15 or over who tune to a radio station within at least a quarter-hour period over the course of a week, and have listened to the station for at least five minutes within that quarter-hour.

Books

A-format, B-format: The two main "sizes" in which paperbacks are published. A-format are smaller (110mm × 178mm) and usually more downmarket; B-format are larger (130mm × 198mm) and usually further upmarket.

acquisition editor: Someone in a publishing house who identifies and negotiates to acquire new titles for publication.

advance: Initial payment to authors against which any royalties are offset.

commissioning editor: Someone in a publishing house who looks for authors to write particular books for publication; sometimes also an acquiring editor.

imprint: The name of the publisher; usually a brand operating under the auspices of a large publishing house.

literary agent: Person who finds marketable authors and tries to sell rights in their work to publishers, taking a commission in the process.

Nielsen Bookscan: Company that produces bestseller lists and further analysis of the UK book industry.

royalties: Payment received by the author as a percentage of sales. Usually set off against the advance.

rights: The main commodity in the books business. Rights can be separated out to include film, television, multimedia, merchandising and rights to publish abroad.

New media

3G: Third-generation mobile phones, capable of video messaging, location mapping and other technical wizardries such as showing Premiership goals.

blog: see *weblog*

broadband: High-speed internet access, usually 512kbps (kilobytes per second) as opposed to the 56kbps of a standard modem. NTL's 150kbps service, advertised as "broadband", is often referred to as "midband".

browser: Software usually used to surf, or "browse", the internet. Microsoft's Internet Explorer is the most popular.

coverage: The percentage of the country or the population that can be reached by a mobile phone network.

Oftel: Outgoing telecommunications regulator. Replaced by Ofcom in December 2003.

search engine: Service allowing you to find a word or image anywhere on the world wide web. Google is the best.

short message service (SMS): Text messaging.

weblog: Diary-style web page in which new entries are added at the top and old ones drift to the bottom; popular among those who want a personal web page but don't necessarily know much about the internet.

Media law

Communications Act: Legislation under which Ofcom becomes the super-regulator for the broadcasting industry. Due to be enacted in December 2003.

contempt of court: A crime punishable by imprisonment or a fine. Journalists might find themselves in contempt of court by publishing prejudicial information about a defendant during a trial, or publishing any information about a person that is specifically banned in a court order or injunction.

culture select committee: Influential cross-party parliamentary committee that examines issues in culture, media and sport.

DCMS: Department of Culture, Media and Sport. Headed by culture secretary Tessa Jowell.

European convention on human rights: European Union legislation, incorporated in British law through the Human Rights Act 1998. Includes articles protecting right to freedom of expression, but also the right to privacy.

European court of human rights: Highest European court dealing with human rights law.

Law commission: Senior lawyers who meet to recommend changes in the law.

libel: A civil "tort", for which a complainant may sue for damages. Generally speaking, a journalist commits libel by publishing or broadcasting something that is defamatory, even by implication, to a person or a small enough group of people; *unless* the journalist can prove that what they wrote or published was true, or it was fair comment based firmly in fact, or it was an accurate, contemporaneous report of something said in parliament or court. But that isn't the half of it: see the latest edition of McNae's Essential Law for Journalists.

Advertising & PR

Advertising Association: Body representing the advertising and promotional marketing industries.

Advertising Standards Authority: Regulator for advertising in the non-broadcast media. Below the line: Marketing services such as PR, direct marketing, market research and sales promotion are said to be "below the line"; advertising directly in media is "above the line".

creatives: In advertising, art directors and copywriters, who often work in pairs on an ad.

display: Advertising in the main body of a publication (as opposed to *classified*).

demographic data: Information defining a population according to factors such as age, sex and income; used to target an ad or marketing campaign.

media agency: Agency that controls the purchase of advertising space.

press release: Information sent by PR agencies and other publicists to journalists, hoping for inclusion: most go in the recycle bin.

solus: In publishing, the only advert on a page.

Careers & training

Bectu: Broadcasting, Entertainment, Cinematograph and Theatre Union. Represents workers in broadcasting, film, theatre, entertainment, leisure and interactive media.

best boy: In broadcasting, the second-in-command of a lighting team.

BJTC: Broadcast journalism training council. Accredits broadcast journalism courses.

grip: In broadcasting, someone who handles the equipment that enables a camera to move.

NCTJ: National Council for the Training of Journalists. Accredits newspaper and magazine journalism courses.

NUJ: National Union of Journalists. Represents journalists.

Pact: Producers' alliance for cinema and television. Represents independent television production companies.

Skillset: National training organisation for broadcast, film, video and interactive media.

Resources

7 Day Press
Glasgow
0141 572 0060
daypress@aol.com
www.7daypress.co.uk

AFX News
London
020 7422 4870
john.manley@afxnews.com
www.afxnews.com

Agence France-Presse, UK
London
020 7353 7461
london.bureau@afp.com
www.afp.com

Airtime Television News
Maidenhead
01628 482763
info@airtimetv.co.uk
www.airtimetv.co.uk

Allscot News Agency
Haddington
01620 822578
allscotnewsuk@compuserve.com

Allstar Picture Library
Scarborough
01723 367264
library@allstarpl.com
www.allstarpl.com

American News Service
London
020 7221 4964

ANSA News Agency
London
020 7240 5514
ansalondra@yahoo.com
www.ansa.it

Apex Photo Agency
Exeter
01392 824024
apex@apexnewspix.com
www.apexnewspix.com

APTN
London
020 7482 7400
aptninfo@ap.org
www.aptn.com

Associated Press News Agency
London
020 7353 1515
www.ap.org

Australian Associated Press
London
020 7353 0153
news.london@aap.com.au
www.aap.com.au

Australian Consolidated Press
London
020 7470 8761
Di@acplon.com
www.acp.com.au

BBC Picture Archives
London
020 8225 7193
commercial.unit@bbc.co.uk
www.bbcresearchcentral.com

Bellis News Agency
Colwyn Bay
01492 549503
bellisd@aol.com

Big Picture Press Agency
London
020 7250 3555
info@bigpictures.co.uk

Bloomberg LP
London
020 7330 7500
aedmonds@bloomberg.net
www.bloomberg.com

Bournemouth News & Picture Service
Bournemouth
01202 558833
news@bnps.co.uk
www.bnps.co.uk

Bruinvels News & Media-Press Media & Broadcasting Agents
Dorking
01306 887680
bruinvelsnewsmedia@supanet.com
www.sourcenet.co.uk/dorking
/services/markpr/bruinvels

Calyx Multimedia
Swindon
01793 520131
richard@calyxpix.com
www.calypix.com

Camera Press
London
020 7378 1300
f.wills@camerapress.com
www.camerapress.com

The Canadian Press
London
020 7353 6355

Capital Pictures
London
020 7253 1122
sales@capitalpictures.com
www.capitalpictures.com

Cassidy & Leigh Southern News Service
Hindhead
01428 607330
denis@cassidyandleigh.com

Caters News Agency
Birmingham
0121 616 1100
news@catersnews.com

Cavendish Press
Manchester
0161 237 1066
newsdesk@cavendish-press.co.uk
www.cavendish-press.co.uk

Central News
London
020 7236 0116
news@centralnews.co.uk
www.centralnews.co.uk

Central News Network
Falkirk
01324 630505
jimdavisofcnn@aol.com

Central Press Features
Bristol
0117 934 3600
mail@central-press.co.uk
www.central-press.co.uk

Chapman & Page
Boston
01205 290477
chapmanpage@internett.demon
.co.uk

Chester News Service
Chester
01244 345562
news@chesterstandard.co.uk
www.chesterstandardnow.co.uk

Chester Press Bureaux
Chester
01244 678575
ron@chesterpb.freeserve.co.uk

Computer Wire
London
020 7919 5000
kevin.white@computerwire.co.uk
www.computerwire.com

Cotswold & Swindon News Service
Swindon
01793 485461
cotswin@stares.co.uk
www.stares.co.uk

Coventry News Service
Coventry
024 7663 3777
adent@advent-communications
.co.uk
www.advent-communications
.co.uk

David Hoffman Photo Library
London
020 8981 5041
lib@hoffmanphotos.com
www.hoffmanphotos.com

DBSP
Glasgow
0141 427 5344
stewart.mcdougall@btclick.com

DobsonAgency.Co.UK
Scarborough
01723 585141
dobsonpix@aol.com
www.dobsonagency.co.uk

Double Red Photographic
Barrow upon Humber
01469 531416
doublered@atlas.co.uk
www.doublered.co.uk

Dow Jones International Marketing Services
London
020 7842 9600
jeremy.ray@dowjones.com
www.dowjones.com

Dow Jones Newswires
London
020 7842 9900
djequitiesnews.london@
dowjones.com
www.dowjones.com

DPA (German Press Agency)
London
020 7233 2888
london@dpa.com
www.dpa.com

Dragon News & Picture Agency
Swansea
01792 464800
mail@dragon-pictures.com
www.dragon-pictures.com

Drivetime (Motoring Press Agency)
Gloucester
01452 522220
drive_edit@yahoo.co.uk

**Edittech International
(IT News Agency)**
Chippenham
01249 444416
elspethwales@aol.com
www.edittech.com

Emirates News Agency
London
020 7228 1060
mia@mia.gb.com
www.mia.gb.com

Empics Sports Photo Agency
Nottingham
0115 8447447
info@empics.com
www.empics.com

Essex News Service
Witham
01376 521222
perfect@essexnews.freeserve.co.uk

Evertons News Agency
Birmingham
0121 4542931
clive.everton@talk21.com

Feature Story News
London
020 7485 0303
wanklyn@featurestory.com
www.featurestory.com

Fleetline News Service
London
020 8444 9183
fleetlinenews@hotmail.com

Frank Ryan News Service
Dumfriess
01387 253700
smeddum@btinternet.com

Freemans Press Agency
Barnstable
01271 324000
tonyfreemanpressagency@bp.com
www.bipp.com

Front Page News Agency
Worcestershire
01527 892123
saralain@btopenworld.com
www.frontpagenewsagency.co.uk

Future Events News Service
London
020 8672 3191
uk@fens.demon.co.uk
www.fens.com

Getty Images
London
0800 376 7981
allsportlondon@gettyimages.com
www.gettyimages.com

Gloucestershire News Service
Gloucester
01452 522270
john.hawkins@glosnews.com
www.glosnews.com

Gosnay's Sports Agency
Leeds
0113 258 5864
gosnays@aol.com

**Government News Network
North West**
Manchester
0161 952 4500
manchester@gnn.gov.uk
www.gnn.gov.uk

**Government News Network
East Midlands**
Nottingham
0115 971 2780
nottingham@gnn.gov.uk
www.gnn.gov.uk

**Government News Network
London**
London
020 7261 8795
london@gnn.gsi.gov.uk
www.gnn.gov.uk

**Government News Network
North East**
Newcastle upon Tyne
0191 202 3600
newcastle@gnn.gov.uk
www.gnn.gov.uk

**Government News Network
West Midlands**
Birmingham
0121 626 2033
birmingham@gnn.gov.uk
www.gnn.gov.uk

**Government News Network
Yorkshire & The Humber**
Leeds
0113 283 6599
leeds@gnn.gsi.gov.uk
www.gnn.gov.uk

Grant Burton Photography
London
020 7253 6111
grant@burtonphoto.co.uk

Harrison Photography
Belfast
028 9066 3100
mail@harrisonphotography.co.uk
www.harrisonphotos.com

Hayters Teamwork
London
020 8808 3300
sport@haytersteamwork.com
www.haytersteamwork.co.uk

Headline Photo Agency
Leicester
0116 232 0310
asp@sports-photos.co.uk
www.sporting-heroes.net

HoldTheFrontPage
Derby
0116 227 3122
pastill@nep.co.uk
www.holdthefrontpage.co.uk

Independent Radio News (IRN)
London
020 7430 4814
irn@itn.co.uk
www.irn.co.uk

Independent Sports Network
London
020 7827 7700
jane.tatnall@isntv.co.uk

Inter-Continental News
Stanmore
020 8954 1294
intercontnews@aol.com

Interpress of London and New York
New York
+1 212 873 0772
itpnyc@aol.com

**Islamic Republic News Agency
(IRNA)**
Middlesex
020 8903 1630
ahmad.nazari@kcl.ac.uk
www.irna.com

ITAR TASS News Agency
London
020 7580 5543
www.itar-tass.com

Jarrold's Press Agency
Ipswich
01473 219193
jarroldspress@cix.compulink.co.uk

Jenkins Group
Rochester
01634 830888
nickjenkins@tesco.net

Jewish Chronicle News Agency
London
020 7415 1500
marketing@thejc.com
www.thejc.com

JIJI Press
London
020 7936 2847
edit@jiji.co.uk
www.jiji.co.jp

John Connor Press Associates
Lewes
01273 486851
news@jcpa.co.uk

John Fairfax (UK)
London
020 7688 2777
fairfax-uk-edit@compuserve.com
www.f2.com

John Wardle Agency
Manchester
0161 861 8015
iwhittell@aol.com

Kent Messenger Group
Aylesford
01622 717880
deales@thekmgroup.co.uk
www.kentonline.co.uk

Kuwait News Agency (KUNA)
London
020 7278 5445
kuwait@btclick.com

Kyodo News
London
020 7766 4400
london@kyodonews.jp
www.kyodo.co.jp

Lakeland Press Agency
Lancashire
01539 431749
craigwilson23@yahoo.co.uk

M&Y News Agency
Portsmouth
023 9282 0311
mynews@dircon.co.uk
www.mynewsagency.co.uk

M2 Communications
Coventry
024 7623 8200
m2pw@m2.com
www.m2.com

Maghreb Arabe Press
London
020 7401 8146
mapldn@aol.com
www.map.co.ma

Market News International
London
020 7634 1655
ukeditorial@marketnews.com
www.marketnews.com

Marshall's Sports Service
Kingswinford
01384 274877
marshall@
    bham-sport.demon.co.uk

Masons News Service
Cambridge
01223 351342
newsdesk@masons-news.co.uk
www.campix.co.uk

Media Features
London
020 7436 3678
leozanelli@aol.com

Meridian News
Southampton
023 8022 2555
news@meridiantv.com
www.meridiantv.com

Mid Glamorgan Press Agency
Porthcawl
01656 782915
midglam@aol.com

**National News Press &
Photographic Agency**
London
020 7684 3000
news@nationalnews.co.uk

News of Australia
London
020 7702 1355
natalie.gray@newsint.co.uk
www.news.com.au

News Team International
Birmingham
0121 246 5511
commercial@newsteam.co.uk
www.newsteam.co.uk

Newsflash Scotland
Stirling
01786 477310
news@nflash.co.uk
www.newsflashscotland.com

Nunn Syndication
London
020 7407 4666
isabel@nunn-syndication.com
www.nunn-syndication.com

The Press Association (PA)
London
020 7963 7000
information@pa.press.net
www.pa.press.net
*National news agency of the UK and
Ireland; provider of real time news
and sports information and images to
every national and regional daily
newspaper, major broadcasters, online
publishers and a wide range
of commercial organisations*

PA News (Birmingham)
Birmingham
0121 224 7686
pa_birmingham@hotmail.com
www.pa.press.net

PA News (Liverpool)
Liverpool
0151 472 2548
paliverpool@pa.press.net
www.pa.press.net

PA News (Scotland)
Glasgow
0870 830 6725
pascotland@pa.press.net
www.pa.press.net

Parliamentary & EU News Service
London
020 7233 8283
info@parliamentary-monitoring
    .co.uk
www.parliamentary-monitoring
    .co.uk

PPP News Service
London
020 8886 2721
wkastor@compuserve.com

Press Agency (Gatwick)
Peacehaven
01273 583103
p.shirley@ukonline.co.uk

Press Trust of India
London
020 7494 0602
ptilondon@aol.com
www.ptinews.com

The Profile Group (UK)
London
020 7405 4455
info@profilegroup.co.uk
www.profilegroup.co.uk

Racenews
London
020 7704 0326
racenews@compuserve.com
www.racenews.co.uk

Raymonds Press Agency
Derby
01332 340404
news@raymondspress.com

The Receipt Supply Agency
Telford
01952 883587
Cecilialaurie.editors@0800dial.com

Reuters
London
020 7250 1122
robert.woodward@reuters.com
www.reuters.com

Rex Features
London
020 7278 7294
rex@rexfeatures.com
www.rexfeatures.com

Richard Harris News
Branton
01228 670381
richardwjharris@aol.com

**Robinsons Parliamentary
News Agency**
London
020 7219 4283

Ross Parry Agency
Farsley
0113 2361842
newsdesk@rossparry.co.uk
www.rossparry.co.uk

Scase News Service
Kings Lynn
01485 600650
news@scase.co.uk
www.scase.co.uk

Scottish News & Sport
Glasgow
0141 221 3602
info@snspix.com
www.snspix.com

Smith Davis Press
Stoke on Trent
01782 829850
smith-davis@smith-davis.co.uk
www.smith-davis.co.uk

Snowmedia Consultancy
London
020 8672 9800
info@snowmedia.net
www.snowmedia.net

Solent News and Photo Agency
Southampton
023 8045 8800
news@solentnews.biz
www.solentnews.biz

Somerset News Service
Taunton
01823 331856
somersetnews@cwcom.net

South West News & Picture Service
Bristol
0117 906 6500
news@swns.com
www.swns.com

Space Press News and Pictures
Cheshire
01477 533403
scoop2001@aol.com

Specialist News Service
London
020 7831 3267
desk@snsnews.co.uk

Speed Media One
Horsham
01403 259661
info@speedmediaone.co.uk
www.speedmediaone.co.uk

The Sport & General Press Agency
London
020 7336 0632
www.alphapress.com

Sportsphoto
Scarborough
01723 367264
library@sportsphoto.co.uk
www.sportsphoto.co.uk

TV News
London
020 7485 0303
london.bureau@featurestory.com
www.fsntv.com

TV News London
Hartfordshire
020 8275 8854
info@tvnewslondon.co.uk
www.tvnewslondon.co.uk

UK Press
London
020 7515 3878
info@ukpress.com
www.ukpress.com

Unique Entertainment News
London
020 7453 1650
amie.oconnor@unique.com
www.unique.com

Universal Pictorial Press & Agency
London
020 7421 6000
contacts@uppa.co.uk
www.uppa.co.uk

Wales News & Picture Service
Cardiff
029 2066 6366
news@walesnews.com
www.walesnews.com

Warwickshire News & Picture Agency
Leamington Spa
01926 424181
barrie@tracynews.co.uk

Wessex Features and Photos Agency
Hungerford
01488 686810
news@britishnews.co.uk
www.britishnews.co.uk

White's Press Agency
Sheffield
0114 255 3975
newsdesk@press-agency.com

World Entertainment News Network
London
020 7607 2757
sales@wenn.com
www.wenn.com

Xinhua News Agency of China
London
020 7586 8437
xinhua@easynet.co.uk
www.xinhuanet.com

Picture libraries

The Advertising Archives
London
020 7435 6540
suzanne@advertisingarchives.co.uk
www.advertisingarchives.co.uk
British and American press ads and magazine illustration

A1PIX Digital Picture Library
London
020 7415 7045
london@a1pix.com
www.a1pix.com
Geography, festivals, travel, nature, lifestyle, business

Alvey & Towers
Leicestershire
01530 45011
alveytower@aol.com
www.alveyandtowers.com
Transport

Andes Press Agency
London
020 7613 5417
apa@andespressagency.com
www.andespressagency.com
Travel and social documentary worldwide, Latin America, UK, Middle East

Andrew N Gagg's Photo Flora
Worcester
01905 748515
a.n.gagg@ntlworld.com
www.ntlworld.com/a.n.gagg/photo/photoflora.html
Plants

Art Directors & Trip Photo Library
Surrey
020 8642 3593
images@artdirectors.co.uk
www.artdirectors.co.uk
Worldwide culture

Artbank Illustration Library
London
020 7608 3333
info@artbank.com
www.artbank.com

Associated Press Photo Archive
London
020 7427 4263
london_photolibrary@ap.org
www.apwideworld.com

Aviation Images – Mark Wagner
London
020 8944 5225
pictures@aviation-images.com
www.aviation-images.com

Aviation Picture Library
London
020 8566 7712
avpix@aol.com
www.aviationpictures.com

Axel Poignant Archive
London
020 7636 2555
Rpoignant@aol.com
Anthropological and ethnographic subjects

BFI Stills, Posters and Designs
London
020 7957 4797
stills.films@bfi.org.uk
www.bfi.org.uk/collections/stills/index.html

British Library Reproductions
London
020 7412 7614
imagesonline@bl.uk
www.bl.uk/imagesonline

Bryan & Cherry Alexander Photography
Dorset
01258 473006
alexander@arcticphoto.co.uk
www.arcticphoto.co.uk
Arctic and Antarctic specialists

Cephas Picture Library
Surrey
020 8979 8647
pictures@cephas.co.uk
www.cephas.com
Wine and vineyards, whisky and brandy, food and drink

Chris Howes/Wild Places Photography
Cardiff
029 2048 6557
photos@wildplaces.co.uk
Travel, topography and natural history, plus action sports and caving

Christie's Images
London
020 7582 1282
imageslondon@christies.com
www.christiesimages.com
Fine and decorative art

Christopher Ware Pictures
Glamorgan
01446 732816
crware@ntlworld.com
South-east Wales including aviation, docks

Chrysalis Images
London
020 7314 1400
Tforshaw@chrysalisbooks.co.uk
www.chrysalisbooks.co.uk
History, transport, cookery, crafts, space

Collections
London
020 8883 0083
collections@btinternet.com
www.collectionspicturelibrary.com
Britain and Ireland: people and traditional culture

Country Life Pictures
London
020 7261 6337
camilla_costello@ipcmedia.com
www.countrylifelibrary.co.uk

David Hoffman Photo Library
London
020 8981 5041
info@hoffmanphotos.com
www.hoffmanphotos.com
Social issues, built from journalistic work since 1970s

David King Collection
London
020 7226 0149
davidkingcollection@
  btopenworld.com
Soviet Union and other Communist movements

E&E Picture Library
Kent
01303 812608
isobel@
  picture-library.freeserve.co.uk
www.picture-library.freeserve.co.uk
World religion

Edifice
London
020 7242 0740
info@edificephoto.com
www.edificephoto.com
Buildings

Education Photos
Surrey
01483 203846
johnwalmsley@
  educationphotos.co.uk
www.educationphotos.co.uk

English Heritage Photo Library
London
020 7973 3338
celia.sterne@
  english-heritage.org.uk
www.english-heritage.org.uk

Exile Images
East Sussex
01273 208741
pics@exileimages.co.uk
www.exileimages.co.uk
Refugees, protest, asylum seekers, conflict

ffotograff
Cardiff
0292 023 6879
ffotograff@easynet.co.uk
www.ffotograff.com
Travel, exploration, the arts, architecture, culture, Wales, Middle East and Far East

Financial Times Pictures
London
020 7873 3671
photosynd@ft.com
Business related

Fogden Wildlife Photographs
Western Isles
01876 580245
susan.fogden@virgin.net
www.fogdenphotos.com
Natural history

Food Features
Surrey
0125 273 5240
frontdesk@foodpix.co.uk
www.foodpix.co.uk
Food and drink

Forest Life Picture Library
Edinburgh
0131 314 6411
n.campbell@forestry.gsi.gov.uk
www.forestry.gov.uk/pictures
Official image bank of the Forestry Commission

Frank Lane Picture Agency
Suffolk
01728 860789
pictures@flpa-images.co.uk
www.flpa-images.co.uk
Natural history, environment, pets and weather.

Galaxy Picture Library
Bucks
01628 521338
robin@galaxypix.com
www.galaxypix.com
Astronomy & the sky

Garden Picture Library
London
020 7228 4332
info@gardenpicture.com
www.gardenpicture.com
Gardening

Geo Aerial Photography
London
020 8764 6292
geo.aerial@geo-group.co.uk
www.geo-group.co.uk
Aerial photographs

Geo Science Features Picture Library
Kent
01233 812707
gsf@geoscience.demon.co.uk
www.geoscience.demon.co.uk
Natural Science and natural history

Geoslides Photography
London
020 8764 6292
geoslides@geo-group.co.uk
www.geo-group.co.uk
Landscape and human interest

Heather Angel/Natural Visions
Surrey
01252 716700
info@naturalvisions.co.uk
www.naturalvisions.co.uk
Online images of worldwide wildlife

Holt Studios International
Berkshire
01488 683523
library@holt-studios.co.uk
www.holt-studios.co.uk
World agriculture and horticulture

Hutchison Picture Library
West Sussex
01273 440113
library@hutchisonpictures.co.uk
www.hutchisonpictures.co.uk
Worldwide contemporary images

Images of Africa Photobank
Staffordshire
01543 262898
info@imagesofafrica.co.uk
www.imagesofafrica.co.uk
130,000 images of 20 African countries

Imperial War Museum Photograph Archive
London
020 7416 5333
photos@iwm.org.uk
www.iwm.org.uk/collections
  /photos.htm
20th-century conflicts

International Photobank
Dorset
01305 854145
peter@internationalphotobank.co.uk
www.internationalphotobank.co.uk
400,000 travel images

Jacqui Hurst
London
020 8743 2315 and 0797 078 1336
jacquih@dircon.co.uk
Designers and applied artists, regional food producers and markets

James Davis Worldwide
West Sussex
01273 452252
library@eyeubiquitous.com
Travel collection

Jessica Strang Photo Library
London
020 7247 8982
jessica.strang@virgin.net
architecture, interiors and gardens

Jim Henderson Photographer & Publisher
Aberdeen
01339 882149
JHende7868@aol.com
www.jimhendersonphotography
  .com
Scenic and general of Aberdeenshire; Aurora Borealis and Egyptology

John Cleare/Mountain Camera
Wiltshire
01747 820320
cleare@btinternet.com
www.mountaincamera.com
Mountains and trekking

John Heseltine Archive
Gloucester
01453 873792
john@heseltine.co.uk
www.heseltine.co.uk
Landscapes, architecture, food and travel: Italy and UK.

Kos Picture Source
London
020 7801 0044
images@kospictures.com
www.kospictures.com
Aquatic images

Lebrecht Music Collection
London
020 7625 5341
pictures@lebrecht.co.uk
www.lebrecht.co.uk
Musical images

Lesley & Roy Adkins
Exeter
01392 811357
mail@adkinsarchaeology.com
www.adkinsarchaeology.com
Archaeology and heritage

London Aerial Photo Library
Surrey
01276 855997
info@flightimages.com
www.londonaerial.co.uk
Aerial imagery (oblique and vertical) covering majority of UK

Mary Evans Picture Library
London
020 8318 0034
pictures@mepl.co.uk
www.mepl.co.uk
Historical images

Monitor Picture Library
Essex
01279 792700
info@monitorpicturelibrary.com
www.monitorpicturelibrary.com
UK and international personalities

Morocco Scapes
Wiltshire
0138 082 8533
chris@realmorocco.com
www.realmorocco.com
Collection of Moroccan material

Museum of London Picture Library
London
020 7814 5604
picturelib@museumoflondon.org.uk
History of London

**National Galleries of Scotland
Picture Library**
Edinburgh
0131 624 6258
picture.library@nationalgalleries.org
www.nationalgalleries.org
Art works

**National Portrait Gallery Picture
Library**
London
020 7312 2474
picturelibrary@npg.org.uk
www.npg.org.uk
Portraits

**Natural History Museum Picture
Library**
London
020 7942 5401
nhmpl@nhm.ac.uk
www.nhm.ac.uk/piclib
Museums collection

Nature Photographers
Hampshire
01256 850661
info@naturephotographers.co.uk
www.naturephotographers.co.uk
Worldwide natural history

Nature Picture Library
Bristol
0117 974 6720
info@naturepl.com
www.naturepl.com
Wildlife

**The Neil Williams Classical
Collection**
Staffordshire
01827 286086
neil@classicalcollection.co.uk
Music

NHPA
West Sussex
01444 892514
nhpa@nhpa.co.uk
www.nhpa.co.uk
Natural history

PA Photos
London
020 7963 7990
paphotos@pa.press.net
www.paphotos.com
*News, entertainment, celebrity and
sports*

Panos Pictures
London
020 7234 0010
pics@panos.co.uk
www.panos.co.uk
*Documentary library specialising in
the developing world*

Papilio
Kent
01227 360996
library@papiliophotos.com
www.papiliophotos.com
Natural history subjects worldwide

Phil Sheldon Golf Picture Library
Herts
020 8440 1986
phil@philsheldongolfpics.co.uk
www.philsheldongolfpics.co.uk
Over 500,000 images of golf

Photofusion
London
020 7733 3500
library@photofusion.org
www.photofusion.org
*Contemporary social and
environmental issues*

The Photolibrary Wales
Cardiff
029 2089 0311
info@photolibrarywales.com
www.photolibrarywales.com
Wales

PPL Photo Agency
West Sussex
01243 555561
ppl@mistral.co.uk
www.pplmedia.com
*Watersports, business and industry,
travel, Sussex scenes and historical
images*

Premaphotos Wildlife
Cornwall
01208 78258
library@premaphotos.co.uk
www.premaphotos.co.uk
Natural history worldwide

The National Archive Image Library
Surrey
020 8392 5225
image-library@
    nationalarchives.gov.uk
www.nationalarchives.gov.uk
British and colonial history

**The Raymond Mander & Joe
Mitchenson Theatre Collection**
London
020 8305 4426
rmangan@tcm.ac.uk
www.mander-and-mitchenson
    .co.uk
Theatre

Redferns Music Picture Library
London
020 7792 9914
info@redferns.com
www.musicpictures.com

Retna Pictures
Bucks
01753 785450
ukinfo@retna.com
www.retna.com
Celebrity and lifestyle

Retrograph Nostalgia Archive
Brighton
01273 687554
retropix1@aol.com
www.retrograph.com
*Vintage consumer advertising art and
decorative art*

Robbie Jack Photography
London
020 8567 9616
robbie@robbiejack.com
Performing arts

Robert Forsythe Picture Library
Northumberland
01661 834511
robert@forsythe.demon.co.uk
www.forsythe.demon.co.uk
*Original ephemera and transparencies
of industrial and transport heritage.*

Royal Air Force Museum
London
020 8205 2266
siouxsie.biswell@rafmuseum.org
www.rafmuseum.org.uk
History of aviation

**Royal Collection Photographic
Services**
Berkshire
01753 868286
photoservices@
    royalcollection.org.uk
www.the-royal-collection.org.uk

RSPB Images
Beds
01767 680551
rspb@thatsgood.biz
www.rspb-images.com
Wildlife

RSPCA Photolibrary
West Sussex
0870 754 0150
pictures@rspcaphotolibrary.com
www.rspcaphotolibrary.com
Natural history

S&O Mathews Photography
Isle of Wight
01983 740809
oliver@mathews-photography.com
www.mathews-photography.com
Gardens, plants and landscapes

Science & Society Picture Library
London
020 7942 4400
piclib@nmsi.ac.uk
www.nmsi.ac.uk/piclib/
*Science museum, railway museum,
photography film and television*

Skishoot-Offshoot
Hampshire
01635 255527
skishootsnow@aol.com
www.skishoot.net
Ski-ing and snowboarding

The Skyscan Photolibrary
Gloucestershire
01242 621357
info@skyscan.co.uk
www.skyscan.co.uk
Aviation & aerial sports

Snookerimages (Eric Whitehead Photography)
Cumbria
015394 48894
eric@snookerimages.co.uk
www.snookerimages.co.uk
Snooker

SOA Photo Library
Taunton
0870 333 6062
info@soaphotoagency.com
www.soaphotoagency.com
Humorous, sports, travel, modern European and reportage

The Still Moving Picture Co
Edinburgh
0131 332 1123
info@stillmovingpictures.com
www.stillmovingpictures.com
Scotland and sport

Still Pictures Photolibrary
London
020 8858 8307
info@stillpictures.com
www.stillpictures.com
Environment, nature, social and Third World issues

Stockfile
Berkshire
01344 872249
info@stockfile.co.uk
www.stockfile.co.uk
Mountain biking and cycling

Sylvia Cordaiy
Wiltshire
01380 728327
info@sylvia-cordaiy.com
www.sylvia-cordaiy.com
160 countries: from obscure to main stock images

Tropix Photo Library
Wirral
0151 632 1698
tropixphoto@talk21.com
www.tropix.co.uk
Worldwide travel; developing nations

True North Photo Library
West Yorkshire
01422 845532
john@trunorth.demon.co.uk
Landscape and life of the North

Ulster Museum Picture Library
Belfast
028 9038 3113
patricia.mclean.um@nics.gov.uk
www.ulstermuseum.org.uk
Art, archaeology, ethnography, natural history, Irish history

V & A Images
London
020 7942 2966
vandaimages@vam.ac.uk
www.vandaimages.com

Valley Green
Stowmarket
01449 736090
pics@valleygreen.co.uk
Perennials

Vaughan Williams Memorial Library
London
020 7485 2206
library@efdss.org
www.efdss.org

VinMag Archive
London
020 8533 7588
piclib@vinmag.com
www.vinmagarchive.com

Waterways Photo Library
London
020 8840 1659
watphot39@aol.com
www.waterwaysphotolibrary.com/

World Pictures
London
020 7437 2121
worldpictures@btinternet.com
www.worldpictures.co.uk

York Archaelogical Trust Picture Library
York
01904 663000
enquiries@yorkarchaeology.co.uk
www.yorkarchaeology.co.uk

Film libraries

BBC Pebble Mill, Information & Archives
Birmingham
0121 432 8922
garry.campbell@bbc.co.uk

BFI Collections
Herts
01442 876301
david.pierce@bfi.org.uk
www.bfi.org.uk/collections
275,000 films and 200,000 TV programmes, dating from 1895 to the present

Central Broadcasting
Birmingham
0121 643 9898

Centre For Mass Communication Research
Leicester
0116 252 3863
cmcr@le.ac.uk
www.le.ac.uk/cmcr

East Anglian Film Archive
Norwich
01603 592664
eafa@uea.ac.uk
www.uea.ac.uk/eafa

Film and Video Archive, Imperial War Museum
London
020 7416 5000
film@iwm.org.uk
www.iwm.org.uk/collections/film.htm
120 million feet of film and 6,500 hours of video tape

Film Institute of Ireland/ Irish Film Archive
Dublin
00 353 1 679 5744
archive@ifc.ie
www.fii.ie

Huntley Film Archive
London
020 7287 8000
films@huntleyarchives.com
www.huntleyarchives.com
Rare and vintage documentary film dating from 1895.

Images Of War
London
020 7267 9198
derek@dircon.co.uk
www.warfootage.com

Institute of Education Library (London)
London
020 7612 6080
lib.enquiries@ioe.ac.uk

International Institute of Communications
London
020 7323 9622
enquiries@iicom.org
www.iicom.org

ITN Archive
London
sales@itnarchive.com
www.itnarchive.com
Archive of moving pictures with over 500,000 hours of news and feature material

Media Archive for Central England
The Institute of Film Studies
Nottingham NG7 2RD
0115 846 6448
james.patterson@nottingham.ac.uk
www.nottingham.ac.uk/film/mace

National Screen and Sound Archive of Wales
Ceredigion
01970 626007
agssc@llgc.org.uk
http://screenandsound.llgc.org.uk

North West Film Archive
Manchester
0161 247 3097
n.w.filmarchive@mmu.ac.uk
www.nwfa.mmu.ac.uk

Northern Ireland Film Commission
Belfast
028 9023 232444
info@nifc.co.uk

Northern Region Film and Television Archive
Middlesbrough TS1 3BA
01642 384022
leo@nrfta.org.uk
www.nrfta.org.uk

Nova Productions
Doncaster
01302 833422
library@novaonline.co.uk
www.novaonline.co.uk/library

Pathé Pictures
London
020 7323 5151
susanna.wyatt@pathe-uk.com
www.pathe.co.uk

Queen's Film Theatre
Belfast
028 9066 7687 x 33

Royal Television Society, Library & Archive
London
020 7430 1000
info@rts.org.uk
www.rts.org.uk

Scottish Screen Archive
Glasgow
0141 337 7400
archive@scottishscreen.com
www.scottishscreen.com

South East Film & Video Archive
Brighton BN2 0JY
01273 643213
sefva@brighton.ac.uk
www.bton.ac.uk/sefva/

South West Film and Television Archive
Plymouth PL1 3RP
01752 202650
elayne@tswfta.co.uk
www.tswfta.co.uk

The Wiener Library
London
020 7636 7247
info@wienerlibrary.co.uk
www.wienerlibrary.co.uk
Modern Jewish history

Vivid – Birmingham's Centre for Media Arts
Birmingham
0121 2334061
vivid@waveriden.co.uk

Wales Film and Television Archive
Dyfed
01970 626007
wftva@aol.com

Wessex Film and Sound Archive
Winchester
01962 847742
sadedm@hants.gov.uk
www.hants.gov.uk
/record-office/film

Yorkshire Film Archive
York YO31 7EX
01904 716550
yfa@yorksj.ac.uk

Media monitoring

BMC Clipserver
London
020 7377 1742
info@bmcnews.com
http//www.clipserver.com
Television, radio, national and European press monitoring

BBC Monitoring
Caversham Park
Reading RG4 8TZ
0118 948 6289
www.bbcmonitoringonline.com
www.monitor.bbc.co.uk

CIS Information Services
London
020 7242 5886
info@cisclip.co.uk
www.cisclip.com
International press monitoring service

Combrogos
Cardiff
029 2062 3359
meic@heoldon.fsnet.co.uk
Arts and media research and editorial services; Welsh books and authors

Daryl Willcox Publishing
Croydon
0870 774 0777
info@dwpub.com
www.dwpub.com
Information services for journalists and PR people

DigiReels Media Monitoring
London
020 7437 7743
peter.godden@digireels.co.uk
www.digireels.co.uk
Online database of tv, radio, poster and press ads

Durrants Press Cuttings
London
020 7674 0200
contact@durrants.co.uk
www.durrants.co.uk
All print media plus internet, newswire and broadcast monitoring

International Booksearch Service
London
020 7639 8900
scfordham@talk21.com
www.scfordham.com
Finds out-of-print books

International Press-Cutting Bureau
London
020 7708 2113
ipcb2000@aol.com
National, provincial, trade, technical and magazine press

John Frost Newspapers
Middlesex
020 8366 1392
andrew@johnfrostnewspapers.com
www.johnfrostnewspapers.co.uk
Original newspapers and press cuttings

Ludvigsen Library
Bury St Edmonds
01284 789246
library@ludvigsen.com
www.ludvigsen.com
Photographic archive and research facilities for writers and publishers.

Media Tenor
Dover
01304 216201
m.klein@mediatenor.com
www.mediatenor.com
Analysis of new and traditional media content

Melanie Wilson
Leicester
0116 260 4442
melaniewilson@bigfoot.com
research service across all media; free worldwide booksearch service

PA News Centre
Leeds
0870 830 6824
palibrary@pa.press.net
www.pa.press.net
Cuttings research service

Parliamentary Monitoring Services
London
020 7233 8283
info@parliamentary-monitoring
.co.uk
www.parliamentary-monitoring
.co.uk/
Confidential monitoring and research services

Romeike Media Intelligence
London
0800 289543
info@romeike.com
www.romeike.com
Monitors all media; back research; analysis and editorial summary service

Television Research Partnership (TRP)
Taunton
01823 424260
partners@trponline.co.uk
www.trponline.co.uk
Media measurement information

Xtreme information
London
020 7377 1742
info@bmcnews.com
http//www.xtremeinformation.com
Television, radio, national and European press monitoring

Specialist libraries and archives

Bank of England Information Centre
Threadneedle Street
London EC2R 8AH
020 7601 4715
informationcentre@
    bankofengland.co.uk
www.bankofengland.co.uk

Barbican Library
Barbican Centre
London EC2Y 8DS
020 7638 0569
barbicanlib@corpoflondon.gov.uk
www.cityoflondon.gov.uk
Emphasis on the arts; Corporation of London's largest lending library

BBC Written Archives Centre
Peppard Road, Caversham Park
Reading, Berkshire RG4 8TZ
0118 948 6281
wac.enquiries@bbc.co.uk
www.bbc.co.uk/thenandnow

BFI Collections
J Paul Getty Jnr Conservation
Centre, Kingshill Way
Berkhamsted, Herts HP4 3TP
01442 876301
david.pierce@bfi.org.uk
www.bfi.org.uk/collections
Contains more than 275,000 films and 200,000 TV programmes, dating from 1895 to the present

BFI National Library, British Film Institute
21 Stephen Street
London W1P 1LN
020 7255 1444
library@bfi.org.uk
www.bfi.org.uk/nationallibrary
    /index.html
World's largest collection of documentation on film and television

British Architectural Library
Royal Institute of British Architects
66 Portland Place
London W1B 1AD
020 7580 5533
bal@inst.riba.org
www.architecture.com

British Library
Reader Admissions Office
96 Euston Road, London NW1 2DB
020 7412 7677
reader-admissions@bl.uk
www.bl.uk

British Newspaper Library
The British Library, Newspaper
Library, Colindale Avenue
London NW9 5HE
020 7412 7353
newspaper@bl.uk
www.bl.uk/catalogues
    /newspapers.html

CAA Library and Information Centre
Aviation House, Gatwick Airport
West Sussex RH6 0YR
01293 573725
library-enquiries@srg.caa.co.uk
www.caa.co.uk
Part of CAA

Catholic Central Library
Lancing Street, London NW1 1ND
020 7383 4333
librarian@catholic-library.org.uk
www.catholic-library.org.uk

City Business Library
1 Brewers' Hall Garden
London EC2V 5BX
020 7332 1812
cbl@corpoflondon.gov.uk
www.cityoflondon.gov.uk
    /citybusinesslibrary

City of Westminster Archives Centre
10 St Ann's Street
London SW1P 2DE
020 7641 5180
archives@westminster.gov.uk
www.westminster.gov.uk/archives

DigiReels Media Monitoring
Paramount House
162–170 Wardour Street
London W1F 8ZX
020 7437 7743
peter.godden@digireels.co.uk
www.digireels.co.uk
Online ad database

Foreign and Commonwealth Office, Library and information services
King Charles Street
London SW1A 2AH
020 7270 3925
library.historical@fco.gov.uk
www.fco.gov.uk

Forestry Commission Library
Forest Research Station
Alice Holt Lodge, Wrecclesham
Farnham, Surrey GU10 4LH
01420 222555
library@forestry.gsi.gov.uk
www.forestry.gov.uk
    /forest_research

French Institute Library
Institut francais
17 Queensberry Place
London SW7 2DT
020 7073 1350
library@ambafrance.org.uk
www.institut.ambafrance.org.uk
French cultural interests

Goethe-Institut Library
50 Princes Gate, Exhibition Road
London SW7 2PH
020 7596 4000
mail@london.goethe.org
www.goethe.de/london
German literature & reference

Harry Price Library of Magical Literature
University of London Library
Senate House, Malet Street
London WC1E 7HU
020 7862 8470
historic@ull.ac.uk
www.ull.ac.uk/historic
    /collections.shtml

Instituto Cervantes
102 Eaton Square
London SW1W 9AN
020 7201 0757
biblon@cervantes.es
www.cervantes.es
Spain

Italian Institute Library
39 Belgrave Square
London SW1X 8NX
020 7396 4425
library@italcultur.org.uk
www.italcultur.org.uk
Italy

Linen Hall Library
17 Donegall Square North
Belfast BT1 5GB
028 9032 1707
info@linenhall.com
www.linenhall.com
Ireland, Northern Ireland political troubles

Llyfrgell Genedlaethol Cymru/ National Library of Wales
Aberystwyth
Ceredigion SY23 3BU
01970 632800
holi@llgc.org.uk
www.llgc.org.uk

London Metropolitan Archives (LMA)
40 Northampton Road
Clerkenwell, London EC1R 0HB
020 7332 3820
ask.lma@corpoflondon.gov.uk
www.cityoflondon.gov.uk/lma
Largest local authority archive in the UK

Murder Files
Dommett Hill Farm, Hare Lane
Buckland St Mary
Somerset TA20 3JS
01460 234065
enquiry@murderfiles.com
www.murderfiles.com
UK murders since 1400

National Archives
Kew, Surrey TW9 4DU
020 8392 5289
jane.crompton@
    nationalarchives.gov.uk
www.nationalarchives.gov.uk
11th–20th century national records

National Library of Scotland
George IV Bridge
Edinburgh EH1 1EW
0131 226 4531
enquiries@nls.uk
www.nls.uk

National Meteorological Archive
The Scott Building, Sterling Centre
Eastern Road, Bracknell
Berkshire RG12 2PW
01344 855960
metarc@metoffice.com
www.metoffice.com

Natural History Museum Library
Cromwell Road, London SW7 5BD
020 7942 5460
library@nhm.ac.uk
www.nhm.ac.uk/library/index.html

Office for National Statistics,
National Statistics Information
and Library Service
1 Drummond Gate
London SW1V 2QQ
0845 601 3034
info@statistics.gov.uk
www.statistics.gov.uk

PA News Centre
Central Park, New Lane
Leeds, West Yorkshire LS11 5DZ
0870 830 6824
palibrary@pa.press.net
www.pa.press.net
*Press cuttings archive dates back
to 1928*

Polish Library
238–246 King Street
London W6 0RF
020 8741 0474
bibliotekapolska@
    posk.library.fsnet.co.uk

**Royal Geographical Society Library
(with the Institute of British
Geographers)**
1 Kensington Gore
London SW7 2AR
020 7591 3000
library@rgs.org
www.rgs.org

Royal Society Library
6 Carlton House Terrace
London SW1Y 5AG
020 7451 2606
library@royalsoc.ac.uk
www.royalsoc.ac.uk
Science

Royal Society of Medicine Library
1 Wimpole Street
London W1G 0AE
020 7290 2940
library@rsm.ac.uk
www.rsm.ac.uk

**Science Fiction Foundation
Research Library**
Liverpool University Library
PO Box 123, Liverpool L69 3DA
0151 794 3142
asawyer@liverpool.ac.uk
www.liv.ac.uk/~asawyer
    /sffchome.html

Science Museum Library
Imperial College Road
London SW7 5NH
020 7942 4242
smlinfo@nmsi.ac.uk
www.nmsi.ac.uk/library

Theatre Museum Library & Archive
1e Tavistock Street
London WC2E 7PR
020 7943 4700
tmenquiries@vam.ac.uk
www.theatremuseum.org

United Nations Information Centre
Millbank Tower (21st Floor)
21–24 Millbank
London SW1P 4QH
020 7630 1981
info@uniclondon.org
www.unitednations.org.uk

Westminster Music Library
Victoria Library
160 Buckingham Palace Road
London SW1W 9UD
020 7641 4292
musiclibrary@westminster.gov.uk
www.westminster.gov.uk
    /libraries/special/music

Wiener Library
4 Devonshire Street
London W1W 5BH
020 7636 7247
info@wienerlibrary.co.uk
www.wienerlibrary.co.uk
Modern Jewish history

Women's Library
Old Castle Street, London E1 7NT
020 7320 2222
moreinfo@thewomenslibrary.ac.uk
www.thewomenslibrary.ac.uk

Zoological Society Library
Regent's Park, London NW1 4RY
020 7449 6293
library@zsl.org
www.zsl.org

Research data

Audit Bureau of Circulations (ABC)
Saxon House, 211 High Street
Berkhamsted
Hertfordshire HP4 1AD
01442 870800
marketing@abc.org.uk
www.abc.org.uk
*Circulation figures for newspapers and
magazines*

**Broadcasters' Audience Research
Board (Barb)**
18 Dering Street, London W1S 1AQ
020 7529 5531
www.barb.co.uk
TV audience data

LemonAd United Kingdom
Nielsen/NetRatings UK
2nd Floor, 4 Elder Street
London E1 6BT
020 7247 7722
sarah@netcrawling.com
www.lemonad.com
Advertising monitoring in Europe

National Readership Survey (NRS)
42 Drury Lane, London WC2B 5RT
020 7632 2915
stevemillington@nrs.co.uk
www.nrs.co.uk
*Newspaper and magazine readership
estimates*

Nielsen BookScan
Woolmead House West, Bear Lane
Farnham, Surrey GU9 7LG
01252 742555
info@nielsenbookscan.co.uk
www.nielsenbookscan.co.uk
*International sales data monitoring
and analysis service for the English-
language book industry worldwide*

Nielsen/NetRatings
ACNielsen House
London Road, Headington
Oxford OX3 9RX
01865 742742
www.nielsen-netratings.com
*Services include the Nielsen/
NetRatings Internet audience
measurement service NetView*

Rajar
Gainsborough House
81 Oxford Street
London W1D 2EU
020 7903 5350
info@rajar.co.uk
www.rajar.co.uk
*Measures and profiles the audiences
of UK radio stations*

Specialist libraries : **Resources**

Research associations

Association of Independent Libraries
Leeds Library
18 Commercial Street, Leeds
West Yorkshire LS1 6AL
0113 245 3071
admin@hlsi.demon.co.uk
www.independentlibraries.co.uk

Association of UK Media Libraries
Editorial Information Services,
Financial Times
One Southwark Bridge
London SE1 9HL
0207 873 3920
Margaret.Katny@bbc.co.uk
www.aukml.org.uk

BAPLA (British Association of Picture Libraries and Agencies)
18 Vine Hill, London EC1R 5DZ
020 7713 1780
enquiries@bapla.org.uk
www.bapla.org

CILIP: The Chartered Institute of Library and Information Professionals
7 Ridgmount Street
London WC1E 7AE
020 7255 0500
info@cilip.org.uk
www.cilip.org.uk

Cilips (Chartered Institute of Library and Information Professionals in Scotland)
1st Floor, Building C,
Brandon Gate, Leechlee Road
Hamilton ML3 6AU
01698 458888
cilips@slainte.org.uk
www.slainte.org.uk

Film Archive Forum
c/o British Universities Film
& Video Council
77 Wells Street, London W1T 3QJ
020 7393 1508
luke@bufvc.ac.uk
www.bufvc.ac.uk/faf

Focal International
Pentax House, South Hill Avenue
South Harrow HA2 0DU
020 8423 5853
info@focalint.org
www.focalint.org
Professional trade association of commercial film/audiovisual libraries & film professionals

International Federation of Film Archives (FIAF)
1 Rue Defacqz
B-1000 Brussels
Belgium
+322 538 3065
info@fiafnet.org
www.fiafnet.org

ISBN Agency
Woolmead House, Bear Lane
Farnham, Surrey GU9 7LG
01252 742590
isbn@whitaker.co.uk
www.whitaker.co.uk/isbn.htm

Picture Research Association
Head Office, 2 Culver Drive
Oxted, Surrey RH8 9HP
01883 730123
pra@lippmann.co.uk
www.picture-research.org.uk

Resource – The Council for Museums, Archives and Libraries
16 Queen Anne's Gate
London SW1H 9AA
020 7273 1444
info@resource.gov.uk
www.resource.gov.uk

Media awards

Amnesty International Media Awards
020 7814 6278
www.amnesty.org.uk/mediaawards
Human rights journalism

British Garden Writers Guild
020 7245 6943
www.gardenwriters.co.uk/awards

British Press Awards
020 8565 3056
www.britishpressawards.com
Organised by Press Gazette

British Society of Magazine Editors
020 8906 4664
www.bsme.com

Catherine Pakenham Award for Young Women Journalists
020 7538 6257

Emmas (Ethnic Multicultural Media Academy awards)
020 7468 3527/3502
www.emma.tv
Multicultural media

Foreign Press Association Annual Media Awards
020 7930 0445
www.foreign-press.org.uk
International journalism by British media

Glenfiddich Food & Drink awards
020 7255 1100
www.glenfiddich.com/foodanddrink

Guardian Student Media Awards
01727 799986
www.media.guardian.co.uk/studentmediaawards
Student journalists, designers and photographers

ICIJ Award for Outstanding International Investigative Reporting
www.icij.org

Local Reporting Awards
020 7636 7014
www.newspapersoc.org.uk
Under-30s

Media Week Awards
020 8565 3056
www.mediaweekawards.co.uk
Strategic thinking and creativity

Medical Journalism Awards
01603 622200
www.norwichunion.co.uk/medical_journalism_awards

NetMedia European Online Journalism Awards
020 7637 7097
www.net-media.co.uk

Newspaper Awards
01895 340788
www.newspaperawards.newstech.co.uk
Technical innovation in newspaper and new media production

Observer Hodge Award
020 7239 9936
www.observer.co.uk/hodgeaward
Young photographers

Picture Editors' Awards
07973 147586
www.pictureawards.net
Photographic journalism

Plain English Media Awards
01663 744409
www.plainenglish.co.uk/mediaawards
Campaign against gobbledygook

PPA Awards
020 7404 4166
www.ppa.co.uk
Magazines

PPAi interactive Awards
020 7404 4166
www.ppai.co.uk
Online publishing

Press Gazette Student Journalism Awards
020 8565 3056
www.pressgazette.co.uk
Open to students enrolled on a journalism course

Race in the Media Awards
020 7939 0000
www.cre.gov.uk/media/rima.html
Organised by Commission for Racial Equality

Regional Press Awards
020 8565 3056
www.regionalpressawards.co.uk
Organised by Press Gazette

The Herald Scottish Student Press Awards 2003
0141 302 6163
www.theherald.co.uk
Open to full-time students in Scotland

What the Papers Say Awards
020 7261 3148
www.whatthepaperssay.co.uk
National newspaper journalists

TV and radio

Bafta Awards
020 7734 0022
www.bafta.com
Film, TV and interactive industries

British Comedy Awards
020 7605 1214
www.britishcomedyawards.co.uk

Broadcast Awards
020 7505 8300
www.broadcastnow.co.uk
Programme ideas and execution

Indie Awards (Pact)
020 7331 6000
www.pact.co.uk

National TV Awards
020 7241 8000
Winners picked by viewers

NTL Commerical Radio Awards
020 7306 2603
www.crca.co.uk

Royal Television Society Journalism Awards
020 7691 2470
www.rts.org.uk

Sony Radio Academy Awards
020 7255 2010
www.radioacademy.org/awards

Books

British Book Design and Production Awards
020 7691 9191
www.publishers.org.uk

Guardian First Book Award
020 7239 9883
www.guardian.co.uk/firstbook
First-time writers of fiction, poetry, biography, memoirs, history, politics, science and current affairs

Man Booker Prize
020 7631 2666
www.themanbookerprize.com
Best novel in English by citizen of Commonwealth, Ireland, Pakistan or South Africa

Orange Prize for Fiction
020 7471 6845
www.orangeprize.co.uk
Women's fiction

Whitbread
020 7202 2822
www.whitbread-bookawards.co.uk
Contemporary British writing

Advertising & PR

British Television Advertising Awards
020 7734 6962
www.btaa.co.uk

Campaign Direct Awards
020 8267 4433
www.brandrepublic.com/magazines/campaign

Campaign Media Awards
020 8267 4433
www.brandrepublic.com/magazines/campaign

Campaign Poster Advertising Awards
020 8267 4433
www.brandrepublic.com/magazines/campaign

Campaign Press Advertising Awards
020 8267 4433
www.brandrepublic.com/magazines/campaign

Cannes Lions International Advertising Festival Awards
020 7291 8444
www.canneslions.com

Creative Juice Awards
020 7636 7014
www.newspapersoc.org.uk
Young creative teams with maximum of three years' experience

Guinness Radio Advertising Awards
00 353 1 667 6471
www.radio-awards.com

Institute of Public Relations Excellence Awards
020 7253 5151
www.ipr.org.uk

London International Advertising Awards
020 8426 1670
www.liaawards.com

Marketing Week Effectiveness Awards
020 7970 4772
www.marketingweek.co.uk

Media Week Awards
020 8565 3056
www.mediaweekawards.co.uk

PR Week Awards
020 8267 4145
www.prweek.com

Scottish PR Awards
020 7253 5151
www.ipr.org.uk

TUC/Bank of Scotland Press and PR Awards
020 7636 4030
www.tuc.org.co.uk
Journalism about Scottish issues and on Scottish publications

Media awards

309

Contacts book

Government: **UK government**

Downing Street

Prime Minister's Office
10 Downing Street
London SW1A 2AA
020 7270 3000
Press: 020 7930 4433
www.number-10.gov.uk
*Prime minister: Tony Blair**

Cabinet Office
70 Whitehall, London SW1A 2AS
020 7270 3000
Press: 020 7276 1191
www.cabinet-office.gov.uk
*Cabinet Office minister:
Douglas Alexander
Leader of the Lords: Lord Williams*;
leader of the Commons and Privy Seal:
Peter Hain*; deputy leader: Phil
Woolas; party chairman: Ian
McCartney**

Government departments

Treasury
1 Horse Guards Road
London SW1A 2HQ
020 7270 5000
Press: 020 7270 5238
www.hm-treasury.gov.uk
*Chancellor of the Exchequer:
Gordon Brown*;
Chief secretary: Paul Boateng*;
paymaster general: Dawn Primarolo;
financial secretary: Ruth Kelly;
economic secretary: John Healey*

Deputy Prime Minister
26 Whitehall, London SW1A 2WH
020 7944 4400
Press: 020 7944 4651
www.odpm.gov.uk
Deputy prime minister: John Prescott;
Local government minister: Nick
Raynsford; regeneration minister:
Lord Rooker; housing/planning
minister: Keith Hill; parliamentary
secretaries: Yvette Cooper, Phil Hope
Prime minister: Tony Blair**

Constitutional Affairs
54 Victoria Street
London SW1E 6QW
020 7210 8500
Press: 020 7210 8512
www.lcd.gov.uk
*Constitutional affairs secretary:
Lord Falconer**

Culture, Media and Sport
2-4 Cockspur Street
London SW1Y 5DH
020 7211 6000
Press: 020 7211 6215
www.culture.gov.uk
Culture secretary: Tessa Jowell
Arts minister: Estelle Morris; sports
minister: Richard Caborn; minister
for media: Lord Mcintosh*

Defence
Horseguards Avenue
London SW1A 2HB
020 7218 9000
Press: 020 7218 3256
www.mod.uk
Defence secretary: Geoff Hoon
Minister: Adam Ingram;
parliamentary secretaries: Lord Bach,
Ivor Caplin*

Education and Skills
Great Smith Street
London SW1P 3BT
020 7925 5000
Press: 020 7925 6789
www.dfes.gov.uk
Education secretary: Charles Clarke
Schools standards minister: David
Miliband; universities minister: Alan
Johnson; minister for children:
Margaret Hodge; parliamentary
secretaries: Baroness Ashton, Ivan
Lewis, Stephen Twigg*

Environment, Food and Rural Affairs
17 Smith Square
London SW1P 3JR
020 7238 3000
Press: 020 7238 6600
www.defra.gov.uk
*Environment secretary:
Margaret Beckett*
Rural affairs minister: Alun Michael;
environment minister: Elliot Morley;
parliamentary secretaries:
Ben Bradshaw, Lord Whitty*

Foreign Office
Whitehall, London SW1A 2AH
020 7270 1500
Press: 020 7008 3100
www.fco.gov.uk
Foreign secretary: Jack Straw
Europe minister: Denis Mcshane;
minister for trade: Mike O'Brien;
Middle East minister: Baroness
Symons; parliamentary secretaries:
Bill Rammell, Chris Mullin*

Health
79 Whitehall, London SW1A 2NS
020 7210 4850
Press: 020 7210 5231
www.doh.gov.uk
Health secretary: John Reid
Ministers: John Hutton, Rosie
Winterton; parliamentary secretaries:
Lord Warner, Melanie Johnson,
Stephen Ladyman*

Home Office
Queen Anne's Gate
London SW1H 9AT
0870 000 1585
Press: 020 7273 4545
www.homeoffice.gov.uk
Home secretary: David Blunkett
Ministers: Hazel Blears, Baroness
Scotland, Beverley Hughes;
parliamentary secretaries: Michael
Wills, Paul Goggins, Fiona
Mactaggart, Caroline Flint*

* cabinet minister

International Development
1 Palace Street, London SW1E 5HE
020 7023 0000
Press: 020 7023 0600
www.dfid.gov.uk
International development secretary:
Baroness Amos*
Ministers: Hillary Benn; parliamen-
tary secretary: Gareth Thomas

Trade and Industry
1 Victoria Street
London SW1H 0ET
020 7215 5000
Press: 020 7215 5954
www.dti.gov.uk
Trade and industry secretary: Patricia
Hewitt*
Energy, e-commerce and postal services
minister: Stephen Timms; industry
and regions minister: Jacqui Smith;
minister for trade: Mike O'Brien;
parliamentary secretaries: Nigel
Griffiths, Lord Sainsbury, Gerry
Sutcliffe

Transport
76 Marsham Street
London SW1P 4DR
020 7944 8300
Press: 020 7944 3066 (Roads)
020 7944 3108 (Marine, Aviation,
Railways)
www.dft.gov.uk
Transport secretary: Alistair Darling*
Minister: Kim Howells; parliamentary
secretaries: David Jamieson, Tony
McNulty

Work and Pensions
79 Whitehall, London SW1A 2NS
020 7238 0800
Press: 020 7238 0866
www.dwp.gov.uk
Pensions secretary: Andrew Smith*
Minister: Des Browne (work),
Malcolm Wicks (pensions);
parliamentary secretaries: Baroness
Hollis, Chis Pond, Maria Eagle,
Baroness Ashton

Law Officers' Department
9 Buckingham Gate
London SW1E 6JP
020 7271 2422
020 7271 2440
www.lslo.gov.uk

Privy Council
2 Carlton Gardens
London SW1Y 5AA
020 7210 3000
Press: 020 7210 1092
www.privy-council.org.uk
President: Lord Williams* (also leader
of the Lords)

* cabinet minister

Wales

Wales Office
Whitehall, London SW1A 2ER
020 7270 0549
Press: 020 7270 0565
/ 029 2089 8267
www.walesoffice.gov.uk
Wales secretary: Peter Hain*
parliamentary secretary: Don Touhig

National Assembly for Wales
Cardiff Bay, Cardiff CF99 1NA
029 2082 5111
Press: 029 2089 8931
/ 029 2089 8763 (first minister)
www.wales.gov.uk
first minister: Rhodri Morgan

Scotland

Scotland Office
Whitehall, London SW1A 2AU
020 7270 6828
Press: 0131 244 9053
www.scottishsecretary.gov.uk
Scottish secretary: Alistair Darling*
parliamentary secretary: Anne
Mcguire

Scottish Executive
St.Andrews House
Edinburgh EH1 3DG
0131 556 8400
Press: 0131 244 1111
www.scotland.gov.uk
first minister: Jack Mcconnell

Northern Ireland

Northern Ireland Office
11 Millbank, London SW1P 4PN
020 7210 3000, 028 9052 0700
Press: 020 7210 6518
/ 028 9052 8220
www.nio.gov.uk

**Northern Ireland Assembly
(suspended October 2002)**
www.ni-assembly.gov.uk

**Northern Ireland Executive
(suspended October 2002)**
www.northernireland.gov.uk

Local and regional government

Local Government Association
020 7664 3131
www.lga.gov.uk
County Councils Network
020 7664 3011
www.lga.gov.uk/ccn/
**Audit Commission for Local
Authorities**
020 7828 1212
www.audit-commission.gov.uk
**Convention of Scottish Local
Authorities**
0131 474 9200
www.cosla.gov.uk
**Improvement and Development
Agency**
020 7296 6600
www.idea.gov.uk
Local government ombudsman
0845 602 1983
www.lgo.org.uk
Scotland
0870 011 5378
www.ombudslgscot.org.uk
Wales
01656 661325
www.ombudsman-wales.org

Professional bodies

**Association of Council Secretaries
and Soliticors**
01772 40404
www.acses.org.uk
**Association of Electoral
Administrators**
0151 281 8246
www.aea-elections.co.uk
**Association of Local Authority Chief
Executives**
01923 727282
www.alace.org.uk

England

London

Greater London Authority
020 7983 4000
www.london.gov.uk
Association of London Government
020 7934 9999
www.alg.gov.uk
Corporation of London
020 7606 3030
www.cityoflondon.gov.uk

London boroughs

Barking and Dagenham
020 8592 4500
Barnet
020 8359 2000
Bexley
020 8303 7777
Brent
020 8937 1234
Bromley
020 8464 3333
Camden
020 7278 4444
Croydon
020 8688 4433
Ealing
020 8825 5866
Enfield
020 8366 6565
Greenwich
020 8854 8888
Hackney
020 8356 5000
Hammersmith and Fulham
020 8748 3020
Haringey
020 8489 0000
Harrow
020 8863 5611
Havering
01708 434343
Hillingdon
01895 250111
Hounslow
020 8583 2000
Islington
020 7527 2000
Kensington and Chelsea
020 7937 5464
Kingston upon Thames
020 8546 2121
Lambeth
020 7926 1000
Lewisham
020 8314 6000
Merton
020 8543 2222
Newham
020 8430 2000
Redbridge
020 8478 3020
Richmond upon Thames
020 8891 1411
Southwark
020 7525 5000
Sutton
020 8770 5000
Tower Hamlets
020 7364 5000
Waltham Forest
020 8496 3000

Wandsworth
020 8871 6000
Westminster
020 7641 6000

County councils

Bedfordshire
01234 363222
Buckinghamshire
01296 395000
Cambridgeshire
01223 717111
Cheshire
01244 602424
Cornwall
01872 270340
Cumbria
01228 606060
Derbyshire
01629 580000
Devon
01392 382000
Dorset
01305 251000
Durham
0191 383 3000
East Sussex
01273 481000
Essex
01245 492211
Gloucestershire
01452 425000
Hampshire
01962 841841
Hertfordshire
01992 555555
Kent
01622 671411
Lancashire
01772 254868
Leicestershire
0116 232 3232
Lincolnshire
01522 552222
Norfolk
01603 222222
North Yorkshire
01609 780780
Northamptonshire
01604 236236
Northumberland
01670 533000
Nottinghamshire
0115 982 3823
Oxfordshire
01865 792422
Shropshire
01743 251000
Somerset
01823 355455
Staffordshire
01785 223121
Suffolk
01473 583000
Surrey
020 8541 8800
Warwickshire
01926 410410
West Sussex
01243 777100
Wiltshire
01225 713000
Worcestershire
01905 763763
Isle of Wight
01983 821000

Rutland
01572 722577

City and district councils

Avon

see **Somerset & Avon**

Bedfordshire

Bedford
01234 267422
Luton
01582 546000
Mid Bedfordshire
01525 402051
South Bedfordshire
01582 472222

Berkshire

Bracknell Forest
01344 424642
Reading
01189 390900
Slough
01753 552288
West Berkshire
01635 42400
Windsor and Maidenhead
01628 798888
Wokingham
01189 746000

Buckinghamshire

Aylesbury Vale
01296 585858
Chiltern
01494 729000
Milton Keynes
01908 691691
South Bucks
01753 533333
Wycombe
01494 461000

Cambridgeshire

Cambridge
01223 457000
Peterborough
01733 563141
East Cambridgeshire
01353 665555
Fenland
01354 654321
Huntingdonshire
01480 388388
South Cambridgeshire
01223 443000

Channel Islands

Isles of Scilly
01720 422537
States of Jersey
01534 603000
www.gov.je
States of Guernsey
01481 717000
www.gov.gg

Cheshire

Chester
01244 324324
Congleton
01270 763231
Crewe and Nantwich
01270 537777

Ellesmere Port and Neston
0151 356 6789
Halton
0151 424 2061
Macclesfield
01625 500500
Vale Royal
01606 862862
Warrington
01925 444400

Cleveland

Hartlepool
01429 266522
Middlesbrough
01642 245432
Redcar and Cleveland
01642 444000

Cornwall

Caradon
01579 341000
Carrick
01872 224400
Kerrier
01209 614000
North Cornwall
01208 893333
Penrith
01736 362341
Restormel
01726 223300

County Durham

Durham
0191 386 6111
Chester-le-Street
0191 387 1919
Dagenham
01325 380651
Derwentside
01207 218000
Easington
0191 527 0501
Sedgefield
01388 816166
Teesdale
01833 690000
Wear Valley
01388 765555

Cumbria

Carlisle
01228 817000
Allerdale
01900 326333
Barrow-in-Furness
01229 894900
Copeland
01946 852585
Eccles
01768 864671
South Lakeland
01539 733333

Derbyshire

Derby
01332 293111
Amber Valley
01779 570222
Bolsover
01248 240000
Chesterfield
01246 345345

315

Derbyshire Dales
01629 761100
Erewash
0115 907 2244
High Peak
0845 129 7777
North East Derbyshire
01246 231111
South Derbyshire
01283 221000

Devon

Exeter
01392 277888
Plymouth
01752 668000
East Devon
01395 516551
Mid Devon
01884 255255
North Devon
01271 327711
South Hams
01803 861234
Teignbridge
01626 361101
Torbay
01803 201201
Torridge
01237 428700
West Devon
01822 813600

Dorset

Bournemouth
01202 451451
Christchurch
01202 495000
East Dorset
01202 886201
North Dorset
01258 454111
Poole
01202 633633
Purbeck
01929 556561
West Dorset
01305 251010
Weymouth and Portland
01305 761222

East Sussex

Brighton and Hove
01273 290000
Eastbourne
01323 410000
Hastings
01424 781066
Lewes
01273 471600
Rother
01424 787878
Wealden
01892 653311

Essex

Basildon
011268 533333
Braintree
01376 552525
Brentwood
01277 261111
Castle Point
01268 882200
Chelmsford
01245 606606

Colchester
01206 282222
Epping Forest
01992 564000
Harlow
01279 446611
Maldon
01621 854477
Rochford
01702 546366
Southend-on-Sea
01702 215000
Tendring
01255 425501
Thurrock
01375 652652
Uttlesford
01799 510510

Gloucestershire

Gloucester
01452 522232
Cheltenham
01242 262626
Cotswold
01285 623000
Forest of Dean
01594 810000
South Gloucestershire
01454 868686
Stroud
01453 766321
Tewkesbury
01684 295010

Greater Manchester

Manchester
0161 234 5000
Bolton
01204 333333
Bury
0161 235000
Oldham
0161 911 3000
Rochdale
01706 647474
Salford
0161 794 4711
Stockport
0161 480 4949
Tameside
0161 342 8355
Trafford
0161 912 2000
Wigan
01942 244991

Hampshire

Portsmouth
02392 822251
Southampton
02380 223855
Basingstoke and Deane
01256 844844
East Hampshire
01730 266551
Eastleigh
02380 688000
Fareham
01329 236100
Gosport
023 9258 4242
Hart
01252 622122
Havant
02392 474174

New Forest
023 8028 5000
Rushmoor
01252 398398
Test Valley
01264 368000
Winchester
01962 840222

Herefordshire

Herefordshire
01432 260000

Hertfordshire

St Albans
01727 866100
Broxbourne
01992 785555
Dacorum
01442 28000
East Hertfordshire
01279 655261
Hertsmere
0208 207 2277
North Hertfordshire
01462 474000
Stevenage
01438 242242
Watford
01923 226400
Welwyn Hatfield
01707 357000

Kent

Canterbury
01227 862000
Ashford
01233 637311
Dartford
01322 343434
Dover
01304 821199
Gravesham
01474 564422
Maidstone
01622 602000
Medway
01634 306000
Sevenoaks
01732 227000
Shepway
01303 850388
Swale
01795 424341
Thanet
01843 577000
Tonbridge and Malling
01732 844522
Tunbridge Wells
01892 526121

Lancashire

Lancaster
01524 582000
Preston
01772 906000
Blackburn with Darwen
01254 585585
Blackpool
01253 477477
Burnley
0128 425011
Chorley
01257 515151
Fylde
01253 721222

Hyndburn
01254 388111
Pendle
01282 661661
Ribble Valley
01200 425111
Rossendale
01706 217777
South Ribble
01772 421491
West Lancashire
01695 577177
Wyre
01253 891000

Leicestershire

Leicester
0116 254 9922
Blaby
0116 275 0555
Boston
01205 314200
Charnwood
01509 263151
Harborough
01858 821100
Hinckley and Bosworth
01455 238141
Melton
01664 502502
North West Leicestershire
01530 454545
Oadby and Wigston
0116 288 8961

Lincolnshire

Lincoln
01522 881188
East Lindsey
01507 601111
North East Lincolnshire
01472 313131
North Kesteven
01529 414155
North Lincolnshire
01724 296296
South Holland
01775 761161
South Kesteven
01476 406080
West Lindsey
01427 615411

Merseyside

Liverpool
0151 233 3000
Knowsley
0151 489 6000
Sefton
01704 533133
St. Helens
01744 456000
Wirral
0151 638 7070

Norfolk

Norwich
01603 622223
Breckland
01362 695333
Broadland
01603 431133
Great Yarmouth
01493 856100

Kings Lynn and West Norfolk
01553 616200
North Norfolk
01263 513811
South Norfolk
01508 533633

North and East Yorkshire

York
01904 613161
Craven
01756 700600
East Riding of Yorkshire
01482 887700
Hambleton
01609 779977
Harrogate
01423 500600
Kingston upon Hull
01482 609100
Richmondshire
01748 829100
Ryedale
01653 600666
Scarborough
01723 232323
Selby
01757 705101
Stockton-on-Tees
01642 393939

Northamptonshire

Corby
01536 402551
Daventry
01327 871100
East Northamptonshire
01832 742000
Kettering
01536 410333
Northampton
01604 233500
South Northamptonshire
01327 322322
Wellingborough
01933 229777

Northumberland

Ainwick
01665 510505
Berwick-upon-Tweed
01289 330044
Blyth Valley
01670 542000
Castle Morpeth
01670 514351
Tynedale
01434 652200
Wansbeck
01670 532200

Nottinghamshire

Nottingham
0115 915 5555
Ashfield
01623 450000
Bassetlaw
01909 533533
Broxtowe
0115 917 7777
Gedling
0115 901 3901
Mansfield
01623 463463

Newark and Sherwood
01636 650000
Rushcliffe
0115 981 9911

Oxfordshire

Oxford
01865 249811
Cherwell
01295 252535
South Oxfordshire
01491 823000
Vale of White Horse
01235 520202
West Oxfordshire
01993 702941

Shropshire

Bridgnorth
01746 713100
North Shropshire
01939 232771
Oswestry
01691 671111
Shrewsbury and Atcham
01743 281000
South Shropshire
01584 813000
Telford & Wrekin
01952 202100

Somerset & Avon

Bath and North East Somerset
01225 477000
Bristol
0117 922 2000
Mendip
01749 343399
North Somerset
01934 888888
Sedgemoor
01278 435435
South Somerset
01935 462462
Taunton Deane
01823 356356
West Somerset
01984 632291

South Yorkshire

Doncaster
01302 734444
Rotherham
01709 382121
Sheffield
0114 272 6444

Staffordshire

Stoke-on-Trent
01782 234567
Cannock Chase
01543 462621
East Staffordshire
01283 508000
Lichfield
01543 308000
Newcastle-under-Lyme
01782 717717
South Staffordshire
01902 696000
Stafford
01785 619000
Staffordshire Moorlands
01538 483483

Tamworth
01827 709709

Suffolk

Babergh
01473 822801
Forest Heath
01638 719000
Ipswich
01473 432000
Mid Suffolk
01449 720711
St. Edmundsbury
01284 763233
Suffolk Coastal
01394 383789
Waveney
01502 562111

Surrey

Elmbridge
01372 474474
Epsom and Ewell
01372 732000
Guildford
01483 505050
Mole Valley
01306 885001
Reigate and Banstead
01737 276000
Runnymede
01932 838383
Spelthorne
01784 451499
Surrey Heath
01276 707100
Tandridge
01883 722000
Waverley
01483 523333
Woking
01483 755855

Tyne and Wear

Gateshead
0191 433 3000
Newcastle upon Tyne
0191 232 8520
North Tyneside
0191 200 6565
South Tyneside
0191 427 1717
Sunderland
0191 553 1000

Warwickshire

North Warwickshire
01827 715341
Nuneaton and Bedworth
02476 376376
Rugby
01788 533533
Stratford-on-Avon
01789 267575
Warwick
01926 450000

West Midlands

Birmingham
0121 303 9944
Coventry
02476 833333
Dudley
501384 818181
Sandwell
0121 569 2200

Solihull
0121 704 6000
Walsall
01922 650000
Wolverhampton
01902 556556

West Sussex

Adur
01273 263000
Arun
01903 737500
Mid Sussex
01444 458166
Chichester
01243 785166
Crawley
01293 438000
Horsham
01403 215100
Worthing
01903 239999

West Yorkshire

Bradford
01274 392718
Calderdale
01422 357257
Kirklees
01484 221000
Leeds
0113 234 8080
Wakefield
01924 306090

Wiltshire

Kennet
01380 724911
North Wiltshire
01249 706111
Salisbury
01722 336272
Swindon
01793 463000
West Wiltshire
01225 776655

Worcestershire

Worcester
01905 723471
Bromsgrove
01527 873232
Malvern Hills
01684 892700
Redditch
01527 64252
Wychavon
01386 565000
Wyre Forest
01562 820505

Wales

National Assembly for Wales
029 2082 5111
Press: 029 2089 8931
Cardiff
029 20 872000
Swansea
01792 636000
Carmarthenshire
01267 234567
Ceredigion
01545 570881
Denbighshire
01824 706000
Flintshire
01352 752121
Gwynedd
01286 672255
Isle of Anglesey
01248 750057
Monmouthshire
01633 644644
Newport
01633 244491
Pembrokeshire
01437 764551
Powys
01597 826000

County borough councils

Blaenau Gwent
01495 350555
Bridgend
01656 643643
Caerphilly
01443 815588
Conwy
01492 574000
Merthyr Tydfil
01685 725000
Neath Port Talbot
01639 763333
Rhondda Cynon Taff
01443 424000
Torfaen
01495 762200
Vale of Glamorgan
01446 700111
Wrexham
01978 292000

Scotland

Scottish Executive
0131 556 8400
press: 0131 244 2019
www.scotland.gov.uk

Aberdeen
01224 522000
Dundee
01382 434000
Edinburgh
0131 200 2000
Glasgow
0141 287 2000

Aberdeenshire
01467 620981
Angus
01307 461460
Argyll and Bute
01546 602127
Clackmannanshire
01259 450000
Dumfries and Galloway
01387 260000
East Ayrshire
01563 576000
East Dunbartonshire
0141 578 8000
East Lothian
01620 827827
East Renfrewshire
0141 577 3000
Falkirk
01324 506070
Fife
01592 414141
Highland
01463 702000
Inverclyde
01475 717171
Midlothian
0131 270 7500
Moray
01343 543451
North Ayrshire
01294 324100
North Lanarkshire
01698 302222
Orkney Islands
01856 873535
Perth and Kinross
01738 475000
Renfrewshire
0141 842 5000
Scottish Borders
01835 824000
Shetland Islands
01595 693535
South Ayrshire
01292 612000
South Lanarkshire
01698 454444
Stirling
0845 277 7000
West Dunbartonshire
01389 737000
West Lothian
01506 777000
Western Isles
01851 703773

Northern Ireland

Belfast
028 90 320202
Lisburn
028 9250 9250

Antrim

Antrim
028 9446 3113
Ballymena
02825 660300
Ballymoney
028 2766 2280
Carrickfergus
028 9335 1604
Larne
028 282 72313
Moyle
028 207 62225
Newtownabbey
028 9034 0000

Armagh

Armagh
028 37 529600
Craigavon
028 38 312400

Down

Ards
02891 824000
Banbridge
028 406 60600
Castlereagh
028 904 94500
Down
028 44 610800
Newry and Mourne
028 3031 3031
North Down
028 91 270371

Fermanagh

Fermanagh
02866 325050

Londonderry

Coleraine
028 7034 7034
Derry
028 713 65151
Limavady
02877 722226
Magherafelt
028 7939 7979

Tyrone

Cookstown
028 86 762205
Dungannon and South Tyrone
028 87 720300
Omagh
028 8224 5321
Strabane
028 71 382204

Government: **Parliament and politics**

Parliaments and assemblies

Parliament
020 7219 3000
www.parliament.uk
Commons information office
020 7219 4272
Lords information office
020 7219 3107
National Assembly for Wales
029 2082 5111
press 029 2089 8931
www.wales.gov.uk
Scottish Parliament
0131 348 5000
press 0131 348 5605
www.scottish.parliament.uk

Main political parties

Labour party
08705 900200
www.labour.org.uk
Conservative party
020 7222 9000
www.conservatives.com
Liberal Democrat party
020 7222 7999
www.libdems.org.uk

Regional parties

Wales

Plaid Cymru
029 2064 6000
www.plaidcymru.org
Wales Labour party
029 2022 1153
www.welshlabour.org.uk
Welsh Conservative party
029 2061 6031
www.welshconservatives.com
Welsh Liberal Democrats
029 2031 3400
www.demrhydcymru.org.uk

Scotland

Scottish Conservative party
0131 247 6890
www.scottishtories.org.uk
Scottish Labour party
0141 572 6900
www.scottishlabour.org.uk
Scottish Liberal Democrats
0131 337 2314
www.scotlibdems.org.uk
Scottish National party
0131 525 8900
www.snp.org.uk
Scottish Socialist party
0141 221 7714
www.scottishsocialistparty.org.uk

Northern Ireland

Alliance Party
028 9032 4274
www.allianceparty.org
Northern Ireland Unionist party
028 9052 1901
www.niup.org
Progressive Unionist party
028 9032 6233
www.pup-ni.org.uk
Sinn Fein
00 3531 8726100
www.sinnfein.ie
Social Democratic and Labour party
028 9024 7700
www.sdlp.ie
UK Unionist party
028 9052 1482
www.ukup.org
Democratic Unionist party
028 9047 1155
www.dup.org.uk
Ulster Unionist party
028 9076 5500
www.uup.org
United Unionist Assembly party
028 9052 1464

Minor parties

British National party
0870 757 6267
www.bnp.org.uk
Communist League party
www.communistleague.org.uk
Communist party of Britain
020 7428 9114
www.communist-party.org.uk
Co-operative party
020 7357 0230
www.co-op-party.org.uk
English Independence party
020 7278 5221
www.englishindependenceparty.com
Green party
020 7272 4474
www.greenparty.org.uk
Liberal party
01562 68361
www.libparty.demon.co.uk
Separate from the Liberal Democrats
National Front
0208 289 1122
www.natfront.com
Natural Law party
01622 812123
www.natural-law-party.org.uk
Official Monster Raving Loonies
01252 878382
www.omrlp.com
Scottish Green party
0131 478 7896
www.scottishgreens.org.uk

Socialist Alliance
020 7609 2999
www.socialistalliance.net
Socialist Equality party
0114 244 3545
www.socialequality.org.net
Socialist party
020 8988 8777
www.socialistparty.org.uk
Socialist Party of Great Britain
020 7720 3665
www.worldsocialism.org
Socialist Workers party
020 7538 5821
www.swp.org.uk
UK Independence party
020 7434 4559
www.independence.org.uk
Workers Revolutionary party
020 7232 1101
www.wrp.org.uk

Parliamentary and electoral bodies

Electoral Commission
020 7271 0500
www.electoralcommission.gov.uk
Electoral Reform Society
020 7928 1622
www.electoral-reform.org.uk
Hansard Society
020 7955 7459
www.hansardsociety.org.uk
Parliamentary Counsel
020 7210 6644
www.parliamentary-counsel.org.uk

Think tanks

Adam Smith Institute
020 7222 4995
www.adamsmith.org
Free market economics
Bow Group
020 7431 6400
www.bowgroup.org
Centre-right
Centre for Economic Policy Research
020 7878 2900
www.cepr.org
European network of research fellows
Centre for Global Energy Studies
020 7235 4334
www.cges.co.uk
Centre for Policy Studies
020 7222 4488
www.cps.org.uk
Established 1974 by Margaret Thatcher and Keith Joseph

Centre for Reform
020 7631 3566
www.cfr.org.uk
Centre for the Study of Financial Innovation
020 7493 0173
www.csfi.org.uk
Chatham House
020 7957 5700
www.riaa.org
International affairs
Civitas
020 7401 5470
www.civitas.org.uk
Demos Independent Think Tank
020 7401 5330
www.demos.co.uk
Fabian Society
020 7227 4900
www.fabian-society.org.uk
Centre-left
Federal Trust
020 7735 4000
www.fedtrust.co.uk
Foreign Policy Centre
020 7401 5350
www.fpc.org.uk
Established 1998 by Labour government
Institute for African Alternatives
020 7482 4662
www.ifaanet.org
International Institute for Environment and Development
020 7388 2117
www.iied.org
Institute for European Environmental Policy
020 7799 2244
www.ieep.org.uk
Institute for Global Ethics
020 7486 1954
www.globalethics.org/uk
Institute for Health Sector Development
020 7253 2222
www.ihsd.org
Institute for Jewish Policy Research
020 7935 8266
www.jpr.org.uk
Institute for Public Policy Research
020 7470 6100
www.ippr.org.uk
Centre-left
International Institute for Strategic Studies
020 7379 7676
www.iiss.org
Institute of Economic Affairs
020 7799 8900
www.iea.org.uk
UK's original free market think tank
Institute of Fiscal Studies
020 7291 4800
www.ifs.org.uk
Institute of Ideas
020 7269 9220
www.instituteofideas.com
New Economics Foundation
020 7820 6300
www.neweconomics.org

New Policy Institute
020 7721 8421
www.npi.org.uk
New Politics Network
020 7278 4443
www.new-politics.net
Overseas Development Institute
020 7820 6300
www.odi.org.uk
Policy Studies Institute
020 7468 0468
www.psi.org.uk
Politeia
020 7240 5070
www.politeia.co.uk
Scottish Council Foundation
0131 225 4709
www.scottishcouncilfoundation.org
The Smith Institute
020 7823 4240
www.smith-institute.org.uk
Social Affairs Unit
020 7637 4356
www.socialaffairsunit.org.uk
Social Market Foundation
020 7222 7060
www.smf.co.uk

Alternative and protest

Anarchist Federation
07946 214 590
www.afed.org.uk
Anti-Fascist Action
07000 569569
www.geocities.com/CapitolHill/senate/5602/
Anti-Fascist Network
www.antifa.net
Anti-Nazi League
020 7924 0333
www.anl.org.uk
Big Green Gathering
01458 834629
www.big-green-gathering.com
British Democracy Campaign
www.britishdemocracycampaign.com
Campaign Against Racism and Facism (CARF)
020 7837 1450
www.carf.demon.co.uk
Charter 88
020 8880 6088
www.charter88.org.uk
Creative Exchange
020 8432 0550
www.creativexchange.org
Democracy Movement
0870 511 0440
www.democracymovement.org.uk
Freedom Association
01746 861267
www.tfa.net
Globalise Resistance
020 7053 2071
www.resist.org.uk
Green Events
020 7281 8483
www.greenevents.fsnet.co.uk

GreenNet
020 7713 1941
www.gn.apc.org
Indymedia
www.indymedia.org.uk
Network of independent media activists
OneWorld
020 7091 4503
www.oneworld.net
Anti-globalisation
Peoples' Global Action
www.agp.org
Protest Net
www.protest.net
Reclaim the Streets
020 7281 4621
www.reclaimthestreets.net
Red Star Research
07960 865601
www.red-star-research.org.uk
Revolutionary Communist Group
020 7837 1688
www.revolutionarycommunist.com
Rising Tide
01865 241097
www.risingtide.org.uk
Squall
www.squall.co.uk
Subvertise
www.subvertise.org
Radical advertising
The Land is Ours
07961 460171
www.tlio.org.uk
Undercurrents
01865 203661
www.undercurrents.org
Alternative news videos
Urban 75
www.urban75.com
Wombles
www.wombles.org.uk

Freemasons

Freemasons
020 7831 9811
www.grandlodge.org.uk

Government: **Global politics**

Government departments

Foreign Office
020 7270 1500
press 020 7008 3100
www.fco.gov.uk
International Development
020 7023 0000
press 020 7023 0600
www.dfid.gov.uk

International

United Nations
UK information centre
020 7630 1981
HQ New York 00 1 212 963 4475
www.un.org
Unicef
020 7405 5592
www.unicef.org.uk
United Nations Conference on Trade & Development (UNCTAD)
00 4122 9071234
www.unctad.org
UN Educational, Scientific & Cultural Organisation (Unesco)
00 4122 9173381
www.unesco.org
UN High Commissioner for Refugees (UNHCR)
00 4122 7398111
www.unhcr.ch
UN High Commissioner for Human Rights (UNHCHR)
00 4122 9179375
www.unhchr.ch
UN Commission on International Trade Law (UNCITRAL)
00 431 260604061
www.uncitral.org
UN Relief & Works Agency for Palestinian Refugees (UNRWA)
000 9728 6777333
www.un.org/unrwa
Inernational Labour Organisation (ILO)
020 7828 6401
www.ilo.org
International Maritime Organisation (IMO)
020 7735 7611
www.imo.org
International Monetary Fund (IMF)
00 202 6237100
www.imf.org
International Whaling Commission
01223 233971
www.iwcoffice.org
Nato
00 322 7077211
www.nato.int
OneWorld
020 7239 7635
www.oneworld.net/uk

World Bank
020 7578 3201
HQ Washington 00 202 4731000
www.worldbank.org
World Health Organisation (WHO)
00 4122 7912222
www.who.int
World Trade Organisation (WTO)
00 4122 7395007
www.wto.org

EU Institutions

European Parliament
press 00 32 2 284 0992
www.europarl.eu.int
European Commission
press 00 32 2 295 3358
www.europa.eu.int/comm
Committee of the Regions of the European Union
press 00 32 2 282 2155
www.cor.eu.int
Council of the European Union
press 00 32 2 285 6423
www.ue.eu.int
Court of Justice of the European Communities
press 00 352 4303 3668/3382
www.curia.eu.int
European Central Bank
00 49 69 13440
www.ecb.int
European Convention
00 32 2 285 5071 / 5072
www.european-convention.eu.int
European Court of Auditors
press 00 352 4398 45410
www.eca.eu.int
European Economic and Social Committee
press 00 32 2 546 9396
www.esc.eu.int
European Environment Agency
00 45 33 367165/68
www.org.eea.eu.int
European Investment Bank
00 352 4379 3122
www.eib.org
European Police Office
00 31 70 302 5000
www.europol.eu.int
Joint Research Centre
00 32 2 295 7624
www.jrc.org
Office for Official Publications of the European Communities
00 352 29291
www.publications.eu.int
The European Ombudsman
00 33 3 8817 2313
www.euro-ombudsman.eu.int

Translation Centre for the Bodies of the European Union
00 352 42 17111
www.cdt.eu.int
Western European Union
00 32 2 500 4415
www.weu.int

Other European contacts

Congress of Local and Regional Authorities of Europe
00 33 3 9021 4475 /
00 33 6 7016 2850
www.coe.fr/cplre
Council of Europe
press 00 33 3 8841 2560
www.coe.int
Council of European Municipalities and Regions
00 32 2 511 7477 / 00 33 1 4450 5959, press 00 32 2 500 0534
www.ccre.org
European Court of Human Rights
00 33 3 8841 2492 /
00 33 3 9021 4215
www.echr.coe.int
European Space Agency
press 00 33 1 5369 7155
www.esa.int
European University Institute, Florence
00 39 055 46851
www.iue.it
European Youth Parliament
01993 70 99 40
www.eyp.org
Organisation for Economic Co-operation and Development
press 00 33 1 4524 8090 / 00 33 1 4524 8097
www.oecd.org
Organisation for Security and Co-operation in Europe
press 00 43 1 5143 6180
www.osce.org

Political parties

Confederal Group of the European United Left / Nordic Green Left
00 32 2 284 2683/2686
press 00 32 475 646628
www.europarl.eu.int/gue
European Liberal Democrats
00 32 2 284 2111
press 00 32 2 284 2077 /
00 32 2 284 2915
www.eld.europarl.eu.int
Greens-European Free Alliance
00 32 2 284 5498
press 00 32 2 284 4683
www.greens-efa.org

Group for a Europe of Democracies and Diversities
fax 00 32 2 284 9144
www.europarl.eu.int/edd/
Group of European People's Party (Christian Democrats) and European Democrats
00 32 2 284 2234
press 00 32 2 479 972144
www.epp-ed.org
Parliamentary Group of the Party of European Socialists
www.socialistgroup.org
Union for Europe of the Nations Group
00 32 2 284 2971
press 00 32 2 284 2147
www.europarl.eu.int/uen/

Pro-Europe and anti-Europe lobbies

Britain in Europe
020 7725 4200
www.britanineurope.org.uk
Pro-Britain in Europe
European Movement
020 7725 4300
www.euromove.org.uk
Pro-European
The No Campaign
020 7378 0436
www.no-euro.com
Pro-Europe, anti-euro
Federation of Small Businesses
01253 348046
www.fsb.org.uk
Powerful anti-euro lobby
Bruges Group
020 7287 4414
www.brugesgroup.com

Commonwealth and British international

British Executive Service Overseas
020 7630 0644
www.beso.org
British Council
0161 957 7755
press 020 7389 4268
www.britcoun.org
Commonwealth Institute
020 7603 4535
www.commonwealth.org.uk
Commonwealth Secretariat
020 7747 6500
www.thecommonwealth.org

British overseas territories

Anguilla
*Small east Caribbean island.
37 sq miles, 11,300 pop*
Governor, Anguilla:
00 1264 4972621
Bermuda
*100 small islands, 20 inhabited, 600 miles off North Carolina, USA.
63,400 pop. 21 sq miles*
Governor, Hamilton:
00 441 2923600
British Antarctic Territory
Uninhabited part of Antarctica, including South Orkney and South Shetland islands. 660,000 sq miles
Commissioner, London:
020 7008 2741
British Indian Ocean Territory
Group of Chagos Archipelago islands in central Indian Ocean, south of India. 21,000 sq miles. Uninhabited, except for UK-US base at Diego Garcia
Commissioner, London:
020 7008 2742
British Virgin Islands
Eastern Caribbean group of 46 islands, 11 inhabited, near Anguilla. 59 sq miles. 19,100 pop
Governor, Tortola: 00 1284 4942345
Cayman Islands
*Three tax-free, wealthy islands south of Cuba. Home to 36,273 people.
100 sq miles*
Governor, Georgetown:
00 345 244 2434
Falkland Islands
*Largest islands in the south Atlantic.
4,700 sq miles. 2,200 pop, plus military*
Governor, Stanley: 00 500 27433
Gibraltar
2.5 sq mile promontory of southernmost Spain. 27,200 pop.
Governor: 00 350 45440
Montserrat
*East Caribbean volcanic island,
39 sq miles. 3,500 pop*
Governor, Olveston:
00 664 4912688
Pitcairn Islands
Eastern group in Pacific, between north New Zealand and Peru. 14 sq miles, 54 pop, all Seventh Day Adventists. Home of mutineers from HMS Bounty, 1790
High Commissioner, Wellington:
00 0964 3660186
St Helena
Island in south Atlantic, 1,100 miles off Angola. 47 sq miles. 5,000 pop, with two dependencies
Governor, Jamestown: 00 290 2555
St Helena Dependent: Ascension Island
*700 miles north-west of St Helena.
34 sq miles, 1,120 pop*
Administrator: 00 247 6311
St Helena Dependent: Tristan da Cunha
Island group 1,850 miles west of Cape Town. 285 pop. 38 sq miles
Administrator: 00 870682 087155

South Georgia & Sandwich Islands
Scattered islands east and south-east of Cape Horn. South Georgia is military, South Sandwich uninhabited and volcanic
Governor, Stanley: 500 27433
Turks & Caicos Islands
*30 Caribbean islands, north of Haiti.
20,000 pop. 193 sq miles*
Governor, Waterloo:
001 649 9462309

International aid

ActionAid
020 7561 7561
www.actionaid.org
Baby Milk Action
01223 464420
www.babymilkaction.org
Book Aid International
020 7733 3577
www.bookaid.org
British Overseas NGOs for Development (Bond)
020 7837 8344
www.bond.org.uk
British Red Cross
020 7201 5027
www.redcross.org.uk
Care International
020 7934 9334
www.careinternational.org.uk
Casa Alianza
info@casa-alianza.org
www.casa-alianza.org
Catholic Agency for Overseas Development
020 7733 7900
www.cafod.org.uk
Christian Aid
020 7620 4444
www.christian-aid.org.uk
Christian Vision
deborahcollier@christianvision.com
www.christianvision.com
Church Mission Society
020 7928 8681
www.cms-uk.org
Disasters Emergency Committee
020 7387 0200
www.dec.org.uk
International Care and Relief
01892 519619
www.icrcharity.com
International Committee of Red Cross
HQ Geneva 00 4122 7346001
www.icrc.org
International Rescue Committee
020 7692 2727
www.theirc.org
Methodist Relief and Development Fund
020 7467 5132
www.mrdf.org.uk
Oxfam
01865 312610
www.oxfam.org.uk

Plan International
01483 755155
www.plan-international.org
Sightsavers
01373 452272
www.sightsavers.org.uk
Tear Fund
0845 355 8355
www.tearfund.org
Voluntary Services Overseas
020 8780 7200
www.vso.org.uk
Wateraid
020 7793 4500
www.wateraid.org.uk
World Vision UK
07939 071337
www.worldvision.org.uk

Human rights

Actionaid
020 7561 7561
www.actionaid.org
Africa Reparations Unit
www.arm.arc.co.uk
Amnesty International
020 7417 6355
www.amnesty.org.uk
Anti-Slavery
020 7501 8920
www.antislavery.org
Asian Human Rights Commission
00 852 26986339
www.ahrchk.net
Association for Civil Rights in Israel
00 9722 6521218
www.acri.org.il
British Institute of Human Rights
020 7401 2712
www.bihr.org
British Refugee Council
020 7820 3044
www.refugeecouncil.org.uk
Burma Campaign
020 7281 7377
www.burmacampaign.org.uk

Campaign Against Criminalising Communities
020 7586 5892
www.cacc.org.uk
Campaign Against Sanctions on Iraq
07789 260207
www.casi.org.uk
Campaign Against the Arms Trade
020 7281 0297
www.caat.org.uk
Campaign to End Genocide
info@endgenocide.org
www.endgenocide.org
Centre for Research on Globalisation
00 1705 7206500
http://globalresearch.ca
Coalition against Slavery in Mauritania and Sudan
00 1212 7744287
http://members.aol.com/casmasalc
Coalition fo the International Criminal Court
00 1212 5991332
www.iccnow.org
Concern Worldwide
020 7738 1033
www.concern.net
Derechos Human Rights
00 3491 5267502
www.derechos.org
Eliminate Child Labour in Tobacco
00 4122 3061444
www.eclt.org
European Roma Rights Centre
00 361 4132200
http://errc.org
Free Tibet Campaign
020 7833 9958
www.freetibet.org
Gendercide Watch
www.gendercide.org
Global Action to Prevent War
www.globalactionpw.org
Global fund for Women
00 415 2027640 x332
www.globalfundforwomen.org

Human Rights Watch
020 7713 1995
www.hrw.org
International Fellowship of Reconciliation
00 31 072 5123014
www.ifor.org
International Physicians for the Prevention of Nuclear War
00 617 8685050
www.ippnw.org
Kurdish Human Rights Project
020 7287 2772
www.khrp.org
Labour Behind the Label
01603 610 993
www.labourbehindthelabel.org
Safer World
020 7881 9290
www.saferworld.co.uk
Stop the War Coalition
07951 235915
www.stopwar.org.uk
Transcend
01914 773 3440
www.transcend.org
Unrepresented Nations and Peoples Organisation
unponl@unpo.org
www.unpo.org
War Resistors International
020 7278 4040
www.wri-irg.org
Womankind Worldwide
020 7549 5700
www.womankind.org.uk
World Commission for Peace and Human Rights Council
worphco@netscape.net
www.worphco.cjb.net
World Organisation Against Torture
00 202 296 5702
www.woatusa.org

Government: **Embassies**

Overseas embassy in UK	UK embassy overseas
Afghanistan	
020 7589 8891	00 9370 221212
Albania	
020 7828 8897	00 355 4234973
Algeria	
020 7221 7800	00 21321 230068
	www.britishembassy.gov.uk/algeria
Andorra	
020 8874 4806	00 376 355660
Angola	
020 7299 9850	00 2442 334582
Antigua and Barbuda	
020 7486 7073	00 268 4620008
www.antigua-barbuda.com	
Argentina	
020 7318 1300	00 5411 48082200
www.argentine-embassy-uk.org; www.britain.org.ar	
Armenia	
020 7938 5435	00 3741 264301
	www.britemb.am
Australia	
020 7379 4334	Canberra 00 61 2 6270 6666
www.australia.org.uk	Melbourne 00 613 96521600
	www.britaus.net
Austria	
020 7235 3731	00 43 1 716130
www.austria.org.uk	www.britishembassy.at
Azerbaijan	
020 7938 5482	00 99 412 975188
www.president.az	
Bahamas	
020 7408 4488	00 1242 325 7471
	www.britishhighcommission.gov.uk/bahamas
Bahrain	
020 7201 9170	00 973 574100
	www.ukembassy.gov.bh
Bangladesh	
020 7584 0081	00 8802 8822705
www.bangladeshhighcommission.co.uk; www.ukinbangladesh.org	
Barbados	
020 7631 4975	00 1246 4307800
	www.britishhc.org
Belarus	
020 7937 3288	00 375 172105920
www.belemb.freeserve.co.uk	
Belgium	
020 7470 3700	00 322 2876211
www.diplobel.org/uk	www.british-embassy.be
Belize	
020 7499 9728	00 501 822 2146
	www.britishhighbze.com

Overseas embassy in UK	UK embassy overseas
Bolivia	
020 7235 4248	00 5912 2433424
www.embassyofbolivia.co.uk	www.britishembassy.gov.uk/bolivia
Bosnia and Herzegovina	
020 7373 0867	00 387 33444429
	www.britishembassy.ba
Botswana	
020 7499 0031	00 267 3952841
	www.britishhighcommission.gov.uk/botswana
Brazil	
020 7499 0877	00 5521 25559600
www.brazil.org.uk	
Brunei	
020 7581 0521	00 6732 222231
	www.britain-brunei.org
Bulgaria	
020 7584 9400	00 3592 9339222
	www.british-embassy.bg
Burma	
020 7499 8841	00 951 256918
www.myanmar.com	
Burundi	
00 322 230535	00 257 827602
Cameroon	
020 7727 0771	00 237 2220545
	www.britcam.org
Canada	
020 7258 6600	Ottowa 00 1613 2371530
www.canada.org.uk	Vancouver 00 1604 6834421
	www.britainincanada.org
Chile	
020 7580 6392	00 562 3704100
	www.britemb.cl
China	
020 7636 9375	Beijing 00 86 10 65321961
www.chinese-embassy.org.uk	Hong Kong 00 852 29013000
	www.britishembassy.org.cn
Colombia	
020 7589 9177	00 571 3176690
Congo	
020 7622 0419	00 242 8844904
Congo (Democratic Republic)	
020 7278 9825	00 243 98169100
Costa Rica	
020 7706 8844	00 506 2582025
www.embcrlon.demon.co.uk	www.embajadabritanica.com
Croatia	
020 7387 2022	00 3851 6009100
	www.britishembassy.gov.uk/croatia
Cuba	
020 7240 2488	00 537 2041771
Cyprus	
020 7499 8272	00 357 22861100
	www.britain.org.cy

Overseas embassy in UK	UK embassy overseas
Czech Republic	
020 7243 1115	00 4202 57402111
www.czech.org.uk	www.britain.cz
Denmark	
020 7333 0200	00 4535 445200
www.denmark.org.uk	www.britishembassy.dk
Dominica, Commonwealth of	
020 7370 5194	00 246 4307800
www.dominica.co.uk	
Dominican Republic	
020 7727 6285	00 1809 4727111
www.serex.gov.do	
Ecuador	
020 7584 2648	00 5932 2970800
	www.britembquito.org.ec
Egypt	
020 7499 3304	00 202 7940852
www.egypt-embassy.org.uk	www.britishembassy.org.eg
El Salvador	
020 7436 8282	00 502 3675425
Eritrea	
020 7713 0096	00 291 1120145
Estonia	
020 7589 7690	00 372 6674700
www.estonia.gov.uk	www.britishembassy.ee
Ethiopia	
020 7589 7212	00 2511 612354
www.ethioembassy.org.uk	
Fiji	
020 7584 3661	00 679 311033
	www.ukinthepacific.bhc.org.fj
Finland	
020 7838 6200	00 35809 22865100
www.finemb.org.uk	www.britishembassy.fi
France	
020 7073 1000	Paris 00 331 44513100
www.ambafrance-uk.org	Marseille 00 334 91157210
	www.amb-grandebretagne.fr
Gabon	
020 7823 9986	00 241 762200
Gambia, The Republic of	
020 7937 6316	
Georgia	
020 7603 7799	00 995 32955497
www.embassyofgeorgia.org.uk; www.britishembassy.org.ge	
Germany	
020 7824 1300	00 4930 20457-0
www.german-embassy.org.uk	www.britischebotschaft.de
Ghana	
020 7235 4142	00 233 21221665
www.ghana-com.co.uk; www.britishhighcommission.gov.uk/ghana	
Greece	
020 7229 3850	00 30210 7272600
www.greekembassy.org.uk	www.british-embassy.gr
Grenada	
020 7631 4277	00 1473 4403222
Guatemala	
020 7351 3042	00 502 3675425
Guinea	
020 57839 2625	00 224 455807

Overseas embassy in UK	UK embassy overseas
Guyana	
020 7229 7684	00 592 2265881
Haiti	
00 509 2573969	
Holy See	
020 8946 1410	00 3906 69923561
Honduras	
020 7486 4880	00 504 2320612
Hungary	
020 7235 5218	00 361 2662888
www.huemblon.org.uk/front.htm; www.britishembassy.hu	
Iceland	
020 7259 3999	00 354 5505100
www.iceland.org.uk	
India	
020 7836 8484	New Delhi 00 9111 26872161
www.hcilondon.org	Bombay 00 9122 2830517
	www.ukinindia.com
Indonesia	
020 7499 7661	00 6221 3156264
www.indonesianembassy.org.uk; www.britain-in-indonesia.or.id	
Iran	
020 7225 3000	00 9821 6705011
www.iran-embassy.org.uk	
Ireland	
020 7235 2171	00 3531 2053700
	www.britishembassy.ie
Israel	
020 7957 9500	00 9723 7251222
www.israel-embassy.org.uk	www.britemb.org.il
Italy	
020 7312 2200	00 3906 42200001
www.embitaly.org.uk	www.britain.it
Ivory Coast (Côte d'Ivoire)	
020 7235 6991	00 225 20300800
	www.britaincdi.com
Jamaica	
020 7823 9911	00 001 876 5100700
www.jhcuk.com; www.britishhighcommission.gov.uk/jamaica	
Japan	
020 7465 6500	00 813 5211-1100
www.embjapan.org.uk	www.uknow.or.jp
Jerusalem	
	00 02 541 410024
	www.britishconsulate.org
Jordan	
020 7937 3685	00 9626 5923100
www.jordanembassyuk.gov.jo	www.britain.org.jo
Kazakhstan	
020 7581 4646	00 73272 508280
	www.britishembassy.gov.uk/kazakhstan
Kenya	
020 7636 2371	00 2542 2714699
	www.britain.or.ke
Kiribati	
	00 686 22501
Korea, DPR (North Korea)	
020 8992 4965	00 850 23817980

Overseas embassy in UK	UK embassy overseas
Korea, Republic of (South Korea)	
020 7227 5500	00 82 2 3210 5500
www.mofat.go.kr/uk.htm	www.britishembassy.or.kr
Kuwait	
020 7590 3400	00 965 240 3334
www.kuwaitinfo.org.uk	www.britishembassy-kuwait.org
Kyrgyzstan	
020 7935 1462	00 996 312 680 815
Latvia	
020 7312 0040	00 371 777 4700
	www.britain.lv
Lebanon	
020 7229 7265	00 961 1990 400
	www.britishembassy.org.lb
Lesotho	
020 7235 5686	00 266 22313961
	www.bhc.org.ls
Liberia	
020 7221 1036	00 231 227468
Libya	
020 7589 6120	00 218 21 335 1084
	www.britain-in-libya.org
Lithuania	
020 7486 6401	00 370 5 246 29 00
	www.britain.lt
Luxembourg	
020 7235 6961	00 352 22 98 64
	www.britain.lu
Macedonia	
020 7935 2823	00 389 2 3299 299
	www.britishembassy.org.mk
Madagascar	
00 45 046211	00 261 20 2249 378
Malawi	
020 7491 4172	00 2651 772400
Malaysia	
020 7235 8033	00 603 21702200
	www.britain.org.my
Maldives	
020 7224 2135	00 941 437336-43
Malta	
020 7292 4800	00 356 23230000
	www.britain.com.mt
Mauritania	
020 7478 9323	00 222 5251756
Mauritius	
020 7225 3331	00 230 2029400
Mexico	
020 7499 8586	00 5255 52428500
www.demon.co.uk/mexuk	www.embajadabritanica.com.mx
Moldova	
00 322 7329300	00 3732 238991
	www.britishembassy.gov.uk/moldova
Mongolia	
020 7937 0150	00 976 11458133
Morocco	
020 7581 5001	00 2120 37238600
	www.britain.org.ma

Overseas embassy in UK	UK embassy overseas
Mozambique	
020 7383 3800	00 2581 320111
Namibia	
020 7636 6244	00 264 61274800
	www.britishhighcommission.gov.uk/namibia
Nepal	
020 7229 1594	00 9771 4410583
www.nepembassy.org.uk	www.britain.gov.np
Netherlands	
020 7590 3200	00 310 704270427
www.netherlands-embassy.org.uk; www.britain.nl	
New Zealand	
020 7930 8422	00 644 9242888
www.nzembassy.com	www.britain.org.nz
Nicaragua	
020 7938 2373	00 505 2780014
Nigeria	
020 7839 1244	00 2349 4132010
www.nigeriahouseuk.com	
Norway	
020 7591 5500	00 4723 132700
www.norway.org.uk	www.britain.no
Oman	
020 7225 0001	00 968 609000
www.uk.gov.om	
Pakistan	
020 7664 9200	Islamabad 00 9251 2206071
www.pakmission-uk.gov.pk	Karachi 00 9221 5872431
	www.britainonline.org.pk
Panama	
020 7493 4646	00 507 2690866
Papua New Guinea	
020 7930 0922	00 675 3251677
Paraguay	
020 7937 1253	00 595 21612611
Peru	
020 7838 9223	00 511 6173000
www.peruembassy-uk.com	www.britemb.org.pe
Philippines	
020 7937 1600	00 632 8167116
	www.britishembassy.gov.uk/philippines
Poland	
0870 774 2700	00 4822 6281001
www.poland-embassy.org.uk	www.britishembassy.pl
Portugal	
020 7235 5331	00 35121 3924000
www.portembassy.gla.ac.uk	www.uk-embassy.pt
Qatar (State of)	
020 7493 2200	00 974 4421991
Romania	
020 7937 9666	00 4021 2017200
www.britishembassy.gov.uk/romania	
	www.embassyhomepage.com/romania
Russian Federation	
020 7229 2666	00 7095 9567200
	www.britemb.msk.ru
Rwanda	
020 7930 2570	00 250 84098
	britishembassykigali.org.rw

Overseas embassy in UK	UK embassy overseas
Saint Christopher and Nevis (St Kitts & Nevis)	
020 7460 6500	00 268462 0008
Saint Lucia	
020 7370 7123	00 001758 4522484
Saint Vincent and the Grenadines	
020 7565 2874	00 784457 1701
Samoa	
00 02 6608454	00 644472 6049
San Marino	
020 7299 9850	00 39055 284133
Saudi Arabia	
020 7917 3000	00 966 14880077
www.saudiembassy.org.uk	www.ukm.org.sa
Senegal	
020 7937 7237	00 221 8237392
Serbia and Montenegro	
020 7370 6105	00 38111 645055
Seychelles	
020 7224 1660	00 248 283666
	www.bhcvictoria.sc
Sierra Leone	
020 7287 9884	00 23222 232961
www.slhc-uk.org.uk	
Singapore	
020 7235 8315	00 656424 4200
www.gov.sg/mfa/london	www.britain.org.sg
Slovakia	
020 7243 0803	00 4212 59982000
www.slovakembassy.co.uk	www.britemb.sk
Slovenia	
020 7222 5400	00 3861 2003910
www.embassy-slovenia.org.uk	www.british-embassy.si
Solomon Islands	
00 322 7327085	00 677 21705
South Africa	
020 7451 7299	00 2721 4052400
	00 2711 5377206
www.southafricahouse.com	
Spain	
020 7235 5555	Madrid 00 3491 7008200
	Barcelona 00 376 355660
	Malaga 00 3495 2352300
	www.ukinspain.com
Sri Lanka	
020 7262 1841	00 941 437336
www.slhclondon.org	
Sudan	
020 7839 8080	00 24911 777105
www.britishembassy.gov.uk/sudan	
Swaziland	
020 7630 6611	00 268 4042581
Sweden	
020 7917 6400	00 468 6713000
www.swedish-embassy.org.uk	
Switzerland	
020 7616 6000	Berne 00 4131 3597700
www.swissembassy.org.uk	Geneva 00 4122 9182300
	www.britain-in-switzerland.ch

Overseas embassy in UK	UK embassy overseas
Syria	
020 7245 9012	00 96311 3739241
Tanzania	
020 7499 8951	00 25522 2110101
www.tanzania-online.gov.uk	
Thailand	
020 7589 2944	00 662 3058333
	www.britishemb.or.th
Tonga	
020 7724 5828	00 676 24285
Trinidad and Tobago	
020 7245 9351	00 1868 6222748
Tunisia	
020 7584 8117	00 21671 846184
	www.britishembassy.gov.uk/tunisia
Turkey	
020 7393 0202	00 90312 4553344
www.turkishembassy-london.com	
Turkmenistan	
020 7255 1071	00 99312 363462
	www.britishembassytm.org.uk
Uganda	
020 7839 5783	00 25678 312000
	www.britain.or.ug
Ukraine	
020 7727 6312	00 38044 4620011
www.ukremb.org.uk	www.britemb-ukraine.net
United Arab Emirates	
020 7581 1281	00 9712 6101100
	www.britain-uae.org
United States	
020 7499 9000	Washington 00 1202 5886500
www.usembassy.org.uk	Los Angeles 00 1310 4810031
	New York 00 1212 745 0200
	Chicago 00 1312 9703852
	www.britainusa.com/embassy
Uruguay	
020 7589 8835	00 5982 6223630
	www.britishembassy.org.uy
Uzbekistan	
020 7229 7679	00 99871 1207852
www.uzbekistanembassy.uk.net	
Vanuatu	
00 678 23100	
Venezuela	
020 7584 4206	00 5821 22638411
www.venezlon.demon.co.uk	www.britain.org.ve
Vietnam	
020 7937 1912	00 844 9360500
	www.uk-vietnam.org
Yemen	
020 7584 6607	00 9671 264081
Zambia	
020 7589 6655	00 260 1251133
	www.britishhighcommission.gov.uk/zambia
Zimbabwe	
020 7836 7755	00 263 4772990
www.zimbabwelink.com	www.britainzw.org

Arts

Government departments

Culture, Media and Sport
020 7211 6000, press 020 7211 6215
www.culture.gov.uk
Education and Skills
020 7925 5000, press 020 7925 6789
www.dfes.gov.uk

Arts councils

Arts Council England
020 7973 6517
www.artscouncil.org.uk
Arts Council for Northern Ireland
028 90 385200
www.artscouncil-ni.org
Design Council
020 7420 5200
www.design-council.org.uk
Film Council
020 7861 7861
www.filmcouncil.org.uk
Scottish Arts Council
0131 226 6051
www.scottisharts.org.uk

Galleries and museums

Association of Independent Museums
samm@ltm.co.uk
www.museums.org.uk/aim
British Museum
020 7323 8299
www.thebritishmuseum.ac.uk
Geffrye Museum
020 7739 9893
www.geffrye-museum.org.uk
Imperial War Museum
020 7416 5320
www.iwm.org.uk
Institute of Contemporary Arts
020 7930 3647
www.ica.org.uk
Museum of London
020 7600 3699
www.museum-london.org.uk
Museums Association
will@museumsassociation.org
www.museumsassociation.org
National Art Collections Fund
020 7225 4800
www.art-fund.org
National Galleries of Scotland
0131 624 6200
www.nationalgalleries.org
National Gallery
020 7747 2885
www.nationalgallery.org.uk
National Maritime Museum
020 8858 4422
www.nmm.ac.uk
National Portrait Gallery
020 7306 0055
www.npg.org.uk
Natural History Museum
020 7942 5000
www.nhm.ac.uk
Royal Academy of Arts
020 7300 8000
www.royalacademy.org.uk
Royal College of Art
020 7590 4500
www.rca.ac.uk
Royal Marines Museum
023 9281 9385
www.royalmarinesmuseum.co.uk
Tate Gallery
020 7887 8008
www.tate.org.uk
Victoria and Albert Museum
020 7942 2000
www.vam.ac.uk
24 Hour Museum
editor@24hourmuseum.org.uk
www.24hourmuseum.org.uk

Performing arts

British Film Institute
020 7255 1444
www.bfi.org.uk
Edinburgh Festival Fringe
0131 226 0026
www.edfringe.com
English National Ballet
020 7581 1245
www.ballet.org.uk
English National Opera
020 7845 9378
www.eno.org
National Theatre
020 7452 3333
www.nt-online.org
Royal Academy of Dance
020 7326 8000
www.rad.org.uk
Royal College of Music
020 7589 3643
www.rcm.ac.uk
Royal Opera House, Covent Garden
020 7240 1200
www.royalopera.org
Royal Shakespeare Company
01789 403404
www.rsc.org.uk
South Bank Centre
020 7921 0600
www.sbc.org.uk
Theatres Trust
020 7836 8591
www.theatrestrust.org.uk

History and heritage

Ancient Monuments Society
office@ancientmonumentssociety
.org.uk
www.ancientmonumentssociety
.org.uk

Architectural Heritage Fund
020 7925 0199
www.ahfund.org.uk

British Archaeological Association
www.britarch.ac.uk/baa

British Cathedrals & Historic Chuches Foundation
00 215 9252688
www.britishchurches.org

Civic Trust
020 7930 0914
www.civictrust.org.uk

Council for British Archaeology
0 1904 671 417
www.britarch.ac.uk

Cultural Heritage search engine
www.culturalheritage.net

English Heritage
0870 333 1181
www.english-heritage.org.uk

Garden History Society
020 7490 2974
www.gardenhistorysociety.org

Historic Royal Palaces
020 7488 5662/3
www.hrp.org.uk

Historical Diving Society
info@thehds.com
www.thehds.com

Historical Manuscripts Collection (The Royal Commission on Historical Manuscripts)
020 7242 1198
www.hmc.gov.uk

Historical Metallurgy Society
01792 233223
http://hist-met.org

Institute of Historic Building Conservation
01747 873133
www.ihbc.org.uk

International Council on Monuments & sites in UK
020 8994 6477
www.icomos.org/uk

Jewish Historical Society of Britain
020 7723 5852
http://www.users.dircon.co.uk/~jhse

Keltek Trust
bells@keltek.org
www.keltek.org
Church bell preservation society

Landmark Trust
01628 825925
www.landmarktrust.co.uk

National Association of Decorative & Fine Arts Associations
020 7430 0730
www.nadfas.org.uk

National Trust
0870 609 5380
www.nationaltrust.org.uk

National Trust for Scotland
0131 243 9300
www.nts.org.uk

Royal Commisssion on the Ancient & Historic Monuments of Wales
01970 621221
www.rcahmw.org.uk

Save Britain's Heritage
020 7253 3500
www.savebritainsheritage.org

Scottish Railway Preservation Society
01506 822298
www.srps.org.uk

Society for the Protection of Ancient Buildings
020 7377 1644
www.spab.org.uk

Ulster Architectural Heritage Society
028 9055 0213
www.uahs.co.uk

United Kingdom Institute for Conservation of Historic & Artistic Works
020 7721 8721
www.ukic.org.uk

Vivat Trust
0845 090 0194
www.vivat.org.uk

Business

Government departments

Treasury
020 7270 5000, press 020 7270 5238
www.hm-treasury.gov.uk
Trade and Industry
020 7215 5000, press 020 7215 5954
www.dti.gov.uk
Work and Pensions
020 7238 0800, press 020 7238 0866
www.dwp.gov.uk

Central banks

Bank of England
020 7601 4444
www.bankofengland.co.uk
European Central Bank
00 49 69 13440
www.ecb.int

FTSE-100 companies

Anglo American
020 7698 8500
www.angloamerican.co.uk
Associated British Foods
020 7589 6363
www.nycomed-amersham.com
Amersham
01494 544000
www.nycomed-amersham.com
Alliance and Leicester
0116 201 1000
www.alliance-leicester.co.uk
Alliance Unichem
01932 870550
www.alliance-unichem.com
Allied Domecq
0117 978 5000
www.allieddomecqplc.com
Abbey National
020 7756 5952
www.abbeynational.co.uk
Amvescap
020 7638 0731
www.amvescap.com
Astra Zeneca
020 7304 5000
www.astrazeneca.com
Aviva
020 7662 7544
www.aviva.com
BAE Systems
media@baesystems.com
www.baesystems.com
BAA
020 7834 9449
www.baa.co.uk
Barclays
020 7699 2658
www.barclays.co.uk
British American Tobacco
020 7845 2888
www.bat.com

Bradford & Bingley
020 7067 5632
www.bbg.co.uk
BG Group
0118 929 3188
www.bg-group.com
British Land
020 7467 2830
www.abbeynational.co.uk
BHP BILLITON
020 7802 4177
www.bhpbilliton.com
BOC Group
01276 807594
www.boc.com
Boots Group
0845 070 8090
www.boots-plc.com
BP
020 7496 4076
www.bp.com
BSkyB
020 7705 3000
www.sky.com
BT Group
020 7356 5369
www.btplc.com
Bunzl
020 7495 4950
www.bunzl.com
Cadbury Schweppes
020 7830 5036
www.cadburyschweppes.com
Carnival
020 7830 5036
www.poprincesscruises.com
Centrica
020 7662 7544
www.centrica.co.uk
Compass Group
01753 494085
www.centrica.co.uk
Cable & Wireless
020 7717 4502
www.cw.com
Diageo
020 7418 2000
www.diageo.com
Daily Mail and General Trust
020 7927 5200
www.dmgt.co.uk
Dixons Group
020 7938 6000
www.dixons-group-plc.co.uk
Emap
020 7278 1452
www.emap.com
Exel Group
020 7795 7000
www.exel.com
Foreign & Colonial Investment Trust
020 7770 5222
www.fandc.com
Friends Provident
01344 744409
www.friendsprovident.co.uk
Granada
01306 654483
www.granadamedia.com

Gallaher Group
020 7620 1620
www.gallaher-group.com
Glaxo SmithKline
01932 859777
www.gsk.com
GUS
020 8047 5502
www.gus.co.uk
GKN
01935 443000
www.gknplc.com
Hanson
020 7245 1245
www.hansonplc.com
HBOS
01483 302203
www.hbosplc.com
Hilton Group
pressoffice@HBOSplc.com
www.hiltongroup.com
HSBC HLDGS
020 7856 8107
www.hsbc.com
ICI
020 7260 8000
www.ici.com
3I Group
020 7009 5000
www.3i.com
Imperial Tobacco
020 7928 3131
www.imperial-tobacco.com
Intercontinental Hotel Group
020 7409 8128
www.intercontinental.com
Johnson Matthey
020 7269 8400
www.matthey.com
Kelda Group
01274 600111
www.keldagroup.com
Kingfisher
020 7821 3529
www.kingfisher.co.uk
Land Securities
020 7372 8008
www.landsecurities.co.uk
Legal and General
020 7004 3150
http://investor.legalandgeneral.com
Liberty International
020 7960 1200
www.liberty-international.co.uk
Lloyds TSB
01737 375353
www.lloydstsb.com
Man Group
01865 204000
www.mangroupplc.com
Marks and Spencer
020 7637 9111
www2.marksandspencer.com
Mitchells & Butlers
0121 498 5770
www.mbplc.com
MMO2
01753 628402
www.mmo2.com

Morrisons Grocery
020 7268 8777
www.morrisons.plc.uk
National Grid
01924 870000
www.nationalgrid.com/uk
Northern Rock
01926 655272
www.northernrock.co.uk
Next
0191 285 7191
www.next.co.uk
Old Mutual
0845 456777
www.oldmutual.com
Prudential
020 7569 0121
www.prudential.co.uk
Pearson
020 7548 3721
www.pearson.com
Provident Financial
01274 731111
www.providentfinancial.com
Reckitt Benckiser
02476 425741
www.reckitt.com
Rentokil Initial
01753 217800
www.rentokil-initial.co.uk
Reuters
01342 833022
www.reuters.com
Rexam
020 7227 4100
www.rexam.com
Royal Bank of Scotland
020 7250 1122
www.rbs.co.uk
Reed Elsevier
0131 523 5659
www.r-e.com
Rio Tinto
020 7227 5657
www.riotinto.com
Rolls Royce
020 7753 2305
www.rolls-royce.com
Royal & Sun Alliance
communications@rolls-royce.com
www.royalsunalliance.com
SABMiller
020 7337 5146
www.sab.co.za
J Sainsbury
020 7659 0120
www.j-sainsbury.co.uk
Scottish & Newcastle
020 7695 7295
www.scottish-newcastle.com
Schroders
0131 528 2131
www.schroders.com
Safeway
020 7658 6166
www.safeway.co.uk
Sage Group
020 8970 3430
www.sage.co.uk
Shell Transport
01912 553036
www2.shell.com
Shire Pharmaceuticals
0800 731 8888
www.shiregroup.com

Smiths Group
01256 894280
www.smiths-group.com
Smith & Nephew
020 8457 8403
www.smith-nephew.com
Scottish Power
020 7401 7646
www.scottishpower.plc.uk
Scottish & Southern Energy
0141 636 4515
www.scottish-southern.co.uk
Standard Chartered
01738 436000
www.standardchartered.com
Severn Trent
020 7280 7163
www.severn-trent.com
Tesco
020 7233 2300
www.tesco.com
Tomkins
020 8871 4544
www.tomkins.co.uk
Unilever
01992 632222
www.unilever.co.uk
United Utilities
020 7822 5252
www.unitedutilities.com
Vodafone
01925 234000
www.vodafone.co.uk
Whitbread
020 7806 5442
www.whitbread.co.uk
Wolseley
01635 674268
www.wolseley.com
WPP Group
0118 929 8700
www.wpp.com
Xstrata
020 7968 2812
www.xstrata.com

Regulators and government agencies

Advertising Standards Authority
020 7580 5555
www.asa.org.uk
British and Irish Ombudsman Association
020 8467 7455
www.bioa.org.uk
British Board of Film Classification
020 7440 1570
www.bbfc.co.uk
British Standards Institution
020 7861 3188
www.bsi-global.com
Competition Commission
020 7271 0100
www.competition-commission.org.uk
Council of Mortgage Lenders
020 7437 0075
www.cml.org.uk
Financial Ombudsman Service
020 7964 1000
www.financial-ombudsman.org.uk

Financial Services Authority
020 7066 1000
www.fsa.gov.uk
Food Standards Agency
020 7276 8000
www.foodstandards.gov.uk
Health and Safety Executive
08701 545500
www.hse.gov.uk
Health and Safety Executive for Northern Ireland
028 9024 3249
www.hseni.gov.uk
Independent Committee for the Supervision of Telephone Information Services
020 7940 7408
www.icstis.org.uk
Information Commissioner
01625 545745
www.dataprotection.gov.uk
Insurance Ombudsman
020 7964 0134
www.theiob.org.uk
National Lottery Commission
020 7016 3430
www.natlotcomm.gov.uk
Office of Fair Trading
08457 224499
www.oft.gov.uk
Office of the Rail Regulator
020 7282 2000, press 020 7282 2002
www.rail-reg.gov.uk
Ofgem
020 7901 7158
www.ofgas.gov.uk/ofgem
Oftel
020 7634 8991
www.oftel.gov.uk
Ofwat
0121 625 1450
hwww.ofwat.gov.uk
Ombudsman for Estate Agents
01722 333306
www.oea.co.uk
Pensions Ombudsman
020 7834 9144
www.pensions-ombudsman.org.uk
Serious Fraud Office
020 7239 7272
www.sfo.org.uk
Small Business Service
0845 001 0031
www.sbs.gov.uk
Trading Standards Institute
0870 872 9000
www.tradingstandards.gov.uk

Industry bodies

Trade Association Forum
020 7395 8283
www.taforum.org
Confederation of British Industry
020 7395 8239
www.cbi.org.uk
Ethnic Minority Business Forum
www.ethnicbusiness.org
Federation of Small Businesses
01253 336000
www.fsb.org.uk

Consumer bodies

Consumer Support Networks
020 7840 7223
www.csnconnect.org.uk
Consumers' Association
020 7770 7000
www.which.net/corporate
**General Consumer Council for
Northern Ireland**
0845 601 6022
www.gccni.org.uk
Internet Watch Foundation UK
01223 237700
www.internetwatch.org.uk
**National Association of Citizens
Advice Bureaux**
www.adviceguide.org.uk
National Consumer Council
020 7730 3469
www.ncc.org.uk
Scottish Consumer Council
0141 226 5261
www.scotconsumer.org.uk
Welsh Consumer Council
029 2025 5454
www.wales-consumer.org.uk

Unions

TUC
Trades Union Congress
020 7636 4030
www.tuc.org.uk
ANGU
The Abbey National Group Union
01442 891122
www.angu.org.uk
Accord
0118 934 1808
www.accord-myunion.org
ALGUS
Alliance and Leicester Group Union
of Staff
0116 285 6585
www.algus.org.uk
*previously Independent Union of
Halifax*
Amicus
020 8462 7755 (Amicus-AEEU)
www.aeeu.org.uk
020 7505 3000; press 020 7420
8934 (Amicus-MSF)
www.msf.org.uk
engineering and electrical
Aslef
Associated Society of Locomotive
Engineers and Firemen
020 7317 8600; press 020 7317 8600
www.aslef.org.uk
manufacturing, union, finance
ACM
Association for College Management
0116 275 5076
www.acm.uk.com
AEP
Association of Educational
Psychologists
0191 384 9512
www.aep.org.uk

AFA
Association of Flight Attendants
020 8276 6723
www.tuc.org.uk
AMO
Association of Magisterial Officers
020 7403 2244
ATL
Association of Teachers and
Lecturers
020 7930 6441; press 020 7782 1589
www.askatl.org.uk
AUT
Association of University Teachers
020 7670 9700
www.aut.org.uk
BFAWU
Bakers, Food and Allied Workers
Union
01707 260150
www.bfawu.org
BSU
Britannia Staff Union
01538 399627
www.britanniasu.org.uk
BALPA
British Air Line Pilots Association
020 8476 4000; press 020 7924 7555
www.balpa.org.uk
BACM-TEAM
British Association of Colliery
Management – Technical, Energy
and Administrative Management
01302 815551
www.bacmteam.org.uk
BDA
British Dietetic Association
0121 200 8080; press 01908 250918
www.bda.uk.com
BOS
British Orthoptic Society
020 7387 7992
www.orthoptics.org.uk
Bectu
Broadcasting, Entertainment,
Cinematograph and Theatre Union
020 7346 0900
www.bectu.org.uk
CSMTS
Card Setting Machine Tenters Society
01924 400206
CATU
Ceramic and Allied Trades Union
01782 272755
CSP
Chartered Society of Physiotherapy
020 7306 6666
press 020 7306 6616/6628
www.csp.org.uk
CWU
Communication Workers Union
020 8971 7200; press 020 8971 7497
www.cwu.org
CDNA
Community and District Nursing
Association
020 8280 5342
www.cdna.tvu.ac.uk

CYWU
Community and Youth Workers'
Union
0121 244 3344
www.cywu.org.uk
Connect
020 8971 6000
professionals in communications
Diageo Staff Association
020 8963 5249
*previously Guinness UDV Staff
Association*
EIS
Educational Institute of Scotland
0131 225 6244
www.eis.org.uk
EFTU
Engineering and Fastener Trade Union
0121 420 2204
Equity
020 7379 6000; press 020 7670 0259
www.equity.org.uk
performers and artists
FDA
020 7343 1111
press 020 7343 1120/1121
www.fda.org.uk
*senior managers and professionals in
public service*
FBU
Fire Brigades Union
020 8541 1765
www.fbu.org.uk
GULO
General Union of Loom Overlookers
01254 51760
GMB
020 8947 3131; press 020 8971 4226
www.gmb.org.uk
general union
GPMU
Graphical, Paper and Media Union
01234 351521
www.gpmu.org.uk
HCSA
Hospital Consultants and Specialists
Association
01256 771777
www.hcsa.com
ISTC
020 7239 1200; press 020 7239 1243
www.istc-tu.org
*steel and metal industry and
communities*
MU
Musicians' Union
020 7582 5566
www.musiciansunion.org.uk
NAPO
020 7223 4887
*probation officers and family court
staff*
NATFHE
020 7837 3636
press 020 7520 1032/3207
www.natfhe.org.uk
university and college lecturers
NACODS
National Association of Colliery
Overmen, Deputies and Shotfirers
01226 203743

NACO
National Association of
Co-operative Officials
0161 351 7900

NAEIAC
National Association of Educational
Inspectors, Advisers and Consultants
01226 383428/383420
www.naeiac.org

NASUWT
National Association of Schoolmasters
Union of Women Teachers
0121 453 6150
www.teachersunion.org.uk

NUDAGO
National Union of Domestic
Appliances and General Operatives
01709 382820

NUJ
National Union of Journalists
020 7278 7916
www.nuj.org.uk

KFAT
National Union of Knitwear, Footwear
and Apparel Trades
0116 255 6703
www.kfat.org.uk

NULMW
National Union of Lock and Metal
Workers
01902 366651

NUMAST
National Union of Marine, Aviation
and Shipping Transport Officers
020 8989 6677
www.numast.org

NUM
National Union of Mineworkers
01226 215555

RMT
National Union of Rail, Maritime and
Transport Workers
020 7387 4771
www.rmt.org.uk

NUT
National Union of Teachers
020 7388 6191
www.teachers.org.uk

NGSU
Nationwide Group Staff Union
01295 710767
www.ngsu.org.uk

POA
Prison Officers Association
020 8803 0255
www.poauk.org.uk

PFA
Professional Footballers Association
0161 236 0575
www.givemefootball.com

Prospect
020 7902 6600
www.prospect.org.uk

PCS
Public and Commercial Services
Union
020 7924 2727; press 020 7801 2820
www.pcs.org.uk

SWSWU
Sheffield Wool Shear Workers Union
17 Galsworthy Road
Sheffield S5 8QX

SCP
Society of Chiropodists and
Podiatrists
020 7234 8620
www.scpod.org

SoR
Society of Radiographers
020 7740 7200
www.sor.org

T&G
Transport and General Workers' Union
020 7611 2500
www.tgwu.org.uk

TSSA
Transport Salaried Staffs' Association
020 7387 2101
www.tssa.org.uk

UBAC
01653 697634
*staff in the Bradford and Bingley
Group and Alltel Mortgage Solutions*

UCAC
Undeb Cenedlaethol Athrawon Cymru
01970 639950

UNIFI
020 8946 9151; press 020 8947 9879
www.unifi.org.uk
finance sector

UCATT
Union of Construction, Allied Trades
and Technicians
0207 622 2442
www.ucatt.org.uk

USDAW
Union of Shop, Distributive and
Allied Workers
0161 224 2804/249 2400

Unison
0845 355 0845
www.unison.org.uk
public service union

WGGB
Writers' Guild of Great Britain
020 7833 0777
www.writersguild.org.uk

YISA
Yorkshire Independent Staff
Association
01482 862058

Employment bodies

Pay & Employment Rights Service
01924 439587
www.pers.org.uk

Employment Tribunals
020 7273 8603
www.employmenttribunals.gov.uk

**Equal Opportunities Commission
(EOC)**
0845 601 5901
www.eoc.org.uk

**Equality Commission for Northern
Ireland**
028 90 500600
www.equalityni.org

Investors in People UK
020 7467 1900
www.iipuk.co.uk

Labour Relations Agency
028 9032 1442
www.lra.org.uk

Low Pay Commission
020 7855 4543/53
www.lowpay.gov.uk

Education

Government department

Education and Skills
020 7925 5000, press 020 7925 6789
www.dfes.gov.uk

Government agencies

Adult Learning Inspectorate
0870 240 7744
www.ali.gov.uk
Arts and Humanities Research Board
0117 987 6500
www.ahrb.ac.uk
Council for Science and Technology
020 7215 5671
www.cst.gov.uk
Education and Learning Wales
08456 088 066
www.elwa.ac.uk
Higher Education Funding Council for England (HEFCE)
0117 931 7317
www.hefce.ac.uk
Learning and Skills Council
0845 019 4170
www.lsc.gov.uk
Learning and Skills Development Agency
020 7297 9000
www.lsda.org.uk
Learning and Teaching Scotland
0141 337 5000
www.ltscotland.com
National Grid for Learning
www.ngfl.gov.uk
Ofsted
020 7421 6800
www.ofsted.gov.uk
Qualifications and Curriculum Authority
020 7509 5555
www.qca.org.uk
Scottish Qualifications Authority
0141 242 2214
www.sqa.org.uk
Sector Skills Development Agency
01709 765444
www.ssda.org.uk
Student Loans Company
0870 242 2211
www.slc.co.uk
Teacher Training Agency (TTA)
0845 600 0991
www.canteach.gov.uk
Ucas
01242 222444
www.ucas.com

Professional bodies

Association of Teachers and Lecturers
020 7930 6441; press 020 7782 1589
www.askatl.org.uk
Association of University Administrators
0161 275 2063
www.aua.ac.uk
Association of University Teachers
020 7670 9700
www.aut.org.uk
British Educational Research Association
01636 819090
www.bera.ac.uk
National Association of Schoolmasters Union of Women Teachers
0121 453 6150
www.teachersunion.org.uk
National Union of Students
020 7272 8900
www.nus.org.uk
National Union of Teachers
020 7388 6191
www.teachers.org.uk

Voluntary bodies

Afasic
020 7490 9410
www.afasic.org.uk
Speech, language & communication charity
Campaign for Learning
020 7930 1111
www.campaign-for-learning.org.uk
CEDC
phil@cedc.org.uk
www.cedc.org.uk
Education Extra
020 8709 9900
www.educationextra.org.uk
Out-of-hours learning
Learning Through Action
01256 883500
www.learning-through-action.org.uk
Life Education Centres
jeani@lifeeducation.org.uk
www.lifeeducation.org.uk
National Literacy Trust
020 7828 2435
www.literacytrust.org.uk
Pupiline
01473 400100
www.pupiline.net
Combats bullying
UFI/ Learn Direct
0114 291 5680
www.ufi.com

Universities

University of Aberdeen
01224 272090/1
www.abdn.ac.uk
University of Abertay Dundee
01382 308080
www.abertay.ac.uk
Anglia Polytechnic University
01245 493131
www.apu.ac.uk
Anglia Polytechnic University
01223 363271
www.apu.ac.uk
Arts Institute at Bournemouth
01202 533011
www.arts-inst-bournemouth.ac.uk
Aston University
0121 359 3611
www.aston.ac.uk
University of Bath
01225 323019
www.bath.ac.uk
Bath Spa University College
01225 875875
www.bathspa.ac.uk
Bell College
01968 283100
www.bell.ac.uk
Bishop Grossteste College
01522 527347
www.bgc.ac.uk
University of Birmingham
0121 414 3344
www.bham.ac.uk
Bolton Institute of Higher Education
01204 900600
www.bolton.ac.uk
Bournemouth University
01202 524111
www.bournemouth.ac.uk
University of Bradford
01274 233081
www.bradford.ac.uk
University of Brighton
01273 600900
www.brighton.ac.uk
University of Bristol
0117 928 9000
www.bris.ac.uk
Brunel University
01895 274000
www.brunel.ac.uk
University of Buckingham
01280 814080
www.buckingham.ac.uk
Buckingham Chilterns University College
01494 603015
www.bcuc.ac.uk
University of Cambridge
01223 332200
www.cam.ac.uk
Christ's College: 01223 334900
www.christs.cam.ac.uk

Churchill College: 01223 336000
www.chu.cam.ac.uk
Clare College: 01223 333246
www.clare.cam.ac.uk
Corpus Christi College:
01223 338057
www.corpus.cam.ac.uk
Downing College: 01223 334800
www.downing.cam.ac.uk
Emmanuel College: 01223 334290
www.emma.cam.ac.uk
Fitzwilliam College: 01223 332000
www.fitz.cam.ac.uk
Girton College: 01223 338999
www.girton.cam.ac.uk
Gonville & Caius College:
01223 332447
www.caius.cam.ac.uk
Homerton College: 01223 411141
www.homerton.cam.ac.uk
Hughes Hall: 01233 334893
www.hughes.cam.ac.uk
Jesus College: 01223 339495
www.jesus.cam.ac.uk
Kings College: 01223 339313
www.kings.cam.ac.uk
Lucy Cavendish College:
01223 332190
www.lucy-cav.cam.ac.uk
Magdalene College: 01223 332100
www.magd.cam.ac.uk
New Hall: 01223 762100
www.newhall.cam.ac.uk
Newnham College: 01223 334700
www.newn.cam.ac.uk
Pembroke College: 01223 338100
www.pem.cam.ac.uk
Peterhouse College: 01223 338200
www.pet.cam.ac.uk
Queen's College: 01223 335540
www.quns.cam.ac.uk
Robinson College: 01223 339100
www.rob.cam.ac.uk
Selwyn College: 01223 335846
www.sel.cam.ac.uk
Sidney Sussex College:
01223 338800
www.sid.cam.ac.uk
St Catharine's College
01223 338300
www.caths.cam.ac.uk
St Edmund's College: 01223 336250
www.stedmunds.cam.ac.uk
St John's College: 01223 338703
www.joh.cam.ac.uk
**Canterbury Christ Church
University College**
01227 767700
www.cant.ac.uk
Cardiff University
029 2087 4404/4839
www.cardiff.ac.uk
**University of Central England in
Birmingham**
0121 331 5595
www.uce.ac.uk
University of Central Lancashire
01772 892400
www.uclan.ac.uk
Speech and Drama
020 7722 8183
www.cssd.ac.uk

**Chester College of Higher
Education**
01244 375444
www.chester.ac.uk
City University
020 7040 5060
www.city.ac.uk
Conservatoire for Dance & Drama
020 7387 0161
www.theplace.org.uk
Conservatoire for Dance & Drama
020 7636 7076
www.rada.org.uk
Coventry University
024 7688 7688
www.coventry.ac.uk
Cumbria Institute of Arts
01228 400300
www.cumbria.ac.uk
Dartington College of Arts
01803 862224
www.dartington.ac.uk
De Montfort University
0116 255 1551
www.dmu.ac.uk
University of Derby
08701 202330
www.derby.ac.uk
University of Dundee
01382 344160
www.dundee.ac.uk
University of Durham
0191 374 2000
www.dur.ac.uk
University of East Anglia
01603 456161
www.uea.ac.uk
University of East London
020 8223 3000
www.uel.ac.uk
Edge Hill College
01695 575171
www.edgehill.ac.uk
University of Edinburgh
0131 650 4360
www.ed.ac.uk
Edinburgh College of Art
0131 221 6000
www.eca.ac.uk
University of Essex
01206 873666
www.essex.ac.uk
University of Exeter
01392 263035
www.ex.ac.uk
Falmouth College of Arts
01326 211077
www.falmouth.ac.uk
University of Glamorgan
01443 483348
www.glam.ac.uk
University of Glasgow
0141 330 3219
www.gla.ac.uk
Glasgow Caledonian
0141 331 3000
www.caledonian.ac.uk
Glasgow School of Art
0141 353 4500
www.gas.ac.uk

University of Gloucestershire
01242 532825
www.chelt.ac.uk, www.glos.ac.uk
Goldsmiths College
020 7919 7171
www.goldsmiths.ac.uk
University of Greenwich
020 8331 8000
www.gre.ac.uk
Heriot-Watt
0131 449 5111
www.hw.ac.uk
University of Hertfordshire
01707 284800
www.herts.ac.uk
University of Huddersfield
01484 422288
www.hud.ac.uk
University of Hull
01482 346311
www.hull.ac.uk
**Imperial College of Science,
Technology and Medicine**
020 7589 5111
www.ic.ac.uk
Keele University
01782 584005
www.keele.ac.uk
University of Kent at Canterbury
01227 827272
www.ukc.ac.uk
Kent Institute of Art & Design
01622 757286
www.kiad.ac.uk
King Alfred's Winchester
01962 841515
www.kingalfreds.ac.uk
King's College London
020 7836 5454
www.kcl.ac.uk
Kingston University London
020 8457 2000
www.kingston.ac.uk
Lancaster University
01524 65201
www.lancs.ac.uk
University of Leeds
0113 233 2332
www.leeds.ac.uk
Leeds Metropolitan
0113 283 3113
www.lmu.ac.uk
University of Leicester
0116 252 5281
www.le.ac.uk
University of Lincoln
01522 882000
www.lincoln.ac.uk
University of Liverpool
0151 794 5928
www.liv.ac.uk
Liverpool John Moores University
0151 231 5090
www.livjm.ac.uk
London Metropolitan
020 7423 0000
www.londonmet.ac.uk
**London School of Economics and
Political Science**
020 7955 7124
www.lse.ac.uk

Loughborough University
01509 263171
www.lboro.ac.uk
University of Luton
01582 489286
www.luton.ac.uk
University of Manchester
0161 275 2077
www.man.ac.uk
University of Manchester Institute of Science and Technology
0161 236 3111
www.umist.ac.uk
Manchester Metropolitan
0161 247 2000
www.mmu.ac.uk
Middlesex University, London
020 8411 5898
www.mdx.ac.uk
Napier University
0500 353570
www.napier.ac.uk
University of Newcastle upon Tyne
0191 222 6000
www.ncl.ac.uk
Newman College of Higher Education
0121 476 1181
www.newman.ac.uk
North East Wales Institute
01978 290666
www.newi.ac.uk
Northern School of Contemporary Dance
0113 219 3000
www.nscd.ac.uk
University of Northumbria at Newcastle
0191 227 4777
www.unn.ac.uk
Norwich School of Art & Design
01603 610561
www.nsad.ac.uk
University of Nottingham
0115 951 5151
www.nottingham.ac.uk
Nottingham Trent
0115 941 8418
www.ntu.ac.uk

University of Oxford
www.ox.ac.uk
Admissions: 01865 270000
  www.admissions.ox.ac.uk
Balliol College: 01865 277777
  www.balliol.ox.ac.uk
Brasenose College: 01865 277510
  www.bnc.ox.ac.uk
Christ Church: 01865 276151
  www.chch.ox.ac.uk
Corpus Christi College:
  01865 276693
  www.ccc.ox.ac.uk
Exeter College: 01865 279660
  www.exeter.ox.ac.uk
Harris Manchester College:
  01865 271009
  www.hmc.ox.ac.uk
Hertford College: 01865 279400
  www.hertford.ox.ac.uk
Jesus College: 01865 279720
  www.jesus.ox.ac.uk

Keble College: 01865 272711
  www.keble.ox.ac.uk
Lady Margaret Hall: 01865 274300
  www.lmh.ox.ac.uk
Lincoln College: 01865 279800
  www.lincoln.ox.ac.uk
Magdalen College: 01865 276063
  www.magd.ox.ac.uk
Mansfield College: 01865 270970
  www.mansfield.ox.ac.uk
Merton College: 01865 276310
  www.merton.ox.ac.uk
New College: 01865 279590
  www.new.oc.ac.uk
Oriel College: 01865 276555
  www.oriel.ox.ac.uk
Pembroke College: 01865 276412
  www.pmb.ox.ac.uk
The Queen's College: 01865 279120
  www.queens.ox.ac.uk
Regent's Park College:
  01865 288120
  www.rpc.ox.ac.uk
Somerville College: 01865 270600
  www.some.ox.ac.uk
St Annes's College: 01865 274825
  www.stannes.ox.ac.uk
St Catherine's: 01865 275800
  www.stcatz.ox.ac.uk
St Edmund Hall: 01865 279008
  www.seh.ox.ac.uk
St Hilda's College: 01865 276884
  www.sthildas.ox.ac.uk
St Hugh's College: 01865 274910
  www.st-hughs.ox.ac.uk
St John's College: 01865 277317
  www.sjc.ox.ac.uk
St Peter's College: 01865 278892
  www.spc.ox.ac.uk
Trinity College: 01865 279910
  www.trinity.ox.ac.uk
University College: 01865 276602
  www.univ.ox.ac.uk
Wadham College: 01865 277946
  www.wadham.ox.ac.uk
Worcester College: 01865 278391
  www.worcester.ox.ac.uk
Oxford Brookes
01865 484040
www.brookes.ac.uk
Queen Margaret University College
0131 317 3000
www.qmuc.ac.uk
Queen Mary, University of London
020 7882 5555
www.qmul.ac.uk
Queen's University Belfast
028 9033 5081
www.qub.ac.uk
University of Paisley
0141 848 3727
www.paisley.ac.uk
University of Plymouth
01752 232137
www.plymouth.ac.uk
University of Portsmouth
023 9284 8484
www.port.ac.uk
Ravensbourne College of Design & Communication
020 8325 8320
www.rave.ac.uk

University of Reading
0118 987 5123
www.reading.ac.uk
Robert Gordon
01224 262000
www.rgu.ac.uk
Roehampton University of Surrey
020 8392 3232
www.roehampton.ac.uk
Rose Bruford College
020 8300 3024
www.bruford.ac.uk
Royal Academy of Music
020 7873 7374
www.ram.ac.uk
Royal Agricultural College
01285 652531
www.royagcol.ac.uk
Royal College of Music
020 7589 3640
www.rcm.ac.uk
Royal Holloway, University of London
01784 434455
www.rhul.ac.uk
Royal Northern College of Music
0161 907 5210
www.rncm.ac.uk
Royal Scottish Academy of Music & Drama
0141 332 4101
www.rsamd.ac.uk
Royal Veterinary College
020 7468 5148
www.rvc.ac.uk
Royal Welsh College of Music & Drama
029 2034 2854
www.rwcmd.ac.uk
University of Salford
0161 295 4545
www.salford.ac.uk
School of Oriental and African Studies (SOAS)
020 7637 2388
www.soas.ac.uk
School of Pharmacy, University of London
020 7753 5831
www.ulsop.ac.uk
Scottish Agricultural College
0800 269453
www.sac.ac.uk/education
University of Sheffield
0114 222 2000
www.sheffield.ac.uk
Sheffield Hallam
0114 225 5555
www.shu.ac.uk
South Bank University
020 7815 7815
www.sbu.ac.uk
University of Southampton
023 8059 5000
www.soton.ac.uk
Southampton Institute
023 8031 9039
www.solent.ac.uk
University of St Andrews
01334 462150
www.st-andrews.ac.uk

St George's Hospital Medical School
020 8725 5992
www.sghms.ac.uk
St Mark & St John College
01752 636890
www.marjon.ac.uk
St Mary's College
020 8240 4000
www.smuc.ac.uk
Staffordshire
01782 294000
www.staffs.ac.uk
University of Stirling
01786 467044
www.stir.ac.uk
Stranmillis University College
028 9038 1271
www.stran-ni.ac.uk
University of Strathclyde
0141 552 4400
www.strath.ac.uk
University of Sunderland
0191 515 3000
www.sunderland.ac.uk
University of Surrey
01483 879305
www.surrey.ac.uk
Surrey Institute of Art & Design, University College
01252 722441
www.surrart.ac.uk
University of Sussex
01273 606755
www.sussex.ac.uk
Swansea Institute of Higher Education
01792 481000
www.sihe.ac.uk

University of Teesside
01642 218121
www.tees.ac.uk
Thames Valley
020 8579 5000
www.tvu.ac.uk
Trinity & All Saints College
0113 283 7123
Trinity College
01267 676767
www.trinity-cm.ac.uk
Trinity College of Music
020 8305 3888
www.tcm.ac.uk
UHI Millennium Institute
01463 27900
www.uhi.ac.uk
University of Ulster at Jordanstown
08700 400700
www.ulster.ac.uk
University College Chichester
01243 816000
www.ucc.ac.uk
University College London
020 7679 2000
www.ucl.ac.uk
University College Northampton
01604 735500
www.northampton.ac.uk
University College Worcester
01905 740800
www.worc.ac.uk
University of Wales, Aberystwyth
Tel: 01970 622021
www.aber.ac.uk
University of Wales College, Newport
01633 432432
www.newport.ac.uk

University of Wales Institute, Cardiff
029 2041 6070
www.uwic.ac.uk
University of Wales, Bangor
01248 382016
www.bangor.ac.uk
University of Wales, Lampeter
01570 422351
www.lamp.ac.uk
University of Wales, Swansea
01792 205678
www.swan.ac.uk
University of Warwick
024 7652 3523
www.warwick.ac.uk
University of the West of England
0117 344 3333
www.uwe.ac.uk
University of Westminster
020 7911 5000
www.westminster.ac.uk
Wimbledon School of Art
020 8408 5000
www.wimbledon.ac.uk
University of Wolverhampton
01902 322222
www.wlv.ac.uk
Writtle College
01245 424200
www.writtle.ac.uk
University of York
01904 430000
Web: www.york.ac.uk
York St John College
01904 624624
www.yorksj.ac.uk

Environment

Government and agencies

Department for the Environment, Food and Rural Affairs
020 7238 3000, press 020 7238 6600
www.defra.gov.uk

Advisory Committee on Pesticides
01904 640500
www.pesticides.gov.uk

British Waterways Board
01923 201120
www.britishwaterways.co.uk

Countryside Agency
01242 521381
www.countryside.gov.uk

Environment Agency
0845 933 3111
www.environment-agency.gov.uk

Food Standards Agency
020 7276 8000
www.foodstandards.gov.uk

Forestry Commission
0131 334 0303
www.forestry.gov.uk

Meat and Livestock Commission
01908 677577
www.mlc.org.uk

United Kingdom Atomic Energy Authority
01235 820220
www.ukaea.org.uk

Rural and environmental bodies

Country Landowners Society
020 7235 0511
www.cla.org.uk

English Heritage
0870 333 1181
www.english-heritage.org.uk

English Nature
01733 455040
www.english-nature.org.uk

Friends of the Earth
0808 800 1111
www.foe.co.uk

Game Conservancy Trust
01425 651000
www.gct.org.uk

Greenpeace
020 7865 8100
www.greenpeace.org.uk

National Farmers Union
020 7331 7200
www.nfu.org.uk

National Trust
0870 609 5380
www.nationaltrust.org.uk

National Trust for Scotland
0131 243 9300
www.nts.org.uk

Ramblers Association
020 7339 8531
www.ramblers.org.uk

Worldwide Fund for Nature UK
01483 426444
www.wwf-uk.org

National parks

Brecon
01874 624437
www.breconbeacons.org

Norfolk & Suffolk Broads
01603 610734
www.broads-authority.gov.uk

Dartmoor
01626 832093
www.dartmoor-npa.gov.uk

Exmoor
01398 323665
www.exmoor-nationalpark.gov.uk

Lake District
01539 724555
www.lake-district.gov.uk

Northumberland
01434 605555
www.northumberland-national-park.org.uk

North Yorkshire Moors
01439 770657
www.moors.uk.net

Peak District
01629 816310
www.peakdistrict.org

Pembrokeshire Coast
0845 634 7275
www.pembrokeshirecoast.org.uk

Snowdonia
0845 130 6229
www.ccw.gov.uk

Yorkshire Dales
01969 650456
www.yorkshiredales.org.uk

Voluntary sector

Animal welfare

Animal Aid
01732 364546
www.animalaid.org.uk

Animal Defenders
020 8846 9777
www.animaldefenders.org.uk

Animal Health Trust
0870 050 2424
www.aht.org.uk

Animal Rights Coalition
01902 711935
http://arc.enviroweb.org

Bat Conservation Trust
020 7627 2629
www.bats.org.uk

Battersea Dogs Home
020 7622 3626
www.dogshome.org

Blue Cross
020 7932 4060
www.bluecross.org.uk
Pet welfare charity

Breach Marine Protection
01405 769375
www.breach.org
Defending the welfare of marine wildlife

British Deer Society
01425 655434
www.bds.org.uk

British Hedgehog Protection Trust
01584 890801
www.software-technics.co.uk/bhps

British Union for Abolition of Vivisection
0207 700 4888
www.buav.org

Butterfly Conservation Trust
0870 774 4309
www.butterfly-conservation.org

Canine Lifeline UK
08707 581401
www.caninelifeline.fsnet.co.uk

Cat Action Trust
01555 660784
www.catactiontrust.co.uk

Cats Protection
08702 099099
www.cats.org.uk

Celia Hammond Animal Trust
01892 783820
www.celiahammond.org

Donkey Sanctuary
01395 578222.
www.thedonkeysanctuary.org.uk

Farm Animal Welfare Council
020 7904 6534
www.fawc.org.uk

Fauna & Flora International
01223 571000
www.fauna-flora.org

Feline Advisory Board
0870 742 2278
www.fabcats.org

Humane Slaughter Society
01582 831919
www.hsa.org.uk

Hunt Saboteurs Organisation
0845 4500727
www.huntsabs.org.uk

International Dolphin Watch
01482 645789
www.idw.org

International Fund for Animal Welfare
020 7587 6700
www.ifaw.org

International League for the Protection of Horses
0870 870 1927
www.ilph.org

League Against Cruel Sports
020 7403 6155
www.league.uk.com
London Wildlife Trust
020 7261 0447
www.wildlondon.org.uk
Mammal Society
020 7350 2200
www.abdn.ac.uk/mammal
Mare & Foal Sanctuary
01626 853085
www.mareandfoal.org.uk
Marine Conservation Society
01989 566017
www.mcsuk.mcmail.com
National Canine Defence League
020 7833 7670
www.ncdl.org.uk
National Federation of Badger Groups
020 7228 6555
www.nfbg.org.uk
Otter Trust
01986 893470
www.ottertrust.org.uk
People and Dogs Society
01924 897732
www.padsonline.org
People for the Ethical treatment of Animals, PETA
020 7357 9229
www.peta.org
People's Dispensary for Sick Animals
01952 290999
www.pdsa.org.uk
Rare Breeds Survival Trust
024 7669 6551
www.rare-breeds.com
Reptile Trust
01207 271766
www.reptiletrust.com
Royal Society for the Prevention of Cruelty to Animals
0870 333 5999
www.rspca.org.uk
Royal Society for the Protection of Birds
01767 680551
www.rspb.org.uk
Save the Rhino
020 7357 7474
www.savetherhino.org
Scottish Wildlife Trust
0131 312 7765
www.swt.org.uk
The Wildlife Trusts
0870 036 7711
www.wildlifetrusts.org
TRAFFIC
01223 277427
www.traffic.org
Combats damaging trade in plants & animals
Ulster Wildlife Trust
028 4483 0282
www.ulsterwildlifetrust.org
Uncaged
0114 272 2220
www.uncaged.co.uk
Anti-vivisection campaigner

Veteran Horse Society
01795 669280
www.veteran-horse-society.co.uk
Whale & Dolphin Conservation Society
0870 870 0027
www.wdcs.org.uk
Wildfowl & Wetlands Trust
01453 891900
www.wwt.org.uk
World Society for the Protection of Animals
020 7587 5000
www.wspa.org.uk
Zoo Federation
01493 369855
www.zoofederation.org.uk

Conservation

Black Environment Network
01286 870715
www.ben-network.co.uk
British Association for Shooting and Conservation
01244 573026
www.basc.org.uk
British Trust for Conservation Volunteers
01491 821600
www.btcv.org
Campaign for Real Events
andi@c-realevents.demon.co.uk
www.c-realevents.demon.co.uk
Provides renewable energy & 'alt tech' support for events
Campaign to Protect Rural England
020 7981 2800
www.cpre.org.uk
Centre for Alternative Technology
01654 705950
www.cat.org.uk
Community Composting Network
0114 258 0483
www.othas.org.uk/ccn
Community Service Volunteers – Environment
0121 322 2008
www.csvenvironment.org.uk
Conservation Foundation
020 7591 3111
www.conservationfoundation.co.uk
Council for Environmental Education
0118 950 2550
www.cee.org.uk
Council for National Parks
020 7924 4077
www.cnp.org.uk
Earth First! In Britain
www.earthfirst.org.uk
Earth Rights
01279 870391
www.earthrights.org.uk
Environmental public interest law firm

Earthwatch Institute
01865 318838
www.uk.earthwatch.org
Conservation of natural environments & cultural heritage
Eco-Village Network
0117 373 0346
http://europe.ecovillage.org/uk
Energywatch
08459 060708
www.energywatch.org.uk
Environmental Campaigns
01942 612639
www.encams.org
European Rivers Network
00 33471 020814
www.rivernet.org
Based in Southern France
Forest Action Network
higgs@envirolink.org
www.fanweb.org/uk
Future Forests
0870 241 1932
www.futureforests.com
Gaia Energy Centre
01840 213321
www.gaiaenergy.co.uk
Promotes renewable energy
Peat Alert
0778 778 2259
www.peatalert.org.uk
People and Planet
01865 245678
www.peopleandplanet.org
UK student action on human rights, poverty & the environment
Rising Tide
07733 017863
www.risingtide.org.uk
Action against climate change
Royal Society for Nature Conservation
0870 036 1000
www.rsnc.org
Solar Energy Society
www.thesolarline.com
Surfers Against Sewage
01273 670153
www.sas.org.uk
UNEP World Conservation Monitoring Centre
01223 277314
www.unep-wcmc.org
Woodland Trust
01476 581135
www.woodland-trust.org.uk

Farming and food

Farm
020 7352 7928
www.farm.org.uk
Campaigners for the future of independent & family farms
Farm Animal Welfare Council
020 7904 6534
www.fawc.org.uk
Farming & Wildlife Advisory Group
02476 696699
www.fwag.org.uk

**Biodynamic Agricultural
Association**
01453 759501
www.anth.org.uk/biodynamic
Campaign for Real Ale
01727 867201
www.camra.org.uk
Compassion in World Farming
01730 264208
www.ciwf.co.uk
Dig it up!
dig-it-up@envoy.dircon.co.uk
www.dig-it-up.uk.net
*Action against planting of
GM rape crops*
Eat the View
01242 533361
www.eat-the-view.org.uk
Food from Britain
020 7233 5111
www.foodfrombritain.com
Promoting sustainable local products
Five Year Freeze Campaign
020 7837 0642
www.fiveyearfreeze.org
Anti-GM activists group
Food & Drink Federation
020 7836 2460
www.fdf.org.uk

Food Dudes
01248 38 3973
www.fooddudes.co.uk
Teaching children about healthy eating
**Foundation for Local Food
Initiatives**
0845 458 9525
www.localfood.org.uk
Free Range Activism Website
www.fraw.org.uk
Future Harvest
LMcDonald@edenproject.com
www.futureharvest.org
*Promoting environmentally sound
agricultural methods*
**Grass Roots Action on Food &
Farming**
01865 793910
www.gaff.org.uk
**Henry Doubleday Research
Society**
024 7630 3517
www.hdra.org.uk
*Researches & promotes organic
methods & produce*
Herb Society
01295 768899
www.herbsociety.co.uk
Herbs for health

**National Association of Farmers
Markets**
01225 787914
www.farmersmarkets.net
National Federation of City Farms
0117 923 1800
www.farmgarden.org.uk
Permaculture Society
0845 458 1805
www.permaculture.org.uk
Pesticide Action Network
020 7274 8895
www.pan-uk.org
Soil Association
0117 929 0661
www.soilassociation.org
Sustain
020 7837 1228
www.sustainweb.org
Alliance for better food & farming
UK Food Group
020 7523 2369
www.ukfg.org.uk
*Network for NGOs working on global
food & agriculture issues*
Veggies Catering Campaign
0845 458 9595
www.veggies.org.uk
Willing Workers on Organic Farms
01273 476286
www.wwoof.org

Health

Department of Health
020 7210 4850, press 020 7210 5231
www.doh.gov.uk
NHS Executive
0113 254 5000
www.doh.gov.uk/nhs.htm
Scottish Executive DoH
0131 244 2440, press 0131 244 2797
www.scotland.gov.uk
Northern Ireland DoH
028 9052 0500, press 028 9052 0636
www.dhsspsni.gov.uk

Government agencies

**Commission for Health
Improvement**
020 7448 9200
www.chi.nhs.uk
Health and Safety Executive
08701 545500
www.hse.gov.uk
Health Protection Agency
020 8200 1295
www.hpa.org.uk
Health Service Ombudsman
0845 015 4033
www.ombudsman.org.uk/hse
**Human Fertilisation and
Embryology Authority**
020 7377 5077
www.hfea.gov.uk
Human Genetics Commission
020 7972 1518
www.hgc.gov.uk
**Joint Committee on Vaccination
and Immunisation**
020 7210 4850
www.doh.gov.uk/jcvi/index.htm
Medical Research Council
020 7636 5422
www.mrc.ac.uk
Medicines Commission
020-7273 0652
www.mca.gov.uk/aboutagency
/regframework/mc
/medcomm.htm
Medicines Regulatory Agency
020 7273 0000
www.mca.gov.uk
Mental Health Task Force
020 7210 4850
www.doh.gov.uk
/mentalhealthtaskforce
Microbiological Research Authority
01980 612100
www.camr.org.uk
National Blood Authority
0113 214 8606
www.blood.co.uk
**National Institute for Clinical
Excellence (NICE)**
020 7067 5800
www.nice.org.uk

National Patient Safety Agency
020 7927 9500
www.npsa.nhs.uk

Professional bodies

British Medical Association
020 7387 4499
www.bma.org.uk
General Medical Council
020 7915 3720
www.gmc-uk.org
Royal College of Nursing
020 7409 3333
www.rcn.org.uk
Academy of Medical Royal Colleges
020 7408 2244
www.aomrc.org.uk
British Dental Association
020 7935 0875
www.bda-dentistry.org.uk
Patients Association
020 8423 9111
www.patients-association.com

Voluntary sector

General health

Action Research
01403 210406
www.actionresearch.co.uk
Alzheimer's Society
020 7306 0606
www.alzheimers.org.uk
Arthritis Care Campaign
020 7380 6500
www.arthritiscare.org.uk
**Association for International
Cancer Research**
01334 477910
www.aicr.org.uk
Bliss
0500 618140
www.bliss.org.uk
*National charity for premature or sick
babies*
Breast Cancer Campaign
020 7749 3700
www.bcc-uk.org
Breast Cancer Care
020 7384 2984
www.breastcancercare.org.uk
British Dietic Association
0121 200 8080
www.bda.uk.com
British Heart Foundation
020 7935 0185
www.bhf.org.uk
British Pregnancy Advisory Service
08457 304030
www.bpas.org

Cancer Research UK
020 7242 0200
www.cancerresearchuk.org
**Consensus Action on Salt and
Health**
0208 725 2409
www.hyp.ac.uk/cash
Cystic Fibrosis Trust
020 8464 7211
www.cftrust.org.uk
Diabetes UK
020 7424 1165
www.diabetes.org.uk
Great Ormond St Children's Charity
020 7916 5678
www.gosh.org
Healthwise
0151 649 3400
www.healthwise.org.uk
Campaigning and providing helplines
Healthy Living Scotland
0845 278 8878
www.healthyliving.gov.uk
Institute of Cancer Research
020 7352 8133
www.icr.ac.uk
International Obesity Taskforce
020 7691 1900
www.iotf.org
Leukaemia Research Fund
020 7405 0101
www.lrf.org.uk
Macmillan Cancer Relief
020 7840 7821
www.macmillan.org.uk
Marie Curie Cancer Care
0207 599 7700
www.mariecurie.org.uk
Marie Stopes International
020 7574 7400
www.mariestopes.org.uk
Reproductive healthcare worldwide
**Motor Neurone Disease
Association**
01604 250505
www.mndassociation.org
Multiple Sclerosis Society
020 8438 0700
www.mssociety.org.uk
National Asthma Campaign
020 7226 2260
www.asthma.org.uk
National Heart Forum
020 7383 7638
www.heartforum.org.uk
**Parkinson's Disease Society
of the UK**
020 7931 8080
www.parkinsons.org.uk
St John Ambulance
020 7324 4210
www.sja.org.uk
The Wellcome Trust
020 7611 8888
www.wellcome.ac.uk

World Cancer Research Fund UK
020 7343 4200
www.wcrf-uk.org

Drugs, alcohol and addiction

Addaction
020 7251 5860
www.addaction.org.uk
Adfam
020 7928 8898
www.adfam.org.uk
Families, drugs and alcohol
Alchemy Project
0845 165 1197
www.alchemyproject.co.uk
Alcohol Concern
020 7928 7377
www.alcoholconcern.org.uk
Alcoholics Anonymous
01904 644026
www.alcoholics-anonymous.org.uk
Arrest Referral Forum
07739 983058
www.drugreferral.org
Support for workers on drugs referral projects
ASH: Action on Smoking and Health
0113 279 4535
www.ash.org.uk
Association of Nurses in Substance Abuse
0870 241 3503
www.ansa.uk.net

Clouds
01747 830733
www.clouds.org.uk
Treatment for addiction
Crew 2000
0131 220 3404
www.crew2000.co.uk
Drinkwise
0141 572 6700
www.drinkwise.co.uk
Drugscope
www.drugscope.org.uk
Information resource
European Association for the Treatment of Addiction
020 7922 8753
www.eata.org.uk
Legalise Cannabis Alliance
07984 255015
www.lca-uk.org
Life or Meth
www.lifeormeth.com
Methamphetamine awareness campaign
Narcotics Anonymous
020 7251 4007
www.ukna.org
National Treatment Agency
020 7972 2274
www.nta.nhs.uk
Parents Against Drug Abuse
admin@pada.org.uk
www.btinternet.com/~padahelp
Promis Recovery Centre
01304 841700
www.promis.co.uk
Multi-awareness and treatment

Release
020 7729 9904
www.release.org.uk
Provides for health, welfare and legal needs of drug users
Re-Solve
www.re-solv.org
The society for the prevention of solvent abuse
Ride Foundation
01372 467708
www.ridefoundation.org.uk
Drug awareness programmes for schools
Sargent Cancer Care for Children
020 8752 2800
www.sargent.org
Scottish Drugs Forum
0141 221 1175
www.sdf.org.uk
Stroke Association
020 7566 0300
www.stroke.org.uk
Substance Misuse Management in General Practice
0161 905 8581
www.smmgp.demon.co.uk
Transform
0117 941 5810
www.transform-drugs.org.uk
anti-prohibition campaign
UK harm reduction alliance
www.ukhra.org
Campaigning for health and ethical treatment of drug users

■ Health helplines

NHS Direct
0845 4647

Alcoholics Anonymous
08457 697555

Alzheimers Helpline
08453 000336

Arthritis Care Helpline
0800 289170

Asthma Helpline
08457 010203

British Allergy Foundation Helpline
020 8303 8583

Cancerlink
0800 132095

Carers Line
0808 808 7777

Contraceptive Education Service
08453 101334

Diabetes UK Careline
020 7424 1030

Doctors' Supportline
08707 650001

Drinkline
0800 917 8282

Drugscope
0800 776600

Healthwise
0151 649 3400

Help with Health Costs Advice Line
0800 917 7711

Menopause and HRT Helpline
01293 413000

Miscarriage Association Helpline
01924 200799

Narcotics Anonymous
020 7730 0009

National Aids Helpline
0800 567123

National Asthma Helpline
08457 010203

National Drugs Helpline
0800 776600

NHS Asian Tobacco Helpline
0800 169 0881 (Urdu)
0800 169 0882 (Punjabi)
0800 169 0883 (Hindi)
0800 169 0884 (Gujerati)
0800 169 0885 (Bengali)

NHS Careers Helpline
0845 606 0655

NHS Pregnancy Smoking Helpline
0800 169 9169

NHS Smoking Helpline
0800 169 0169

Organ Donor Line
0845 606 0400

Parents Against Drug Abuse
08457 023867

re-solve
0808 800 2345

RNID tinnitus helpline
0808 808 6666

Smokers Quitline
0800 002200

Still Births and Neonatal Deaths Helpline
020 7436 5881

Talk to Frank
0800 776600

Women's Health Concern Helpline
01628 483612

Women's Health Enquiry Line
020 7251 6580

NHS hospitals: England

A

Abberton Day Hospital, Colchester
01206 228704

Abingdon Community Hospital, Abingdon
01235 522717

Accrington Victoria Community Hospital, Accrington
01254 263555

Acre Day Hospital, Worthing
01903 216807

Acton Hospital, London
020 8383 1133

Acute Mental Health Services, Shaftesbury
01747 824949

Addenbrooke's Hospital, Cambridge
01223 245151

Adult Psychiatry Day Hospital, Manchester
0161 447 4367

Airedale General Hospital, Keighley
01535 652511

Alcester Hospital, Alcester
01789 762470

Aldeburgh & District Community Hospital, Aldeburgh
01728 452778

Alder Hey Children's Hospital, Liverpool
0151 228 4811

Alderney Hospital, Poole
01202 735537

Alexander Day Hospital, Manchester
0161 748 4022 ext 2766

Alexandra Hospital, Redditch
01527 503030

Alfred Bean Hospital, Driffield
01377 241124

All Saints Hospital, Birmingham
0121 623 5500

All Saints Hospital, Eastbourne
01323 417400

Allenby Ward, Louth County Hospital, Louth
01507 600100

Alnwick Infirmary
01665 626700

Alton Community Hospital, Alton
01420 82811

Altrincham General Hospital, Altrincham
0161 928 6111

Amberstone Hospital, Hailsham
01323 440022

Amersham Hospital, Amersham
01494 434 411

Ancoats Hospital, Manchester
0161 795 4567

Andover War Memorial Community Hospital, Andover
01264 358811

Arundel & District Hospital
01903 882543

Ashburton & Buckfastleigh Hospital
01364 652203

Ashby & District Hospital, Ashby de la Zouch
01530 414222

Ashby Rehabilitation Centre, Lincoln
01522 577055

Ashfield Community Hospital, Kirkby in Ashfield
01623 785050

Ashford Hospital
01932 872000

Ashington Hospital
01670 521212

Ashley House, Grantham
01476 573985

Ashmore House, Poole
01202 660846

Ashurst Child And Family Health Centre, Southampton
023 8074 3000

Aston Hall Hospital (Learning Disabilities), Aston on Trent
01332 792412

Atkinson Morley's Hospital & Wolfson Neurorehabilitation Centre, Wimbledon
020 8946 7711

Atu Day Hospital, Manchester
0161 447 4312

Avondale Unit (Adult Acute Psychiatry), Preston
01772 710651

Axminster Hospital, Axminster
01297 32071

B

Babington Hospital, Belper
01773 824171

Barking Hospital
020 8983 8000

Barnes Hospital, Cheadle
0161 491 2300

Barnes Hospital, London
020 8878 4981

Barnet Community Healthcare NHS Trust
020 8370 6520

Barnet Hospital
020 8216 4000

Barnet Psychiatric Unit
020 8216 4400

Barnsley District General Hospital
01226 730000

Barrow Hospital, Bristol
01275 392811

Bartlet Hospital, Felixstowe
01394 284292

Barton Under Needwood Cottage Hospital, Barton Under Needwood
01283 712323

Basildon Hospital
01268 533911

Basingstoke BSU, Basingstoke
01256 473202

Bassetlaw District General Hospital, Worksop
01909 500990

Battle Hospital, Reading
0118 958 3666

Beccles & District War Memorial Hospital, Beccles
01502 712164

Beckenham Hospital, Beckenham
020 8289 6600

Becontree Day Hospital, Dagenham
020 8984 1234

Bedford Hospital, Bedford
01234 355122

Beech House Mental Health Day Hospital, Camberley
01276 670911

Beech House, Boston
01205 354988

Beighton Community Hospital, Sheffield
0114 271 6572

Bensham Hospital, Gateshead
0191 482 0000

Berkeley Hospital, Berkley
01453 562000

Berwick Infirmary, Berwick on Tweed
01289 307484

Bethlem Royal Hospital, Manchester
020 8777 6611

Bexhill Hospital, Bexhill on Sea
01424 730077

Bexley Hospital, Bexley
01322 625754

Bicester Community Hospital, Bicester
01869 876500

Bideford Hospital, Bideford
01237 420200

Biggleswade Hospital, Biggleswade
01767 224906

Billinge Hospital, Wigan
01942 244000

Bingley Hospital, Bingley
01274 563438

Birch Hill Hospital, Rochdale
01706 377777

Birchfield, Shoreham by Sea
01273 455622

Birmingham and Midland Eye Centre, Birmingham
0121 554 3801

Birmingham Heartlands Hospital
0121 424 1263

Birmingham Skin Centre, Birmingham
0121 554 3801

Birmingham Women's Hospital
0121 472 1377

Bishop Auckland General Hospital
01388 455000

Bishops Castle Community Hospital, Bishops Castle
01588 638220

Blackberry Hill Hospital, Bristol
0117 965 6061

Blackburn Royal Infirmary, Blackburn
01254 263555

Blackpool Victoria Hospital
01253 300000

Blandford Community Hospital, Blandford
01258 456541

Bletchley Community Hospital, Milton Keynes
01908 376415

Bloxwich Hospital, Walsall
01922 858600

Blyth Community Hospital, Blyth
01670 396400

Bognor Regis War Memorial Hospital, Bognor Regis
01243 865418

Bolingbroke Hospital, Wandsworth Common
020 7223 7411

Bolsover Local Hospital
01246 827901

Booth Hall Children's Hospital, Manchester
0161 795 7000

Bootham Park Hospital, York
01904 610777

Bovey Tracey Hospital, Bovey Tracey
01626 832279

Bradford on Avon Community Hospital, Bradford-on-Avon
01225 862975

Bradford Royal Infirmary, Bradford
01274 542200

Bradwell Hospital, Newcastle
01782 425400

Bramcote Hospital,
Nuneaton
024 7638 8200
Brampton War Memorial
Community Hospital,
Brampton
016977 2534
Brentry Hospital, Bristol
0117 908 5000
Brentwood Community
Hospital
01277 212244
Bridgnorth Hospital,
Bridgnorth
01746 762641
Bridgwater Community
Hospital
01278 451501
Bridlington & District
Hospital
01262 606666
Bridport Community
Hospital
01308 422345
Brighton General Hospital
01273 696955
Bristol Eye Hospital
0117 923 0000
Bristol General Hospital
0117 923 0000
Bristol Homoeopathic
Hospital, Bristol
0117 9731231
Bristol Royal Hospital
for Children
0117 927 6998
Bristol Royal Infirmary
0117 923 0000
Brixham Hospital
01803 882153
Broadgreen Hospital,
Liverpool
0151 706 2000
Bromley Hospital
020 8289 7000
Bromyard Community
Hospital, Bromyard
01885 488080
Brookfields Hospital,
Cambridge
01223 723001
Brooklands, Birmingham
0121 779 6981
Broomfield Hospital,
Chelmsford
01245 440761
Brumby Hospital,
Scunthorpe
01724 290402
Buckingham Hospital,
Buckingham
01280 813243
Buckland Hospital, Dover
01304 200 0624
Bucknall Hospital, Stoke-
on-Trent
01782 273510
Budleigh Salterton
Hospital, Budleigh
Salterton
01395 442020

Burden Neurological
Hospital, Bristol
0117 956 7444
Burnley General Hospital
01282 425071
Burton House Day
Hospital, Manchester
0161 447 4509
Bushey Fields Hospital,
Dudley
01384 457373
Butleigh Hospital,
Glastonbury
01458 850237
Buxton Hospital
01298 214000

C

Calderdale Royal Hospital,
Halifax
01422 357171
Calderstones Hospital,
Clitheroe
01254 822121
Cambourne/Redruth
Community Hospital,
Redruth
01209 881688
Cannock Chase Hospital,
Cannock
01543 572757
Cardiothoracic Centre
Liverpool, Liverpool
0151 228 1616
Carlton Court, Lowestoft
01582 538008
Carter Bequest Hospital,
Middlesbrough
01642 850911
Cassel Hospital, Richmond
020 8237 2922
Castle Hill Hospital,
Cottingham
01482 875875
Castle Hill House, Poole
01202 747416
Castle Hospital,
Okehampton
01837 52411
Castleberg Hospital, Settle
01729 823515
Castleford Normanton &
District Hospital,
Castleford
01977 605500
Caterham Dene Hospital,
Caterham
01883 837500
Cathedral View Day
Hospital, Gloucester
01452 307814
Cavendish Hospital,
Buxton
01298 79236
Central Middlesex
Hospital, London
020 8965 5733
Chadwell Heath Hospital,
Romford
020 8983 8000

Chalfonts & Gerrards
Cross Hospital,
Chalfont St Peter
01753 883821
Chapel Allerton Hospital,
Leeds
0113 392 4595
Chard & District Hospital,
Chard
01460 63175
Charing Cross Hospital,
London
020 8846 1234
Charles Clifford Dental
Hospital, Sheffield
0114 271 7800
Chase Farm Hospital,
Enfield
020 8366 6600
Chase Hospital, Whitehall
01420 488801
Cheadle Hospital,
Stoke-on-Trent
01538 487500
Chelsea and Westminster
Hospital, London
020 8746 8000
Cheltenham General
Hospital, Cheltenham
01242 222222
Cherry Knowle Hospital,
Sunderland
0191 565 6256
Cherry Tree Hospital,
Stockport
0161 483 1010
Chesham Hospital
01494 783961
Cheshunt Community
Hospital, Cheshunt
01992 622157
Chester le Street Hospital
0191 333 6262
Chesterfield & North
Derbyshire Royal
Hospital, Chesterfield
01246 277271
Chesterton Hospital,
Cambridge
01223 363415
Chippenham Community
Hospital, Chippenham
01249 447100
Chipping Norton
Community Hospital,
Chipping Norton
01608 628000
Chorley & South Ribble
District General Hospital,
Chorley
01257 261222
Christchurch Hospital,
Christchurch
01202 486361
Christie Hospital,
Manchester
0161 446 3000
Churchill Hospital,
Headington
01865 741841

Cirencester Hospital,
Cirencester
01285 884632
City General Hospital,
Stoke-on-Trent
01782 715444
City Hospital, Birmingham
0121 554 3801
Clacton & District Hospital,
Clacton on Sea
01255 253520
Clacton Hospital, Clacton
01255 201717
Clatterbridge Hospital,
Wirral
0151 334 4000
Clay Cross Community
Hospital
01246 863031
Clayponds Hospital,
London
020 8560 4011
Clayton Hospital,
Wakefield
01924 201688
Clevedon Hospital,
Clevedon
01275 341473
Clifton Hospital, Lytham
St Annes
01253 306204
Clitheroe Hospital
01772 782216
Coalville Community
Hospital, Coalville
01530 510510
Cobham Cottage Hospital,
Cobham
01932 584200
Cockermouth Cottage
Hospital, Cockermouth
01900 822226
Colchester General
Hospital, Colchester
01206 747474
Colindale Hospital, London
020 8200 1555
Coltman Street Day
Hospital, Hull
01482 328807
Colwood Hospital,
Haywards Heath
01444 441881
Community Day Hospital,
Runcorn
01928 753047
Congleton & District
War Memorial Hospital,
Congleton
01260 272227
Conquest Hospital,
St Leonards on Sea
01424 755255
Cookridge Hospital, Leeds
0113 392 4253
Coppetts Wood Hospital,
London
020 7794 0500
Coquetdale Cottage
Hospital, Morpeth
01669 620555

Corbett House,
Stourbridge
01384 456111
Corby Community
Hospital, Corby
01536 400070
Coronation Hospital, Ilkley
01943 609 666
Cossham Hospital, Bristol
0117 9671661
Cottage Day Hospital,
Oldham
0161 627 8068
Countess of Chester
Hospital, Chester
01244 365000
County Hospital, Durham
0191 333 6262
County Hospital, Hereford
01432 355444
Coventry and Warwickshire
Hospital, Coventry
024 7622 4055
Cranleigh Village Hospital,
Cranleigh
01483 782400
Crawley Hospital, Crawley
01293 600300
Crediton Hospital, Crediton
01363 775588
Crewkerne Hospital,
Crewkerne
01460 72491
Cromer Hospital, Cromer
01263 513571
Crowborough War
Memorial Hospital,
Crowborough
01892 652284
Cumberland Infirmary,
Carlisle
01228 523444

D

Dane Garth, Mental Health
Unit, Barrow in Furness
01229 870870
Darent Valley Hospital,
Dartford
01322 428100
Darlington Memorial
Hospital
01325 380100
Dartmouth & Kingswear
Hospital, Dartmouth
01803 832255
Dawlish Hospital, Dawlish
01626 863219
Day Hospital for the Elderly,
Grimsby
01472 874111
Defoe Day Hospital,
Colchester
01206 228928
Delancey Assessment &
Rehabilitation Hospital,
Cheltenham
01242 222222
Dellwood Hospital,
Reading
0118 958 9195

Dental Hospital, Bristol
0117 923 0000
Derby City General
Hospital
01332 340131
Derby Royal Infirmary
01332 347141
Derbyshire Children's
Hospital, Derby
01332 340131
Dereham Hospital
01362 692391
Derriford Hospital,
Plymouth
01752 777111
Devizes Community
Hospital
01380 723511
Devonshire Road Hospital,
Blackpool
01253 303364
Devonshire Royal Hospital,
Buxton
01298 72222
Dewsbury and District
Hospital, Dewsbury
01924 512000
Diana, Princess of Wales
Children's Hospital,
Birmingham
0121 333 9999
Diana, Princess of Wales
Hospital, Grimsby
01472 874111
Didcot Community
Hospital
01235 517900
Dilke Memorial Hospital,
Gloucester
01594 598100
Doddington Hospital,
March
01354 644299
Doncaster Gate Hospital,
Rotherham
01709 304802
Doncaster Royal Infirmary
& Montagu Hospital,
Doncaster
01302 366666
Dorking Hospital
01737 768511
Dorothy Pattison Hospital,
Walsall
01922 858000
Dorset County Hospital,
Dorchester
01305 251150
Dryden Road Day Hospital,
Gateshead
0191 402 6600
Dunston Hill Hospital,
Gateshead
0191 482 0000

E

Ealing Hospital, Southall
020 8967 5000
Earls House Hospital,
Durham
0191 333 6262
East Cleveland Hospital,
Saltburn by Sea
01287 676205
East Cornwall Hospital,
Bodmin
01208 251560
East Ham Memorial
Hospital, London
020 8586 5000
East Surrey and Crawley
Hospitals, Redhill
01737 768511
Eastbourne District
General Hospital,
Eastbourne
01323 417400
Eastman Dental Hospital,
London
020 7915 1000
Edenbridge & District
War Memorial Hospital,
Edenbridge
01732 862137
Edgware Community
Hospital
0208 952 2381
Edith Cavell Hospital,
Peterborough
01733 874000
Edward Bolitho House NHS
Nursing Home, Penzance
01736 575555
Edward Hain Hospital,
St Ives
01736 576100
Edward Street Hospital,
West Bromwich
0121 553 7676
Elizabeth Garrett Anderson
Hospital, London
020 7387 9300
Ellen Badger Hospital,
Shipston-on-Tour
01608 661410
Ellesmere Port Hospital,
Elllesmere Port
01244 365000
EMI Unit (Hillview) Day
Hospital, Blackburn
01254 293365
Enfield Community Care
Centre, Enfield
020 8366 6600
Epsom General Hospital,
Epsom
01372 735735
Erith & District Hospital,
Erith
020 8302 2678
Essex County Hospital,
Colchester
01206 747474
Evesham Community
Hospital, Evesham
01386 502538

Exmouth Hospital,
Exmouth
01395 226005

F

Fair Mile Hospital,
Wallingford
020 8366 9174/9193
Fairfield General Hospital,
Bury
0161 764 6081
Fairford Hospital, Fairford
01285 712212
Fairmile Hospital,
Wallingford
01491 651281
Fall Birch Hospital, Bolton
01204 695 5714
Falmouth Hospital
01326 434700
Farnham Community
Hospital, Farnham
01483 782000
Farnham Road Mental
Health & Community
Hospital Health Services,
Guildford
01483 443535
Faversham Cottage
Hospital, Faversham
01795 562066
Feilding Palmer Hospital,
Lutterworth
01455 552150
Felixstowe General
Hospital, Felixstowe
01394 282214
Fenwick Hospital,
Lyndhurst
023 8028 2782
Fieldhead Hospital,
Wakefield
01924 327000
Finchley Memorial
Hospital, London
020 8349 3121
Fleet Community Hospital,
Fleet
01483 782700
Fleetwood Hospital
01253 303364
Florence Desmond Day
Hospital, Guildford
01483 571122
Fordingbridge Hospital,
Fordingbridge
01425 652255
Fowey Hospital
01726 832241
Franklyn Hospital, Exeter
01392 208400
Freeland Court Day
Hospital, Clacton on Sea
01255 253602
Freeman Hospital,
Newcastle General
Hospital, Royal Victoria
Infirmary, Newcastle
Upon Tyne
0191 284 3111
Frenchay Hospital, Bristol
0117 970 1070

Friarage Hospital,
Northallerton
01609 779911
Frimley Park Hospital,
Frimley
01276 604604
Fulbourn Hospital,
Cambridge
01223 243961
Furness General Hospital,
Barrow-in-Furness
01229 870870

G

Gables Day Hospital,
Braintree
01376 555700
General Hospital, Hereford
01432 355444
George Eliot Hospital,
Nuneaton
02476 351351
Gilbert Bain Hospital,
Lerwick
01595 743000
Glenfield Hospital,
Leicester
0116 287 1471
Gloucestershire Royal
Hospital, Gloucester
01452 528555
Goldie Leigh Hospital,
London
020 8311 5128
Good Hope District
General Hospital, Sutton
Coldfield
0121 378 2211
Goodmayes Hospital, Ilford
020 8983 8000
Goole & District Hospital,
Goole
01405 720720
Gordon Hospital, London
020 8746 5505
Gorse Hill Hospital,
Leicester
0116 225 5200
Goscote Hospital, Walsall
01922 710710
Gosport War Memorial
Hospital, Gosport
023 9252 4611
Grantham & District
Hospital, Grantham
01476 565232
Gravesend & North Kent
Hospital, Gravesend
01474 564333
Graylingwell Hospital,
Chichester
01243 787970
Great Ormond Street
Hospital for Children,
London
020 7405 9200
Great Western Hospital,
Swindon
01793 604020
Green Lane Hospital,
Devizes
01380 731200

Grimsby Maternity
Hospital, Grimsby
01472 874111
Grove Hospital, Derby
01332 792210
Guild Park, Preston
01772 865531
Guisborough General
Hospital, Guisborough
01287 284000
Gulson Hospital
02476 553344
Guy's Hospital, London
020 7955 5000

H

Hallam Day Hospital,
West Bromwich
0121 553 1831
Hallam Street Hospital,
West Bromwich
0121 607 3900
Halstead Hospital,
Halstead
01787 291010
Haltwhistle War Memorial
Hospital,
Northumberland
01434 320225
Ham Green Hospital,
Bristol
01275 812661
Hammersmith Hospital,
London
020 8383 4692
Hammerwich Hospital,
Burntwood
01543 686224
Hanham Hall Hospital,
Bristol
0117 908 5000
Harefield Hospital,
Harefield
01895 823737
Harold Wood Hospital,
Romford
01708 345533
Harpenden Memorial
Hospital, Harpenden
01582 460429
Harrogate District Hospital,
Harrogate
01423 885959
Harry Watton House,
Birmingham
0121 623 5500
Hartismere Hospital, Eye
01379 870543
Harwich & District Hospital,
Harwich
01255 201200
Harwich Day Hospital,
Harwich
01255 207400
Haslemere Community
Hospital, Haslemere
01483 782300
Havant War Memorial
Hospital, Havant
023 9248 4256

Hawkhurst Cottage
Hospital, Hawkhurst
01580 753345
Head and Neck Centre,
Shrewsbury
01743 261000
Heanor Memorial Hospital
01773 710711
Heart Hospital, London
020 7573 8888
Heath Lane Hospital, West
Bromwich
0121 553 7676
Heatherwood Hospital,
Ascot
01753 633000
Hellesdon Hospital &
Wensum Meadows,
Norwich
01603 421421
Helston Community
Hospital
01326 435800
Hemel Hempstead General
Hospital, Hemel
Hempstead
01442 213141
Herbert Hospital,
Bournemouth
01020 765323
Hertford County Hospital,
Hertford
01707 328111
Herts & Essex General
Hospital, Bishop's
Stortford
01279 444455
Herts & Essex Hospital,
Bishop's Stortford
01279 655191
Hexham General Hospital,
Hexham
01434 655655
High Royds Hospital,
Leeds
01943 876151
High Wood Hospital,
Brentwood
01708 465000
Highbury Hospital,
Nottingham
0115 977 0000
Highcroft Hospital,
Birmingham
0121 623 5500
Highfield Day Hospital,
Chester le Street
0191 333 6262
Hill Crest Mental Health
Unit, Redditch
01527 500575
Hillingdon Hospital,
Uxbridge
01895 238282
Hinchingbrooke Hospital,
Huntingdon
01480 416416
Hinckley & District
Hospital, Hinckley
01455 441800

Hinckley Sunnyside
Hospital, Hinckley
01455 251188
Hitchin Hospital, Hitchin
01438 314333
Holme Valley Memorial
Hospital, Holmfirth
01484 681711
Holsworthy Hospital,
Holsworthy
01409 253424
Holywell Rehabiltation
Unit, St Albans
01727 897411
Homeopathic Hospital,
Tunbridge Wells
01892 542977
Homerton University
Hospital, London
020 8510 5555
Honiton Hospital, Honiton
01404 540540
Hope Hospital, Salford
0161 789 7373
Horn Hall Hospital,
Stanhope
01388 528233
Horncastle War Memorial
Hospital, Horncastle
01507 522349
Hornsea Cottage Hospital,
Hornsea
01964 533146
Hornsey Central Hospital,
London
020 8219 1700
Horsham Hospital
(Community and Mental
Health), Horsham
01403 227000
Horsham Hospital,
Horsham
01403 227000
Horton Hospital, Banbury
01295 275500
Hospital for Tropical
Diseases, London
020 7387 9300 or
020 7387 4411
Hospital of St Cross, Rugby
01788 572831
Hospital of St John and
St Elizabeth, London
020 7806 4000
Huddersfield Royal
Infirmary
01484 342000
Hull Royal Infirmary, Hull
01482 328541
Hulton Hospital, Bolton
01204 390390
Hyde Hospital, Cheshire
0161 366 8833
Hythe Hospital,
Southampton
023 8084 6046

I

Ilfracombe Hospital, Ilfracombe
01271 863448
Ilkeston Community Hospital
0115 930 5522
Ipswich Hospital, Ipswich
01473 712233
Isebrook Hospital, Wellingborough
01933 440099

J

James Cook University Hospital, Middlesbrough
01642 850850
James Paget Hospital, Great Yarmouth
01493 452452
John Coupland Hospital, Gainsborough
01427 816500
John Radcliffe Hospital, Oxford
01865 741166
John Taylor Hospice, Birmingham
0121 2552400
Johnson Hospital, Spalding
01775 722386
Julian Hospital, Norwich
01603 421421

K

Kelling Hospital, Holt
01263 713333
Kendray Hospital, Barnsley
01226 777811
Kent & Canterbury Hospital, Canterbury
01227 766877
Kent and Sussex Hospital, Tunbridge Wells
01892 526111
Kent County Ophthalmic & Aural Hospital, Maidstone
01622 673444
Kettering General Hospital, Kettering
01536 492000
Keycol Hospital, Sittingbourne
01634 810900
Keynsham Hospital, Bristol
0117 986 2356
Kidderminster Hospital, Kidderminster
01562 823424
King Edward VII Hospital, Windsor
01753 860441
King George Hospital, Ilford
020 8983 8000
King's College Hospital (Dulwich), London
0207 737 4000

King's College Hospital, London
0207 737 4000
King's Mill Hospital, Sutton in Ashfield
01623 622515
Kings Park Hospital, Bournemouth
01202 303757
Kingsbury Community Hospital, London
020 8903 1323
Kingston General Hospital, Hull
01482 328631
Kingston Hospital, Kingston upon Thames
020 8546 7711
Kingsway Hospital, Derby
01332 362221
Kington Cottage Hospital, Kington
01544 230317
Knutsford and District Community Hospital, Knutsford
01565 632112

L

Lambert Memorial Hospital, Thirsk
01845 522292
Lamellion Hospital, Liskeard
01579 335300
Langdon Hospital, Dawlish
01626 888372
Lanthorne Hospital, Leytonstone
020 8539 5511
Larchwood Hospital, Haywards Heath
01444 252248
Launceston General Hospital
01566 765650
Lea Castle Hospital, Kidderminster
01562 850461
Leatherhead Hospital, Leatherhead
01372 384384
Ledbury Cottage Hospital, Ledbury
01531 632488
Leeds General Infirmary
0113 243 2799
Leeds Road Hospital, Bradford
01274 494194
Leeds/Wakefield BSU, Leeds
0113 264 8164
Leek Moorlands Hospital, Leek
01538 487100
Leicester Frith Hospital, Leicester
0116 225 5200
Leicester General Hospital, Leicester
0116 249 0490

Leicester Royal Infirmary, Leicester
0116 254 1414
Leigh House Hospital, Winchester
01962 825800
Leigh Infirmary, Leigh
01942 672333
Leighton Hospital, Crewe
01270 255141
Leominster Community Hospital, Leominster
01568 614211
Lichfield Victoria Hospital, Lichfield
01543 442000
Lincoln County Hospital, Lincoln
01522 512512
Lings Bar Hospital, Nottingham
0115 945 5577
Lister Hospital, Stevenage
01438 314333
Little Bromwich Centre for Elderly Mental Health, Birmingham
0121 623 5500
Little Plumstead Hospital, Norwich
01603 711227
Littlehampton Hospital, Littlehampton
01903 717101
Littlemore Mental Health Centre, Oxford
01865 778911
Liverpool Women's Hospital, Liverpool
0151 708 9988
Livingstone Hospital, Dartford
01322 622222
London Chest Hospital
0207 377 7000
Longton Cottage Hospital, Stoke-on-Trent
01782 425600
Lord Mayor Treloar Hospital, Alton
01420 82811
Lothingland Community Unit, Lowestoft
01502 560111
Loughborough General Hospital, Loughborough
01509 611600
Loughborough Hospital, Loughborough
01509 611600
Louth County Hospital, Louth
01507 600100
Loversall Hospital, Doncaster
01302 796000
Lowestoft Hospital, Lowestoft
01502 587311
Lucy Baldwyn Hospital, Stourport-on-Severn
01299 827327

Ludlow Hospital, Ludlow
01584 872201
Luton & Dunstable Hospital, Luton
01582 491122
Lymington Hospital, Lymington
01590 677011
Lymington Infirmary, Lymington
01590 676081
Lynfield Mount Hospital, Bradford
01274 494194
Lytham Hospital, Lytham St Annes
01253 303980

M

Macclesfield District General Hospital, Macclesfield
01625 421000
Maidstone Hospital, Maidstone
01622 729000
Malmesbury Community Hospital, Malmesbury
01666 823358
Malton Norton & District Hospital, Malton
01653 693041
Malvern Community Hospital, Malvern
01684 612600
Manchester Royal Eye Hospital, Manchester
0161 276 1234
Manchester Royal Infirmary, Manchester
0161 276 1234
Manor Hospital (Walsall), Walsall
01922 721172
Mansfield Community Hospital, Mansfield
01623 785050
Mapleton Day Hospital (Elderly Services), Derby
01332 340131
Market Harborough & District Hospital, Market Harborough
01858 410500
Marlow Community Hospital
01628 482292
Martello Court Day Hospital, Clacton on Sea
01255 253540
Mary Hewetson Community Hospital, Keswick
017687 72012
Mary Hewetson Cottage Hospital, Keswick
01768 772012
Maternity Hospital, Hull
01482 376215
Maudsley Hospital, London
020 7703 6333

Mayday University
Hospital, Croydon
020 8401 3000

Meadowbrook Hospital,
Manchester
0161 772 3700

Medway Maritime Hospital,
Gillingham
01634 830000

Melksham Community
Hospital, Melksham
01225 703088

Melton Mowbray & District
War Memorial Hospital,
Melton Mowbray
01664 854901

Memorial Hospital, London
020 8856 5511

Memorial Hospital,
Woolwich
020 8836 6000

Middlesbrough General
Hospital, Middlesbrough
01642 850850

Midhurst Eastbourne &
District Cottage Hospital,
Midhurst
01730 813105

Mile End Hospital, London
020 7377 7000

Milford Rehabilitation
Hospital, Godalming
01483 782000

Milford-on-sea Hospital,
Milford-on-sea
01590 648100

Mill View hospital, Hove
01273 696011

Millbrook Macclesfield
District General Hospital,
Macclesfield
01625 663306

Millom Cottage Hospital,
Millom
01229 772631

Milton Keynes General
NHS Hospital,
Milton Keynes
01908 660033

Minehead & West
Somerset Hospital,
Minehead
01643 707251

Molesey Hospital, West
Molesey
020 8941 4481

Monkwearmouth Hospital,
Sunderland
0191 565 6256

Montfield Hospital, Lerwick
01595 743000

Moore Cottage Hospital,
Cheltenham
01451 820228

Moorfields Eye Hospital,
London
0207 253 3411

Moorgreen Hospital,
Southampton
02380 472258

Moreton District Hospital,
Moreton in Marsh
01608 650456

Moretonhampstead
Hospital, Newton Abbot
01647 440217

Morpeth Cottage Hospital,
Morpeth
01670 395600

Morton Ward, John
Coupland Hospital,
Gainsborough
01427 614751

Moseley Hall Hospital,
Birmingham
0121 4424321

Mossley Hill Hospital,
Liverpool
0151 250 3000

Mount Gould Hospital,
Plymouth
01752 268011

Mount Hospital, Eastleigh
01703 612335

Mount Vernon Hospital,
Barnsley
01226 777835

Mount Vernon Hospital,
Northwood
01923 826111

N

National Hospital for
Neurology &
Neurosurgery, London
020 7837 3611

Nelson Hospital, Merton
020 8296 2000

New Cross Hospital,
Wolverhampton
01902 307999

Newark Hospital
01636 681681

Newbury Community
Hospital, Newbury
01635 32500

Newcastle Dental Hospital,
Newcastle upon Tyne
0191 232 5131

Newcastle General
Hospital, Newcastle
Upon Tyne
0191 273 8811

Newham General Hospital,
London
020 7476 4000

Newhaven Downs House,
Newhaven
01273 513441

Newholme Hospital,
Bakewell
01629 812525

Newmarket Hospital,
Newmarket
01638 564000

Newquay and District
Hospital
01637 893600

Newton Abbot Hospital,
Newton Abbot
01626 354321

Newton Community
Hospital, Newton-le-
Willows
01925 222731

Newtown Hospital,
Worcester
01905 763333

Norfolk & Norwich
University Hospital,
Norwich
01603 286286

North Cambridgeshire
Hospital, Wisbech
01945 585781

North Devon District
Hospital, Barnstaple
01271 322577

North Hampshire Hospital,
Basingstoke
01256 473202

North Manchester General
Hospital Day Surgery
Unit, Manchester
0161 795 4567

North Manchester General
Hospital, Manchester
0161 795 4567

North Middlesex University
Hospital, London
020 8887 2000

North Riding Infirmary,
Middlesbrough
01642 850850

North Staffordshire Royal
Infirmary, Stoke-on-Trent
01782 715444

North Tyneside General
Hospital, North Shields
0191 259 6660

North Walsham Cottage
Hospital, North Walsham
01692 500560

Northampton General
Hospital, Northampton
01604 634700

Northern Centre for Cancer
Treatment, Newcastle
Upon Tyne
0191 273 8811

Northern General Hospital,
Sheffield
0114 243 4343

Northgate Hospital, Great
Yarmouth
01493 452452

Northgate Hospital,
Morpeth
01670 394000

Northowram Hospital,
Halifax
01422 201101

Northwick Park Hospital,
Harrow
020 8864 3232

Northwood & Pinner
Community Hospital,
Northwood
01923 824182/3/4

Nottingham City Hospital,
Nottingham
0115 969 1169

Nunnery Fields Hospital,
Canterbury
01227 766877

O

Okehampton & District
Hospital, Okehampton
01837 52188

Old Manor Hospital,
Salisbury
01722 336262

Oldchurch Hospital,
Romford
01708 345533

Ongar War Memorial
Hospital, Ongar
01277 362629

Ormskirk and District
General Hospital,
Ormskirk
01695 577111

Orpington Hospital
01689 815000

Orsett Hospital, Grays
01268 533911

Orsett Hospital, Thurrock
01268 533911

Ottery St Mary Hospital,
Ottery St Mary
01404 816000

Oxford Community
Hospital, Oxford
01865 225501

Oxted and Limpsfield
Hospital, Oxted
01883 714334

P

Paignton Hospital,
Paignton
01803 557425

Palmer Community
Hospital, Jarrow
0191 451 6000

Papworth Hospital,
Cambridge
01480 830541

Park Hospital for Children,
Headington
01865 226213

Park View Resource
Centre, King's Lynn
01553 613613/ext.5502

Parklands Hospital,
Basingstoke
01256 817718

Patrick House, Sutton
Coldfield
0121 685 6685

Patrick Stead Hospital,
Halesworth
01986 872124

Paulton Memorial Hospital,
Bristol
01761 412315

Pembury Hospital,
Pembury
01892 823535

Pendle Community
Hospital, Nelson
01282 474900

Penn Hospital,
Wolverhampton
01902 444141

Penrith Hospital, Penrith
01768 245300

Pershore Cottage Hospital,
Pershore
01386 502070

Peterborough District
Hospital, Peterborough
01733 874000

Peterlee Community
Hospital, Peterlee
01642 617617

Petersfield Hospital,
Petersfield
01730 263221

Pilgrim Hospital, Boston
01205 364801

Pinderfields General
Hospital, Wakefield
01924 201688

Plaistow Hospital, London
020 8586 6200

Plympton Hospital,
Plymouth
01752 338484

Poltair Hospital, Penzance
01736 575578

Pontefract General
Infirmary, Pontefract
01977 600600

Poole Hospital, Poole
01202 665511

Portland Hospital for
Women and Children,
London
020 75804400

Portland Hospital, Portland
01305 820341

Preston Hall Hospital,
Aylesford
01622 710161

Prestwich Hospital,
Manchester
0161 772 9121

Primrose Hill Hospital,
Jarrow
0191 451 6375

Princess Alexandra
Hospital, Harlow
01279 444455

Princess Anne Hospital,
Southampton
023 8077 7222

Princess Louise Hospital,
London
020 8969 2488

Princess Margaret
Hospital, Swindon
01793 604020

Princess Marina Hospital,
Northampton
01604 752323

Princess of Wales
Community Hospital,
Bromsgrove
01527 488000

Princess of Wales Hospital
and Oliver Zangwill
Centre For
Neuropsychologica, Ely
01353 652000

Princess Royal Hospital,
Haywards Heath
01444 441881

Princess Royal Hospital,
Hull
01482 701151

Princess Royal Hospital,
Telford
01952 641222

Princess Royal University
Hospital, Orpington
01689 814000

Prudhoe Hospital, Prudhoe
01670 394000

Purley War Memorial
Hospital, Purley
020 8401 3000

Putney Hospital, London
020 8789 6611

Q

Queen Alexandra Hospital,
Cosham
023 9228 6941

Queen Alexandra Hospital,
Portsmouth
02392 286000

Queen Elizabeth Hospital,
Gateshead
0191 482 0000

Queen Elizabeth Hospital,
King's Lynn
01553 613613

Queen Elizabeth Hospital,
London
020 8836 6000

Queen Elizabeth II Hospital,
Welwyn Garden City
01707 328111

Queen Elizabeth Medical
Centre, Birmingham
0121 472 1311

Queen Elizabeth
Psychiatric Hospital,
Birmingham
0121 627 2999

Queen Elizabeth The
Queen Mother Hospital,
Margate
01843 225544

Queen Mary's Hospital
for Children, Carshalton
020 8296 2000

Queen Mary's Hospital,
London
020 8789 6611

Queen Mary's Hospital,
Sidcup
020 8302 2678

Queen Victoria Hospital
(Morecambe),
Morecambe
01524 411661

Queen Victoria Hospital,
East Grinstead
01342 410210

Queen Victoria Memorial
Hospital, Herne Bay
01227 594700

Queen Victoria Memorial
Hospital, Welwyn
01707 365291

Queen's Hospital,
Burton-on-Trent
01283 566333

Queen's Medical Centre,
Nottingham
0115 924 9924

Queens Park Hospital,
Blackburn
01254 263555

Queen's Park Psychiatric
Day Hospital,
Blackburn
01254 293427

R

Radcliffe Infirmary,
Oxford
01865 311188

Rainbow Cottage,
Bournemouth
01202 534692

Ramsbottom Cottage
Hospital, Bury
01706 823123

Rathbone Hospital,
Liverpool
0151 250 3000

Retford Hospital, Retford
01777 705261

Ribchester Hospital,
Preston
01772 782216

Richardson Hospital,
Barnard Castle
01833 637436

Richmond Healthcare
Hamlet, Richmond
020 8940 3331

Richmond Royal,
Richmond
020 8940 3331

Richmond Victoria
Hospital, Richmond
01748 822109

Ridge Lea Hospital,
Lancaster
01524 586200

Ridings, Shoreham by Sea
01273 455622

Ripley Hospital
01773 743456

Ripon Community Hospital,
Ripon
01765 602546

Rochdale Infirmary,
Rochdale
01706 377777

Rochford Hospital,
Wickford
01702 578000

Romsey Hospital, Romsey
01794 512343

Rosie Hospital, Cambridge
01223 245151

Ross Community Hospital,
Ross-on-Wye
01989 562100

Rossall Hospital,
Fleetwood
01253 303800

Rotherham District General
Hospital, Rotherham
01709 820000

Roundwell Place Day
Centre, Stoke-on-Trent
01782 425740

Rowley Regis Hospital
0121 607 3465

Royal Albert Edward
Infirmary, Wigan
01942 244000

Royal Alexandra Hospital
for Sick Children,
Brighton
01273 328145

Royal Berkshire & Battle
Hospitals, Reading
0118 987 5111

Royal Bolton Hospital
01204 390390

Royal Bournemouth
Hospital, Bournemouth
01202 303626

Royal Brompton Hospital,
London
020 7352 8121

Royal Cornwall Hospital,
Truro
01872 250000

Royal Devon & Exeter
Hospital, Exeter
01392 411611

Royal Eye Infirmary,
Plymouth
01752 662078

Royal Free Hospital,
London
020 7794 0500

Royal Halifax Infirmary
01422 357222

Royal Hallamshire Hospital,
Sheffield
0114 271 1900

Royal Hampshire County
Hospital, Winchester
01962 863535

Royal Lancaster Infirmary,
Lancaster
01524 65944

Royal Leamington Spa
Rehabilitation Hospital,
Warwick
01926 317700

Royal Liverpool University
Hospital, Liverpool
0151 7062000

Royal London
Homeopathic Hospital,
London
020 7837 8833

Royal London Hospital
020 7377 7000

Royal Manchester
Children's Hospital,
Manchester
0161 794 4696
Royal Marsden Hospital,
London
020 7352 8171
Royal National Hospital for
Rheumatic Diseases,
Bath
01225 465941
Royal National
Orthopaedic Hospital,
Stanmore
020 8954 2300
Royal National Throat,
Nose and Ear Hospital,
London
020 7837 8855
Royal Oldham Hospital
0161 624 0420
Royal Orthopaedic
Hospital, Birmingham
0121 685 4000
Royal Preston Hospital
01772 716565
Royal Shrewsbury
Hospital, Shrewsbury
01743 261000
Royal South Hants
Hospital, Southampton
02380 634288
Royal Surrey County
Hospital, Guildford
01483 571122
Royal Sussex County
Hospital, Brighton
01273 696955
Royal United Hospital, Bath
01225 428331
Royal Victoria Hospital,
Folkestone
01303 850202
Royal Victoria Infirmary,
Newcastle Upon Tyne
0191 232 5131
Royston Hospital, Royston
01763 242134
Runwell Hospital, Wickford
01268 366000
Rushden Hospital,
Rushden
01933 440666
Russells Hall, Wordsley,
Corbett & Guest
Hospitals, Stourbridge
01384 456111
Ruth Lancaster James
Cottage Hospital, Alston
01434 381218
Rutland Memorial Hospital,
Rutland
01572 722552
Rutson Hospital,
Northallerton
01609 779911
Ryhope Hospital,
Sunderland
0191 565 6256

S

Saffron Walden Community
Hospital, Saffron Walden
01799 562900
St Albans City Hospital,
St Albans
01727 866122
St Andrew's Hospital, Bow
020 7476 4000
St Anne's Hospital,
Altrincham
0161 928 5851
St Anns Hospital, London
020 8442 6000
St Ann's Hospital, Poole
01202 708881
St Austell Community
Hospital
01726 291100
St Barnabas Hospital,
Saltash
01752 843101
St Bartholomew's Day
Hospital, Liverpool
0151 489 6241
St Bartholomew's Hospital,
London
020 7377 7000
St Bernards Hospital,
Southall
020 8354 8027
St Catherines Hospital,
Birkenhead
0151 678 7272
St Catherines Hospital,
Bradford
01274 227599
St Catherine's Hospital,
Doncaster
01302 796000
St Charles Hospital,
London
020 8969 2488
St Christophers Hospital,
Fareham
01329 286321
St Clements Hospital,
Ipswich
01473 715111
St Clements Hospital,
London
020 7377 7000
St Edmunds Hospital,
Northampton
01604 637221
St Edmunds Nursing
Home, Ipswich
01473 254709
St Edwards Hospital, Leek
01538 360421
St Francis Unit, City
Hospital, Nottingham
0115 969 1169
St Georges Hospital,
Hornchurch
01708 465000
St George's Hospital,
Lincoln
01522 512512
St George's Hospital,
London
020 8672 1255

St George's Hospital,
Morpeth
01670 512121
St Georges Hospital,
Stafford
01785 257888
St Helens Hospital
0151 4261600
St Helier Hospital,
Carshalton
020 8296 2000
St James Hospital,
Portsmouth
023 9282 2444
St James's University
Hospital, Leeds
0113 243 3144
St Johns & Amyand House,
Twickenham
020 8744 9943
St Johns Health Centre,
Twickenham
020 8891 3101
St John's Hospital,
Chelmsford
01245 491149
St Lawrences Hospital,
Bodmin
01208 251300
St Leonard's Hospital,
Ringwood
01202 871165
St Leonards Hospital,
Sudbury
01787 371341
St Leonard's, London
020 7301 3000
St Luke's Hospital,
Bradford
01274 734744
St Luke's Hospital,
Huddersfield
01484 343000
St Lukes Hospital, London
020 8219 1800
St Luke's Hospital, Market
Harborough
01858 410300
St Luke's Hospital,
Middlesbrough
01642 850850
St Margaret's Hospital,
Epping
01279 444455
St Mark's Hospital,
Maidenhead
01628 632012
St Mark's, Harrow
020 8235 4000
St Martins Hospital, Bath
01225 832383
St Martin's Hospital,
Canterbury
01227 459371
St Mary's Hospital for
Women and Children
(Manchester),
Manchester
0161 276 1234
St Mary's Hospital,
Isles of Scilly
01720 422392

St Marys Hospital,
Kettering
01536 410141
St Mary's Hospital, Leeds
0113 279 0121
St Mary's Hospital, London
020 7886 6666
St Mary's Hospital, Melton
Mowbray
01664 854800
St Mary's Hospital,
Newport
01983 524081
St Marys Hospital,
Portsmouth
023 9228 6892
St Michael's Hospital,
Aylsham
01263 732341
St Michael's Hospital,
Braintree
01376 551221
St Michael's Hospital,
Bristol
0117 921 5411
St Michael's Hospital,
Hayle
01736 753234
St Michael's Hospital,
Lichfield
01543 414555
St Michael's Hospital,
Warwick
01926 496241
St Monica's Hospital, York
01347 821214
St Nicholas Hospital,
Gosforth
0191 273 6666
St Nicholas Hospital,
Newcastle upon Tyne
0191 273 6666
St Oswalds Hospital,
Ashbourne
01335 342121
St Pancras Hospital,
London
020 7530 3500
St Peter's Hospital,
Chertsey
01932 872000
St Peter's Hospital, Maldon
01621 854344
St Richard's Hospital,
Chichester
01243 788122
St Thomas' Hospital,
London
020 7928 9292
Salisbury District Hospital,
Salisbury
01722 336262
Sanderson Hospital,
Gosforth
0191 285 0171
Sanderson Hospital,
Newcastle upon Tyne
0191 285 0171
Sandwell General Hospital,
West Bromwich
0121 553 1831

Savernake Hospital,
Marlborough
01672 514571
Scarborough General
Hospital, Scarborough
01723 368111
Scott Clinic, St Helens
0151 430 6300
Scott Hospital, Plymouth
01752 284370
Scunthorpe General
Hospital, Scunthorpe
01724 282282
Seacroft Hospital, Leeds
0113 264 8164
Seaton & District
Community Hospital,
Seaton
01297 23901
Sedgefield Community
Hospital, Stockton-on-
Tees
01740 626600
Selby War Memorial
Hospital, Selby
01757 702664
Selly Oak Hospital,
Birmingham
0121 627 1627
Sevenoaks Hospital,
Sevenoaks
01732 455155
Sharoe Green Hospital,
Preston
01772 716565
Sheffield Children's
Hospital, Sheffield
0114 271 7000
Sheldon Nursing Home,
Birmingham
0121 4756100
Shelton Hospital,
Shrewsbury
01743 261000
Shepherd House, Worthing
01903 843390
Sheppey Community
Hospital, Isle of Sheppey
01795 879100
Shepton Mallet Community
Hospital
01749 342931
Shipley Hospital
01274 773390
Shire Hill Hospital, Glossop
01457 866021
Shotley Bridge Day
Hospital for the Elderly,
Consett
01207 583583
Shotley Bridge General
Hospital, Consett
01207 214444
Sidmouth Hospital,
Sidmouth
01395 512842
Sir Alfred Jones Memorial
Hospital, Liverpool
0151 250 3000
Sir GB Hunter Memorial
Hospital, Tyne & Wear
0191 220 5953

Sir Robert Peel Hospital,
Tamworth
01827 263800
Sittingbourne Memorial
Hospital, Sittingbourne
01795 418300
Skegness & District
Hospital, Skegness
01754 762401
Skipton General Hospital
01756 792233
Small Heath Health Centre,
Birmingham
0121 685 7204
Smallwood Health Centre,
Redditch
01527 60121
Smallwood House,
Redditch
01527 488600
Snowdon House,
Southampton
023 8029 3636
Solihull Hospital
0121 424 2000
South Hams Hospital,
Kingsbridge
01548 852349
South Molton Hospital,
South Molton
01769 572164
South Moor Hospital,
Stanley
0191 333 6262
South Petherton Hospital,
South Petherton
01460 241106
South Shore Hospital,
Blackpool
01253 306106
South Tyneside District
Hospital, South Shields
0191 454 8888
Southampton General
Hospital, Southampton
02380 777222
Southend Hospital,
Westcliff-on-Sea
01702 435555
Southlands Hospital,
Shoreham by Sea
01273 455622
Southmead Hospital,
Bristol
0117 950 5050
Southmoor Hospital,
Pontefract
01977 465630
Southport & Formby
District General Hospital,
Southport
01704 547471
Southport & Ormskirk
District General Hospital,
Southport
01704 547471
Southport General
Infirmary, Southport
01704 547471
Southwold & District
Hospital, Southwold
01502 723333

Southwood Hospital,
London
020 8340 8778
Southwood House,
Bridgwater
01278 456561
Springbourne House,
Bournemouth
01202 300024
Springfield University
Hospital, London
020 8672 9911
Staffordshire General
Hospital, Stafford
01785 257731
Stamford & Rutland
Hospital, Stamford
01780 764151
Standish Hospital,
Stonehouse
01453 822481
Stanfield Hospital,
Stoke-on-Trent
01782 835721
Stead Memorial Hospital,
Redcar
01642 282282
Stepping Hill Hospital,
Stockport
0161 483 1010
Steppingley Hospital,
Steppingley
01525 716601
Stewart Day Hospital,
St Helens
01744 458380
Stoke Mandeville Hospital,
Aylesbury
01296 315000
Stonebury Day Hospital,
Lydney
01594 598260
Stoney Ridge Hospital,
Bingley
01274 495737
Stow Lodge Centre,
Stowmarket
01449 614024
Stratfield House,
Wellington
01823 661663
Stratford upon Avon
Hospital, Stratford-upon-
Avon
01926 495321
Stratton Hospital, Bude
01288 352161
Stretford Memorial
Hospital, Manchester
0161 881 5353
Stroud General Hospital,
Stroud
01453 562200
Stroud Maternity Hospital,
Stroud
01453 562140
Stroud Road Mental Health
Centre, Gloucester
01452 891200
Sunderland Eye Infirmary,
Sunderland
0191 5283616

Sunderland Royal Hospital,
Sunderland
0191 565 6256
Surbiton Hospital, Surbiton
020 8399 7111
Surrey BSU, Farnham
01483 782000
Sussex Eye Hospital,
Brighton
01273 606126
Sutherland Centre,
Stoke-on-Trent
01782 425560
Sutton Coldfield Cottage
Hospital
0121 2554000
Swaffham Community
Hospital, Swaffham
01760 721363
Swanage Hospital,
Swanage
01929 422282
Sycamores Day Hospital,
Oldham
0161 627 8101

T

Tameside General Hospital,
Ashton-Under-Lyne
0161 331 6000
Tatchbury Mount,
Southampton
023 8087 4000
Taunton & Somerset
Hospital, Taunton
01823 333444
Tavistock General Hospital,
Tavistock
01822 612233
Teddington Memorial
Hospital, Teddington
020 8408 8210
Teignmouth Hospital,
Teignmouth
01626 772161
Tenbury District Hospital,
Tenbury Wells
01584 810643
Tewkesbury Hospital,
Tewkesbury
01684 293303
Thame Community
Hospital, Thame
01844 212727
Thanet Mental Health Unit,
Margate
01843 225544
Thetford Cottage Hospital
01842 752490
Thornbury Hospital, Bristol
01454 412636
Thorpe Coombe Hospital,
Walthamstow
020 8520 8971
Thurrock Community
Hospital, Grays
01375 390044
Tickhill Road Hospital,
Doncaster
01302 796000

Tiddington Fields,
Stratford-upon-Avon
01789 414923

Tiverton & District Hospital,
Tiverton
01884 253251

Tolworth Hospital, Tolworth
020 8390 0101

Tonbridge Cottage
Hospital, Tonbridge
01732 353653

Torbay District General
Hospital, Torquay
01803 614567

Torrington Hospital,
Torrington
01805 622208

Totnes Community
Hospital, Totnes
01803 862622

Towers Hospital, Leicester
0116 225 6000

Townlands Hospital,
Henley-on-Thames
01491 572544

Trafford General Hospital,
Manchester
0161 748 4022

Trengweath Hospital,
Redruth
01209 881900

Trowbridge Community
Hospital, Trowbridge
01225 752558

U

Uckfield Community
Hospital, Uckfield
01825 769999

Ulverston Hospital,
Ulverston
01229 583635

University College London
Hospital
020 7636 8333

University Hospital Aintree,
Liverpool
0151 525 5980

University Hospital
Lewisham, London
020 8333 3000

University Hospital of
Hartlepool, Hartlepool
01429 266654

University Hospital of North
Durham, Dryburn
0191 333 2333

University Hospital of North
Tees, Stockton-on-Tees
01429 266654

Upton Hospital, Slough
01753 821441

Upton Road Day Hospital,
Bexleyheath
020 8303 3577

V

Verrington Hospital,
Wincanton
01963 32006

Victoria Central Hospital,
Wirral
0151 678 7272

Victoria Cottage Hospital,
Emsworth
01243 376041

Victoria Cottage Hospital,
Maryport
01900 812634

Victoria Eye Hospital
(Hereford), Hereford
01432 355444

Victoria Hospital, Deal
01304 865400

Victoria Hospital, Frome
01373 463591

Victoria Hospital, Lewes
01273 474153

Victoria Hospital, Swindon
01793 481182

Victoria House, Margate
01843 224541

Victoria Infirmary,
Northwich
01606 74331

Violet Hill Day Hospital,
Stowmarket
01449 673872

W

Walkergate Hospital,
Newcastle Upon Tyne
0191 219 4300

Wallingford Community
Hospital, Wallingford
01491 208500

Walnuttree Hospital,
Sudbury
01787 371404

Walsgrave Hospital,
Coventry
024 7660 2020

Walton Centre for
Neurology and
Neurosurgery, Liverpool
0151 525 3611

Walton Community
Hospital
01932 220060

Walton Hospital,
Chesterfield
01246 277271

Wanford House Hospital,
Exeter
01392 403433

Wansbeck General
Hospital, Ashington
01670 521212

Wantage Community
Hospital, Wantage
01235 205801

Wareham Health Centre,
Wareham
01929 556422

Wareham Hospital,
Wareham
01929 552433

Warley Hospital,
Brentwood
01708 465000

Warminster Community
Hospital, Warminster
01985 212076

Warrington Hospital,
Warrington
01925 635911

Warrington, Halton,
St Helens & Knowsley
BSU, Warrington
01925 635911

Warwick Hospital, Warwick
01926 495321

Warwickshire, Solihull &
Coventry BSU, Coventry
02476 224055

Waterloo Day Hospital,
Liverpool
0151 928 7243

Waterside Hospital,
Londonderry
01504 860007

Watford General Hospital,
Watford
01923 244366

Wathwood Hospital,
Rotherham
01709 873106

Wayland Hospital,
Attleborough
01953 452181

Welland Hospital, Spalding
01775 766800

Wellington & District
Cottage Hospital,
Wellington
01823 662663

Wells & District Hospital
01749 673154

Wells Cottage Hospital,
Wells next the Sea
01328 710218

Wembley Community
Hospital, Wembley
020 8903 1323

Wesham Park Hospital,
Preston
01253 303280

West Bank Hospital,
Telford
01952 243482

West Cheshire Hospital,
Chester
01244 365000

West Cornwall Hospital,
Penzance
01736 874000

West Cumberland Hospital,
Whitehaven
01946 693181

West Haven Hospital,
Weymouth
01305 786116

West Heath Hospital,
Birmingham
0121 627 1627

West Howe Clinic,
Bournemouth
01202 572501

West Lane Hospital,
Middlesbrough
01642 850619

West Middlesex University
Hospital, Isleworth
020 8560 2121

West Norwich Hospital,
Norwich
01603 286286

West Park Hospital,
Wolverhampton
01902 444000

West Suffolk Hospital, Bury
St Edmunds
01284 713000

West View Hospital,
Tenterden
01580 763677

Westbourne, Plymouth
01752 550741

Westbury Community
Hospital, Westbury
01373 823616

Westcliffe Hospital,
Stoke-on-Trent
01782 425860

Western Community
Hospital, Southampton
02380 475401

Western Eye Hospital,
London
020 7886 3231

Western House Hospital,
Ware
01920 468954

Westminster Memorial
Hospital, Shaftesbury
01747 851535

Westmorland General
Hospital, Kendal
01539 732288

Weston General Hospital,
Weston-super-Mare
01934 636363

Weston Park Hospital,
Sheffield
0114 226 5000

Westwood Hospital,
Beverley
01482 886600

Westwood Hospital,
Beverley
01482 875875

Wexham Park Hospital,
Slough
01753 633000

Weybridge Hospital
01932 852931

Weymouth Community
Hospital, Weymouth
01305 760022

Wharfdale General
Hospital, Leeds
0113 392 2000

Whelley Hospital, Wigan
01942 244000

Whipps Cross University
Hospital, London
020 8539 5522

Whipton Hospital, Exeter
01392 208333

Whiston Hospital, Prescot
0151 426 1600
Whitby Hospital, Whitby
01947 604851
Whiteabbey Hospital,
Newtownabbey
02890 865181
Whitstable & Tankerton
Hospital, Tankerton
01227 594400
Whittington Hospital,
London
020 7272 3070
Whitton Clinic, Whitton
020 8894 0306/4293
Whitworth Hospital,
Matlock
01629 580211
Wigton Community
Hospital, Wigton
016973 66600
Willesden Community
Hospital, London
020 8459 1292
William Harvey Hospital,
Ashford
01233 633331
William Julien Courtauld
Hospital, Braintree
01376 551221
Williton & District Hospital,
Williton
01984 632422
Wimborne Hospital,
Wimborne
01202 841101
Winchcombe & District
Hospital, Winchcombe
01242 602341
Windsor Day Hospital,
Shepton Mallet
01749 343911
Wirral Hospital (Arrowe
Park & Clatterbridge),
Wirral
0151 678 5111
Withernsea Hospital,
Withernsea
01964 614666
Withington Hospital,
Manchester
0161 445 8111
Witney Community
Hospital, Witney
01993 602900
Woking Community
Hospital
01483 715911
Wokingham Hospital
0118 949 5000
Wolverhampton Eye
Infirmary, Wolverhampton
01902 307999
Women's Hospital,
Doncaster Royal
Infirmary
01302 366666
Wonford House Hospital,
Exeter
01392 403475

Woodlands Hospital,
Manchester
0161 790 4222
Woodlands Hospital,
St Leonards on Sea
01424 755255
Woods Hospital, Glossop
01457 860783
Woodside Health Centre,
London
020 8656 0213
Worcester Royal Infirmary
(Castle Street Branch)
01905 763333
Worcester Royal Infirmary
(Newtown Branch)
01905 763333
Worcester Royal Infirmary
(Ronkswood Branch)
01905 763333
Worcestershire Royal
Hospital, Worcester
01905 763333
Wordsley Hospital,
Stourbridge
01384 456111
Wordsworth House Child
Development Centre,
Southampton
023 8079 6657
Workington Infirmary,
Workington
01900 602244
Worthing Hospital,
Worthing
01903 205111
Wotton Lawn Acute
Hospital, Gloucester
01452 891500
Wrightington Hospital,
Wigan
01257 252211
Wycombe Hospital,
High Wycombe
01494 526161
Wythenshawe Hospital,
Manchester
0161 998 7070

Y

Yeatman Hospital,
Sherborne
01935 813991
Yeovil District Hospital,
Yeovil
01935 475122
York District Hospital, York
01904 631313

Z

Zachary Merton
Community Hospital,
Rustington
01903 784155

Aberaeron Cottage
Hospital
01545 570225
Aberdare General Hospital,
Aberdare
01685 872411
Abergele Hospital
01745 832295
Abergoed Hospital,
Abergoed
01443 821821
Abertillery & District
Hospital, Abertillery
01496 214123
Amman Valley Hospital,
Ammanford
01269 822226
Barry Hospital
01446 704000
Blaina & District Hospital,
Nantyglo
01495 290230
Brecon War Memorial
Hospital, Brecon
01874 622443
Bro Cerwyn Psychiatric
Day Hospital,
Haverfordwest
01437 773157
Bro Ddyfi Community
Hospital, Powys
01654 702266/7
Bro Morgannwg NHS Trust,
Bridgend
01656 752752
Bronglais General Hospital,
Aberystwyth
01970 623131
Bronllys Hospital, Brecon
01874 711255
Bryn Beryl Hospital,
Pwllheli
01758 701122
Brynhaul Day Hospital,
Llanelli
01554 756567
Brynmair Day Hospital,
Llanelli
01554 772768
Bryntirion Hospital, Llanelli
01554 756567
Builth Cottage Hospital,
Builth Wells
01982 552221
Caerphilly District Miners'
Hospital, Caerphilly
02920 851811
Cardigan and District
Memorial Hospital
01239 612214
Chepstow Community
Hospital, Chepstow
01291 636636
Chirk Community Hospital,
Chirk
01691 772430
Colwyn Bay Community
Hospital
01492 515218

Conwy Hospital
01492 592333
County Hospital, Torfeen
01495 768768
Cymla Hospital
01639 641161
Deeside Community
Hospital, Deeside
01244 830461
Denbigh Community
Hospital
01745 812624
Dolgellau & Barmouth
Hospital, Dolgellau
01341 422479
Ebbw Vale Hospital,
Ebbw Vale
01495 302483
Fairwood Hospital,
Swansea
01792 203192
Glan Clwyd District General
Hospital, Rhyl
01745 583910
Glanrhyd Hospital,
Bridgend
01656 752752
Groeswen Hospital,
Port Talbot
01639 641161
Hensol Hospital, Pontyclun
01656 752752
Hill House Hospital,
Swansea
01792 203551
HM Stanley Hospital,
St Asaph
01745 583275
Knighton Hospital,
Knighton
01547 528633
Llandough Hospital,
Penarth
029 20711711
Llandrindod Wells Hospital,
Llandrindod Wells
01597 822951
Llandudno General
Hospital, Llandudno
01492 860066
Llanfrechfa Grange
Hospital, Cwmbran
01633 623623
Llangollen Community
Hospital
01978 860226
Llanidloes War Memorial
Hospital, Llanidloes
01686 412121
Lluesty Hospital, Holywell
01352 710581
Llwynypia Hospital,
Rhondda
01443 440440
Maesgwyn Hospital,
Bryncethin
01656 720371
Maesteg Hospital, Maesteg
01654 732732
Maindiff Court Hospital,
Abergavenny
01873 735500

Mid-Wales Hospital,
Brecon
01874 711661

Monmouth Hospital,
Monmouth
01600 713522

Montgomery County
Infirmary, Newtown
01686 627722

Morriston Hospital,
Swansea
01792 702222

Mountain Ash General,
Mountain Ash
01685 872411

Neath General Hospital,
Neath
01639 862000

Neath Port Talbot Hospital,
Port Talbot
01639 862000

Nevill Hall Hospital,
Abergavenny
01873 732732

Oakdale Hospital,
Blackwood
01495 225207

Port Talbot Hospital
01639 641161

Porth Hospital, Porth
01443 440440

Prestatyn Community
Hospital
01745 853487

Prince Charles Hospital,
Merthyr Tydfil
01685 721721

Prince Philip Hospital,
Llanelli
01554 756567

Princess of Wales Hospital,
Bridgend
01656 752752

Redwood Memorial
Hospital, Rhymney
01685 840314

Robert Jones & Agnes
Hunt Orthopaedic and
District Hospital,
Oswestry
01691 404000

Royal Alexandra Hospital,
Rhyl
01745 343188

Royal Glamorgan Hospital,
Llantrisant
01443 443443

Royal Gwent Hospital,
Newport
01633 234234

Ruthin Hospital
01824 702692

St Brynach's Day Hospital,
Haverfordwest
01437 764545

St Cadoc's Hospital,
Newport
01633 436700

St David's Hospital
(Carmarthen),
Carmarthen
01267 237481

St Tydfil's Hospital,
Merthyr Tydfil
01685 723244

St Woolos Hospital,
Newport
01633 234234

Singleton Hospital,
Swansea
01792 205666

South Pembrokeshire
Hospital, Pembroke Dock
01646 682114

Swn-Y-Gwynt Day
Hospital, Ammanford
01269 595473

Tenby Cottage Hospital,
Tenby
01834 842040

Tonna Hospital, Neath
01639 641161

Tredegar General Hospital,
Tredegar
01495 722271

Tregaron Hospital
01974 298203

Ty Sirhowy Health Centre,
Blackwood
01495 229010

Tywyn & District War
Memorial Hospital, Tywyn
01654 710411

University Hospital of
Wales, Cardiff
029 2074 7747

Velindre Hospital, Cardiff
02920 615888

Victoria Memorial Hospital,
Welshpool
01938 553133

West Wales General
Hospital, Carmarthen
01267 235151

Whitchurch Hospital,
Cardiff
029 2069 3191

Whitechurch Hospital,
Whitechurch
01948 666292

Withybush General
Hospital, Haverfordwest
01437 764545

Wrexham Maelor Hospital,
Wrexham
01978 291100

Ystrad Mynach Hospital,
Hangoed
01443 812201

Ystradgynlais Community
Hospital, Swansea
01639 844777

Aberdeen Maternity
Hospital, Aberdeen
01224 840606

Aberdeen Royal Infirmary,
Aberdeen
01224 681818

Aberfeldy Cottage
Hospital, Aberfeldy
01887 820314

Aboyne Hospital, Aboyne
01339 886433

Acorn Street Day Hospital,
Glasgow
0141 556 4789

Adamson Hospital, Fife
01334 652901

Ailsa Hospital, Ayr
01292 610556

Alexander Hospital,
Coatbridge
01236 422661

Annan Hospital, Annan
01461 203425

Arbroath Infirmary,
Arbroath
01241 872584

Argyll & Bute Hospital,
Argyll
01546 602323

Arran War Memorial
Hospital, Lamlash
01770 600777

Ashludie Day Hospital,
Dundee
01382 527830

Astley Ainslie Hospital,
Edinburgh
0131 537 9000

Ayr Hospital, Ayr
01292 614500

Ayrshire Central Hospital
01294 274191

Balfour Hospital, Kirkwall
01856 885400

Bangour Village Hospital,
Broxburn
01506 419666

Bannockburn Hospital,
Bannockburn
01786 813016

Belford Hospital, Fort
William
01397 702481

Belhaven Hospital, Dunbar
01368 862246

Bellsdyke Hospital, Larbert
01324 570700

Benbecula Hospital,
Benbecula
01870 603603

Birch Avenue Day Hospital,
Perth
01738 553920/553500

Birkwood Hospital,
Lesmahagow
01555 892382

Blairgowrie Cottage
Hospital, Blairgowrie
01250 874466

Blawathill Hospital, Glagow
0141 954 9000

Bo'ness Hospital, Bo'ness
01506 823032

Bonnybridge Hospital
01324 814685

Borders General Hospital,
Melrose
01896 826000

Brechin Infirmary, Brechin
01356 622291

Brooksby House Hospital,
Largs
01475 672285

Caithness General
Hospital, Wick
01955 605050

Cameron Hospital, Fife
01592 712472

Campbell Hospital, Banff
01261 842202

Campbeltown Hospital,
Argyll
01586 552224

Canniesburn Hospital,
Glasgow
0141 211 5845

Castle Douglas Hospital,
Castle Douglas
01556 502333

Chalmers Hospital, Banff
01261 812567

Chalmers Hospital,
Edinburgh
0131 536 1000

City Hospital, Aberdeen
01224 663131

City Hospital, Edinburgh
0131 536 1000

Clackmannan County Day
Hospital, Alloa
01259 723840

Clackmannan County
Hospital, Alloa
01259 723840

Cleland Hospital,
Motherwell
01698 860293

Coathill Hospital,
Coatbridge
01698 245000

Coldstream Cottage
Hospital, Coldstream
01890 882417

Corstorphine Hospital,
Edinburgh
0131 537 6250

Cottage Day Hospital,
Dumbarton
01389 763151

County Hospital,
Invergordon
01349 852496

Cresswell Maternity
Hospital, Dumfries
01387 246246

Crieff Hospital, Crieff
01764 653173

Crosshouse Hospital,
Kilmarnock
01563 521133

Dalrymple Hospital,
Dumfries
01776 706900

Davidson Cottage Hospital,
Girvan
01465 712571

Dingleton Hospital,
Melrose
01896 822727

Dr Gray's Hospital, Elgin
01343 543131

Dr MacKinnon Memorial
Hospital, Isle of Skye
01471 822137

Drumchapel Hospital,
Glasgow
0141 211 6000

Dumbarton Joint Hospital,
Dumbarton
01389 762317

Dumfries and Galloway
Royal Infirmary, Dumfries
01387 246246

Dunaros Hospital/Salen
Sick Bay Hospital,
& Eventide Home,
Isle of Mull
01680 300392

Dunbar Hospital, Caithness
01847 893263

Dunoon & District General
Hospital, Dunoon
01369 704341

Dunrowan Day Hospital,
Falkirk
01324 639009

Dykebar Hospital, Paisley
0141 884 5122

Eastern General Hospital,
Edinburgh
0131 536 7000

Edenhall Hospital,
Musselburgh
0131 536 8000

Edinburgh Dental Institute,
Edinburgh
0131 536 4900

Edington Cottage Hospital,
North Berwick
01620 897040

Falkirk & District Royal
Infirmary, Falkirk
01324 624000

Fernbank Street Day
Hospital, Glasgow
0131 537 6246

Fleming Hospital, Aberlour
01340 871464

Florence Street Day
Hospital, Glasgow
0141 429 2878

Forfar Infirmary, Angus
01307 464551

Forth Park Hospital,
Kirkcaldy
01592 643355

Fraserburgh Hospital,
Fraserburgh
01346 513151

Garrick Hospital, Stranraer
01776 702323

Gartnavel General Hospital,
Glasgow
0141 211 3000

Gartnavel Royal Hospital,
Glasgow
0141 211 3600

Gesto Hospital, Edinbane
01470 582262

Glasgow Homoeopathic
Hospital, Glasgow
0141 2113000

Glasgow Royal Infirmary
0141 211 4000

Glaxo Day Hospital,
Dundee
01382 532101 ex 170

Glen O'Dee Hospital,
Banchory
01330 822233

Glencoe Hospital, Glencoe
01855 811254

Glenrothes Hospital,
Glenrothes
01592 743505

Hairmyres Hospital,
Glasgow
01355 585000

Hartwoodhill Hospital,
Shotts
01698 245000

Hawick Cottage Hospital
01450 372162

Hawkhead Hospital,
Paisley
0141 889 8151

Hawkhill Day Hospital,
Dundee
01382 668300

Haylodge Hospital,
Peebles
01721 722080

Herdmanflat Hospital,
Haddington
0131 536 8300

Holmhead Hospital,
Cumnock
01290 422220

Ian Charles Hospital,
Grantown-on-Spey
01479 872528

Insch & District War
Memorial Hospital, Insch
01464 820213

Inverclyde Royal Hospital,
Greenock
01475 633777

Inverurie Hospital, Inverurie
01467 620454

Irvine Memorial Hospital,
Pitlochry
01796 472050

Islay Hospital, Isle of Islay
01496 810219

Johnstone Hospital,
Johnstone
01505 331471

Jubilee Hospital, Huntly
01466 792116

Kello Hospital, Biggar
01899 220077

Kelso Hospital
01573 223441

Kildean Hospital, Stirling
01786 458600

Kilsyth Victoria Memorial
Hospital, Kilsyth
01236 822172

Kincardine Community
Hospital, Stonehaven
01569 762022

Kincardine O'Neill War
Memorial Hospital,
Torphins
01339 882302

King's Cross Hospital,
Dundee
01382 660111

Kirkcudbright Hospital,
Kirkcudbright
01557 330549

Kirklands Hospital,
Bothwell
01698 245000

Kirklandside Hospital,
Kilmarnock
01563 524355

Knightswood Hospital,
Glasgow
0141 211 6900

Knoll Hospital, Duns
01361 883373

Lady Home Hospital,
Lanark
01555 851210

Lady Margaret Hospital,
Isle of Cumbrae
01475 530307

Ladysbridge Hospital,
Banff
01261 861361

Law Hospital, Carluke
01698 361100

Lawson Memorial Hospital
& Cambusavie Unit,
Sutherland
01408 633157

Lawson Memorial Hospital,
Sutherland
01408 633157

Leanchoil Hospital, Forres
01309 672284

Leverndale Hospital,
Glasgow
0141 211 6400

Liberton Hospital,
Edinburgh
0131 536 7800

Lightburn Hospital,
Glasgow
0141 211 1500

Little Cairnie Hospital,
Arbroath
01241 872584

Loanhead Hospital,
Loanhead
0131 440 0174

Lochmaben Hospital,
Lochmaben
01387 810255

Lockhart Hospital, Lanark
01555 662496

Lorn and Islands District
General Hospital, Oban
01631 567500

Lynebank Hospital, Fife
01383 623623

MacKinnon House,
Glasgow
0141 531 3100

Macmillan House, Perth
01738 639303

Maud Hospital, Maud
01771 613236

Meigle Community Day
Hospital, Meigle
01828 640211

Merchiston Hospital,
Johnstone
01505 328261

Mid Argyll Hospital, Argyll
01546 602952

Migdale Hospital,
Sutherland
01863 766211

Moffat Hospital, Moffat
01683 220031

Monklands Hospital,
Airdrie
01236 748748

Montrose Royal Infirmary,
Montrose
01674 830361

Murray Royal Hospital,
Perth
01738 621151/8

Netherlea Hospital,
Newport-on-Tay
01382 543223

Newton Stewart Hospital,
Newton Stewart
01671 402015

Ninewells Hospital, Dundee
01382 660111

Nithbank Hospital,
Dumfries
01387 241950

Orleans Day Hospital,
Dundee
01382 667322

Parkhead Hospital,
Glasgow
0141 211 8300

Perth Royal Infirmary, Perth
01738 623311

Peterhead Hospital,
Peterhead
01779 478234

Portree Hospital, Portree
01478 613200

Princes Street Day
Hospital, Stirling
01786 474230

Princess Alexandra Eye
Pavilion, Edinburgh
0131 536 3899

Princess Margaret Rose
Orthopaedic Hospital,
Edinburgh
0131 536 4600

Princess Royal Maternity
Hospital, Glasgow
0141 211 5400

Queen Margaret Hospital,
Dunfermline
01383 623623

Queen Mother's Hospital,
Glasgow
0141 201 0550

Raigmore Hospital,
Inverness
01463 704000

Randolph Wemyss
Memorial Hospital,
Buckhaven
01592 712427

Ravenscraig Hospital,
Greenock
01475 633777

Red Deer Day Hospital,
Glasgow
01355 244254

Roadmeetings Hospital,
Carluke
01555 772271

Roodlands Hospital,
Haddington
0131 536 8300

Roseangle Day Hospital,
Dundee
01382 24073

Rosemount Day Hospital,
Arbroath
01241 872584

Ross Memorial Hospital,
Dingwall
01349 663313

Rosslynlee Hospital,
Midlothian
0131 536 7608

Roxburghe House,
Aberdeen
01224 681818

Royal Aberdeen Children's
Hospital, Aberdeen
01224 681818

Royal Alexandra Hospital,
Paisley
0141 887 9111

Royal Cornhill Hospital,
Aberdeen
01224 663131

Royal Dundee Liff Hospital,
Dundee
01382 423038

Royal Edinburgh Hospital
0131 537 6000

Royal Hospital for Sick
Children, Edinburgh
0131 536 0000

Royal Hospital for Sick
Children, Glasgow
0141 201 0000

Royal Infirmary of
Edinburgh, Edinburgh
0131 536 1000

Royal Northern Infirmary,
Inverness
01463 242860

Royal Scottish National
Hospital, Larbert
01324 570700

Royal Victoria Hospital,
Dundee
01382 423123

Royal Victoria Hospital,
Edinburgh
0131 537 5000

St Andrews Memorial
Hospital, Fife
01334 472327

St John's Hospital at
Howden, Livingston
01506 419666

St Margaret's Hospital,
Auchterarder
01764 662246

St Michael's Hospital,
Linlithgow
01506 842053

St Vincent's Hospital,
Kingussie
01540 661219

Sauchie Hospital, Alloa
01259 722060

Seafield Hospital, Buckie
01542 832081

Shettleston Day Hospital,
Glasgow
0141 778 8381

Sister Margaret Hospital,
Jedburgh
01835 863212

Southern General Hospital,
Glasgow
0141 201 1100

Southfield Hospital,
Edinburgh
0131 664 1788

Spynie Hospital, Moray
01343 543131

Stephen Hospital,
Dufftown
01340 820215

Stirling Royal Infirmary,
Stirling
01786 434000

Stobhill Hospital, Glasgow
0141 201 3000

Stonehouse Hospital,
Larkhall
01698 793521

Stracathro Hospital,
Brechin
01356 647291

Strathclyde Hospital,
Motherwell
01698 245000

Stratheden Hospital, Fife
01334 652611

Strathmartine Hospital,
Dundee
01382 423000

Sunnyside Royal Hospital,
Montrose
01674 830361

Thomas Hope Hospital,
Langholm
01387 380417

Thornhill Hospital, Thornhill
01848 330205

Tippethill House, Bathgate
01501 740342

Tor-Na-Dee Hospital,
Aberdeen
01224 681818

Town & Country Hospital,
Caithness
01955 604025

Town & Country Hospital,
Nairn
01667 452101

Threshold Day Hospital,
Dundee
01382 322026

Turner Memorial Hospital,
Keith
01542 882526

Turriff Cottage Hospital,
Turriff
01888 563293

Udston Hospital, Hamilton
01698 823255

Ugie Hospital, Peterhead
01779 472011

Vale of Leven District
General Hospital,
Alexandria
01389 754121

Victoria Annex Hospital,
Isle of Bute
01700 502943

Victoria Hospital, Isle of
Bute
01700 503938

Victoria Hospital, Kirkcaldy
01592 643355

Victoria Infirmary, Glasgow
0141 201 6000

Victoria Infirmary,
Helensburgh
01436 672158

Weddenburn House Day
Hospital, Dundee
01382 346000

Westbank Day Hospital,
Falkirk
01324 624111

Wester Moffat Hospital,
Airdrie
01236 763377

Western General Hospital,
Edinburgh
0131 537 1000

Western Infirmary, Glasgow
0141 211 2000

Western Isles Hospital,
Stornoway
01851 704704

Weston Day Hospital, Fife
01334 652163

Whitehills Hospital, Angus
01307 464551

Whittingham Gardens Day
Hospital, Glasgow
0141 211 3616

Whytemans Brae Day
Hospital, Fife
01592 643355

Whytemans Brae Hospital,
Fife
01592 643355

Wishaw General Hospital,
Wishaw
01698 361100

Woodend Hospital,
Aberdeen
01224 663131

Woodlands Hospital,
Aberdeen
01224 663131

NHS hospitals: Northern Ireland

Albert Bridge Road Day
Hospital, Belfast
01232 456007

Alexandra Gardens Day
Hospital, Belfast
01232 773311

Altnagelvin Area Hospital,
Londonderry
028 71345171

Antrim Hospital, Antrim
028 9442 4000

Ards Hospital,
Newtownards
01247 812661

Armagh Community
Hospital, Armagh
01861 522381

Bangor Hospital, Bangor
01247 454184

Beaver Park Hospital,
Belfast
028 9069 9069

Belfast City Hospital
028 9032 9241

Braid Valley Hospital,
Ballymena
01266 655200

Causeway Hospital,
Coleraine
028 7032 7032

Coleraine Hospital
028 904 4177

Craigavon Area Hospital
028 3833 4444

Craigavon Area Hospital
(Psychiatric Unit),
Portadown
028 3833 4444

Daisy Hill Hospital, Newry
02830 835000

Dalriada Hospital,
Ballycastle
028 2076 2666

Downe Hospital,
Downpatrick
028 4461 3311

Erne Hospital, Enniskillen
028 6632 4711

Forster Green Hospital,
Belfast
028 9079 3681

Gransha Hospital,
Londonderry
01504 860261

Holywell Hospital, Antrim
028 9446 5211

Lagan Valley Hospital,
Lisburn
028 9266 5141

Longstone Hospital,
Armagh
01861 522381

Lurgan Hospital (Day
Hospital)
01762 323262

Mater Hospital, Belfast
028 9074 1211

Mid-Ulster Hospital,
Magherafelt
028 7963 1031

Mourne Hospital, Newry
016937 62235

Moyle Hospital, Larne
01574 275431

Muckamore Abbey
Hospital, Muckamore
028 9446 3333

Mullinure Hospital, Armagh
01861 522381

Musgrave Park Hospital,
Belfast
028 9066 9501

Robinson Memorial
Hospital, Ballymoney
028 2766 0332

Route Hospital,
Ballymoney
028 2766 6600

Royal Belfast Hospital for
Sick Children, Belfast
028 9024 0503

Royal Maternity Hospital,
Belfast
01232 894656

Royal Victoria Hospital,
Belfast
028 9026 3000

St Luke's Hospital
(Armagh), Armagh
01861 522381

Shaftsbury Square
Hospital, Belfast
01232 329808

South Tyrone Hospital,
Dungannon
01868 722381

Stradreagh Hospital,
Londonderry
01504 860261

Royal Hospitals, Belfast
028 9024 0503

Thompson House Hospital,
Lisburn
01846 665646

Tyrone and Fermanagh
Hospital, Omagh
0288 224 5211

Tyrone County Hospital,
Omagh
02882 245211

Ulster Hospital, Dundonald
028 9048 4511

Ireland

Abbeyleix District Hospital,
Laois
00 353 502 31 204

Adelaide and Meath
Hospital (Tallaght
Hospital), Dublin
00 353 1 414 2000

Beaumont Hospital, Dublin
00 353 1 837 7755

Birr District Hospital, Offaly
00 353 509 20 819

Carlow District Hospital,
Carlow
00 353 505 364 58

Castlecomer District
Hospital, Castlecomer
00 353 56 412 46

Cavan General Hospital,
Lisdarn
00 353 49 436 1388

Cherry Orchard Hospital,
Dublin
00 353 1 626 4702

Cork University Hospital,
Cork
00 353 21 546 400

Ennis General Hospital,
Ennis
00 353 65 682 4464

Gorey District Hospital
00 353 55 211 02

James Connolly Memorial
Hospital, Dublin
00 353 1 821 3844

Letterkenny General
Hospital, Letterkenny
00 353 74 258 88

Limerick Regional Hospital,
Limerick
00 353 61 301111

Longford/Westmeath
General Hospital,
Westmeath
00 353 44 40 221

Lourdes Regional
Orthopaedic Hospital,
Kilkenny
00 353 56 52465

Louth County Hospital,
Dundalk
00 353 42 933 4701

Mallow General Hospital,
Mallow
022 212 51

Mater Misericordiae
Hospital, Dublin
00 353 1 803 2000

Mayo General Hospital,
Castlebar
094 217 33

Mercy Hospital, Cork
00 353 21 271 971

Merlin Park Regional
Hospital, Galway
00 353 91 757 631

Monaghan General
Hospital, Monaghan
00 353 47 81811

Naas General Hospital,
Kildare
00 353 45 897 221

Nenagh General Hospital,
Nenagh
00 353 67 31 491

Our Lady of Lourdes,
Drogheda
00 353 41 983 7601

Our Lady's County and
Surgical Hospital, Cashel
00 353 62 61022

Our Lady's Hospital,
Navan, Navan
00 353 46 21210

Portiuncula Hospital,
Galway
00 353 905 42140

Portlaoise General
Hospital, Portlaoise
00 353 502 21364

Roscommon County
Hospital, Roscommon
Town
00 353 903 262 00

St Bridget's District
Hospital, Carrick on Suir
00 353 51 640 025

St Columcille's Hospital,
Dublin
00 353 1 282 5800

St Finbarr's Hospital, Cork
00 353 21 966 555

St James's Hospital, Dublin
00 353 1 453 7941

St John's Hospital,
Limerick
00 353 61 415 822

St Joseph's County
Medical and Maternity
Hospital, Clonmel
00 353 52 7700

St Luke's General Hospital,
Kilkenny
00 353 56 51133

St Mary's Hospital, Dublin
00 353 1 677 8132

St Mary's Orthopaedic
Hospital, Cork
00 353 21 303264

St Michael's Hospital,
Dublin
00 353 1 280 6901

St Nessan's Orthopaedic
Hospital, Croom
00 353 61 397276

St Teresa's District
Hospital, Clogheen
00 353 52 652 05

St Vincent University
Hospital, Dublin
00 353 1 269 4533

St Vincent's District
Hospital, Dungarvan
00 353 58 411 25

Sligo General Hospital,
Sligo Town
00 353 71 71111

South Infirmary / Victoria
Hospital, Cork
00 353 21 964 333

Temple Street – The
Children's Hospital,
Dublin
00 353 1 8748763

Tralee General Hospital,
Tralee
00 353 66 712 6222

Tullamore General
Hospital, Tullamore
00 353 506 21501

University College
Hospital, Galway
00 353 91 524 222

Waterford Regional
Hospital, Waterford
00 353 51 873321

Wexford General Hospital,
Wexford Town
00 353 53 42233

Private hospitals

Abbey Caldew Hospital
01228 31713

Abbey Carrick Glen
Hospital
01292 288882

Abbey Gisburne Park
01200 445693

Abbey Kings Park Hospital
01786 451669

Abbey Park Hospital
01229 813388

Abbey Sefton Hospital
0151 257 6700

Alexandra Hospital,
Cheadle
0161 428 3656

Ashtead Hospital
01372 221400

Beaumont Hospital
01204 404404

Benenden Hospital
01580 240333

Berkshire Independent
Hospital
0118 902 8000

Birkdale Clinic
01709 828928

Birth Centre
020 8767 8294

BMI Albyn Hospital
01224 595993

BMI Bath Clinic
01225 835555

BMI Bishops Wood
Hospital
01923 835814

BMI Chatsworth Suite
01246 544400

BMI Chelsfield Park
Hospital
01689 877855

BMI Esperance Hospital
01323 411188

BMI Fernbrae Hospital
01382 667203

BMI Meriden Wing
01203 602772

BMI Park Hospital
0115 967 0670

BMI Ross Hall Hospital
0141 810 3151

BMI Shirley Oaks Hospital
020 8655 5500

BMI The Alexandra
Hospital Victoria Park
0161 257 2233

BMI The Beardwood
Hospital
01254 507607

BMI The Blackheath
Hospital
020 8318 7722

BMI The Chaucer Hospital
01227 825100

BMI The Chiltern Hospital
01494 890890

BMI The Clementine
Churchill Hospital
020 8872 3872

BMI The Droitwich Spa
Hospital
01905 793333

BMI The Garden Hospital
020 8457 4500

BMI The Highfield Hospital
01706 655121

BMI The Manor Hospital
01234 364252

BMI The Princess Margaret
Hospital
01753 743434

BMI The Priory Hospital
0121 440 2323

BMI The Ridgeway
Hospital
01793 814848

BMI The Runnymede
Hospital
01932 877800

BMI The Sandringham
Hospital
01553 769770

BMI The Sloane Hospital
0208 466 6911

BMI The Somerfield
Hospital
01622 208000

BMI Three Shires Hospital
01604 620311

BMI Winterbourne Hospital
01305 263252

Bridge Centre
020 7403 3363

British Pregnancy Advisory
Sevice
0345 304030

Bupa Alexandra Hospital
01634 687166

Bupa Belvedere Hospital
01723 365363

Bupa Cambridge Lea
Hospital
01223 266900

Bupa Dunedin Hospital
0118 958 7676

Bupa Fylde Coast Hospital
01253 394188

Bupa Gatwick Park
Hospital
01293 785511

Bupa Hartswood Hospital
01277 232525

Bupa Hospital Bristol
0117 973 2562

Bupa Hospital Bushey
020 8950 9090

Bupa Hospital Cardiff
029 2073 5515

Bupa Hospital Clare Park
01252 850216

Bupa Hospital Elland
01422 324000

Bupa Hospital Harpenden
01582 763191

Bupa Hospital Hastings
01424 757400

Bupa Hospital Leeds
0113 269 3939

Bupa Hospital Leicester
0116 272 0888

Bupa Hospital Little Aston
0121 353 2444

Bupa Hospital Manchester
0161 226 0112

Bupa Hospital Norwich
01603 456181

Bupa Hospital Portsmouth
023 9245 6000

Bupa Hospital
Southampton
023 8077 5544

Bupa Hospital Tunbridge
Wells
01892 740047

Bupa Hospital Washington
0191 415 1272

Bupa Hull And East Riding
Hospital
01482 659471

Bupa Methley Park
Hospital
01977 518518

Bupa Murrayfield Hospital
Edinburgh
0131 334 0363

Bupa Murrayfield Hospital
Wirral
0151 648 7000

Bupa North Cheshire
Hospital
01925 265000

Bupa Parkway Hospital
0121 704 1451

Bupa Redwood Hospital
01737 277277

Bupa Regency Hospital
01625 501150

Bupa Roding Hospital
020 8551 1100

Bupa South Bank Hospital
01905 350003

Bupa St Saviour's Hospital
01303 265581

Bupa Wellesley Hospital
01702 462944

Bupa Yale Hospital
01978 291306

Chalfont Centre for
Epilepsy
01494 874646

Cheadle Royal
0161 428 9511

Chesterfield Nuffield
Hospital
0117 987 2727

Churchill Private Clinic
0207 928 5633

Claremont Hospital
0114 263 0330

Cromwell Hospital
020 7460 2000

Devonshire Hospital
0207 486 7131

Duchy Hospital
01872 226100

Euxton Hall Hospital
01257 276261

Fairfield Independent
Hospital
01744 739311

Farm Place
01306 627742

Fawkham Manor Hospital
01474 879900

Fitzwilliam Hospital
01733 261717

Florence Nightingale Clinic
Chelsea
0800 783 0594

Florence Nightingale
Hospital Liverpool
0151 928 8351

Florence Nightingale, The
020 7258 3828

Foscote Private Hospital
01295 252281

Fulwood Hall Hospital
01772 704111

Gainsborough Clinic, The
020 7928 5633

Goring Hall Hospital
01903 506699

Grosvenor Nuffield
Hospital
01244 680444

Grovelands Priory Hospital
020 8882 8191

Guthrie Clinic, The
020 7346 3192/3

Hampshire Clinic
01256 357 111

Harbour Hospital
01202 244200

Harley Street Clinic
020 7935 7700

Hayes Grove Priory
Hospital
020 8462 7722

HCI International Medical
Centre
0141 951 5000

Heart Hospital, The
020 7573 8888

Heath House Priory
Hospital
0117 952 5255

Highbank Rehabilitation
Centre
01706 829540

Highgate Private Hospital
020 8341 4182

Holly House Hospital
020 8505 3311

Holy Cross Hospital
01428 643311

Horder Centre for Arthritis,
The
01892 665577

Hospital of St John and
St Elizabeth
020 7806 4000

HRH Princess Christians
Nuffield Hospital
01753 853121

Huddersfield Nuffield
Hospital
01484 533131

Hull IVF Unit
01482 676541

Huntercombe Manor
Hospital
01628 667881

International Centre for
Excellence in Dentistry
020 7905 1234
King Edward VII Hospital
01730 812341
King Edward VII's Hospital
Sister Agnes
020 7486 4411
King's Oak Hospital
020 8370 9500
Leeds Nuffield Hospital
0113 388 2000
Leicester Nuffield Hospital
0116 276 9401
Lister Hospital, The
020 7730 3417
London Bridge Hospital
020 7407 3100
London Clinic, The
020 7935 4444
London Independent
Hospital
020 7780 2400
London IRYO Centre
020 8202 7272
Lourdes Hospital
0151 733 7123
Manchester Fertility
Services
0161 862 9567
Mcindoe Surgical Centre
01342 330300
Mid Yorkshire Nuffield
Hospital
0113 258 8756
Mount Alvernia Hospital
01483 570122
Mount Stuart Hospital
01803 313881
New Hall Hospital
01722 422333
New Victoria Hospital
020 8949 9000
Newcastle Nuffield
Hospital
0191 281 6131
North Downs Hospital
01883 348981
Nuffield Derwent Suite
01202 729480
Nuffield Hospital Acland
01865 404142
Nuffield Hospital
Birmingham
0121 456 2000
Nuffield Hospital
Bournemouth
01202 291866
Nuffield Hospital
Brentwood
01277 695695
Nuffield Hospital Brighton
01273 624488
Nuffield Hospital Bristol
0117 973 0391
Nuffield Hospital Bury St
Edmunds
01284 701371
Nuffield Hospital
Cambridge
01223 303336

Nuffield Hospital
Cheltenham
01242 246500
Nuffield Hospital
Chichester
01243 530600
Nuffield Hospital Derby
01332 517891
Nuffield Hospital Enfield
020 8366 2122
Nuffield Hospital Exeter
01392 276591
Nuffield Hospital Glasgow
0141 334 9441
Nuffield Hospital Guildford
01483 555800
Nuffield Hospital Harrogate
01423 567136
Nuffield Hospital Haywards
Heath
01444 456999
Nuffield Hospital Hereford
01432 355131
Nuffield Hospital Hove
01273 779471
Nuffield Hospital Hull
01482 623500
Nuffield Hospital Ipswich
01473 279100
Nuffield Hospital Lancaster
01524 62345
Nuffield Hospital
Leamington Spa
01926 427971
Nuffield Hospital Lincoln
01522 578000
Nuffield Hospital
Newcastle-under-Lyme
01782 625431
Nuffield Hospital
Nottingham
0115 920 9209
Nuffield Hospital
Shrewsbury
01743 282500
Nuffield Hospital Taunton
01823 286991
Nuffield Hospital Teesside
01642 360100
Nuffield Hospital
Wolverhampton
01902 754177
Nuneaton Private Hospital
02476 357500
Oaklands Hospital
0161 787 7700
Oaks Hospital, The
01206 752121
Orchard Hospital, The
01983 520022
Paddocks Hospital
01844 346951
Park Hill Hospital
01302 730300
Parkside Hospital
020 8971 8000
Pinehill Hospital
01462 422822
Plymouth Nuffield Hospital
01752 775861

Portland Hospital for
Women and Children, The
020 7580 4400
Princess Grace Hospital,
The
020 7486 1234
Priory Clinic Keats House,
The
Priory Clinic Nottingham,
The
0115 969 3388
Priory Hospital
Chelmsford, The
01245 345 345
Priory Hospital Glasgow,
The
0141 636 6116
Priory Hospital
Marchwood, The
023 8084 0044
Priory Hospital North
London, The
020 8882 8191
Priory Hospital
Roehampton, The
Priory Hospital Sturt, The
01737 814488
Priory Hospital Woking,
The
01483 489211
Priory Hospital, The
0161 904 0050
Priory Ticehurst House,
The
01580 200391
Purey Cust Nuffield
Hospital
01904 641571
Renacres Hall Hospital
01704 841133
Rivers Hospital, The
01279 600282
Rowley Hall Hospital
01785 223203
Royal Hospital for
Neuro-disability
020 8780 4500
St Anthony's Hospital
020 8337 6691
St Hugh's Hospital
01472 251100
St John of God Hospital
01748 811535
St Joseph's Hospital
01633 820300
St Luke's Hospital for the
Clergy
020 7388 4954
Sancta Maria Hospital
01792 479040
Sarum Road Hospital
01962 841555
Saxon Clinic
01908 665533
Shelburne
01494 888700
Sketchley Hall
01455 890023
South Cheshire Private
Hospital
01270 500411

Springfield Hospital
01245 234000
Stamford Hospital, The
020 8636 9000
Stockton Hall Hospital
01904 400500
Suffolk Nuffield at
Christchurch Park
Hospital
01473 256071
Surgicare Birmingham
01827 263831
Surgicare Manchester
0161 945 8688
Thames Valley Nuffield
Hospital
01753 662241
Thornbury Hospital
0114 266 1133
Tunbridge Wells Nuffield
Hospital
01892 531111
Ulster Independent Clinic
028 9066 1212
Unsted Park Hospital
01483 892061
Waterside Suite
01934 647000
Wellington Hospital, The
020 7586 5959
Werndale Hospital
01267 211500
Wessex Maternity Centre
02380 464721
Wessex Nuffield Hospital
02380 266377
West Midlands Hospital
01384 560123
Winfield Hospital
01452 331111
Woking Nuffield Hospital
01483 227800
Woodbourne Priory
Hospital, The
0121 434 4343
Woodland Hospital
01536 414515
Woodlands Hospital
01325 341700
Yorkshire Clinic
01274 560311
Yorkshire Laser Centre
01724 290456

Health

359

Law

Home Office
0870 000 1585; press 020 7273 4545
www.homeoffice.gov.uk

Attorney General's Office
020 7271 2450
press office 020 7271 2440

Department for Constitutional Affairs
020 7210 8512
www.lcd.gov.uk

Crown Office and Procurator Fiscal Service, Scotland
0131 226 2626
www.crownoffice.gov.uk

Scottish Executive: justice department
0131 244 212, press 0131 244 2718
www.scotland.gov.uk

Court, legal and prison services

Appeals Service
020 7712 2640
www.appeals-service.gov.uk

Court Service
020 7210 2266
www.courtservice.gov.uk

Court Service, Northern Ireland
028 9032 8594
www.courtsni.gov.uk

Crown Prosecution Service
020 7796 8000
www.cps.gov.uk

Scottish Courts Administration
0131 226 9200
www.scotcourts.gov.uk

Magistrates Court Service Inspectorate
020 7217 4344
www.mcsi.gov.uk

Prison Service
020 7217 6633
www.hmprisonservice.gov.uk
Press 020 7273 4545
victim helpline 0845 758 5112

Scottish Prison Service
0131 244 8745
www.sps.gov.uk
Chief executive: 0131 244 8522

N Ireland Prison Service
028 9052 5065
www.niprisonservice.gov.uk

Appeal courts

Court of Appeal
020 7947 6000
www.courtservice.gov.uk/cms
/supremecourt.htm

High Court
020 7947 6000
www.courtservice.gov.uk/cms
/supremecourt.htm

High Court, Scotland
0131 225 2595

High Court of Justiciary, Scotland
0131 240 6906

Court of Session, Scotland
0131 240 6743

Supreme Court of Judicature, N Ireland
028 9023 5111

Judicial Committee of the Privy Council
020 7270 0483

House of Lords Appellate Committee
020 7219 3000

Other agencies

Civil Justice Council
020 7947 6670
www.civiljusticecouncil.gov.uk

Criminal Cases Review Commission
0121 633 1800
www.ccrc.gov.uk

Criminal Records Bureau
0870 909 0811
www.crb.gov.uk

Customs and Excise
0845 010 9000, press 020 7620 1313
www.hmce.gov.uk

Human Rights Unit
020 7273 4172
www.homeoffice.gov.uk/hract

Law Commission
020 7453 1220
www.lawcom.gov.uk

Legal Services Commission
020 7759 0493
www.legalservices.gov.uk

Legal Services Ombudsman
0161 839 7262
www.olso.org

Scottish Legal Services Ombudsman
0131 556 9123
www.slso.org.uk

Youth Justice Boards for England and Wales
020 7271 3033
www.youth-justice-board.gov.uk

Professional bodies

Administrative Law Bar Association
020 7832 1111
www.adminlaw.org.uk

Association of Personal Injury Lawyers
0115 958 0585
www.apil.com

Association of Women Barristers
020 7482 7070
www.womenbarristers.co.uk

Bar Council
020 7242 0082
www.barcouncil.org.uk

Chancery Bar Association
020 8883 1700
www.chba.org.uk

Commercial Bar Association
020 7404 2022
www.combar.com

Family Law Bar Association
020 7242 1289
www.flba.co.uk

Institute of Barristers' Clerks
020 7831 7144
www.barristersclerks.com

Institute of Legal Executives
01234 841 0000
www.ilex.org.uk

Justices' Clerks' Society
www.jc-society.co.uk

Law Society
020 7320 5810
www.lawsoc.org.uk

Legal Aid Practitioners' Group
020 7336 8565
www.lapg.co.uk

Magistrates' Association
020 7387 2353
www.magistrates-association.org.uk

Solicitors' Criminal Law Association
01273 676725
www.clsa.co.uk

Solicitors' Family Law Association
01689 850227
www.sfla.org.uk

Crown courts

Central Criminal Court – Old Bailey
020 7248 3277
Aylesbury
01296 434401
Barnstaple
01271 373286
Barrow-in-Furness
01772 832300
Basildon Combined Court
01268 458000
Birmingham
0121 681 3300
Blackfriars
020 7922 5800
Bolton Combined Court Centre
01204 392881
Bournemouth
01202 502800
Bradford Combined Court Centre
01274 840274
Bristol
0117 976 3030
Burnley Combined Court Centre
01282 416899
Bury St Edmonds
01284 762676
Caernarfon
01286 675200
Cambridge
01223 224666
Canterbury Combined Court Centre
01227 819200
Cardiff
029 2041 4400
Carlisle Combined Court Centre
01228 520619
Carmarthen
01267 236071
Chelmsford
01245 603000
Chester
01244 317606
Chichester Combined Court Centre
01243 520742
Coventry Combined Court Centre
024 7653 6166
Croydon Combined Court Centre
020 8410 4700
Derby Combined Court Centre
01332 622600
Dolgellau
01286 675200
Doncaster
01302 322211
Dorchester
01305 778684
Durham
0191 386 6714

Exeter Combined Court Centre
01392 210655
Gloucester
01452 529351
Great Grimsby Combined Court Centre
01472 311811
Guildford
01483 468500
Harrow
020 8424 2294
Haverfordwest
01437 764782
Hereford
01432 276118
Inner London
020 7234 3100
Ipswich
01473 220750
Isleworth
020 8380 4500
Kingston-upon-Hull Combined Court Centre
01482 586161
Kingston-upon-Thames
020 8240 2500
Knutsford
01685 388307
Leeds Combined Court Centre
0113 283 0040
Lewes Combined Court Centre
01273 480400
Lincoln
01522 525222
Liverpool Combined Court Centre
0151 473 7373
Luton
01582 522000
Maidstone
01622 202000
Manchester (Crown Square)
0161 954 1702
Manchester at Minshull St
0161 954 7500
Merthyr Tydfil Combined Court Centre
01685 358222
Middlesex Guildhall
020 7202 0370
Mold
01244 356709
Newcastle-upon-Tyne Combined Court Centre
0191 201 2000
Newport (South Wales)
01633 266211
Newport, I.O.W.
01983 821569
Northampton Combined Court
01604 470400
Norwich Combined Court Centre
01603 728200
Nottingham
0115 910 3551

Oxford Combined Court Centre
01865 264200
Peterborough Combined Court Centre
01733 349161
Plymouth Combined Court
01752 677400
Portsmouth Combined Court Centre
023 9289 3000
Preston Combined Court Centre
01772 832300
Reading
0118 967 4400
Salisbury Combined Court Centre
01722 325444
Sheffield Combined Court Centre
0114 281 2400
Shrewsbury
01743 355775
Snaresbrook
020 8530 0000
Southampton Combined Court Centre
023 8021 3200
Southwark
020 7522 7200
St. Albans
01727 753220
Stafford Combined Court Centre
01785 610730
Stoke-on-Trent Combined Court
01782 854000
Swansea
01792 510200
Swindon Combined Court
01793 690514
Taunton
01823 326685
Teesside Combined Court Centre
01642 340000
Truro Combined Court Centre
01872 222340
Warrington Combined Court Centre
01925 256700
Warwick Combined Court Centre
01926 495428
Welshpool
01938 553144
Weymouth and Dorchester Combined Court Centre
01305 788684
Winchester Combined Court Centre
01962 841212
Wolverhampton Combined Court Centre
01902 48100
Wood Green
020 8881 1400

Woolwich
020 8312 7000
Worcester Combined Court Centre
01905 730800
York
01904 645121

Northern Ireland courts

Court Service, Northern Ireland
028 9032 8594
www.courtsni.gov.uk
Antrim
028 9446 2661
Armagh
028 3572 2816
Ballymena
028 2564 9416
Belfast
028 9024 2099
Craigavon
028 3834 1324
Downpatrick
028 4461 4621
Enniskillen
028 6632 2356
Londonderry
028 7136 3448
Newry
028 4062 3622
Omagh
028 8224 2056

Sheriff courts, Scotland

Scottish Courts Administration
0131 226 9200
www.scotcourts.gov.uk
Aberdeen
01224 657200
Airdrie
01236 751121
Alloa
01259 722734
Arbroath
01241 876600
Ayr
01292 268474
Banff
01261 812140
Campbelltown
01586 552503
Cupar
01334 652121
Dingwall
01349 863153
Dornoch
01862 810224
Dumbarton
01389 763266
Dumfries
01387 262334
Dundee
01382 229961

Dunfermline
01383 724666
Dunoon
01369 704166
Duns
01361 883719
Edinburgh
0131 225 2525
Elgin
01343 542505
Falkirk
01324 620822
Forfar
01307 462186
Fort William
01397 702087
Glasgow
0141 429 8888
Greenock
01475 787073
Hamilton
01698 282957
Inverness
01463 230782
Jedburgh
01835 863231
Kilmarnock
01563 520211
Kirkcudbright
01557 330574
Kirkwall
01856 872110
Lanark
01555 661531
Lerwick
01595 693914
Linlithgow
01506 842922
Lochmaddy
01876 500340
Oban
01631 562414
Paisley
0141 887 5291
Peebles
01721 720204
Perth
01738 620546
Peterhead
01779 476676
Portree
01478 612191
Rothesay
01700 502982
Stirling
01786 462191
Stonehaven
01569 762758
Stornoway
01851 702231
Stranraer
01776 702138
Tain
01862 892518
Wick
01955 602846

County courts

Aberdare
01685 874779
Aberystwyth
01970 636370
Accrington
01254 237490
Aldershot & Farnham
01252 321639
Altrincham
0161 975 4760
Ashford
01233 632464
Aylesbury
01296 393498
Banbury
01295 265799
Barnet
020 8343 4272
Barnsley
01226 203471
Barnstaple
01271 372252
Barrow-In-Furness
01229 820046
Basildon Combined Court
01268 458000
Basingstoke
01256 318200
Bath
01225 310282
Bedford
01234 760400
Birkenhead
0151 647 8826
Birmingham Civil Justice
Centre
0121 681 4441
Bishop Auckland
01388 602423
Blackburn
01254 680640
Blackpool
01253 293178
Blackwood
01495 223197
Bodmin
01208 74224
Bolton Combined Court
01204 392881
Boston
01205 366080
Bournemouth
01202 502800
Bow
020 8536 5200
Bradford Combined Court
Centre
01274 840274
Brecknock
01874 622671
Brentford
020 8580 7300
Bridgend
01656 768881
Brighton
01273 674421
Bristol
0117 929 4414
Bromley
020 8464 9727

Burnley Combined Court
01282 416899
Bury
0161 7641344
Bury St Edmunds
01284 753254
Burton upon Trent
01283 568241
Buxton
01298 23734
Caernarfon
01286 678911
Cambridge
01223 224500
Canterbury Combined
Court
01227 819200
Cardiff Civil Justice Centre
029 2037 6400
Carlisle Combined Court
Centre
01228 520619
Carmarthen
01267 228010
Central London
020 7917 5000
Cheltenham
01242 519983
Chelmsford
01245 264670
Chester Civil Justice
Centre
01244 404200
Chesterfield
01246 501200
Chichester
01243 520700
Chorley
01257 262778
Clerkenwell
020 7359 7347
Colchester
01206 572743
Consett
01207 502854
Conwy & Colwyn
01492 530807
Coventry Combined Court
Centre
01203 536166
Crewe
01270 212255
Croydon Combined Court
020 8410 4700
Darlington
01325 463224
Dartford
01322 629820
Derby Combined Court
01332 622600
Dewsbury
01924 466135
Doncaster
01302 365400
Dudley
01384 480799
Durham
0191 386 5941
Eastbourne
01323 735195
Edmonton
020 8807 1666

Epsom
01372 721801
Evesham
01386 442287
Exeter Combined Court
01392 210655
Gateshead
0191 477 2445
Gloucester
01452 529351
Grantham
01476 563638
Gravesend
01474 321771
Great Grimsby Combined
Court
01472 311811
Guildford
01483 595200
Halifax
01422 344700
Harlow
01279 443291
Harrogate
01423 503921
Hartlepool
01429 268198
Hastings
01424 435128
Haverfordwest
01437 772060
Haywards Heath
01444 456326
Hertford
01992 503954
Hereford
01432 357233
High Wycombe
01494 436374
Hitchin
01462 450011
Holywell
01352 711027
Horsham
01403 252474
Hove Court Centre
01273 770643
Hove Trial Centre
01273 770643
Huddersfield
01484 421 043
Huntingdon
01480 450932
Ilford
020 8478 1132
Ipswich
01473 214256
Keighley
01535 602803
Kendal
01539 721218
Kettering
01536 512471
Kidderminster
01562 822480
King's Lynn
01553 772067
Kingston upon Hull
01482 586161
Kingston-upon-Thames
020 8546 8843

Lambeth
020 7091 4410
Lancaster
01524 68112
Leeds
0113 283 0040
Leicester
0116 222 2323
Leigh
01942 673639
Lewes Combined Court
01273 480400
Lichfield
01543 262137
Lincoln Combined Court
01522 883000
Liverpool Combined Court
0151 473 7373
Llanelli
01554 757171
Llangefni
01248 750225
Lowestoft
01502 586047
Ludlow
01584 872091
Luton
01582 506700
Macclesfield
01625 422872
Maidstone Combined
Court
01622 202000
Manchester
0161 954 1800
Mansfield
01623 656406
Mayor's & City Of London
Court
020 7796 5400
Medway
01634 402881
Melton Mowbray
01664 568336
Merthyr Tydfil Combined
Court
01685 358200
Milton Keynes
01908 668855
Mold
01352 700313
Morpeth & Berwick
01670 512221
Neath and Port Talbot
01639 642267
Nelson
01282 601177
Newark
01636 703607
Newcastle Combined
Court
0191 201 2000
Newbury
01635 40928
Newport
01633 227150
Newport (Isle Of Wight)
01983 526821
North Shields
0191 257 5866

Northampton (County
Court Bulk Centre)
01604 601636
Northampton Combined
Court
01604 470452
Northwich
01606 42554
Norwich Combined Court
01603 728200
Nottingham
01159 103500
Nuneaton
01203 386134
Oldham
01612 904200
Oswestry
01691 652127
Oxford Combined Court
Centre
01865 264200
Penrith
01768 862535
Penzance
01736 362987
Peterborough Combined
Court
01733 349161
Plymouth Combined Court
01752 208284
Pontefract
01977 702357
Pontypool
01495 762248
Pontypridd
01443 402471
Poole
01202 741150
Portsmouth Combined
Court
023 9289 3000
Preston Combined Court
01772 832300
Rawtenstall
01706 214614
Reading
0118 987 0500
Redditch
01527 67822
Reigate
01737 763637
Rhyl
01745 330216
Romford
01708 750677
Rotherham
01709 364786
Rugby
01788 542543
Runcorn
01928 716533
Salford
0161 7457511
Salisbury
01722 325444
Scarborough
01723 366361
Scunthorpe
01724 289111
Sheffield Combined Court
0114 281 2400

Shoreditch
0207 253 0956
Shrewsbury
01743 289069
Skegness
01754 762429
Skipton
01756 793315
Slough
01753 690300
South Shields
0191 4563343
Southampton Combined
Court
023 8021 3200
Southend
01702 601991
Southport
01704 531541
St Albans
01727 856925
St Helens
01744 27544
Stafford
01785 610730
Staines
01784 459175
Stockport
01614 747707
Stoke On Trent Combined
Court
01782 854000
Stourbridge
01384 394232
Stratford upon Avon
01789 293056
Sunderland
0191 568 0750
Swansea Civil Justice
Centre
01792 510350
Swindon Combined Court
01793 690500
Tameside
01613 391711
Tamworth
01827 62664
Taunton
01823 335972
Teesside Combined Court
01642 340000
Telford
01952 291045
Thanet
01843 228771
Torquay & Newton Abbot
01803 616791
Trowbridge
01225 752101
Truro Combined Court
01872 222340
Tunbridge Wells
01892 515515
Uxbridge
020 8561 8562
Wakefield
01924 370268
Walsall
0845 351 3513
Wandsworth
020 8333 4351

Warrington Combined
Court
01925 256700
Warwick Combined Court
Centre
01926 495428
Watford
01923 249666
Wellingborough
01933 226168
Welshpool and Newtown
01938 552004
West London
020 7602 8444
Weston Super Mare
01934 626967
Weymouth & Dorchester
01305 778684
Whitehaven
01946 67788
Wigan
01942 246481
Winchester Combined
Court
01962 841212
Willesden
020 8963 8200
Wolverhampton
Combined Court
01902 481000
Woolwich
020 8854 2127
Worcester Combined
Court
01905 730807
Worksop
01909 472358
Worthing
01903 206721
Wrexham
01978 351738
Yeovil
01935 474133
York
01904 629935

Law centres

Law Centres Federation
020 7387 8570
www.lawcentres.org.uk
Avon & Bristol
0117 924 8662
Barnet
020 8203 4141
Battersea
020 7585 0716
Bradford
01274 306617
Brent Community
020 8451 1122
Bury
0161 272 0666
Camden Community
020 7284 6510
Cardiff
029 2049 8117
Carlisle
01228 515129
Central London
020 7839 2998
Chesterfield
01246 550674
Coventry
024 7622 3053
Derby
01332 344557

Devon
01752 519794
Gateshead
0191 478 2847
Gloucester
01452 423492
Greenwich Community
020 8305 3350
Hackney Community
020 8985 8364
Hammersmith & Fulham
020 8741 4021
Harehills & Chapeltown
0113 249 1100
Hillingdon
020 8561 9400
Hounslow
020 8570 9505
Humberside
01482 211 180
Islington
020 7607 2461
Lambeth
020 7737 9780
Northern Ireland: Belfast
028 9024 4401
Northern Ireland: western area
028 7126 2433

Leicester
0116 255 3781
Lewisham
020 8692 5355
Liverpool
0151 709 7222
Luton
01582 481000
Newcastle
0191 230 4777
North Kensington
020 8969 7473
North Manchester
0161 205 9031
Nottingham
0115 978 7813
Oldham
0161 627 0925
Paddington
020 8960 3155
Plumstead Community
020 8855 9817
Rochdale
01706 657766
Saltley & Nechells
0121 328 2307
Sheffield
0114 273 1888

South Manchester
0161 225 5111
Southwark
020 7732 2008
Springfield
020 8767 6884
Stockport
0161 476 6336
Thamesmead
020 8311 0555
Tottenham
020 8800 5354
Tower Hamlets
020 7247 8998
Vauxhall Law and Information Centre
0151 330 0239
Wandsworth & Merton
020 8767 2777
Warrington Community
01925 651104
Wiltshire
01793 486926
Wythenshawe
0161 498 0905

Legal advice

Activists Legal Project
01865 243 772
www.activistslegalproject.org.uk
Legal information for activists
Asylum Aid
020 7377 5123
www.asylumaid.org.uk
CHAS Housing Aid Society
020 7723 5928
www.chasnational.org.uk
Children's Legal Centre
01206 873820
www.childrenslegalcentre.com
Community Legal Service
020 7759 1020
www.justask.org.uk
Counsel & Care
0845 300 7585
www.counselandcare.org.uk
Detainee Support & Help Unit
020 7703 5435
www.dshu.org.uk
Disability Law Service
020 7791 9800
advice@dls.org.uk

Environmental Law Foundation
020 7404 1030
www.elflaw.org
Help & Advice for Relatives of Prisoners (HARP)
0808 808 2003
www.harpinfo.org.uk
Joint Council for the Welfare of Immigrants
020 7251 8706
www.jcwi.org.uk
Legal Action Group
020 7833 7430
www.lag.org.uk
Legal Services Research Centre
information@lsrc.org.uk
www.lsrc.org.uk
Lesbian & Gay Employment Rights (LAGER)
Gay men 020 7704 6066; lesbians
020 7704 6067
www.lager.dircon.co.uk

Liberty (the National Council for Civil Liberties)
020 7378 8659
www.yourrights.org.uk
Maternity Alliance
020 7588 8582
www.maternityalliance.org.uk
National Youth Advocacy Service
0800 616101
www.nyas.net
Public Law Project
020 7269 0570
www.publiclawproject.org.uk
Refugee Legal Centre
020 7780 3200
www.refugee-legal-centre.org.uk
Scottish Human Rights Centre
0141 332 5960
www.scottishhumanrightscentre
.org.uk
UK Legal
0845 2801976
www.uklegal.com

Prison Service
020 7217 6633
www.hmprisonservice.gov.uk
Press 020 7273 4545
victim helpline 0845 7585 112

Scottish Prison Service
0131 244 8745
www.sps.gov.uk
Chief executive: 0131 244 8522

N Ireland Prison Service
028 9052 5065
www.niprisonservice.gov.uk

Agencies

Parole Board for England and Wales
020 7217 5314
www.paroleboard.gov.uk
Press 020 7217 5266

Prisons Ombudsman for England and Wales
020 7276 2876

Scottish Parole Board
0131 244 8755

Scottish Prisons Inspectorate
0131 244 8481

Chief Inspector of Prisons
0870 267 4298
www.homeoffice.gov.uk/justice
/prisons/inspprisons

Professional bodies

Prison Governors Association
020 7217 8591
www.prisongovernors.org.uk

Prison Officers Association
020 8803 0255
www.poauk.org.uk

National Association of Prison Visitors
01234 359763

National Association of Probation Officers
020 7223 4887

Campaign groups

Apex Trust
0870 608 4567
www.apextrust.com

Campaign for Freedom of Information
020 7831 7477
www.cfoi.org.uk

Campaign for the Accountability of American Bases
01943 466405
www.caab.org.uk

Committee on the Administration of Justice (Northern Ireland)
028 9096 1122
www.caj.org.uk

Crimestoppers
020 8254 3200
www.crimestoppers-uk.org

Federation of Prisoners' Families Support Groups
020 8741 4578

Howard League for Prison Reform
020 7249 7373
www.howardleague.org

Inquest
020 7263 1111
www.inquest.org.uk

Justice
020 7329 5100
www.justice.org.uk

Liberty
020 7403 3888
www.liberty-human-rights.org.uk

Lifers Campaign
01992 769632

Minority Rights Group
020 7978 9498
www.minorityrights.org

National Association for the Care & Resettlement of Offenders
020 7582 6500
www.nacro.org.uk

Prison Reform Trust
020 7251 5070
www.prisonreformtrust.org.uk

Prisoners Advice Service
01634 247350
www.unlockprison.org.uk

Prisoners Family and Friends
020 7403 4091

Replay Trust
01844 214193

Unit for the Arts & Offenders
01227 470629
www.a4offenders.org.uk

Unlock
01634 247350
www.tphbook.dircon.co.uk
/unlock

Women in Prison
020 7226 5879
www.womeninprison.org.uk

Prisons for men

Acklington
01670 762300

Albany
01983 556300

Altcourse*
0151 522 2000

Ashfield*
0117 303 8000
Adults and young offenders

Ashwell
01572 774100

Aylesbury
01296 444000
Young offenders

Bedford
01234 373000

Belmarsh
020 8317 2436
High security

Birmingham
0121 345 2500

Blakenhurst
01527 400500

Blantyre House
01580 211060

Blundeston
01502 734500

Brinsford
01902 532450
Young offenders

Bristol
0117 980 8100

Brixton
020 8588 6283

Brockhill
01527 552650

Buckley Hall
01706 514300

Bullingdon
01869 353100

Camp Hill
01983 554600

Canterbury
01227 862800

Cardiff
029 2043 3100

Castington
01670 762100
Adults and young offenders

Channings Wood
01803 814600

Chelmsford
01245 272000
Adults and young offenders

Coldingley
01483 804300

Dartmoor
01822 892000

Deerbolt
01833 633200
Young offenders

Doncaster*
01302 760851
Adults and young offenders

Dorchester
01305 214500

Dovegate*
01283 820066

Downview
020 8929 3300

Durham
0191 332 3400
High security

Elmley
01795 882100

Erlestoke
01380 814250

Everthorpe
01430 426500

Featherstone
01902 703001

Feltham
020 8844 5000
Young offenders and remand

Ford
01903 663000

Forest Bank*
0161 9257000
Adults and young offenders

Foston Hall
01283 584301

Frankland
0191 332 3000
High security

Full Sutton
01759 375100
High security

Garth
01772 443300

Gartree
01858 436600

Glen Parva
0116 264 3000
Young offenders and remand

Gloucester
01452 453000
Adults and young offenders

Grendon
01296 443000

Guys Marsh
01747 856400
Adults and young offenders

Haverigg
01229 713000

Hewell Grange
01527 552000

High Down
020 8722 6300

Highpoint
01440 823099
Adults and young offenders

Hindley
01942 855000
Young offenders

Hollesley Bay
01394 412400

Holme House
01642 744000

Hull
01482 282200

Huntercombe
01491 643100
Young offenders
Kingston
023 9289 1100
Kirkham
01772 675400
Kirklevington Grange
01642 792600
Lancaster Farms
01524 563450
Adults and young offenders
Latchmere House
020 8588 6650
Leeds
0113 203 2600
Leicester
0116 228 3000
Lewes
01273 405100
Adults and young offenders
Leyhill
01454 264000
Lincoln
01522 663000
Lindholme
01302 848700
Littlehey
01480 333000
Liverpool
0151 525 5971
High security
Long Lartin
01386 835100
High security
Lowdham Grange*
0115 966 9220
Maidstone
01622 775300
Manchester
0161 817 5600
High security
Moorland
01302 523000
Adults and young offenders
Morton Hall
01522 866750
The Mount
01442 836300
Northallerton
01609 785100
Young offenders
North Sea Camp
01205 769300
Norwich
01603 708600
Adults and young offenders
Nottingham
0115 872 3000
Onley
01788 523400
Young offenders
Parc*
01656 300200
Adults and young offenders
Parkhurst
01983 554000
Pentonville
020 7023 7000
Portland
01305 825600
Young offenders
Prescoed
01291 672231
Adults and young offenders

Preston
01772 444550
Ranby
01777 862000
Reading
0118 908 5000
Rochester
01634 838100
Rye Hill*
01788 523300
Shepton Mallett
01749 823300
Shrewsbury
01743 273000
Send
01483 471000
Spring Hill
01296 443000
Stafford
01785 773000
Standford Hill
01795 884500
Stocken
01780 485100
Stoke Heath
01630 636000
Young offenders
Sudbury
01283 584000
Swaleside
01795 884100
Swansea
01792 485300
Swinfen Hall
01543 48400
Young offenders
Thorn Cross
01925 605100
Young offenders
Usk
01291 671600
The Verne
01305 825000
Wakefield
01924 246000
High security
Wandsworth
020 8588 4000
Warren Hill
01394 412400
Young offenders
Wayland
01953 858100
Wealstun
01937 848500
The Weare
01305 825400
Wellingborough
01933 232700
Werrington
01782 463300
Young offenders
Wetherby
01937 544200
Whatton
01949 859200
Whitemoor
01354 602350
High security
Winchester
01962 723000
Wolds*
01430 421588

Woodhill
01908 722000
High security
Wormwood Scrubs
020 8588 3200
Wymott
01722 444000

* private prisons

Prisons for women

Askham Grange
01904 772000
Adults and young offenders
Bullwood Hall
01702 562801
Young offenders
Cookham Wood
01634 202500
Drake Hall
01785 858100
Adults and young offenders
East Sutton Park
01622 845000
Adults and young offenders
Eastwood Park
01454 382100
Adults and young offenders
Exeter
01392 415650
Adults and young offenders
Holloway
020 7979 4400
Adults and young offenders
Low Newton
0191 376 4000
New Hall
01924 844200
Adults and young offenders
Risley
01925 733000
Styal
01625 553000
Adults and young offenders

Immigration removal centres

Dover
01304 246400
Haslar
023 9260 4000

Aberdeen
01224 238300
Men and women
Barlinnie
0141 770 2000
Castle Huntly
01382 360265
Cornton Vale
01786 832591
Women and young offenders
Dumfries
01387 261218
Edinburgh
0131 444 3000
Glenochil
01259 760471
Greenock
01475 787801
Inverness
01463 229000
Men and women
Kilmarnock
01563 548800
Low Moss
0141 7624848
Noranside
01356 665300
Perth
01738 622293
Peterhead
01779 479101
Polmont
01324 711558
Young offenders
Shotts
01501 824000
High security

Prisons in Northern Ireland

Hydebank Wood
028 9025 3666
Young offenders
Maghaberry
028 9261 1888
*High security,
men and women*
Magilligan
028 7776 3311

Religion

Inter Faith Network for the UK
020 7388 0008
www.interfaith.org.uk

Anglicanism

Anglican Communion
020 7620 1110
www.anglicancommunion.org
Archbishop of Canterbury
020 7898 1200
www.archbishopofcanterbury.org
Archbishop of York
01904 707021
www.bishopthorpepalace.co.uk
/archbishop
Church in Wales
029 2034 8200
www.churchinwales.org.uk
Church of England
020 7898 1000
www.cofe.anglican.org
Church of Ireland
00 353 1497 8422
www.ireland.anglican.org
Record Centre
020 7898 1030
www.lambethpalacelibrary.org
Scottish Episcopal Church
0131 225 6357
www.scotland.anglican.org

Catholicism

Catholic Church
020 7233 8196
www.catholic-ew.org.uk
Media Office
020 7901 4800
Provinces/Archbishops
Armagh 00 028 375 22045
Birmingham 0121 236 5535
Edinburgh 0131 452 8244
Glasgow 0141 226 5898
Cardiff 029 2022 0411
Liverpool 0151 522 1000
Southwark 020 7928 5592
Westminster 020 7798 9055

Other Christian

Baptist Union
01235 517700
www.baptist.org.uk
Church of Christ, Scientist
020 7371 0600
www.themotherchurch.org
**Church of Jesus Christ of Latter
Day Saints (Mormons)**
0121 712 1200
www.lds.org
Church of Scotland
0131 225 5722
www.churchofscotland.org.uk
**Churches Together in Britain &
Ireland**
020 7523 2121
www.ctbi.org.uk
Congressional Federation
0115 911 1460
www.congregational.org.uk
Council of Churches for Britain
020 7620 4444
Eastern Orthodox Churches
Greek 020 7723 4787 Russian 020
7584 0096
www.eastern-christian-churches.net
Free Church Federal Council
020 7387 8413
Free Church of England
020 7387 2564
www.fcofe.freeserve.co.uk
**Free Presbyterian Church of
Scotland**
0131 229 0649
www.fpchurch.org.uk
Independent Methodist Churches
01942 223526
www.fimc.org.uk
International Churches of Christ
020 7247 6480
www.icoc.org.uk
Jehovah's Witnesses
020 8906 2211
www.watchtower.org
Jesus Army
020 8992 0100
www.jesusarmy.org.uk
Lutheran Council of GB
020 7554 2900
www.lutheran.org.uk
Methodist Church
020 7467 5191
www.methodist.org.uk
Moravian Church
020 8883 3409
www.moravian.org.uk
Pentecostal Assemblies of God
0115 921 7272
www.aog.org.uk
Presbyterian Church in Ireland
028 9032 2284
www.presbyterianireland.org

Presbyterian Church of Wales
029 2049 4913
www.ebcpcw.org.uk
Quakers
020 7663 1000
www.quaker.org.uk
Salvation Army
020 7332 0101
www.salvationarmy.org
Seventh Day Adventist Church
01923 672251
www.adventist.org
Unification Church
020 7223 0721
www.unification.org
Unitarian Churches
020 7240 2384
www.unitarian.org.uk
United Free Church of Scotland
0131 332 3435
www.ufcos.org.uk
United Reform Church
020 7916 2020
www.urc.org.uk
World Council of Churches
41 22 791 6153
www.wcc-coe.org

Buddhism

BuddhaNet
www.buddhanet.net
Buddhist Centre London
020 7916 2282
www.buddhismlondon.demon.co.uk
The Buddha Vihara
020 8470 1879
www.buddha-vihara.org.uk
The Buddhist Society
020 7834 5858
www.thebuddhistsociety.org.uk
Cardiff Buddhist Centre
029 2046 2492
www.cardiffbuddhistcentre.com/
Edinburgh Buddhist Centre
0131 228 3333
www.edinburghbuddhistcentre.org.uk
**Friends of the Western Buddhist
Order**
0121 449 8272
Network of Buddhist Organisations
020 7582 5797
www.nbo.org.uk
Potala Buddhist Centre, Belfast
028 9023 8090
www.potalacentre.org.uk
Society Krishna Consciousness
01923 857244
www.iskcon.org.uk

Islam

Islamic Centre of England
020 7604 5500
www.ic-el.org
Islamic Cultural Centre
020 7724 3363
www.islamicculturalcentre.co.uk
Islamic Digest
www.islamicdigest.org
Muslim Council of Britain
020 8432 0585
www.mcb.org.uk
Muslim Directory
020 8840 0020
www.muslimdirectory.co.uk

Hinduism

Hindu Centre, London
020 7485 8200
Hindunet
www.hindunet.org
Hindu Links
www.hindulinks.org

Judaism

Board of Deputies of British Jews
020 7543 5400
www.bod.org.uk
Jewish Network
07974 439668
www.jewish.co.uk
Reform Synagogue
020 8349 4731
www.refsyn.org.uk
United Synagogue
020 8343 8989
www.unitedsynagogue.org.uk

Sikhism

Sikh Missionary Society
020 8574 1902
www.sikhs.org
Sikhnet
www.sikhnet.com
Sikh Women's Network
Sikhwomen.com

Spiritualism and paganism

Aetherius Society
020 7736 4187
www.aetherius.org
British Druid Order
sparrowhawk@britishdruidorder.co.uk
www.druidorder.demon.co.uk
Order of Bards, Ovates & Druids
obod@druidry.org
www.druidry.org
Pagan Federation
01295 277244
www.paganfed.demon.co.uk
PaganLink
www.paganlink.org
Satanism
www.churchofsatan.com
**Spiritualist Association
of Great Britain**
020 7235 3351
www.spiritualuk.com
Spiritualists' National Union
023 8044 2642.
www.snu.org.uk
Theosophical Society
020 7935 9261
Transcendental Meditation
0870 514 3733
www.transcendental-meditation
.org.uk.

Other religions

Church of Scientology
01342 318229
www.scientology.org
Baha'i Community of UK
020 7584 2566
www.bahai.org.uk
Jainism
www.jainworld.com
World Zoroastrian Organisation
President@w-z-o.org
www.w-z-o.org

Humanism and atheism

Association of Irish Humanists
00 353 12869870
www.irish-humanists.org
British Humanist Assoc
020 7430 0908
www.humanism.org.uk
**Gay and Lesbian Humanist
Association**
019268 58450
www.galha.freeserve.co.uk/galha.htm
**International Humanist and Ethical
Union**
020 7831 4816
www.iheu.org
National Secular Society
020 7404 3126
www.secularism.org.uk
Rationalist Press Association
020 7430 1371
www.rationalist.org.uk
South Place Ethical Society
020 7242 8034
www.ethicalsoc.org.uk

Society

Government departments

Deputy Prime Minister
020 7944 4400, press 020 7944 4651
www.odpm.gov.uk
Health
020 7210 4850, press 020 7210 5113
www.doh.gov.uk
Home Office
0870 0001585, press 020 7273 4545
www.homeoffice.gov.uk
Work and Pensions
020 7238 0800, press 020 7238 0866
www.dwp.gov.uk

Government agencies

Benefits Agency
020 7712 2171
www.dwp.gov.uk/lifeevent/benefits
British Council
020 7561 7561
www.britcoun.org
Charity Commission
020 7674 2322
www.charity-commission.gov.uk

Children and young people

Child Support Agency
helpline 08457 133133
press 020 7238 0866
www.csa.gov.uk
Children's Task Force
www.doh.gov.uk/childrenstaskforce
government
Connexions
080 800 13219
www.connexions.gov.uk
Advice and support for 13–19 year olds
**Adoption and Fostering Information
Line**
www.adoption.org.uk
Anna Freud Centre
020 7794 2313
www.annafreudcentre.org
Psychoanalysis for children
Barnardo's
020 8550 8822
www.barnardos.org.uk
BBC Children in Need
020 8576 7788
www.bbc.co.uk/cin
Bliss
0870 770337
www.bliss.org.uk
*National charity for premature or
sick babies*
Care and relief for the Young
01489 788300
www.cry.org.uk

Child Concern
0161 832 8113
www.childconcern.org.uk
Child Hope
020 7833 0868
www.childhopeuk.org
Defending street children worldwide
Childline Charitable trust
020 7650 3240
www.childline.org.uk
Children and Armed Conflict Unit
01206 873483
www.essex.ac.uk/armedcon
Children's Society
0845 300 1128
www.the-childrens-society.org.uk
Coram Family
020 7520 0300
www.coram.org.uk
Working with vulnerable children
End Child Poverty
020 7843 1913
www.ecpc.org.uk
Foyle Foundation
020 7430 9119
www.foylefoundation.org.uk
Great Ormond St Children's Charity
020 7916 5678
www.gosh.org
Hope
01442 234561
www.hope-for-children.org
*International charity for "handicapped,
orphaned, poor and exploited children"*
**Hyperactive Children's Support
Group**
01243 551313
www.hacsg.org.uk
**International Planned Parenthood
Federation**
020 7487 7900
www.ippf.org
Kids Clubs Network
020 7512 2100
www.kidsclubs.org.uk
National Children's Bureau
020 7843 6000
www.ncb.org.uk
**National Confederation of Parent
Teacher Associations**
01732 748850
www.ncpta.org.uk
NCH Action for Children
020 7704 7111
www.nch.org.uk
NSPCC
020 7825 2500
www.nspcc.org.uk
Prince's Trust
020 7543 7411
www.princes-trust.org.uk
Relate
020 7387 3127
www.relate.org.uk
Relationship Guidance

Ride Foundation
01372 467708
htwww.ridefoundation.org.uk
*Drug awareness, life skills and
citizenship programmes for schools*
Save the Children
020 7703 5400
www.savethechildren.org.uk
Second Chance
02392 872790
www.second-chance.org.uk
*Camping and fishing for
disavantaged children*
The Site
020 7288 7311
www.thesite.org.uk
Advice and help for young people
Task Brazil
020 7394 1177
www.taskbrasil.org.uk
UK charity for street children in Brazil
Trident Trust
020 7014 1400
www.thetridenttrust.org.uk
Unicef
020 7405 5592
www.unicef.org.uk
United Kingdom Missing Children
www.missingkids.co.uk
War Child UK
020 7916 9276
www.warchild.co.uk
Whizz Kidz
020 7233 6600
www.whizz-kidz.org.uk
Young Enterprise UK
01865 776845
www.young-enterprise.org.uk

Women

Breast Cancer Campaign
020 7749 3700
www.bcc-uk.org
Breast Cancer Care
020 7384 2984
www.breastcancercare.org.uk
**British Association of Women
Entrepreneurs**
020 7935 0085
www.bawe.org
**Campaign Against Domestic
Violence**
020 8520 5881
www.cadv.org.uk
**Child and Woman Abuse Studies
Unit**
020 7753 5037
www.cwasu.org
Emily's List
emily@emilyslist.org.uk
www.emilyslist.org.uk
Campaign for Labour women MPs

European Women's Lobby
00 32 2 217 9020
www.womenlobby.org
Everywoman
0870 746 1800
www.everywoman.co.uk
FEM Vision
0118 973 2291
www.femvision.org
Feminist Library
020 7928 7789
Justice for Women
0113 226 8863
www.jfw.org.uk
League of Jewish Women
020 7242 8300
www.leagueofjewishwomen.org.uk
Meet A Mum Association
01525 217064
www.mama.org.uk
National Abortion Campaign
020 7923 4976
www.gn.apc.org/nac
**National Association for
Premenstrual Syndrome**
0870 777 2178
www.pms.org.uk
National Council of Women
020 7354 2395
www.ncwgb.org
**National Federation of Women's
Institutes**
020 7371 9300
www.womens-institute.co.uk
Older Feminist Network
020 8346 1900
www.ofn.org.uk
Rights of Women
020 7251 6575
www.row.org.uk
Scottish Women's Aid
0131 475 2372
www.scottishwomensaid.co.uk
Single Parent Action Network
0117 951 4231
www.spanuk.org.uk
Suzy Lamplugh Trust
icps@suzylamplugh.org
www.suzylamplugh.org
The 300 Group
01403 733797
www.300group.org.uk
The Fawcett Society
020 7253 2598
www.fawcettsociety.org.uk
The Hypatia Trust
01736 360549
www.hypatia-trust.org.uk
The Women's Library
020 7320 2222
www.thewomenslibrary.ac.uk
Womankind Worldwide
020 7549 5700
www.womankind.org.uk
Women and Manual Trades
020 7251 9192
www.wamt.org
Women Connect
020 7226 5375
www.womenconnect.org.uk

Women's Aid
0117 944 4411
www.womensaid.org.uk
Women's Link
020 7248 1200
www.womenslink.org.uk
Women's National Commission
020 7276 2555
www.thewnc.org.uk
YWCA (London)
020 7383 0133
www.ywca-gb.org.uk/london

Community

Anchor Trust
020 7759 9104
www.anchor.org.uk
**Association for Citizenship
Teaching**
020 7367 0510
www.teachingcitizenship.org.uk
*Information and direct action across a
number of areas*
**Centre for Citizenship Studies in
Education**
0116 252361
www.le.ac.uk/se/centres
/citizenship/cs.html
Changemakers
01458 834767
www.changemakers.org.uk
Citizens Advice Bureaux
020 7833 2181
www.nacab.org.uk
Citizenship Foundation
020 7367 0518
www.citizenshipfoundation.org.uk
Civil Service Benevolent Fund
020 8240 2400
www.csbf.org.uk
Coalfields Regeneration Trust
01709 765576
www.coalfields-regen.org.uk
Communities that Care
020 7619 0123
www.communitiesthatcare.org.uk
**Community Development
Foundation**
020 7226 5375
www.cdf.org.uk
Community Service Volunteers
020 7278 6601
www.csv.org.uk
Directory of Social Change
020 7391 4800
www.dsc.org.uk
Erskine Hospital
0141 8123733
www.erskine.org
*For ex-service men and women in
Scotland*
Groundwork
0121 236 8565
www.groundwork.org.uk
*Community improvement schemes in
rundown areas*
Hansard Society
020 7955 7459
www.hansardsociety.org.uk

Jewish Care
020 8922 2000
www.jewishcare.org
JustdoSomething
020 7608 8100
www.justdosomething.net
Nacro
020 7582 6500
www.nacro.org.uk
Crime reduction charity
**National Federation of Community
Organisations**
020 7837 7887
www.communitymatters.org.uk
National Youth Agency
0116 285 3700
www.nya.org.uk
Neighbourhood Renewal Unit
neighbourhoodrenewal@odpm
.gsi.gov.uk
www.neighbourhood.gov.uk
Norwood Ravenswood Foundation
020 8954 4555
www.nwrw.org
Prince's Trust
020 7543 7411.
www.princes-trust.org.uk
Quest Trust
01225 466222
www.quest-net.org
Rathbone Community Industry
020 8983 4101
www.rathbonetraining.co.uk
*Learning and training support for the
disadvantaged*
Royal British Legion
0845 772 5725
www.britishlegion.org.uk
Samaritans
020 8394 8300
www.samaritans.org.uk
**Soldiers', Sailors', Airmen and
Families Association Forces Help**
020 7403 8783
www.ssafa.org.uk
St Christopher's Hospice
020 8768 4500
www.stchristophers.org.uk
Sue Ryder Care
020 7400 0440
www.suerydercare.org
*National volunteering campaign for
community welfare*
Time Bank
020 7401 5420
www.timebank.org.uk
Time for Citizenship
www.timeforcitizenship.com
Victim Support
020 7896 3809
www.victimsupport.com

Disability

Disability Rights Commission
08457 622633
www.drc-gb.org
Independent body established by statute
Action for Blind People
020 7635 4800
www.afbp.org
Afasic
020 7490 9410
www.afasic.org.uk
For children and young adults with communication impairments
British Wheelchair Sports Foundation
01296 395995
www.britishwheelchairsports.org
Council for Disabled Children
020 7843 1900
www.ncb.org.uk
Dogs For the Disabled
01295 252600
www.dogsforthedisabled.org
Elizabeth Foundation for Pre-School Deaf Children
023 9237 2735
www.elizabeth-foundation.org
Employment Opportunities for People with Disabilities
020 7481 2727
www.opportunities.org.uk
emPower
020 8355 2341
www.empowernet.org/empower
Aiming to influence policy on disability equipment services
First Asian Support Trust
0161 740 3399
www.fast-uk.org
Support for Asians with disabilities
Guide Dogs for the Blind
0870 600 2323
www.gdba.org.uk
Guide Dogs for the Blind Association
0870 600 2323
www.gdba.org.uk
Leonard Cheshire
020 7802 8200
www.leonard-cheshire.org
Creating opportunities with disabled people
Mencap
020 7454 0454
www.mencap.org.uk
Mind
0845 766 0163
www.mind.org.uk
For better mental health
National Autistic Society
020 7903 3593
www.nas.org.uk
National Deaf Children's Society
020 7490 8656
www.ndcs.org.uk
Physically Handicapped and Able Bodied Children
020 8667 9443
www.phabengland.org.uk

Riding for the Disabled
024 7669 6510
www.riding-for-disabled.org.uk
Royal National Institute for the Deaf
020 7296 8000
www.rnid.org.uk
Royal National Institute for the Blind
020 7391 2356
www.rnib.org.uk
Royal Star and Garter Home
020 8340 3314
www.starandgarter.org
For disabled ex-service men and women
Scope
0800 800 3333
www.scope.org.uk
Disability organisation focusing on cerebral palsy
Sense
020 7272 7774
www.sense.org.uk
Charity for the deafblind
St Dunstans
020 7723 5021
www.st-dunstans.org.uk
For blind ex-service personnel
The Shaw Trust
01225 716350
www.shaw-trust.org.uk
Provides training and work opportunities
United Response
020 8246 5200
www.united-response.co.uk
Support for those with learning difficulties and mental health problems
Whizz Kidz
020 7233 6600
www.whizz-kidz.org.uk

Asylum and refugees

Immigration and Nationality Directorate
0870 000 1585
www.ind.homeoffice.gov.uk
Office of the Immigration Services Commissioner
020 7211 1500
www.oisc.gov.uk
Asylum Aid
020 7377 5123
www.asylumaid.org.uk
Immigration Advisory Service
020 7967 1200
www.iasuk.org
Immigration Law Practitioners' Association
020 7251 8383
www.ilpa.org.uk
Joint Council for the Welfare of Immigrants
020 7251 8708
www.jcwi.org.uk
Human rights for immigrants & asylum seekers in UK
Migration Research Unit
020 7679 7569
www.geog.ucl.ac.uk/mru

Refugee Action
020 7654 7700
www.refugee-action.org.uk
Refugee Council
020 7820 3044
www.refugeecouncil.org.uk
Refugee Safe Haven Campaign
01237 441426
www.safe-haven.org.uk
Scottish Asylum Seekers Consortium
0141 287 3623
www.asylumscotland.org.uk
Scottish Refugee Council
0141 248 9799
www.scottishrefugeecouncil.org.uk

Diversity

Equal Opportunities Commission
0845 601 5901
www.eoc.org.uk

Race

Commission for Racial Equality (CRE)
020 7939 0000
www.cre.gov.uk
1990 Trust
020 7582 1990
www.blink.org.uk
Black community organisation
Black Enterprise
020 7498 5656
www.blackenterprise.co.uk
Ethnic Minority Foundation
020 8432 0307
www.emf-cemvo.co.uk

Age

Age Concern England
020 8765 7200
www.ageconcern.org.uk
Help the Aged
020 7278 1114
www.helptheaged.org.uk
Age Positive
www.agepositive.gov.uk/
Age diversity in employment

Sexuality

Armed Forces Lesbian and Gay Association
0870 740 7755
www.aflaga.org.uk
Beyond Barriers
0141 574 0242
www.beyondbarriers.org.uk
Gay and Lesbian Association of Doctors and Dentists
0870 765 5606
www.gladd.org.uk
Lesbian and Gay Christian Movement
020 7739 1249
www.lgcm.org.uk

Lesbian and Gay Employment Rights
lager@dircon.co.uk
www.lager.dircon.co.uk
Metro Centre
020 8265 3311
www.themetro.dircon.co.uk
Services for people questioning their sexuality
Outrage
020 8240 0222
http://outrage.nabumedia.com
Direct action for gay rights
Out-Side-In
osiuk@hotmail.com
http://www.users.globalnet.co.uk
/~quequeg/osi.html
Support for gay prisoners
Queerspace
info@queerspace.org.uk
www.queerspace.org.uk
Northern Ireland
Stonewall
020 7881 9440
www.stonewall.org.uk
The Gay Vote
www.thegayvote.co.uk
UK Lesbian and Gay Immigration Group
0870 241 0645
www.uklgig.org.uk

►► DIVERSITY IN THE MEDIA,
page 261

Housing

Housing Corporation
020 7393 2000
www.housingcorp.gov.uk
Funding and regulation of housing associations
Advisory Service for Squatters
020 7359 8814
www.squat.freeserve.co.uk
Broadway
020 7089 9500
www.broadwaylondon.org
Working to house the homeless
Centrepoint
020 7426 5300
www.centrepoint.org.uk
Agency for young homeless
Chartered Institute of Housing
020 7685 1700
www.cih.org
Promoting high standards in housing provision
Connection at St Martin's
020 7766 5555
www.london-connection.org.uk
Facilities for London's homeless
Crash
020 8742 0717
www.crash.org.uk
Construction and property industry homeless charity
Crisis
0870 011 3335
www.crisis.org.uk
Homeless charity
Defend Council Housing
020 7987 9989
www.defendcouncilhousing.org.uk
Empty Homes Agency
020 7828 6288
www.emptyhomes.com
FEANTSA
00 3202 5386699
www.feantsa.org
European federation of homeless organisations
Foyer Federation
020 7430 2212
www.foyer.net
Accommodation and opportunities for the young
Groundswell
020 7737 5500
www.groundswell.org.uk
Support projects for the homeless

Homeless Link
020 7960 3010
www.homeless.org.uk
UK membership network for homeless agencies
Homes for Homeless People
01582 481426
www.homeline.dircon.co.uk
Housing Quality Network
01723 350099
www.hqnetwork.org.uk
Aims to improve quality of housing services
Joseph Rowntree Foundation
01904 629241
www.jrf.org.uk
Policy research and action on housing and social care
National Housing Federation
020 7278 6571
www.housing.org.uk
Representing the independent social housing sector
Paddington Churches Housing Association
020 8537 4100
www.pcha.org.uk
London housing association founded 1965
Peabody Trust
020 7928 7811
www.peabody.org.uk
London housing association
Room
020 7929 9494
www.room.org.uk
Forum for debate on housing and regeneration issues
Royal Masonic Benevolent Institution
020 7596 2400
www.rmbi.org.uk
Housing and care needs for elderly masons
Rural Housing Trust
020 7793 8114
www.ruralhousing.org.uk
Affordable housing in English villages
Shelter
020 7505 2162
www.shelter.org.uk
Thamesreach
020 7702 5646
www.thamesreach.org.uk
London homeless charity
UK Co-Housing Network
dweston@cqm.org.uk
www.cohousing.org.uk
Network of resident-developed neighbourhoods

■ Society helplines

Afasic
08453 555577

Benefit Enquiry Line
0800 882200

Childline
0800 1111

Churches Child Protection Advisory Service
08451 204551

Deafblind UK
0800 132320

Diasability Alliance – Rights Advice Line
020 7247 8763

Disability Living Allowance
08457 123456

Domestic Violence – First Step Centre
0800 281281

Elder Abuse Responseline
020 8679 7074

Gamblers Anonymous
08700 508880

Gay Men's Employment Rights
020 7704 6066

Gingerbread Advice Line
0800 018 4318

Kidscape
08451 205204

Learning Disability Helpline
0808 808111

Lesbian Employment Rights
020 7704 8066

NSPCC National Child Protection Helpline
0800 800500

Parent Line
08088 002222

Refugee Helpline
0800 413848

Relate
0845 1 304010

Samaritans
020 8394 8300

Saneline
0845 767 8000

Shelter London Line
0800 800444

Supportline for Survivors of Professional Abuse
0845 450 0300

Victim Supportline
0845 303 0900

Welfare Foods Helpline
0800 056 2665

Winter Warmth Advice Line
0800 085 7000

Women's Aid National Domestic Violence Helpline
08457 023468

Sport

Department for Culture, Media and Sport
020 7211 6000
press 020 7211 6215
www.culture.gov.uk

Official bodies

UK Sport
020 7211 5100
www.uksport.gov.uk
Sport England
020 72731500
www.sportengland.org
Regional offices:
East 01234 345222
East Midlands 0115 982 1887
London 020 8778 8600
North 0191 384 9595
North-west 0161 834 0338
South-east 0118 948 3311
South-west 01460 73491
West Midlands 0121 456 3444
Yorkshire 0113 243 6443
Sport Scotland
0131 317 7200
www.sportscotland.org.uk
Sports Council for N Ireland
028 9038 1222
www.sportni.net
Sports Council for Wales
029 2030 0500
www.sports-council-wales.co.uk

Olympics 2004

International Olympic Committee
00 4121 621 6111
www.olympic.org
International Paralympic Committee
00 49 228 209 7200
www.paralympic.org
Organising Committee for Athens 2004
00 30210 200 4000
www.athens2004.com
Greek Undersecretariat of Sports
www.sport.gov.gr/main_en.html
British Olympic Association
020 8871 2677
www.olympics.org.uk
British Paralympic Association
020 7662 8882
www.paralympics.org.uk

Football

Governing bodies

FA
020 7262 4542
www.the-fa.org
FA Premier League
020 7745 4545
www.premierleague.com
Football League
0870 4420 1888
www.football-league.co.uk
Nationwide Conference
01322 411021
www.football.nationwide.co.uk
Irish Football Association
028 9066 9458
www.irishfa.com
Scottish Football Association
0141 616 6000
www.scottishfa.co.uk
Football Association of Wales
029 2037 2325
www.faw.org.uk
Women's Football Association
01707 651840
www.thefa.com/football
Scottish Women's Football Association
0141 353 1162
www.scottishfa.co.uk/affiliates /womens
Portuguese Football Federation (Euro 2004)
00 351 213 252 700
www.fpf.pt, www.euro2004.com
Uefa
00 4122 994 4444
www.uefa.com
Fifa
00 4113 849595
www.fifa.com

National stadium

Millennium stadium
0870 013 8600
www.cardiff-stadium.co.uk

Premiership 2003–04

Arsenal FC
020 7704 4000
www.arsenal.com
Aston Villa FC
0121 327 2299
www.avfc.co.uk
Birmingham FC
0121 772 0101
www.blues.premiumtv.co.uk
Blackburn Rovers FC
01254 691919
www.rovers.co.uk
Bolton Wanderers FC
01204 673673
www.bwfc.co.uk

Charlton AFC
020 8333 4000
www.cafc.co.uk
Chelsea FC
020 7385 5545
www.chelseafc.co.uk
Everton FC
0151 330 2307
www.evertonfc.com
Fulham FC
020 7893 8383
www.fulham-fc.co.uk
Leeds United FC
0113 367 3000
www.lufc.co.uk
Leicester City FC
0116 291 5033
www.lcfc.co.uk
Liverpool FC
0151 330 2200
www.liverpoolfc.net
Manchester City FC
0161 224 5000
www.mcfc.co.uk
Manchester United FC
0161 868 8000
www.manutd.com
Middlesbrough FC
01642 877 700
www.mfc.co.uk
Newcastle United FC
0191 201 8400
www.nufc.co.uk
Portsmouth FC
023 9261 8777
www.pompeyfc.co.uk
Southampton FC
0870 220 0000
www.saintsfc.co.uk
Tottenham Hotspur FC
020 8365 5000
www.spurs.co.uk
Wolverhampton Wanderers FC
01902 653653
www.wolves.co.uk

Other bodies

Professional Footballers' Association
0161 236 0575
www.thepfa.co.uk
Referees Association
02476 601701
www.footballreferee.org
Football Supporters' Federation
01634 319461
www.fsf.org.uk
Let's Kick Racism Out of Football
020 1684 4884
racism hotline 0800 169 9414
www.kickitout.org
Show Racism the Red Card
0191 291 0160
www.srtrc.org

Other Sports

American football

British American Football Association
01661 843179

Angling

National Federation of Anglers
01283 734835
www.the-nfa.org.uk
National Federation of Sea Anglers
01626 331300
www.nfsa.org.uk
Salmon and Trout Association
020 7283 5838
www.salmon-trout.org.uk

Archery

The Grand National Archery Society
01952 677888
www.gnas.org

Athletics

International Association of Athletics Federations
00 377 9310 8888
www.iaaf.org
UK Athletics
0121 456 5098
www.ukathletics.org

Badminton

Badminton Association of England
01908 268400
www.baofe.co.uk
Ulster Branch Badminton Union of Ireland
028 9038 3810
www.badmintonireland.com
Scottish Badminton Union
0141 445 1218
www.scotbadminton.demon.co.uk
Welsh Badminton Union
029 2022 2082
www.welshbadminton.force9.co.uk

Ballooning

British Balloon & Airship Club
01562 850750
www.bbac.org

Baseball

British Baseball Federation
020 7453 7055
www.baseballsoftballuk.com

Basketball

English Basketball Association
0113 236 1166
www.basketballengland.org.uk
Ulster Basketball Association
028 9064 8000
www.ulsterbasketball.com
Basketball Scotland
0131 317 7260
www.basketball-scotland.com
Basketball Association of Wales
029 2049 6696
www.hoopscymru.net

Biathlon

British Biathlon Union
01874 730562
www.britishbiathlon.com

Bobsleigh

British Bobsleigh Association
01225 826802
www.british-bobsleigh.com

Bowling

English Bowling Association
01903 820222
www.bowlsengland.com
Irish Bowling Association
028 9044 8348
Scottish Bowling Association
0141 221 8999
www.scottish-bowling.co.uk
Welsh Bowling Association
01446 733745
www.welsh-bowling-association.org.uk

Boxing

Amateur Boxing Association of England
020 8778 0251
www.abae.org.uk
Irish Amateur Boxing Association
028 796 2840
www.iaba.ie
Amateur Boxing Scotland
0131 317 8908
Welsh Amateur Boxing Association
029 2062 3566
British Boxing Board of Control
020 7403 5879
www.bbbofc.com
World Boxing Organisation
00 1 787 765 4444
www.wbo-int.com
International Boxing Federation
00 1 973 414 0300
www.ibf-usba-boxing.com
World Boxing Association (Venezuela)
00 58 414 343 6499
www.wbaonline.com

Canoeing

British Canoe Union
0115 982 1100
www.bcu.org.uk

Caving

National Caving Association
020 8422 9668
www.nca.org

Cricket

England and Wales Cricket Board
020 7432 1200
www.ecb.co.uk
Scottish Cricket Union
0131 317 7247
www.scu.org.uk
Marylebone Cricket Club
020 7616 8500
www.lords.org.uk

Croquet

Croquet Association
020 736 3148
www.croquet.org.uk

Curling

British Curling Association
01772 634154
www.britishcurlingassociation.org.uk
Royal Caledonian Curling Club
0131 333 3003
www.rccc.org

Cycling

British Cycling Federation
0161 230 2301
www.bcf.uk.com

Equestrianism

British Equestrian Federation
024 7669 8871
www.bef.co.uk
British Show Jumping Association
024 7669 8800
www.bsja.co.uk

Fencing

British Fencing Association
020 8742 3032
www.britishfencing.com

Golf

English Golf Union
01526 354500
www.englishgolfunion.org
Golfing Union of Ireland (Ulster Branch)
028 9042 3708
www.gui.ie
Scottish Golf Union
01382 549500
www.scottishgolf.com
Welsh Golfing Union
01633 430830
www.welshgolf.org
Ladies Golf Union
01334 475811
www.lgu.org
St Andrews
01334 466666
www.standrews.org.uk

Gymnastics

British Gymnastics
01952 820330
www.baga.co.uk

Handball

British Handball Association
01706 229354
www.britsport.com/handball

Hockey

Great Britain Olympic Hockey Board
01908 544644
English Hockey Association
01908 544644
www.hockeyonline.co.uk
Irish Hockey Assoc (Ulster Branch)
028 9038 3819
www.hockey.ie

Scottish Hockey Union
0131 312 8870
www.scottish-hockey.org.uk
Welsh Hockey Union
029 2023 3257
www.welsh-hockey.co.uk

Horse racing

The Jockey Club
01638 664151
www.thejockeyclub.co.uk
The Tote
020 8874 6411
www.tote.co.uk
Ascot
01344 622211
www.ascot.co.uk
Aintree (Grand National)
0151 523 2600
www.aintree.co.uk
Epsom (Derby)
01372 470047
www.epsomderby.co.uk

Ice hockey

Ice Hockey UK
0115 924 1441
www.icehockeyuk.co.uk

Ice skating

**National Ice Skating Association
of UK**
0115 853 3100
www.iceskating.org.uk

Martial arts

British Aikido Board
01753 577878
www.aikido-baa.org.uk
British Ju-Jitsu Association
01277 224057
www.bjjagb.com
British Judo Association
0116 255 9669
www.britishjudo.org.uk
British Kendo Association
01788 891975
www.kendo.org.uk
English Karate Governing Body
01302 337645
www.ekgb.org.uk
**Tae Kwon-Do Association of
Great Britain**
0800 052 5960
www.tagb.biz

Korfball

British Korfball Association
01622 813115
www.british-korfball.org.uk

Lacrosse

English Lacrosse Association
0121 773 4422
www.englishlacrosse.co.uk

Luge

Great Britain Luge Association
01684 576604
www.gbla.co.uk

Modern pentathlon

**Modern Pentathlon Association
of Great Britain**
0118 981 7181
www.mpagb.org.uk

Motor sports

Auto-Cycle Union
motorcycling
01788 566400
www.acu.org.uk
**Federation Internationale de
L'Automobile (FIA)**
motor sports
00 33143 124455
www.fia.com
**Royal Automobile Club Motor
Sports Association**
motor sports
01753 681736
www.msauk.org

Mountaineering

British Mountaineering Council
0161 445 4747
www.thebmc.co.uk

Netball

All England Netball Association Ltd
01462 442344
www.england-netball.co.uk
Netball Scotland
0141 570 4016
www.netballscotland.com
Welsh Netball Association
029 2023 7048
www.welshnetball.co.uk

Orienteering

British Orienteering Federation
01629 734042
www.britishorienteering.org.uk

Parachuting

British Parachute Association
0116 278 5271
www.bpa.org.uk

Petanque

British Petanque Association
024 7642 1408
www.britishpetanque.org.uk

Polo

Hurlingham Polo Association
01367 242828
www.hpa-polo.co.uk

Pool

English Pool Association
01706 642770
www.epa.org.uk

Rounders

National Rounders Association
0115 938 5478
www.rounders.punters.co.uk

Rowing

Amateur Rowing Association
020 8748 3632
www.ara-rowing.org

Rugby

The Rugby Football League
0113 232 9111
www.rugby-league.org
**British Amateur Rugby League
Association**
01484 544131
www.barla.org.uk
Rugby Football Union
020 8892 2000
www.rfu.com
Scottish Rugby Union
0131 346 5000
www.sru.org.uk
Welsh Rugby Union
029 2078 1700
www.wru.co.uk
Irish Rugby Union
00 3531 647 3800
www.irishrugby.ie
Rugby Football Union for Women
01635 42333
www.rfu-women.co.uk

Sailing

Royal Yachting Association
023 8062 7400
www.rya.org.uk

Scuba diving

British Sub-Aqua Club
0151 350 6200
www.bsac.com

Shooting

**Great Britain Target Shooting
Federation**
01702 219395
www.leadshot.com

Skiing and snowboarding

British Ski & Snowboard Federation
0131 445 7676
www.bssf.co.uk
Snowsport Scotland
0131 445 4151
www.snsc.demon.co.uk

Softball

British Softball Federation
020 7453 7055
www.baseballsoftballuk.com

Squash

England Squash
0161 231 4499
www.englandsquash.com
Ulster Squash
028 9038 1222
www.ulstersquash.com
Scottish Squash
0131 317 7343
www.scottishsquash.org
Squash Wales
01633 682108
www.squashwales.co.uk

Surfing

British Surfing Association
01736 360250
www.britsurf.co.uk

Swimming

Amateur Swimming Federation of Great Britain
01509 618700
www.britishswimming.org

Table tennis

English Table Tennis Association
01424 722525
www.etta.co.uk

Tennis

Lawn Tennis Association
020 7381 7000
www.lta.org.uk
Tennis and Rackets Association
020 7386 3448
www.irtpa.com

Tenpin bowling

British Tenpin Bowling Association
020 8478 1745
www.btba.org.uk

Triathlon

British Triathlon Association
01530 414234
www.britishtriathlon.co.uk

Volleyball

English Volleyball Association
0115 981 6324
www.volleyballengland.org

Water skiing

British Water Ski Federation
020 7833 2855
www.britishwaterski.co.uk

Weightlifting

British Weight Lifting Association
01865 200339
www.bawla.com

Wrestling

British Amateur Wrestling Association
0161 832 9209
www.britishwrestling.org

Yoga

British Wheel of Yoga
01529 306851
www.members.aol.com/wheelyoga

Sport centres

Bisham Abbey, Bucks
01628 476911
www.leisureconnection.co.uk/bisham
Crystal Palace, South London
020 8778 9876
www.crystalpalacensc.co.uk
Cumbrae, Ayrshire
01475 530757
Glenmore Lodge, Aviemore
01479 861256
www.glenmorelodge.org.uk
Holme Pierrepoint, Notts
01159 821212
www.nationalwatersports.co.uk
Inverclyde, Largs
01475 674666
Lilleshall, Shropshire
01952 603003
www.lilleshallnsc.co.uk
Plas Menai, Gwynedd
01248 670964
www.plasmenai.co.uk
Plas y Brenin, Conwy
01690 720214
www.pyb.co.uk
Welsh Institute, Cardiff
029 2030 0500
www.welsh-institute-sport.co.uk
Tollymore, County Down
028 4372 2158
www.tollymoremc.com

Sport and education

British Universities Sports Association
020 7357 8555
www.busa.org.uk
Central Council of Physical Recreation
020 7828 3163
www.ccpr.org.uk
National Council for School Sport
0115 923 1229
www.schoolsport.freeserve.co.uk
Physical Education Association of UK
0118 931 6240
www.pea.uk.com
Youth Sport Trust
01509 228293
www.youthsport.net

Sport and disability

British Amputee and Les Autres Sports Association
0121 605 9549
www.chap14.freeserve.co.uk/balasa
British Blind Sport
01926 424247
British Deaf Sports Council
01943 850214
www.britishdeafsportscouncil.org.uk
British Wheelchair Sports Foundation
01296 395995
www.britishwheelchairsports.org
United Kingdom Sports Association for People with Learning Disability
020 7354 1030
Wheelchair Sports Foundation
01296 395995
www.britishwheelchairsports.org

Other bodies

National Lottery Charities Board
08457 919191
www.nlcb.org.uk
National Sports Medicine Institute
020 7908 3636
www.nsmi.org.uk
Sports Aid Foundation
020 7387 9380
www.sportsaid.org.uk
Sports Coach UK
0113 274 4802
www.sportscoachuk.org
Women's Sports Foundation
020 8697 5370
www.wsf.org.uk

Travel

Government agencies

Department for Transport
020 7944 8300
press 020 7944 3066 (roads)
020 7944 3108 (sea, air, rail)
www.dft.gov.uk
Commission for Integrated Transport
cfit@dft.gsi.gov.uk
www.cfit.gov.uk
Transport 2000
01628 524900
www.transport2000.org.uk
National independent transport advisory body

Transport in London

Transport for London
020 7941 4500
www.tfl.gov.uk/tfl
London Underground
0845 330 9880
tube.tfl.gov.uk
London Transport Users Committee
020 7505 9000
London River Services
020 7941 4500
www.tfl.gov.uk/river
London Buses
020 7918 4300
www.tfl.gov.uk/buses
Congestion charge
020 7941 4500
www.cclondon.com

Rail travel

Rail: official bodies

Network Rail
Headquarters 020 7557 8000
Press 020 7557 8292
Helpline 08457 114141
www.networkrail.co.uk
Strategic Rail Authority
020 7654 6000
www.sra.gov.uk
Office of the Rail Regulator
020 7282 2002
www.rail-reg.gov.uk
Rail Safety & Standards Board
020 7904 7518
www.railwaysafety.org.uk
Health and Safety Executive: railways
020 7717 6000
www.hse.gov.uk/railways
Continental route planning & ticket sales
National Rail Enquiries
08457 484950
www.nationalrail.co.uk

Rail: passenger councils

Rail Passengers Council: Wales
029 2022 7247
www.railpassengers.org.uk
Rail Passengers Council: Midlands
0121 212 2133
www.railpassengers.org.uk
Rail Passengers Council: southern England
020 7222 0391
www.railpassengers.org.uk
Rail Passengers Council: north-western England
0161 244 5982
www.railpassengers.org.uk
Rail Passengers Council: western England
0117 926 5703
www.railpassengers.org.uk
Rail Passengers Council: eastern England
01733 312188
www.railpassengers.org.uk
Rail Passengers Council: north-eastern England
01904 787711
www.railpassengers.org.uk
Rail Passengers Council: Scotland
0141 221 7760
www.railpassengers.org.uk
Rail Passengers Council: Northern Ireland
020 7420 5308
www.railpassengers.org.uk

Rail: train operating companies

Association of Train Operating Companies
020 7904 3000
www.atoc.org
Anglia Railways Train Services
01473 693929
www.angliarailways.co.uk
Arriva Trains Northern
0191 520 4000
www.arrivatrainsnorthern.co.uk
C2C
0845 601 4873
www.c2c-online.co.uk
Central Trains
0121 654 1200
www.centraltrains.co.uk
Chiltern Railways
01296 332113
www.chilternrailways.co.uk
Connex
0870 603 0405
www.connex.co.uk
Docklands Light Rail
020 7491 4500
www.tfl.gov.uk/dlr
English Welsh & Scottish Railways
020 7713 2426
www.ews-railway.co.uk

Eurostar
0870 518 6186
www.eurostar.com
First Great Eastern
08459 505000
www.ger.co.uk
First Great Western
0845 600 5604
www.firstgreatwestern.co.uk
First North Western
0845 600 1159
www.firstnorthwestern.co.uk
Freightliner
020 7200 3902
www.freightliner.co.uk
Gatwick Express
020 8750 6622
www.gatwickexpress.co.uk
GNER
08457 225333
www.gner.co.uk
Heathrow Express
0845 600 1515
www.heathrowexpress.co.uk
Hull Trains
01482 606388
www.hulltrains.co.uk
Island Line
01983 812591
www.island-line.co.uk
Midland Mainline
01332 262010
www.midlandmainline.com
NI Railways
www.nirailways.co.uk
Scotrail
0845 601 5929
www.scotrail.co.uk
Silverlink
01923 207818
www.silverlink-trains.com
South Central
0191 232 3123
www.southcentraltrains.co.uk
South West Trains
0845 600 0650
www.swtrains.co.uk
Think Thameslink
0845 330 6333
www.thameslink.co.uk
Thames Trains
0118 908 3678
www.thamestrains.co.uk
Valley Lines
029 2044 9944
www.valleylines.co.uk
Virgin Trains
0870 789 1111
www.virgintrains.co.uk
Wales & Borders Trains
0870 900 0766
www.walesandborderstrains.co.uk
West Anglia Great Northern Railway (WAGN)
08457 818919
www.wagn.co.uk
Wessex Trains
0845 600 0880
www.wessextrains.co.uk

Air travel

Air: official bodies

Airport Operators Authority
020 7222 2249
www.aoa.org.uk
Air Transport Users Council
020 7240 6061
www.auc.org.uk
British Airline Pilots Association
020 8476 4000
www.balpa.org
British Airports Authority
020 7834 9449
www.baa.co.uk
Civil Aviation Authority
020 7379 7311
www.caa.co.uk
International Air Transport Association
020 8607 6262
www.iata.org
National Air Traffic Services
020 7497 5888
www.nats.co.uk

Airports

Battersea Heliport
020 7228 0181
London City
020 7646 0000
www.londoncityairport.com
London Gatwick
01293 535353
www.baa.co.uk/main/airports
/gatwick
London Heathrow
0870 000 0123
www.baa.com/main/airports
/heathrow
London Stansted
01279 680500
www.baa.com/main/airports/stansted
London Luton
01582 405100
www.london-luton.co.uk
London Manston (Kent)
01843 825063
www.london-manston.com
Aberdeen
01224 722331
www.baa.co.uk/main/airports
/aberdeen
Barra
01871 890283
www.hial.co.uk/barra-airport.html
Belfast (City)
028 9045 7745
www.belfastcityairport.com
Belfast (Aldergrove)
01849 422888
Benbecula
01870 602051
www.hial.co.uk/benbecula-airport
.html
Biggin Hill
028 9448 4848
www.bial.co.uk
Birmingham
0121 767 5511
www.bhx.co.uk

Blackpool
01253 343434
www.blackpoolairport.com
Bournemouth
01202 364000
www.flybournemouth.com
Bristol
01275 474444
www.bristolairport.co.uk
RAF Brize Norton
01993 842551
Cambridge
01223 373737
www.cambridgecityairport.com
Campbeltown
01586 553797
www.hial.co.uk
/campbeltown-airport.html
Cardiff
01446 712626
www.cardiffairportonline.com
Carlisle
01446 711111
Channel Islands:
Alderney 01481 822551
www.alderney.gov.gg/index
.php/pid/40
Guernsey 01481 237766
www.guernsey-airport.gov.gg
Jersey 01534 492000
www.jersey-airport.com
Coventry
02476 762220
www.coventryairport.co.uk
RNAS Culdrose
01326 574121
www.aviator.co.uk/aerodromes
/culdrose.htm
Dundee
01382 662200
www.dundeecity.gov.uk/airport
East Midlands
01331 852852
www.eastmidlandsairport.com
Edinburgh
0131 333 1000
www.baa.co.uk/main/airports
/edinburgh
Exeter
01392 367433
www.exeter-airport.co.uk
Glasgow
0141 887 1111
www.baa.co.uk/main/airports
/glasgow
Gloucester
01452 857700
www.gloucestershireairport.co.uk
Inverness
01667 464000
www.hial.co.uk/inverness-
airport.html
Ipswich
01473 720111
www.aviator.co.uk/aerodromes
/ipswich.htm
Islay
www.hial.co.uk/islay-airport.html
Isle of Man (Ronaldsway)
01624 821600
www.iom-airport.com
Lands End
01736 788771
www.sennen-cove.com

Leeds
0113 250 9696
www.lbia.co.uk
Liverpool (Speke)
0151 288 5000
Lydd
01797 322411
www.lydd-airport.co.uk
Manchester
0161 489 3000
www.manairport.co.uk
Newcastle
0191 286 0966
www.newcastleairport.com
RAF Northolt
020 8845 2300
www.rafnortholt.com
Norwich
01603 411923
www.norwichairport.co.uk
Orkney (Kirkwall)
01856 886210
www.hial.co.uk/kirkwall-airport.html
Penzance Heliport
01736 363871
www.penzance.co.uk/transport
/air.htm
Plymouth
0345 222111
www.plymouthcity.co.uk/airport.html
Prestwick
01292 511000
www.gpia.co.uk
St Mawgan
01637 860551
www.a2bairports.co.uk/newquay
.shtml
Scilly Isles
St Mary's 01720 422646
Tresco Heliport 01720 422970
Shetland
01595 840246
Shoreham
01273 296900
www.shorehamairport.co.uk
Southampton
023 8062 9600
www.baa.co.uk/main/airports
/southampton
Southend
01702 608100
www.southendairport.net
Stornoway
01851 702256
www.hial.co.uk/stornoway
-airport.html
Teesside
01325 332811
www.teessideairport.com
Tiree
01879 220456
www.hial.co.uk/tiree-airport.html
Wick
01955 602215
www.hial.co.uk/wick-airport.html

Airlines

Aer Lingus
0845 084 4111
www.aerlingus.ie
Aeroflot
00 212 944 2300
www.aeroflot.com
Air Canada
08705 247226
www.aircanada.ca
Air France
0845 084 5010
www.airfrance.com
Air India
airindpr@vsnl.com
www.airindia.com
Air Malta
00 356 21690890
www.airmalta.com
Air New Zealand
0800 028 4149
www.airnewzealand.com
Air Seychelles
01293 596656
www.airseychelles.net
Alitalia
020 8745 8297
www.alitalia.com
Alaska Airlines
01992 441517
www.alaskaair.com
America West Airlines
00 480 6935729
www.americawest.com
American Airlines
00 817 9671577
www.aa.com
ANA Europe
020 7224 8866
www.anaskyweb.com
ATA
www.ata.com
Austrian Airlines
020 7766 0300
www.aua.com
Avianca (Columbia)
0870 576 7747
www.avianca.com
British Airways
020 8738 5100
www.british-airways.com
BMI (British Midland)
01332 854687
www.britishmidland.com
Cathay Pacific
020 8834 8888
www.cathaypacific.com
China Airlines
020 7291 9233
www.china-airlines.com
Continental Airlines
01293 822690
www.continental.com
Cyprus Airways
00 357 22663054
www.cyprusair.com
Delta Express
0800 414767
www.delta.com
El Al Israel Airlines
020 7957 4299
www.elal.com

Emirates
0870 243 2222
www.emirates.com
Finnair
0207 629 4349
www.finnair.com
Gulf Air
0870 777 1700
www.gulfairco.com
Iberia
0845 601 2854
www.iberia.com
Icelandair
020 7874 1007
www.icelandair.com
Kenya Airways
01784 888299
www.kenya-airways.com
Kuwait Airways
00 965 240 4628
www.kuwait-airways.com
Japan Airlines
08457 747700
www.jal.com
JAT – Yugoslav Airlines
020 7629 2007
www.jat.com
KLM Royal Dutch
08705 074074
www.klm.com
LanChile
0800 917 0572
www.lanchile.com
LOT – Polish Airlines
0845 601 0949
www.lot.com
Lufthansa
020 8750 3408
www.lufthansa.com
Malaysia Airlines
0870 333 1238
www.malaysia-airlines.com
Olympic Airways
020 8745 7339
www.olympic-airways.gr
Portugalia Airlines
0161 489 5039
www.pga.pt
Qantas Airways
0845 774 7767
www.quantas.com.au
Royal Jordanian Airlines
rja@rja.com.jo
www.rja.com.jo
SAS Scandinavian Airlines
020 8990 7060
www.scandinavian.net
Saudi Arabian Airlines
01784 266244
www.saudiairlines.com
Singapore Airlines
020 8754 4151
www.singaporeair.com
South African Airways
020 8897 3645
www.flysaa.com
Spanair
00 971 492553
www.spanair.com
Sri Lankan Airlines
020 8538 2001
www.airlanka.com
Swiss
0845 601 0956
www.swiss.com

Thai Airways
0870 606 0911
www.thaiairways.com
United Airlines
0845 844 4777
www.ual.com
Varig – Brazilian Airlines
020 7287 3131
www.varig.com.br
Virgin Atlantic
01293 747373
www.virgin-atlantic.com
Yemen Airways
020 7409 1120
www.yemenairways.co.uk

Water travel

Boats and shipping: authorities

Associated British Ports
020 7430 1177
www.abports.co.uk
Association of Inland Navigation Authorities
01642 590257
www.aina.org.uk
British Marine Industries Federation
01784 473377
www.bmif.co.uk
British Ports Association
020 7242 1200
www.britishports.org.uk
British Waterways Board
01923 201120
www.british-waterways.org
Hydrographic Office
01823 723366
www.hydro.gov.uk
Inland Waterways Association
01923 711114
www.waterways.org.uk
International Maritime Organisation
020 7735 7611
www.imo.org
Lloyd's Register – Fairplay
01737 379000
www.fairplay.co.uk
Lloyd's Register
020 7423 2040
www.lr.org
London River Services
020 7941 4500
www.tfl.gov.uk/river
Lloyd's List
020 7553 1374
www.lloydslist.com
Maritime & Coastguard Agency
023 8032 9100
www.mcagency.org.uk
Register of Shipping & Seamen
029 2074 7333
Marine information services
Royal Institute of Navigation
020 7591 3130
www.rin.org.uk
Royal Yachting Association
0845 345 0400
www.rya.org.uk
UK Harbours Directory
www.harbours.co.uk

Ports

Aberdeen
01224 597000
www.aberdeen-harbour.co.uk
Ardrossan
01294 463972
Ayr
01292 281687
www.abports.co.uk
Barrow
01229 822911
www.abports.co.uk
Barry
0870 609 6699
www.abports.co.uk
Belfast
028 9055 4422
www.belfast-harbour.co.uk
Boston
01205 365571
www.portofboston.co.uk
Brightlingsea
01206 302370
Bristol
0117 982 0000
www.bristolport.co.uk
Brixham
01803 853321
Cardiff
029 2040 0500
www.abports.co.uk
Cowes
01983 293952
www.cowes.co.uk
Dartmouth
01803 832337
www.dartharbour.org.uk
Dover Harbour Board
01304 865260
www.doverport.co.uk
Dundee
01382 224121
www.forthports.co.uk
**Ellesmore Port
(Manchester Ship Canal)**
0151 355 3311
Eyemouth
01890 750223
Falmouth
01326 211376
www.falmouthport.co.uk
Felixstowe
01394 604500
www.portoffelixstowe.co.uk
Fishguard
01348 404453
www.abergwaun.com
Fleetwood
01253 872323
www.abports.co.uk
Folkestone
01304 865260
Forth Ports
0131 555 8700
www.forthports.co.uk
Garston
0151 427 5971
www.abports.co.uk
Goole
01405 762691
www.abports.co.uk
Great Yarmouth
01493 335500
www.gypa.co.uk

Grimsby
01472 359181
www.abports.co.uk
Harwich
01255 243030
www.hha.co.uk
Heysham
01524 852 3730
Hull
01482 327171
www.abports.co.uk
Immingham
01469 571555
www.abports.co.uk
Inverness Harbour Trust
01463 715715
www.invernessharbour.co.uk
Ipswich
01473 231010
www.abports.co.uk
Isle of Man
01624 686628
Kings Lynn
01553 691555
www.abports.co.uk
Larne
01574 872100
Lerwick
01596 692991
Liverpool
0151 949 6391
www.merseydocks.co.uk
Port of London
020 7743 7900
www.portoflondon.co.uk
Londonderry
028 7186 0555
www.londonderryport.com
London Tillbury
01375 852342
Lowestoft
01502 572286
www.abports.co.uk
Medway Ports
01795 561234
**Mersey Docks & Harbour Company,
Birkenhead**
0151 647 8074
www.merseydocks.co.uk
Milford Haven
01646 693091
Montrose Port Authority
01674 467 2302
Mostyn Docks, Holywell
01745 560335
Newhaven
01273 514131
Newport
0870 609 6699
www.abports.co.uk
Peterhead
01779 474281
Plymouth
01752 662191
www.abports.co.uk
Poole
01202 440200
www.phc.co.uk
Portsmouth
023 9229 7395
www.portsmouthand.co.uk
Port Talbot
0870 609 6699
www.abports.co.uk
Ramsgate
01843 592277

Saundersfoot
01834 812094
Scarborough
01723 373530
Seaham
0191 581 3877
Shoreham
01273 598100
Silloth
016973 31358
www.abports.co.uk
Southampton
023 8048 8800
www.abports.co.uk
St Ives
01736 795018
Stonehaven
01569 762741
Stornaway
01851 702688
Sunderland
0191 553 2100
Swansea
01792 633000
www.abports.co.uk
Tees & Hartlepool
01642 877000
Teignmouth
01626 774044
www.abports.co.uk
Troon
01292 281687
www.abports.co.uk
Tyne, Port of
0191 257 0407
Weymouth
01305 206421
Whitby, Port of
01947 602272
www.portofwhitby.co.uk
Whitby Harbour
01947 602354
www.whitby-uk.com

Ferries

Brittany Ferries
020 7610 4028
www.brittany-ferries.com
Caledonian MacBrayne Limited
01475 650100
www.calmac.co.uk
Condor Ferries Limited
01202 207207
www.condorferries.co.uk
DFDS Seaways Limited
020 7233 2300
www.dfdsseaways.co.uk
Fjord Line
01491 614660
www.fjordline.com
Hoverspeed Limited
0870 460 7132
www.hoverspeed.com
Hovertravel
01983 811000
www.hovertravel.co.uk
Irish Ferries Limited
020 7886 8440
www.irishferries.com
Isle of Man Steam Packet Company
01624 645645
www.steam-packet.com

Mersey Ferries
0151 330 1444
www.mersey ferries.co.uk
Norfolk Line
01227 728044
www.norfolkline.com
Orkney Ferries
01856 872044
www.orkneyferries.co.uk
P&O Ferries (Dover – Calais)
01304 863833
www.poferries.com
P&O Ferries (Hull, Rotterdam and Zeebrugge)
01304 863833
www.poferries.com
P&O Ferries (Portsmouth, Le Havre, Cherbourg and Bilbao)
023 9230 1220
www.poportsmouth.com
P&O Irish Sea
028 2887 2182
www.poferries.com
P&O Scottish Ferries Limited
01224 421227
www.posf.co.uk
Red Funnel Ferries
020 7233 2300
www.ferryinformationservice.co.uk
Sea Containers Irish Sea Operations
020 7805 5926
www.seacontainers.com
SeaFrance Limited
020 7233 2300
www.seafrance.com
Stena Line
08705 747474
www.stenaline.com
Superfast Ferries Scotland
0870 234 0870
www.superfast.com
Swansea Cork Ferries
01792 456116
www.swansea-cork.ie
Wightlink Limited
01798 874177
www.wightlink.co.uk
Woolwich Ferry
020 8854 8888
www.yellins.co.uk/woolwichferry

Road travel

Motoring bodies

AA
0870 600 0371
www.theaa.co.uk
British Motorcyclists Federation
0116 254 8818
www.bmf.co.uk
British Parking Association
01444 447300
www.parking.co.uk
Coach Operators Federation
somerbus@tinyworld.co.uk
www.users.tinyworld.co.uk
/somerbus/COFmembers.html
Confederation of Passenger Transport
01893 380709
www.carlton-group.co.uk
/passtransport.html
DVLA (Drivers & Vehicles Licensing Authority)
Licence 0870 240 0009
Vehicle 0870 240 0010
www.dvla.gov.uk
Greenflag
0113 399 1427
www.greenflag.com
Institute of Logistics & Transport
01536 740100
www.iolt.org.uk
Institute of the Motor Industry
01992 511521
www.motor.org.uk
International Road Transport Union
www.iru.org
Licensed Taxi Drivers Association
020 7286 1046
www.ltda.co.uk
Motor Industry Research Association
01268 290100
www.mira.co.uk
National Federation of Bus Users
023 9281 4493
www.nfbu.org
RAC
020 8917 2500
www.rac.co.uk
Road Haulage Association
01932 841515
www.rha.net
Road Operators Safety Council
01865 775552
www.rosco.org.uk
Society of Motor Manufacturers
020 7235 7000
www.smmt.co.uk
Transport & General Workers Union
020 7611 2500
www.tgwu.org.uk
World Road Association (PIARC)
00 33 147 968121
www.aipcr.lcpc.fr

Pedestrians, cyclists and campaign groups

Brake
01484 559909
www.brake.org.uk
Road Safety charity
British Cycling Federation
0870 871 2000
www.bcf.uk.com
Campaign Against Drinking & Driving
0870 744 3003
www.cadd.org.uk
Cycle Campaign Network
ccn@cyclenetwork.org.uk
www.cyclenetwork.org.uk
Cyclists Touring Club
0870 873 0063
www.ctc.org.uk
Don't Choke London
editor@dontchokelondon.co.uk
www.dontchokelondon.co.uk
Environmental Transport Association
020 7963 5770
www.eta.org.uk
Environmental Transport Association
01932 828882
www.eta.co.uk
Environmental campaigner & provider of roadside recovery service
European Federation of Road Victims
00 4122 7767413
www.fevr.org
Lift Share
08700 780225
www.liftshare.com
Online car sharing scheme
Living Streets
020 7820 1010
www.livingstreets.org.uk
Campaign for better streets and public spaces
London Cycling Campaign
020 7928 7220
www.lcc.org.uk
Motorcycle Action Group
0870 444 8448
www.mag-uk.org
National Cycle Network
0117 929 0888
www.sustrans.org.uk
Nationwide Cycle Registration
0117 964 2187
www.cycleregistration.com
Ramblers Association
020 7339 8531
www.ramblers.org.uk
Reclaim the Streets
rts@gn.apc.org
http://rts.gn.apc.org/
RoadPeace
020 8838 5102
www.roadpeace.org
Slower Speeds Initiative
info@slower-speeds.org.uk
www.slower-speeds.org.uk
Smart Moves
01484 483061
www.smartmoves.co.uk

Sustrans
0117 927 7555
www.sustrans.org.uk

Buses

Arriva
0191 520 4000
www.arriva.co.uk
Firstgroup
020 7291 0505
www.firstgroup.com
The Go-ahead Group
0191 232 3123
www.go-ahead.com
London United Busways
020 8400 6665
www.lonutd.co.uk
Lothian Buses Plc
0131 558 8011
www.lothianbuses.co.uk
Metroline
020 8218 8888
www.metroline.co.uk
National Express
08705 808080
www.nationalexpress.com
Scottish Citylink
0141 332 9644
www.citylink.co.uk
Stagecoach
01738 442111
www.stagecoachplc.com
Ulsterbus
028 9066 6630
www.ulsterbus.co.uk

Tourism

Air Travel Organisers' Licensing (ATOL)
020 7379 7311
www.caa.co.uk/cpg/atol
Association of British Travel Agents
020 7307 1900
www.abtanet.com
British Tourist Authority
020 8846 9000
www.britishtouristauthority.org
Tourism Concern
020 7753 3330
www.tourismconcern.org.uk
Youth Hostels Association
01629 592600
www.yha.org.uk

Utilities

Gas and electricity

Ofgem – regulator
020 7901 7217
www.ofgem.gov.uk
Energywatch
08459 060708
www.energywatch.org.uk
National Grid
024 7653 7777
www.nationalgrid.com/uk
Transco
0121 626 4431
www.transco.uk.com
British Gas
www.gas.co.uk
EDF Energy
020 7242 9050
www.edfenergy.com
npower
0845 070 2807
www.npower.co.uk
Powergen
024 7642 5741
www.powergen.co.uk
Scottish and Southern
0870 900 0410
www.scottish-southern.co.uk
Scottish Power
0141 636 4515
www.scottishpower.com

Water

Ofwat – regulator
0121 625 1300
www.ofwat.gov.uk
Anglian
01480 323000
www.anglianwater.co.uk
Welsh
01443 452300
www.dwrcymru.co.uk
Northumbrian
0191 383 2222
www.nwl.co.uk
Severn Trent
0121 722 4000
www.stwater.co.uk
South West
01392 446688
www.southwestwater.co.uk
Southern
01903 264444
www.southernwater.co.uk
Thames
0118 373 8000
www.thames-water.com
United Utilities
01925 234000
www.unitedutilities.com
Wessex
01225 526000
www.wessexwater.co.uk
Yorkshire
01274 691111
www.yorkshirewater.com

Post

Postal Services Commission – regulator
020 7593 2100
www.postcomm.gov.uk
Royal Mail
press.office@royalmail.com
www.royalmail.com

Telecoms

Ofcom – regulator
020 7981 3000
www.ofcom.gov.uk
British Telecom
020 7356 5369
www.bt.com
Cable and Wireless
020 7315 4495
www.cableandwireless.co.uk
Colt
0800 358 9945
www.colt.co.uk
Energis
0808 172 7272
www.energis.co.uk
Hutchinson 3G
0207 010 9312
www.three.co.uk
Kingston Communications
01482 602100
www.kcltd.co.uk
MCI WorldCom
0118 905 5000
www1.worldcom.com/uk
mmO2
01753 628402
www.mmo2.com
NTL
01256 752000
www.ntl.com
Orange
07973 100150
www.orange.co.uk
Telewest
01483 750900
www.telewest.co.uk
Thus
0141 537 1234
www.thus.co.uk
T-Mobile
0845 412 5000
www.t-mobile.co.uk
Virgin Mobile
020 7484 4300
www.virginmobile.com
Vodafone
07000 500100
www.vodafone.co.uk

Emergency and services

see separate panel for police, fire, ambulance, page 386

Police

Home Office
0870 0001585, press 020 7273 4545
www.homeoffice.gov.uk
Police Service
www.police.uk
National Crime Squad
020 7238 500, press 020 7238 2510
www.nationalcrimesquad.police.uk
National Criminal Intelligence Service
020 7238 8000, press 020 7238 8431
www.ncis.gov.uk
Forensic Science Service
0121 607 6800
www.forensic.gov.uk
Centrex (national police training)
01256 602100, press 01256 602725
www.centrex.police.uk
HM Inspectors of Constabulary
01527 882000
www.homeoffice.gov.uk/hmic
/hmic.htm
Interpol
020 7238 8600
www.interpol.int
Metropolitan Police, London
020 7230 1212, press 020 7230 2171
www.met.police.uk
Missing Persons Helpline
0500 700 700, press 020 8392 4510
www.missingpersons.org
National Identification Service
020 7230 2780
www.met.police.uk/so/nis.htm
Northern Ireland Police Service
028 9065 0222
www.psni.police.uk
Northern Ireland Policing Board
028 9040 8500
www.policingboard.org.uk
Police Forces in Scotland
www.scottish.police.uk
Police Complaints Authority
020 7273 6450, press 020 7273 8029
www.pca.gov.uk
Police IT Organisation (national computer)
020 8358 5555
www.pito.org.uk
Police Skills and Standards Organisation
0114 261 1499
www.psso.org.uk

Professional bodies

Police Federation
020 8335 1000
www.polfed.org
Police Federation for Northern Ireland
028 9076 4200
www.policefed-ni.org.uk
Police Superintendents' Association
0118 984 4005
www.policesupers.com
Association of Chief Police Officers
020 7227 3434
www.acpo.police.uk
Association of Chief Police Officers in Scotland
www.scottish.police.uk/main
/acpos/acpos.htm
Association of Police Authorities
020 7664 3185
www.apa.police.uk
Institute of Traffic Accident Investigators
01332 292447
www.itai.org
British Association for Women in Policing
01706 216331
www.bawp.org

Fire

Office of the Deputy Prime Minister
020 7944 4400
www.odpm.gov.uk
Fire Policy Division
020 7944 6923
HM Fire Service Inspectorate
020 7944 5569
Northern Ireland Fire Authority
028 9266 4221
Fire Kills campaign
www.firekills.gov.uk

Professional bodies

Fire Brigades Union
020 8541 1765
www.fbu.org.uk
Chief and Assistant Chief Fire Officers' Association
www.fire-uk.org
Fire Protection Association
020 7902 5300
www.thefpa.co.uk

Ambulance

Department of Health
020 7210 4850, press 020 7210 5113
www.doh.gov.uk
Ambulance Service Association
020 7928 9620
www.the-asa.org
Association of Professional Ambulance Personnel
0870 167 0999
www.apap.org.uk

Search and rescue

Mountain Rescue Council of England and Wales
www.mountain-rescue.org.uk
Links to all mountain rescue bodies in the UK
RAF Mountain Rescue Association
0174 335 2173
www.rafmra.org.uk
Search and Rescue Dog Association
www.nsarda.org.uk
Maritime and Coastguard Agency
0870 600 6505
www.mcga.gov.uk

Military

Ministry of Defence
0870 607 4455
020 7218 2629/7907
www.mod.uk
British Army
www.army.mod.uk
Royal Air Force
www.raf.mod.uk
Royal Navy
www.royal-navy.mod.uk
MI5
press 020 7273 4545 (Home Office)
www.mi5.gov.uk
UK's defensive security intelligence agency
MI6
press 020 7008 3100 (Foreign Office)
www.fco.gov.uk
Secret intelligence service
GCHQ (Government Communications Headquarters)
press 01242 221491 ext 33847
www.gchq.gov.uk
Territorial Army
0845 603 8000
www.ta.mod.uk
reserve force
MoD police
press 01371 854416
www.mod.uk/mdp

Military associations

Army Base Repair Organisation
01264 383295
www.abrodev.co.uk

Army Training and Recruitment Agency
01980 615041
www.atra.mod.uk

Central Data Management Authority
01793 555391
www.cdma.mod.uk
Tri service organisation helping enable IS interoperability.

Commonwealth War Graves Commission
press 01628 634221
www.cwgc.org

Computer Emergency Response Team
020 7218 8715
www.mod.uk/cert

Defence Analytical Services Agency
020 7807 8792 (publications)
www.dasa.mod.uk
UK defence statistics

Defence Procurement Agency
press 0117 91 30636 /
0117 91 30638
www.mod.uk/dpa

Defence Scientific Advisory Council
020 7218 0333
www.mod.uk/dsac
Provides independent advice to the defence secretary

D-Notice system
020 7218 2206
www.dnotice.org.uk
Issued by the defence, press and broadcasting advisory committee

Hydrographic Office
press 01823 337900 ext 4837
www.hydro.gov.uk
Responsible for surveying the seas around the UK

International Visits Control Office
020 7218 9000 (MoD)
www.mod.uk/ivco
Provides security clearance and advice for visitors to and from the UK defence industry

Military Heraldry Society
01952 408830 / 270221

Military Historical Society
020 7730 0717

Orders and Medals Research Society
01295 690009
www.omrs.org.uk

Reserve Forces and Cadets Association
www.rfca.org.uk

Royal British Legion
020 7973 7353 / 7280
www.britishlegion.org.uk

Sabre
0800 389 5459, 0800 389 5459
www.sabre.mod.uk
Supporting Britain's reservists and employers

SSAFA Forces Help
020 7403 8783
www.ssafa.org.uk
National charity helping serving and ex-service men, women and their families

Veterans Agency
0800 169 2277 / 01253 866043
www.veteransagency.mod.uk
MoD contact for veterans and dependants

Emergency planning

Government

Air Accidents Investigation Branch
01252 510300
www.aaib.dft.gov.uk

Civil Contingencies Secretariat
020 7276 3000
www.ukresilience.info
Formerly the Emergency Planning Division

Emergency Planning College, Easingwold
01347 822877
www.ukresilience.info/college
Government training college

Emergency Services Action Team
020 7210 4850
www.doh.gov.uk/esat.htm

London Fire and Emergency Planning Authority
020 7587 2000
www.london-fire.gov.uk

London Prepared
www.londonprepared.gov.uk

National Infrastructure Security Co-ordination Centre (NISCC)
020 7821 1330
www.niscc.gov.uk

National Radiological Protection Board
01235 831600
www.nrpb.org

Scottish Executive Justice Department
0131 244 2122, 0131 244 2718
www.scotland.gov.uk

Anti-Terrorist Hotline
0800 789321

Professional body

Emergency Planning Society
020 8579 7971
www.emergplansoc.org.uk

Voluntary services

Basics
0870 165 4999
www.basics.org.uk
Medical help at disasters

British Red Cross
020 7235 5454
www.redcross.org.uk

Casualties Union
08700 780590
www.casualtiesunion.org.uk
Simulated injuries for emergency exercises

Royal Life Saving Society
01789 773 994, 024 7621 7398
www.lifesavers.org.uk

Royal National Lifeboat Institution
0800 543210
www.rnli.org.uk

St Andrews Ambulance Association
0141 332 4031
www.firstaid.org.uk

St John Ambulance
08700 104950, 020 7324 4210
www.sja.org.uk

Victim Support
020 7735 9166
www.victimsupport.com
Supports fire and crime victims

■ Fire, police and ambulance

Avon
FIRE 0117 926 2061
POLICE 01275 816350
AMBULANCE 0117 927 7046

Bedfordshire
FIRE 01234 351081
POLICE 01234 842390
AMBULANCE 01234 408967

Berkshire
FIRE 0118 945 2888
POLICE 01865 846000
AMBULANCE 0118 936 5500

Buckinghamshire
FIRE 01296 424666
POLICE 01865 846000
AMBULANCE 01908 262422

Cambridgeshire
FIRE 01480 444575
POLICE 01480 422393
AMBULANCE 01603 422700

Cheshire
FIRE 01606 868700
POLICE 01244 612030
AMBULANCE 0151 260 5220

Cleveland
FIRE 01429 872311
POLICE 01642 326326
AMBULANCE 01642 850088

Cornwall
FIRE 01872 273117
POLICE 08705 777444
AMBULANCE 01392 261500

Cumbria
FIRE 01900 822503
POLICE 01768 891999
AMBULANCE 01228 596909

Derbyshire
FIRE 01332 771221
POLICE 01773 570100
AMBULANCE 0115 929615

Devon
FIRE 01392 872200
POLICE 08705 777444
AMBULANCE 01392 261500

Dorset
FIRE 01305 251133
POLICE 01929 462727
AMBULANCE 01202 438970

Durham
FIRE 0191 384 3381
POLICE 0191 386 4929
AMBULANCE 0191 273 1212

East Sussex
FIRE 0845 130 8855
POLICE 0845 607 0999
AMBULANCE 01273 489444

Essex
FIRE 01277 222531
POLICE 01245 491491
AMBULANCE 01245 443344

Gloucestershire
FIRE 01242 512041
POLICE 0845 090 1234
AMBULANCE 01452 753030

Greater Manchester
FIRE 0161 736 5866
POLICE 0161 872 5050
AMBULANCE 0161 796 7222

Hampshire
FIRE 023 8064 4000
POLICE 0845 045 4545
AMBULANCE 01962 863511

Hereford and Worcester
FIRE 01905 24454
POLICE 01905 723000
AMBULANCE 01886 834200

Hertfordshire
FIRE 01992 507507
POLICE 01707 354200
AMBULANCE 01234 408967

Humberside
FIRE 01482 565333
POLICE 01482 326111
AMBULANCE 01482 354277

Isle of Wight
FIRE 01983 823194
POLICE 0845 045 4545
AMBULANCE 01983 524081

Kent
FIRE 01622 692121
POLICE 01622 690690
AMBULANCE 01622 747010

Lancashire
FIRE 01772 862545
POLICE 01772 614444
AMBULANCE 01772 862666

Leicestershire
FIRE 0116 287 2241
POLICE 0116 222 2222
AMBULANCE 0115 929615

Lincolnshire
FIRE 01522 553960
POLICE 01522 532222
AMBULANCE 01522 545171

London
FIRE 020 7587 2000
POLICE 020 7230 2171*
AMBULANCE 020 7921 5100

Merseyside
FIRE 0151 296 4000
POLICE 0151 709 6010
AMBULANCE 0151 260 5220

Norfolk
FIRE 01603 810351
POLICE 01953 424242
AMBULANCE 01603 422700

North Yorkshire
FIRE 01609 780150
POLICE 01609 789000
AMBULANCE 01904 666000

Northamptonshire
FIRE 01604 797000
POLICE 01604 700700
AMBULANCE 01908 262422

Northumberland
FIRE 01670 534700
POLICE 01661 872555
AMBULANCE 0191 273 1212

Nottinghamshire
FIRE 0115 967 0880
POLICE 0115 967 0999
AMBULANCE 0115 9296151

Oxfordshire
FIRE 01865 842999
POLICE 01865 846000
AMBULANCE 01865 740100

Shropshire
FIRE 01743 260200
POLICE 01905 723000
AMBULANCE 01384 215555

Somerset
FIRE 01823 364501
POLICE 01275 818181
AMBULANCE 01392 261500

South Yorkshire
FIRE 0114 272 7202
POLICE 0114 220 2020
AMBULANCE 01709 820520

Staffordshire
FIRE 01785 813234
POLICE 01785 257717
AMBULANCE 01785 253521

Suffolk
FIRE 01473 588888
POLICE 01473 613500
AMBULANCE 01603 422700

Surrey
FIRE 01737 242444
POLICE 01483 571212
AMBULANCE 01737 353333

Tyne and Wear
FIRE 0191 235 2902
POLICE 01661 872555
AMBULANCE 0191 273 1212

Warwickshire
FIRE 01926 423231
POLICE 01926 415000
AMBULANCE 01926 881331

West Midlands
FIRE 0121 380 6906
POLICE 0845 113 5000
AMBULANCE 01384 215555

West Sussex
FIRE 01243 786211
POLICE 0845 607 0999
AMBULANCE 01273 489444

West Yorkshire
FIRE 01274 682311
POLICE 01924 375222
AMBULANCE 01274 707070

Wiltshire
FIRE 01380 723601
POLICE 01380 722341
AMBULANCE 01249 443939

Metropolitan Police

City of London police
020 7601 2222

Wales

Mid Wales
FIRE 01267 211444
POLICE 01267 222020
AMBULANCE 01745 583900

West Wales
FIRE 01267 211444
POLICE 01633 838111
AMBULANCE 01745 583900

North Wales
FIRE 01745 343431
POLICE 01492 517171
AMBULANCE 01745 583900

South Wales
FIRE 01443 232000
POLICE 01656 655555
AMBULANCE 01745 583900

Scotland

Central Scotland
FIRE 01324 716996
POLICE 01786 456000
AMBULANCE 0131 446 7000

Dumfries and Galloway
FIRE 01387 252222
POLICE 01387 252112
AMBULANCE 0131 446 7000

Fife
FIRE 01592 774451
POLICE 01592 418888
AMBULANCE 0131 446 7000

Grampian
FIRE 01224 696666
POLICE 01224 386000
AMBULANCE 0131 446 7000

Highland and Islands
FIRE 01463 227000
POLICE 01463 715555
AMBULANCE 0131 446 7000

Lothian and Borders
FIRE 0131 228 2401
POLICE 0131 311 3131
AMBULANCE 0131 446 7000

Strathclyde
FIRE 01698 300999
POLICE 0141 532 2000
AMBULANCE 0131 446 7000

Tayside
FIRE 01382 322222
POLICE 01382 223200
AMBULANCE 0131 446 7000

Northern Ireland

HQ, Lisburn
FIRE 028 9266 4221
POLICE 028 9065 0222
AMBULANCE 028 9040 0999

Index

Subject index

Subject index

F – Z

Contacts index

B

Contacts index

C

D

F

I

K

In–Ku

Contacts index

N

Sh – St

Contacts index

U

X

Y

Z

The **Guardian**

NHS and Social Services Directory 2003-04

Edited by Alun M Llewellyn
Foreword by Jacqui Smith MP, Minister of State for Health
Introduction by David Brindle, Editor, Guardian Society

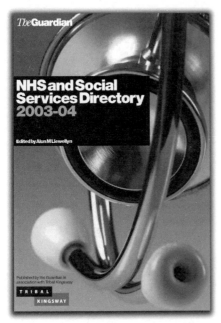

A fully revised and updated edition of this user-friendly guide charts the continuing organisational changes being made to the NHS.

It provides the most up-to-date statistical information and contact details available for both the NHS and Social Services in the UK including a significant number of address changes for PCTs in England.

Other key features include an overview of the structure of the NHS in the UK, a chapter outlining the key NHS agencies and organisations and contributions from key NHS personnel, including Sir Nigel Crisp, NHS Chief Executive.

If you work in the NHS, the public, voluntary and charitable sectors, this is an essential resource at an affordable price.

"Better than anything produced so far"
Mary Humphrey
Secretary, National Homecare Council

Only £20

- A to Z of Strategic Health Authorities, Primary Care Trusts, NHS Trusts, Care Trusts and Social Services Departments in England;

- A to Z of NHS Boards, NHS Trusts and Social Work Departments in Scotland;

- A to Z of Local Health Boards, NHS Trusts and Social Services Departments in Wales;

- A to Z of Health and Social Services Boards and Health and Social Services Trusts in Northern Ireland.

To order call 0870 066 7847

Or, send a UK cheque, made payable to 'The Guardian', to: The Guardian NHS & Social Services Directory, PO Box 582, Norwich, NR11WN. Alternatively, fill in the coupon below and send to the address above. (UK p&p Free; £3.95+ Europe; £6.95+ World). Delivery within 14 days. Calls charged at national rate.

Name

Address

Credit Card Number

Expiry Date

Signature

Please send me _____ copy (ies) of

The Guardian NHS & Social Services Directory 2003-04

The Guardian

The Guardian Local Authority Directory 2004

Edited by Alun M Llewellyn
Foreword by Nick Raynsford MP
Sponsored by the New Local Government Network

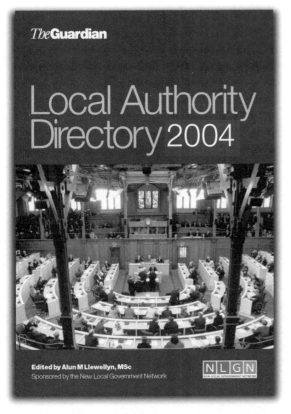

NEW EDITION OUT JANUARY

This fully revised and updated directory includes a detailed A to Z of all the UK's 468 local authorities, with over 2000 updates to contact details since the last edition.

If you work in or provide services to the NHS, the public, voluntary and charitable sectors, this is an essential resource at an affordable price.

Key features include:

• An overview of local government structure and functions

• Contributions from six Beacon Councils on change and innovation

• Facts on the National and European political scene; the cabinet, government team, Scottish Parliament, Welsh Assembly, Northern Ireland Assembly and the UK members of the European Parliament

• General local authority information; population tables, council tax figures, Regional Development Agencies, Beacon Councils and comprehensive performance assessment results for county and single tier authorities in England

• Details of the Government's regional offices and information about police and fire authorities, National Parks and PTEs

"Its user-friendliness and ease of reference make it an essential purchase"

Professor Steve Leach, De Montfort University

To order your copy priced at **£20,** call 0870 066 7847. Or, send a UK cheque, made payable to 'The Guardian', to: GLAD 2004, Guardian Books, PO Box 582, Norwich, NR1 1WN. Alternatively, fill in the form below and send to the address above. (UK p&p free; Europe £3.95+; World £6.95). Delivery within 14 days. Calls charged at national rate. Please allow up to eight weeks for official orders/pro-formas to be processed.

Name	
Address	
Credit Card Number	Expiry Date
Signature	
Please send me _____ copy (ies) of The Guardian Local Authority Directory 2004	

'An invaluable and clear-headed guide to those about to enter the daunting, and often confusing, world of the law. If you can, keep your feet out of the law courts; if you can't, go armed with *The Home Lawyer*'
John Mortimer

'It is clear that there is an increasing need in the community for the services – for any number of reasons – of lawyers. This unique book aims to meet that need by explaining how to find a good lawyer. I cannot recommend it too highly.' Sir Ludovic Kennedy

Whoever you are, wherever you are and whatever you're doing, you're potentially never far from the law. Whether buying a house, getting married, negotiating a contract, seeking compensation, resisting discrimination, confronting institutional intransigence or enforcing basic civil rights, you will almost certainly require the services of an experienced and trustworthy lawyer. This need usually arises without warning and knowing where to go for help is often left to chance. This book is unique in offering:

- A concise, user-friendly analysis of all the main areas of the law – from consumer, criminal, disability, education, employment, family and health to housing, immigration, inquests, libel, prisoners' rights and welfare

- A comprehensive list of legal organisations and advice centres

- Detailed and up-to-date information on the important protections now available to people since the European Convention on Human Rights in 2000.

Michael Mansfield QC has represented defendants in many well-known criminal trials and appeals, most notably the family of Stephen Lawrence, Barry George and the families of victims at the on-going Bloody Sunday inquiry. He founded his chambers, Tooks Court, in 1984 and is President of the National Civil Rights Movement. He is a regular contributor to public debates on human rights issues.

Edited by **Yvette Vanson**

To order call 0870 066 7850 or send a UK cheque payable to
Guardian Books, PO Box 582, Norwich, NR1 1WN